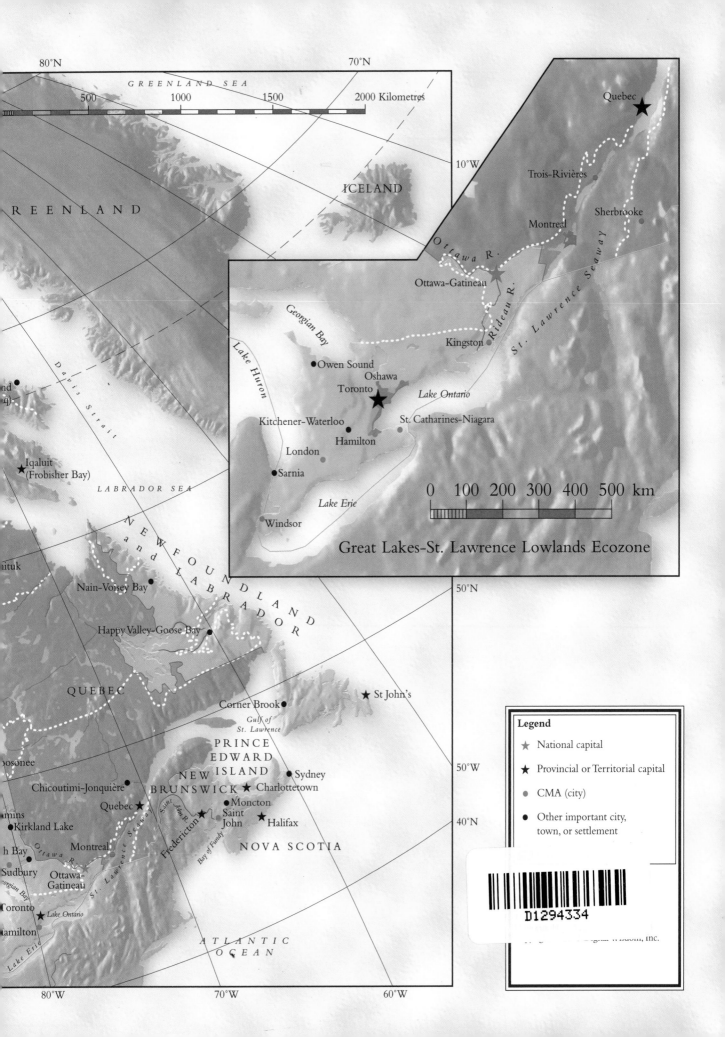

GREENLAND SEA

500   1000   1500   2000 Kilometres

ICELAND

10°W

GREENLAND

Davis Strait

Iqaluit
(Frobisher Bay)

LABRADOR SEA

NEWFOUNDLAND
and LABRADOR

Nain-Voisey Bay

Happy Valley-Goose Bay

QUEBEC

Corner Brook

Gulf of
St. Lawrence

St John's

PRINCE
EDWARD
ISLAND

NEW
BRUNSWICK

Chicoutimi-Jonquière

Quebec

Saint John R.

Fredericton

Sydney

Charlottetown

Moncton
Saint
John

Halifax

NOVA SCOTIA

Kirkland Lake

Montreal

St. Lawrence Seaway

Ottawa R.

Bay of Fundy

Sudbury

Ottawa-
Gatineau

Toronto

Lake Ontario

Hamilton

Lake Erie

ATLANTIC
OCEAN

Great Lakes–St. Lawrence Lowlands Ecozone

Quebec

Trois-Rivières

Sherbrooke

Montreal

Ottawa R.

Ottawa-Gatineau

Rideau R.

Kingston

St. Lawrence Seaway

Georgian Bay

Lake Huron

Owen Sound

Oshawa

Toronto

Lake Ontario

Kitchener-Waterloo

St. Catharines-Niagara

Hamilton

London

Sarnia

Lake Erie

Windsor

0   100   200   300   400   500 km

80°N   70°N   50°N   50°N   40°N   80°W   70°W   60°W

Legend

★ National capital

★ Provincial or Territorial capital

● CMA (city)

● Other important city,
town, or settlement

D1294334

global

connections: canadian and world issues
second edition

bruce clark ■ john wallace

PEARSON

The authors of this book have benefited from the knowledge, skills, and dedication of many people. We would like to extend our sincere appreciation to the publisher, editors, coordinators, designers, formatters, and artists at Pearson Education Canada. Many of the materials were field tested by our students and we are indebted to them for their assistance. Finally, we would like to thank our partners in life, June Wan and Laurie Wallace, for their support, advice, and patience over the many hours of work on this book.

Bruce Clark and John Wallace

PEARSON

Copyright © 2009 Pearson Education Canada, a division of Pearson Canada Inc., 26 Prince Andrew Place, Don Mills, ON M3C 2T8. This publication is protected by copyright and permission should be obtained from the publisher prior to any published reproduction, storage in a retrieval system, or transmission in any form or by any means, electronic, mechanical, photocopying, recording, or likewise. For information regarding permission(s), write to the Permissions Department.

ISBN 13: 978-0-13-206940-3
ISBN 10: 0-13-206940-7

Publisher: Susan Cox
Research and Communications Manager: Aerin Guy
Managing Editor: Gaynor Fitzpatrick
Coordinating Editor: Marg Bukta
Developmental Editors: Jane Clark, Cara James, Judith Scott
Production Editor: Geraldine Kikuta
Production Coordinator: Sharlene Ross
Senior Manufacturing Coordinator: Jane Schell
Copy Editor: Jessica Westhead
Proofreader: Christine Higdon
Cover Image: F001192903C014 - © Yann Arthus-Bertrand / Altitude
Nuclear power station at Saint-Laurent-Nouan, Loir-et-Cher, France
Art Coordination: Carolyn E. Sebestyen
Maps: Crowle Art Group
Index: Audrey Dorsch
Photo Researchers and Permissions: Allana Barron, Sandy Cooke, Dominic Farrell, Geraldine Kikuta

Printed and bound in Canada
3 4 5 TC 14 13 12

Contents

Preface and Acknowledgements / vi

UNIT 1   LOOKING AT THE WORLD 1

CHAPTER 1   **Exploring Canadian and World Issues / 2**
Introduction 3 ■ What Is Perspective? 3 ■ What Is an Issue? 5 ■
How to Validate Information From a Source 8 ■ Media 9 ■
Distinguishing Opinions From Facts 11 ■ Can Opinions About Facts
Alter Behaviour? 12 ■ Can Bias Be Detected? 15

CHAPTER 2   **Globalization and Sustainability: Two Themes for World Issues / 21**
Globalization: The Example of Dubai 22 ■ The Nature of Globalization
25 ■ Concerns About Globalization 30 ■ A Final Observation About
Globalization…for Now 31 ■ Sustainability in Dubai 31 ■ Closer to
Home—the Mountain Pine Beetle 32 ■ A Historical Perspective on
Sustainability 33 ■ Different Views of Our World Today 35 ■
Resources and Resource Use 36

CHAPTER 3   **Different Ways of Looking at the World / 40**
Grouping Countries 41 ■ Other Ways to Group Countries 50

UNIT 2   HUMAN POPULATION 55

CHAPTER 4   **Demography / 56**
Trends in Population 58 ■ Technological Change and Population Growth
61 ■ Measuring Demographics 63

CHAPTER 5   **Population Theories / 69**
The Theory of Demographic Transition 70 ■ Differing Ideas About
Population Growth 79 ■ Population Projections 80

CHAPTER 6   **Population Explosion and Control / 84**
The Population Explosion 85 ■ Population Control 86 ■ The Future
of Population Control 95

CHAPTER 7   **Population Futures / 100**
Different Assumptions → Different Predictions → Different Futures 101 ■
Population Futures in the Old Core and Eastern Europe 102 ■ What Are
the Implications of the Birth Dearth? 104 ■ Why Is the Birth Dearth
Happening? 109 ■ Can We Prevent a Population Implosion? 109 ■
What Will Happen? 110

CHAPTER 8   **Population Migration / 113**
Nature of Migration 115 ■ An Overview of Important Migration Issues
119

CHAPTER 9   **Rural to Urban Migration / 128**
Global Patterns of Urbanization 129 ■ Urban Changes Worldwide 134
■ Urban Problems in Old Core Countries 136 ■ Urban Problems in the
New Core, Near Core, and Far Periphery 138 ■ The Urban Future—Is
There a Better Way? 142

UNIT 3 ECONOMIC ISSUES 145

CHAPTER 10 Food and Agricultural Issues / 146
The Nature of Hunger—A Vocabulary 147 ■ The Geography of Hunger 149 ■ The Nature of Agriculture 150 ■ The Green Revolution 151 ■ Food Production Issues 155 ■ The Search for Sustainable Agriculture 161 ■ The Future of the Global Agricultural System 162

CHAPTER 11 Geographic Models of Development and Change / 167
Stages of Economic Development 169 ■ Colonialism Past and Present 171 ■ Current Economic Colonialism 174 ■ Economic Systems 175 ■ How Will You Vote? 178

CHAPTER 12 The Growth of Economic Globalization / 181
Transnational Corporations 182 ■ Growth of Free Trade in the World 188 ■ Doha Round and Beyond 192

CHAPTER 13 Economic Disparity in the World / 196
The Nature of Economic Disparity 197 ■ Disparity Among Nations 199 ■ Addressing the Problem 203 ■ Role of Remittances 208 ■ Income Disparity Within Countries 209

CHAPTER 14 The International Debt Crisis / 213
The Burden of International Debt 215 ■ How the Debt Crisis Happened 219 ■ Dealing With the Debt Crisis 221 ■ Debt Relief for Developing Countries 222

UNIT 4 THE EARTH IN BALANCE 227

CHAPTER 15 Land Issues / 228
Types of Land Degradation 230 ■ Causes of Land Degradation 233 ■ Solid Waste Management 235 ■ World Protected Areas 240

CHAPTER 16 Forest Issues / 245
The State of the World's Forests 246 ■ Take These Trees and... 247 ■ Take These Trees and Defend Them... 248 ■ Effective Use of Forest Resources 249 ■ Balancing Competing Interests 251 ■ Promoting Sustainability 255

CHAPTER 17 Earth's Water Resources / 258
Preserving Our Water Resources 259 ■ Fresh Water 259 ■ Preserving Our Oceans 273

CHAPTER 18 Earth's Fragile Atmosphere / 277
The Atmosphere 278 ■ Poisons in the Atmosphere 278 ■ The Dilemma of Acid Rain 280 ■ A London Smog or an LA Smog? 283 ■ The Ozone Layer 286 ■ The Future of Life on Earth 288

CHAPTER 19 Energy Choices / 291
Are You Part of the Problem, or Part of the Solution? 292 ■ A Guided Tour of World Energy 293 ■ Is There a Better Way to Produce and Use Energy? 307 ■ Alternative Sources of Energy 308

CHAPTER 20 Climate Change—the 21st Century Issue / 316
The Tipping Point Has Been Reached 317 ■ Climate Change Is Not New 318 ■ The Greenhouse Effect 319 ■ Impact of Global Warming 321 ■ Loops and Global Warming 326 ■ Politics of Climate Change 327 What's Next Politically? 329 ■ Possible Solutions to the Climate Change Problem 332

UNIT 5   CONFLICT AND COOPERATION   337

CHAPTER 21   An Introduction to Geopolitics / 338
What Is Geopolitics? 339 ■ The Nation State 339 ■ What Is an Ideology? 343 ■ Geopolitics and Conflict 345

CHAPTER 22   Conflict in the 21st Century / 349
Nature of Conflict 350 ■ The Role of Hard and Soft Power in Conflicts 352 ■ Causes of Conflict 353 ■ A Clash of Civilizations or a Clash of Globalizations? 360

CHAPTER 23   The Globalization of Terrorism / 364
What Exactly Is Terrorism? 365 ■ Geography of Terrorism 366 ■ Objectives of Terrorism 370 ■ State Terrorism 371 ■ Motivations for Terrorism 371 ■ Freedom Fighter or Terrorist? 372 ■ Changing Nature of Terrorist Threats 373 ■ Fighting Terrorism—Is a "War on Terror" Possible? 374

CHAPTER 24   Toward 2050—Changing Global Power Structures / 377
World Power Structures Today and Tomorrow 378

CHAPTER 25   Working Together to Build a Better World / 395
Solving Problems in the Real World 397 ■ Using Treaties to Make the World Better 401 ■ The Role of Individuals and NGOs 404 ■ Are World Peace and Social Development Possible? 406

UNIT 6   QUALITY OF LIFE   409

CHAPTER 26   Globalization of Disease / 410
Infectious and Lifestyle Diseases 411 ■ Infectious Diseases: HIV/AIDS 411 ■ Lifestyle Diseases: The Obesity Pandemic 416 ■ The Next Pandemic 419

CHAPTER 27   Human Rights Issues / 424
What Are Human Rights Issues? 425 ■ What Are Universal Human Rights? 428 ■ Women and Political Power 428 ■ Human Rights and War 432 ■ Human Rights and Children 433 ■ Slavery in the 21st Century 435 ■ The Issue of Cultural Exceptionalism 435

CHAPTER 28   Empowerment in a Globalized World / 438
Powerlessness Versus Empowerment 439 ■ Socially Responsible Investing 439 ■ Microcredit and Bangladesh's Grameen Bank 440 ■ Free Trade and Fair Trade 443 ■ Taking the Initiative in Your Community 446

UNIT 7   RESPONSIBILITY AND HOPE FOR THE FUTURE   449

CHAPTER 29   Achieving a Sustainable Future in a Globalized World / 450
Economic Growth and Sustainability 451 ■ Measuring Sustainable Development 451 ■ Achieving a More Sustainable Future 456 ■ Changing Our Behaviour 459

CHAPTER 30   The Geography of Hope / 462
Time for Some Good News? 463 ■ The International Year of Planet Earth 463 ■ Positive Aspects of Globalization 463 ■ Achieving Sustainability 467 ■ A Call to Action 469

Culminating Activity 472 ■ Glossary 476 ■ Index 485 ■ Credits and Sources 490

Preface

The Geography of Hope

You are about to discover the significant issues facing people around the world. Many of these issues also affect you as a citizen of Canada. As the world becomes increasingly interdependent and globalized, new issues arise and existing ones often become more complex.

This textbook will broaden your horizons as you explore some of these issues. It will provide you with opportunities to develop analytical skills and encourage you to think critically about your values and beliefs.

When examining Canadian and world issues, it is possible to become overwhelmed by the enormity of the issues and the apparent difficulty of resolving them. This book attempts to give you a realistic view of world issues but at the same time show there is often progress toward solutions. The last unit entitled "Responsibility and Hope for the Future" aims to provide you with a sense of optimism because it is your idealism, your enthusiasm, and your efforts that will be needed to meet the challenges of the future.

How to Use this Text

A number of special features in this book will help you in your studies. The book is divided into 30 chapters that are grouped into seven units. These units organize the issues facing the world into broad, general topics. All chapters within each of the seven units are linked by two themes: *globalization* and *sustainability*. These themes will become the lenses through which you will view the issues. The case studies, questions, and activities also centre around these two themes.

Each chapter begins with a list of the **Key Terms** that appear in bold throughout the chapter. These key terms are defined in the text and in the **Glossary** to help you fully understand each concept. In addition, **Key Questions** to be addressed in the chapter also appear on the first page of each chapter and will provide a focus for your reading. Take a moment to think about these before starting the chapter.

Throughout the book there are also Internet references that direct you to a central Pearson Education Web site where you can link to additional material about a particular topic. The **Working It Out** feature and **Questions** at the end of each chapter provide a wide variety of activities. By doing these activities, you will further examine specific aspects of an issue. You will also use and develop skills such as interpreting statistics, creating and interpreting graphs, and working with others to solve a problem or develop a point of view. The **In the News** feature provides opportunities to research important people or organizations that affect world issues. It is our hope this book will encourage students to think and do more about global issues as Canadian and world citizens.

Acknowledgements

Pearson Canada would like to thank the teachers who helped to shape *Global Connections*, Second Edition through survey information, discussions, and manuscript reviews:

Gerry Bell, Port Colborne High School

Brad Coppin, Holy Trinity Secondary School

Andrew Cresswell, The Humberview School

Mike Farley, Western Technical-Commercial School

Brian Gallagher, Sacred Heart High School

William Holla, Eastview Secondary School

Ivan Ius, St James Catholic High School

Joe Maurice, Sir James Dunn Collegiate and Vocational School

Nadine Morrison, Westdale Secondary School

Arnis Pukitis, Vivian Outdoor Resources Centre and Whitchurch Highlands Public School

Archie Robinson, Sir Wilfrid Laurier Secondary School

Liz Smith, Medway High School

Chris Somr, South Secondary School

Ken VenHuizen, Program Services—Thames Valley District School Board

UNIT 1   LOOKING AT THE WORLD

The world is a complex, wonderful, exciting, and at times, frightening place. In your study of global issues, you will come to understand the world better using the ideas of globalization and sustainability as organizing principles.

CHAPTER I

Exploring Canadian and World Issues

Key Terms

perspective
socio-economic status
life experiences
NGO
issue
polls
media
mainstream media source
alternative media source
opinions
values
subjective
facts
objective
bias
libel
Copenhagen Consensus

What you see in these images depends on your perspective.

Key Questions

By the end of this chapter you will be able to answer the following questions.

■ How does my perspective influence my opinion on a particular issue?

■ What methods can I use to recognize sources of inaccurate or biased information?

■ How can I distinguish between fact and opinion?

■ How can I address some of the global issues we face?

Introduction

Throughout this course, you will be asked to explore issues, seek out information through research and statistical analysis, examine and weigh facts, and develop ideas through reading and discussion. Before you begin, however, you should think about the **perspective**, or point of view, you hold as a Canadian student, and how it might influence your thoughts on a particular issue. In this chapter, you will also learn what is meant by the terms "issue" and "bias," how to differentiate a fact from an opinion, and how to evaluate the validity of a source. By doing all these things, you will gain skills necessary for the study of Canadian and world issues.

What Is Perspective?

On the evening news, there is a report on the discovery of a large quantity of diamonds in Canada's North. People listening to the report might have very different reactions or opinions, depending on who they are and what interests them. To someone who lives in the area where the diamonds have been found, the discovery might mean the prospect of a well-paying job and economic security; to someone in the environmental movement, it might raise concerns about the effects of diamond mining on the environment. That is, your reaction, or opinion, depends on your perspective, or point of view.

Many factors affect your perspective. Your **socio-economic status** (SES), which is a measure of an individual's or group's position in a community, is determined by such factors as your parents' occupations, income, education, and place of residence. Your gender, ethnic background, age, schooling, religious beliefs, and the places you have lived in and visited determine your **life experiences**. Both your life experiences and your socio-economic status may influence your opinions and how you view the issues presented in this course.

Consider Figure 1–1. What do you see in this photo—police maintaining law and order in the face of violent demonstrators, or citizens fighting for their rights in the face of a repressive government? What you see

Figure 1–1 What do *you* see in this photo?

depends on your perspective. It is important to remember that other people will have perspectives different from yours; it is critical that you understand and respect these perspectives. Many of the issues examined in *Global Connections* exist, or are *exacerbated* (made worse), because one group of people is ignorant or intolerant of the perspectives of others. In fact, people in some areas of the world accuse others of practising ethnocentrism, the belief that one's country, area, or culture is naturally superior to others.

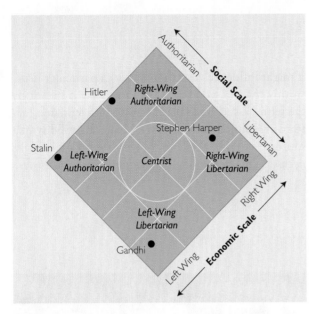

Figure 1–2 Where would your perspectives place you on this graph?

Social and Economic Perspectives

You have just learned that your perspective will influence how you view the issues presented in this course. Your perspective will also influence your opinion on how you think society should operate (see Figure 1–2). For instance, you probably have a particular opinion on how you should be governed, how social issues should be handled, and how government should manage the economy. The terms "right wing" and "left wing" are commonly used to describe two opposing perspectives, but these terms tend to oversimplify complex issues. Here are five terms that describe a broader range of social and economic perspectives:

- **Right-Wing Authoritarian.** Someone in this category believes the economy works best if the government does not interfere with business or trade, but exerts a significant measure of social control.

- **Left-Wing Authoritarian.** Someone in this category believes the economy works best if the government exerts considerable control over business and trade, while also exerting a significant measure of social control.

- **Left-Wing Libertarian.** Someone in this category feels the government has an important role to play in the economy, but feels government should allow people to make their own social decisions.

Figure 1–3 Gandhi used non-violent civil disobedience to protest unjust taxation of the poor and discrimination against women and people in the lowest caste ("untouch-ables"). He was a prominent leader in the movement for India's independence from Great Britain. His theories about non-violence inspired Martin Luther King Jr. and Nelson Mandela.

- **Right-Wing Libertarian.** Someone in this category wants to minimize the role of government in all aspects of life.

- **Centrist.** Someone in this category believes social and economic controls should be applied if they are for the public good, or dismantled if they do not benefit society.

People's perspectives, as well as those of entire governments, can and do change (see Figure 1–3). They change because people live through new experiences or alter their opinions as they grow older. Individuals may also hold a "left-wing" position on one issue, but a very different position on another.

Perhaps the best example of a government that changed its perspective is China. The China of Communist leader Mao Zedong was an extreme example of left-wing authoritarianism. Since Mao's death, the country has changed dramatically. While China's government remains distinctly authoritarian, economically it has become quite right wing.

What Is an Issue?

This course is called *Canadian and World Issues: A Geographic Analysis*. When you chose to take this course, you undoubtedly expected to learn about issues. But what exactly is an **issue**? More specifically, what are Canadian issues and what are world issues? Are they similar or different?

WORKING IT OUT   FOCUS ON ISSUES

By completing the following activity, you should gain a better understanding of what is meant by the term "issue," as well as which issues are primarily Canadian in nature, which are primarily global, and which span both geographical perspectives.

Defining an Issue

1. In a group of three or four, discuss the question "What is an issue?" Write down your group's definition of "issue."

2. Choose a representative from your group to write your definition for the class to see.

3. As a class, examine each group's definition, and then arrive at a consensus in answering the question, "What is an issue?"

What Are Today's Major Issues?

4. In your group, make a list of major issues facing humanity today.

5. Your teacher will now help you combine the group lists to create a class master list of issues facing humanity. How many issues in total has your class identified?

6. As a class, create four or five headings under which the issues may be categorized (for example, environmental issues, economic issues). With the help of your teacher, place each issue under the appropriate heading.

Which Issues Are Local, National, or Global?

7. In your group, examine your city's daily newspaper or a local Internet news site and determine which events could be considered issues. Decide whether the issues are local, national, or global. Discuss whether any of the local or national issues have global consequences.

8. Refer to the class master list of issues categorized under the headings in question 6. With your group, identify which are local, national, global, or a combination of two or more.

9. In your group, draw a flow chart or make a web diagram to illustrate how one issue in the class master list may be related to other issues in the list.

Analyzing Issues in the Arts

10. a) Working in your group, find a musical selection, a poem, or a visual (for example, a cartoon, painting, print advertisement, or TV commercial) that addresses a world issue.

    b) Interpret the song/poem/visual. What is its purpose? Analyze the lyrics of the song/poem, or the images (and text) of the visual.
    - If your choice was a song, explain how the words and music together convey the message.
    - If your choice was a poem, explain how the structure and the metre of the poem convey the message.
    - If your choice was a visual, explain how the images (and any accompanying text) convey the message.

    c) How successful is the song/poem/visual in achieving its goal? Explain.

    d) Who created the song, poem, or visual you chose to analyze? What particular political, economic, environmental, or social perspective does the work convey? Why did the author present this perspective?

From your group and class discussions in the previous activity, you should now realize that issues are important subjects or problems open to discussion and debate. They are multi-faceted and usually have or involve

- complex causes
- interrelated environmental, social, political, and economic components
- groups of people with different points of view
- groups of people who are involved in disputes because they cannot resolve their different points of view
- people unwilling to compromise

- complex, often imperfect, solutions
- local, national, and/or global implications

This complexity means people will have different explanations for, and perspectives on, the issues that concern them. Trying to understand such complex issues will make demands on your intellect and patience. You will need skills that help you identify the issue, research information, compile the facts, evaluate various points of view, draw conclusions, and recommend *viable* (useful or workable) courses of action.

The table in Figure 1–4 provides a framework to help you complete these tasks. This framework will help you investigate and analyze issues, not solve them. Modify the questions and/or their order, or leave out a step (or steps) altogether to best meet your needs.

Steps to Follow	Questions to Ask	Possible Strategies
1. Identify the issue.	• What is this issue about?	• Ask questions to differentiate this issue from another, e.g., Is this issue about ozone depletion, or is it about air pollution?
2. What do you currently know about this issue?	• What are all the aspects of this issue?	• Use a web diagram such as the following to analyze your issue.  • Use brainstorming to identify what you currently know and where there may be gaps in your knowledge.
3. Define the scope of the issue.	• Is this issue local, national, or global in scope? • Are there connections among the three levels? • Are the causes of this issue local, national, or global? • How does this issue impact Earth, people, or animals and plants? • During what time period was this issue of concern? • What individuals or groups are involved and why? • What are the effects and implications of this issue?	• Conduct some initial research to answer the questions in the previous column. Since you are still exploring the scope of the issue, you do not need to do in-depth research into each of these questions.

Figure 1–4 Framework for investigating and analyzing issues

Steps to Follow	Questions to Ask	Possible Strategies
4. Organize the information.	• What are the environmental, social, cultural, political, and economic aspects of the issue?	• Organize the information you currently have about the issue under the headings listed in the previous column.
5. Conduct more intensive research to add to your knowledge of the environmental, social, cultural, political, and economic aspects of the issue. Review the questions in the "Questions to Ask" column to make sure they are answered adequately.	• What information is missing from my current knowledge? • What sources do I need to consult to fill in missing information? • Should I conduct my own primary research?	• Examine various types of mainstream and alternative media (Internet Web sites, Weblogs [blogs], periodicals, newspapers, magazines, and TV and radio programs). • Look at information from the UN and government sources, as well as information from *NGOs* (non-governmental organizations, such as Greenpeace and Amnesty International, that promote courses of action or try to influence the actions of governments, corporations, and other organizations). • Conduct your own primary research using interviews, surveys, and fieldwork.
6. Organize your new information under the headings you established in step 4, or modify the organizational structure as needed.	• What organizational format best suits my needs?	• Use a graphic organizer, a chart, or other organizational structure. • Modify any format you have used as needed.
7. Analyze the information you have collected.	• Have I considered all points of view? • Am I leaving any questions unanswered? • Have I separated fact from opinion? • Are there viewpoints I have not considered? • Have I challenged commonly held assumptions? • What relationships exist between people and the environment? • Do I understand the environmental, social, political, and economic contexts associated with the issue? • Have I used the best sources? • Do I have the information I need to come to an informed conclusion?	• Assess the credibility of each source of information. • Analyze statistics. • Identify any trends and patterns. • Look for significant relationships. • Evaluate the evidence that supports each point of view.
8. Draw conclusions.	• What conclusions can I reach about this issue, based on my analysis and evaluation?	• Draw logical conclusions from your research based on your arguments and supporting evidence.

Figure 1–4 *continued*

How to Validate Information From a Source

During this course, you will be asked to obtain information about certain issues by examining a wide variety of sources. These sources include:

- books
- newspapers and magazines
- radio and television programs
- Web sites, blogs, and podcasts
- databases
- census data
- documents from companies, governments, and non-governmental organizations
- data from **polls**, where people are asked questions to determine their beliefs or opinions about a particular issue

How can you be sure the information you obtain from these sources is accurate? The information may seem relevant to your issue, but it may be *biased* (presented from only one point of view) and *unsubstantiated* (not verified by evidence). For example, there is no check on the validity of information on many Web sites because the people posting the information are accountable to no one, and there is no control on what is posted. Although you can never be 100 percent sure your information is accurate, there are some things you can do to help validate it. Examine the following set of questions in "Evaluating the Validity of Information" to discover what these things are.

Evaluating the Validity of Information

Ask the following questions to help determine the validity of the information presented by your source.

- What is the purpose of the information?

- Does it inform, persuade, entertain, influence, or deflect criticism?

- How was the information collected? For example, was the information obtained through phone surveys, credible academic research, or controlled experiments?

- What is the form of the information (for example, article, TV or radio program, cartoon, blog, archive, transcript, brochure)? You should know some forms are less reliable than others; for example, a blog may be less accurate than a document from a respected academic journal.

- What organization published the document? Does this organization have a particular point of view or agenda that might bias the information?

- Who are the authors of the information? What positions do they hold in the organization they work for? Do they have reputable credentials? Do they have a vested interest in the position they hold?

- What is the date or time frame of the information? The information may be out of date or not cover the time during which the issue occurred.

- What types of data (for example, statistics, arguments, facts, opinions, poll results) are used to support the point of view? The data may not be relevant to the issue.

- Did the authors rely on documented materials to support their arguments?

- Was information on some aspect of the issue left out? If so, what was left out and why?

- Does the information match information from other reliable sources?

Media

We need information to build our knowledge and understanding. Most of our information comes from the **media** (see Figure 1–5). The term "media" refers to the various forms of mass communication—for example, newspapers, television, radio, and the Internet—and the people involved in their production. **Mainstream media sources** include mass communication organizations such as newspapers, television and radio broadcasters, and magazine publishers that are generally owned by large corporations and usually present views held by the general population. The term **alternative media sources** refers to organizations that are generally small, not affiliated with large corporations, and offer alternative views to those found in mainstream sources. They may provide points of view that advocate a specific social perspective or political leaning (which is often the trademark of the organization).

If information in the media is accurate, without bias, and presented from many viewpoints, the public can develop informed opinions about issues that concern them. It is a well-recognized fact that what the media have to say often has a profound, sometimes crucial, effect on political, economic, social, and environmental issues throughout the world.

Modern communications technology has allowed the transmission of huge amounts of information across great distances at very high speed for relatively little cost. Communications satellites, the Internet, videos and DVDs, and even your cellphone, among a host of other electronic technologies, have contributed to the proliferation of information around the globe. Because of modern communications technology, the amount of information available to us about world issues has increased exponentially, often making it difficult to determine what is true. You may overcome this difficulty somewhat when you learn who owns the media, how the media gather and present information, and how journalists perceive their role.

Figure 1–5 Mainstream and alternative media. Identify two mainstream publications and two alternative publications.

Answer these questions, conducting research as needed.

1. Define the following terms:

a) mass media
b) publicly funded media
c) digital divide
d) podcasts
e) alternative media
f) propaganda
g) jargon
h) spin
i) doublespeak
j) euphemism
k) sound bite
l) blogs

Select five terms and find an example of each.

2. The first sentence of a newspaper article, the "lead," contains the main idea of the story. It "hooks" readers so they will read the rest of the article. Using three newspapers from different parts of the world, select one story from each on the same topic.

a) Write down the lead from each story.

b) How similar or different is the perspective in each lead?

c) Explain which lead is the most effective in
   • grabbing your attention
   • correctly conveying the idea of the article
   • being objective

3. a) From what sources do you get your news?

b) Which of the print and electronic media sources listed in part a) do you rely on most for your news? Explain why.

c) Surveys show a large number of young Canadians and Americans get their news from "faux-news" comedy programs such as *This Hour Has 22 Minutes* and *The Daily Show*.
   • Do you think this is odd? Explain.
   • In what ways is this good and bad?

4. There is a great deal of contradictory information in the media. How do you determine what is correct?

5. a) What do you think is the role of journalists?

b) What factors might hinder journalists in this role?

6. Not everyone in the world has equal media access. This is sometimes called the "information gap."

a) What groups of people have most access?

b) What groups of people have limited access?

c) What should be done, if anything, about this?

 For a comprehensive listing of online newspapers from around the world, visit the link on our Web site.

7. The media plays an important role in shaping public opinion. Using the editorial cartoon in Figure 1–6, explain how it

a) provides an accurate view of reality

b) provides a distorted view of reality

c) influences public opinion

Figure 1–6

8. In some large cities and regions, media ownership is concentrated in one or two companies. Each company may own several types of media outlets. As a result, the news that consumers in that market receive may be limited or biased according to the perspective of the company. On a national or international level, one large corporation may own many media outlets (see Figure 1–7) in one country or in several.

Could this control over media outlets present a problem? Explain your answer.

9. The news media has been criticized for "making news into theatre."

a) What does this mean? Give a specific example from recent news coverage.

b) Does this type of reporting affect your understanding of news events? Explain.

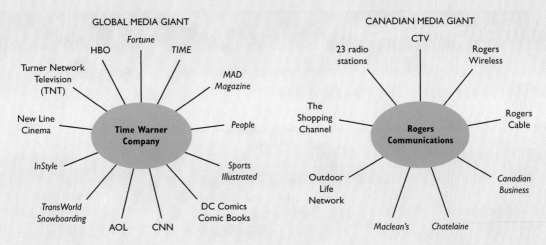

Figure 1–7 Large media companies own a wide range of print and electronic outlets. What effect might this have on your perspective of local or world events?

Distinguishing Opinions From Facts

In the exercise "Focus on Issues" on page 5, you were asked to list the most important issues facing humanity today. Even though you and your classmates may lead similar lives, you probably noticed some of the issues you selected were not the same as theirs.

Your **opinions** reflect the beliefs you hold about the events in the world around you. They develop as you consider the facts and make judgments about these facts in light of your **values** (principles or moral standards), life experiences, and the ideas of others. Your opinions are **subjective**, meaning they form as a result of your perspective. When two people have differing opinions about an issue, they will often argue about them. So, we can say opinions are not only subjective, but also arguable. Being able to use facts to develop an informed opinion and defend it is one of the most useful skills you can possess.

Before you can judge an issue and form your subjective opinion, you have to know the facts. **Facts** are indisputable truths—knowledge that is certain, concrete, and incontestable. They can be verified by accurate observation and measurement; for example, the types and amounts of chemicals found in a lake. You cannot argue about facts because they are reality, or as close to reality as current measurements will allow. Your own personal experience cannot change the nature of factual information. In other words, facts are **objective**.

Here is an example that uses population and food supply to illustrate the difference between a fact and an opinion. It is a fact, as close as current measurements

allow, that the world's population reached 6.6 billion in 2007. Accepting this fact, an environmentalist might conclude there will not be enough food to feed the world's future inhabitants because most of the world's *arable land* (land suitable for growing crops) is already in use. On the other hand, an *agronomist* (a person who studies soil management, climate trends, and innovations in crop production) might conclude there will be enough food for billions more people in the future. Although the fact is the same, the two opinions are highly subjective and very different, and each opinion reflects the experience of the observer.

Polling companies ask people (called "respondents") questions to determine their beliefs or opinions about a particular issue. When the opinions of a small number of people have been obtained, the information is *extrapolated* (extended for the purpose of drawing conclusions about something unknown) to represent the opinions of a much larger group of people. The extrapolated information is often presented as a percentage, or as a statement such as "the majority of Canadians think..." or "one in ten Canadians thinks..." These statements, however, may represent information obtained in a way that *skews* (distorts or biases) the results toward one position or another. To skew information is to misrepresent something by presenting it with a slant. To ensure the information obtained from polling truly reflects the opinions of the respondents, you should ask the following questions listed in "Validating Poll Results."

The objective of a poll is to obtain an opinion from a small group of people that accurately reflects the opinion of a much larger group. Therefore, the people in the small group, called a "sample," must be selected in a way that reflects the same language, ethnicity, gender, age, urban/rural location, and region of the larger group.

Questions to Ask

- Who paid for the poll? Was it commissioned by a political party, association, or company with a particular ideological position or point to make?

- Who conducted the poll? Was the poll conducted by an independent polling company, or by an organization affiliated with a political party, association, or company?

- How were the questions phrased? Small changes in wording can produce different results.

How might this be related to the sponsor or conductor of the poll?

- How large is the sample (in other words, how many people were polled)? If the results of a poll indicated that 67 percent of respondents felt a certain course of action was needed to resolve an issue, there would appear to be overwhelming support for that action. But if only three people had been polled, the accuracy of the statement would be in question. If the sample is chosen correctly, a representative sample of approximately 1000 respondents will produce a high degree of accuracy in terms of the way the entire population of Canada views a particular issue.

- How was the poll administered? There can be problems associated with obtaining information. For example, in face-to-face interviews, respondents may answer in different ways depending on the age, gender, or race of the interviewer, or what they think is the expected or "right" answer. With self-administered polls, results may be skewed because people who take the time to fill out the questionnaire may have strong feelings about the issue in the first place.

- When was the poll taken? A poll is a "snapshot" of the opinions of people at a moment in time. The timing of a poll can be a critical factor in people's opinion. For example, if a survey was conducted on a pipeline route shortly after there was a major oil spill, the response might tell more about the public's emotional response to the disaster than to its long-term beliefs about oil pipelines. Surveys should be conducted at regular intervals to determine the respondents' true opinion on the issue.

Can Opinions About Facts Alter Behaviour?

There is an important, *subtle* (not immediately obvious) relationship between opinion and fact that might surprise you. Your opinion, which should be based on fact as much as possible, can cause a change in human behaviour. That change can then alter the information on which your opinion was originally based. Look at the example in Figure 1–8 to see how opinion can influence behaviour. Opinion based on fact does not always alter human behaviour, however, because different interpretations of the facts are possible. This range of interpretation may make it difficult to find the "right" answer for some problems, or the best solution for an

issue. Some developing countries still produce and use DDT because they believe its low cost and high degree of effectiveness against pests outweigh the environmental damage it causes. For example, the most cost-effective method of combating malaria is to spray DDT inside people's houses. The mosquitoes are either killed or driven away. Studies indicate that when DDT spraying stops, the incidence of malaria increases. In South Africa, when spraying was stopped in 1996, the number of malaria cases increased by 150 percent. When spraying resumed a few years later, the number of cases dropped dramatically.

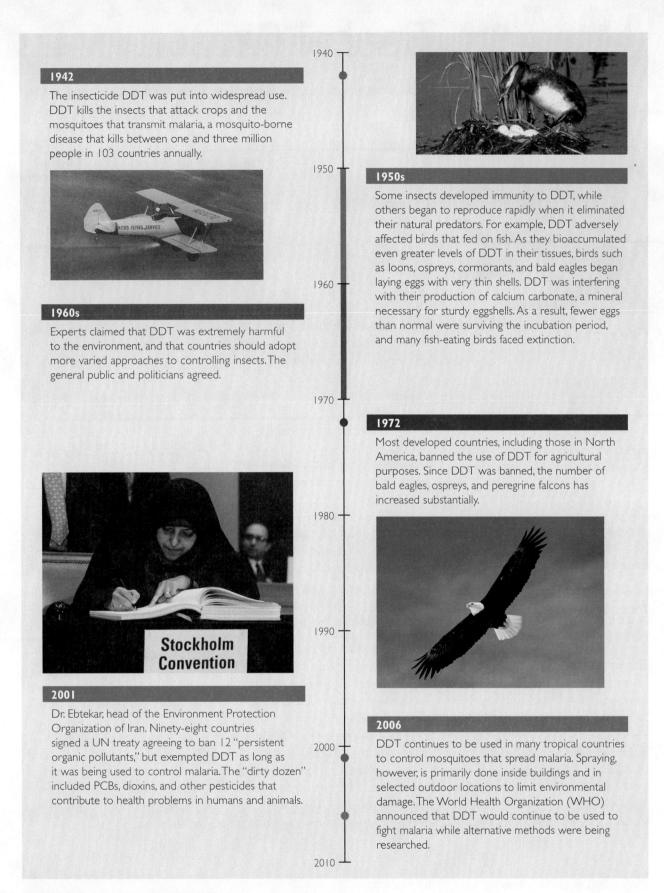

1942

The insecticide DDT was put into widespread use. DDT kills the insects that attack crops and the mosquitoes that transmit malaria, a mosquito-borne disease that kills between one and three million people in 103 countries annually.

1960s

Experts claimed that DDT was extremely harmful to the environment, and that countries should adopt more varied approaches to controlling insects. The general public and politicians agreed.

2001

Dr. Ebtekar, head of the Environment Protection Organization of Iran. Ninety-eight countries signed a UN treaty agreeing to ban 12 "persistent organic pollutants," but exempted DDT as long as it was being used to control malaria. The "dirty dozen" included PCBs, dioxins, and other pesticides that contribute to health problems in humans and animals.

1950s

Some insects developed immunity to DDT, while others began to reproduce rapidly when it eliminated their natural predators. For example, DDT adversely affected birds that fed on fish. As they bioaccumulated even greater levels of DDT in their tissues, birds such as loons, ospreys, cormorants, and bald eagles began laying eggs with very thin shells. DDT was interfering with their production of calcium carbonate, a mineral necessary for sturdy eggshells. As a result, fewer eggs than normal were surviving the incubation period, and many fish-eating birds faced extinction.

1972

Most developed countries, including those in North America, banned the use of DDT for agricultural purposes. Since DDT was banned, the number of bald eagles, ospreys, and peregrine falcons has increased substantially.

2006

DDT continues to be used in many tropical countries to control mosquitoes that spread malaria. Spraying, however, is primarily done inside buildings and in selected outdoor locations to limit environmental damage. The World Health Organization (WHO) announced that DDT would continue to be used to fight malaria while alternative methods were being researched.

1940 · 1950 · 1960 · 1970 · 1980 · 1990 · 2000 · 2010

Figure 1–8 The chronology of DDT

Rachel Carson

Figure 1–9 Rachel Carson in 1962

Throughout this book, you will be asked to research people or organizations who have made or are making a significant impact on the global issues you are studying. You can use the following as an example of how you might structure your research.

The Issue: The adverse effects of the widespread use of synthetic chemical pesticides after World War II on human health and the natural environment

Name: Rachel Carson (1907–1964)

Nationality: American

Education: Carson studied biology at the Pennsylvania College for Women (known today as Chatham University), where she graduated with honours in 1929.

She continued her studies at Johns Hopkins University, where she earned a Master's degree in zoology in 1932.

She wanted to continue studying for her doctorate, but in 1934 she took a full-time teaching position to support her parents.

Major Influences: When she was young, her mother taught her how to study nature on their small family farm in Pennsylvania.

A biology course in her junior year at college reawakened her interest in the natural world, and she switched from English to biology.

Career: In 1936, Carson wrote the US Civil Service exam and scored the highest mark of all the applicants. The Bureau of Fisheries (later the Fish and Wildlife Service) hired her as a junior aquatic biologist. She was the second woman hired for a full-time professional position with the Bureau.

She wrote a number of articles for the *Baltimore Sun*, the *Atlantic Monthly*, and *Nature*. By 1949, Carson was the chief editor of publications for the Fish and Wildlife Service.

In 1950, sections of a book Carson was working on appeared in *Science Digest*, the *Yale Review*, the *New Yorker*, and *Reader's Digest*. The completed book, *The Sea Around Us*, won the 1952 National Book Award and was made into an Oscar-winning documentary film. This work resulted in the award of two honorary doctorates.

In 1952, Carson gave up her job with the Fish and Wildlife Service to concentrate full-time on her writing career.

Achievements: During the 1940s, Carson became interested in the effects of synthetic pesticides on the environment, but it wasn't until the late 1950s that she began a serious study of the effects of exposure to DDT and other pesticides on both humans and the environment. This work resulted in the publication of her landmark book *Silent Spring* in 1962. The book's title refers to the loss of birdsong in the spring as a result of birds dying from pesticide poisoning.

Criticisms: The release of *Silent Spring* resulted in attacks by the former Secretary of Agriculture and scientists associated with the chemical industry. Some threatened lawsuits against her. Some critics attacked her scientific credentials because she was not a biochemist. Others criticized her for calling for a ban on pesticides, which in fact she did not do. Instead, she called for the responsible and careful management of pesticides in order that they would not adversely affect humans and the environment.

Recognition: *Silent Spring* was reviewed positively by those not associated with the agricultural and chemical industries; it became a bestseller in the US and in other parts of the world.

Carson testified before President Kennedy's Science Advisory Committee, which issued a 1963 report largely agreeing with her scientific findings.

In 1963, Carson won the Audubon Medal from the American Geographical Society and many other honours.

Carson died of cancer at the age of 56 in 1964, before she could see the banning of DDT. In 1980, she was posthumously awarded the Presidential Medal of Freedom, the highest civilian honour in the US.

Impact: *Silent Spring* was one of the major influences in the development of the modern environmental movement.

In 1991, the Rachel Carson Prize was created in Norway to recognize women who have made a contribution to environmental protection.

Legacy: Today, *Silent Spring* is seen as the cornerstone of modern environmentalism.

Carson helped to make environmentalism respectable, and *TIME* magazine named her one of the 100 most influential people of the 20th century.

Can Bias Be Detected?

When evaluating an issue, you should remember that viewpoints are often biased. **Bias** arises when an issue is presented from only one point of view. Today, you and your peers can get information about almost any event or issue if you have access to the Internet. But be careful. Although some of the information you collect may be true, your sources may have, consciously or unconsciously, included only those facts that support their point of view. Personal biases may have led your sources to omit other data.

Bias can be detected by examining your source's use of language, especially the choice of verbs and adjectives. For example, one observer might describe a protest march in the following terms: "A well-organized, peaceful group of marchers arrived at the government offices." Another observer might describe the same scene this way: "An unruly mob descended on the government offices." Biased words have great power to persuade the unwary toward opinions they might not otherwise hold.

You may want to think of the reliability of your sources in terms of three levels of confidence:

■ You should have the highest level of confidence in academic articles, professional journals, and most scholarly books because independent editorial boards review them (peer review) before they are published.

■ You should have a lower level of confidence in magazines and newspapers that are not subject to peer review, but at least these sources can be held financially responsible for what they print; that is, they can be sued for **libel**, a published statement that damages someone's name or reputation.

■ You should have the lowest level of confidence in sources where peer review or financial accountability are absent. For example, most Web sites have not been scrutinized by independent reviewers and are not accountable to anyone for their point of view.

Your sources—whether newspapers, journal articles, Web sites, films, television documentaries, or personal accounts from friends—may reflect a bias, and you have to be aware that you may not be getting an objective point of view. The following questions can be used as guidelines when you are trying to detect bias in sources of information.

Sniffing Out Bias

Ask yourself the following questions in order to detect bias in your information sources:

■ Who wrote the information, and why did he or she write it? If it was published by an organization, does the organization have a particular point of view or agenda that might bias the information?

■ Was the author or organization closely involved in the event? What effect might that have had on what was written?

■ Do the arguments and evidence support only one side of an issue?

■ Are generalizations and simplified solutions used to explain complex points of view to the point of being inaccurate?

■ Are emotion-laden adjectives used? For what purpose?

■ Are stereotypical comments used?

■ If counter arguments are given, are they developed and presented as thoroughly as the original arguments?

WHICH SOLUTIONS WOULD YOU FUND FIRST?

In 2004, Bjørn Lomborg, Associate Professor of Statistics at the University of Aarhus, in Denmark, organized an international conference of some of the world's top economists in Copenhagen. The participants in the **Copenhagen Consensus** did exactly what you did in the "Focus on Issues" activity on page 5. They identified the most pressing issues facing humanity, and came up with a list of 32 "challenges" or issues. The 32 issues were then narrowed down to a more manageable list of ten. For these ten issues, they came up with more than 30 solutions. The participants were then asked to imagine they had US$50 billion, and to decide which solutions they would spend the money on to best advance the welfare of humanity.

1. Your teacher will give you a copy of Figure 1–10. Fill in the blanks to complete the Copenhagen Consensus list of 32 issues, a description of each, and one possible solution for each.

Issue	One-Sentence Description of the Issue	One Possible Solution to the Problem
ECONOMY		
Digital divide	■	Build and distribute $100 hand-cranked laptop computers to children in developing countries
Financial instability	Inflation and banking crises dramatically impact the standard of living for millions of people	■
Lack of intellectual property rights	The widespread creation and sale of pirated copies of movies, music, and other media harm the interests of producers and damage the world's economy	■
Money laundering	■	Monitor the movement of large sums of money through bank accounts
Subsidies and trade barriers	■	Eliminate subsidies in wealthy countries
GOVERNANCE		
Arms proliferation	The rapid increase in the number of weapons acquired by countries	■
■	Disagreements or open warfare between opposing groups or nation states	Use a third-party mediator to resolve the reason for the conflict
Corruption	■	Formulate and enforce strict laws to prosecute people engaged in corruption
■	The lack of knowledge and abilities gained through learning at school	Provide funding to build schools in poor countries
Terrorism	The use of violence and intimidation to achieve political or ideological goals	■

Figure 1–10 Copenhagen Consensus

Issue	One-Sentence Description of the Issue	One Possible Solution to the Problem
HEALTH AND POPULATION		
Illegal drugs	▪	Destroy illegal drug-manufacturing laboratories
HIV/AIDS	The epidemic of the disease of the immune system, caused by the retrovirus HIV, that is infecting and killing millions of people in many parts of the world	▪
Problems in human settlements	Problems such as poverty, overcrowding, pollution, and lack of adequate drinking water and sewage treatment facilities affect the quality of life in human settlements	▪
▪	As populations in developed countries age, the number of people of working age decreases to the point where there are not enough workers to replace those who retire	Encourage immigration of young people from other countries
▪	Over one billion people live in areas where mosquitoes transmit this disease, which kills between one million and three million people annually	Use pesticides
Living conditions of children	▪	Support NGOs that assist homeless children
▪	Women who live in poverty or war zones, or without proper education and access to political power, do not have an opportunity to reach their full potential	Foreign aid to countries should be conditional on meeting the needs of women in the society
Non-communicable diseases	Diseases such as cancer, arthritis, diabetes, and heart disease, which are not passed from one person to another	▪
Undernutrition/hunger	People lack the basic food intake that provides the energy the human body requires to function properly	▪
Unsafe water and lack of sanitation	Clean drinking water and sewage-treatment plants are not available in many parts of the world	▪
Vaccine-preventable diseases	▪	Instruct and fund governments in developing countries to develop vaccination programs aimed especially at children

Issue	One-Sentence Description of the Issue	One Possible Solution to the Problem
ENVIRONMENT		
▪	The release of harmful substances, such as chemicals, aerosols, and particulate matter into the atmosphere	Impose strict regulations on industry and vehicles to prevent emissions of harmful substances
Chemical pollution and hazardous waste	Toxic pesticides and industrial chemicals are dumped onto the land, or released into the air or water	▪
Climate change	▪	Impose carbon taxes on large emitters
Deforestation	The complete removal of trees from a region by human (e.g., clear-cutting) or natural (e.g., forest fire) causes	▪
Depletion of the ozone layer	▪	Stop the release of chlorofluorocarbons (CFCs) and other pollutants into the atmosphere through international agreements
▪	The excessive use or pollution of freshwater resources	Limit the amount of water removed from the water body
Lack of energy	Insufficient energy to meet the needs of the world's population	▪
Land degradation	Deterioration of the productive capacity of soil for present or future use	▪
▪	A decline in the variety of animal and plant life on Earth	Enforce the preservation of species habitat
Vulnerability to natural disasters	▪	Discourage or restrict people from living or developing businesses on flood plains

2. a) In the group you were part of for the "Focus on Issues" activity, compare the list of 32 issues developed by the Copenhagen Consensus (Figure 1–10) to
- your group's list of issues facing humanity
- the class master list of issues drawn up in "Focus on Issues," page 5

b) Which issues did your group miss? Why do you think you missed them?

c) Which issues did the class miss? Why do you think the class missed these issues?

d) How many issues in your list and in the class master list correspond to the 32 issues in the Copenhagen Consensus list? How did you and the class score?

Score	Categories
0–5	Do you read the newspaper, other than the comics?
6–10	You have a lot of learning ahead of you.
11–15	You have some work to do.
16–20	You are on the way to gaining a good knowledge of major issues.
21–25	You have a good grasp of major issues.
26–30	You have an excellent knowledge of major issues.
31–32	You should represent Canada at the UN.

3. a) If your group had US$50 billion to spend on issues that would advance global welfare, which ten issues would you choose that could be best solved with this amount of money?

b) Compare your group's top ten to the list your teacher will provide of the top ten selected by the Copenhagen Consensus. Which issues on their list did you not select? Why do you think you missed these issues?

4. In your group, brainstorm three solutions for each of the top ten issues you selected in question 3. a). For example, if you selected climate change, your solutions might be to

• provide funds to support research into methods of reversing climate change

• give tax incentives to encourage the use of alternative fuels

• institute a tax against carbon emissions, for example, $150 per tonne of emissions

a) You have now formulated about 30 solutions to the top ten issues, as did the Copenhagen Consensus. But here comes the difficult part. Keeping in mind some of the solutions are attainable for less money than others (cost/benefit analysis), select the ten most desirable solutions from the list of 30. Rank the ten solutions from one to ten, with number one being the solution for which you think you will get the best value for the money you spend. Copy the following table into your notebook and write these solutions in the second column, based on your ranking.

Ranking	Solution
1	
2	
3	
4	
5	
6	
7	
8	
9	
10	

b) Your teacher will now tell you the top ten solutions and their rationale, as selected by the Copenhagen Consensus.

c) Do you agree with the ranking of the solutions by the Copenhagen Consensus? Explain.

Chapter Questions

Knowledge and Understanding

1. a) What is an issue?

   b) "Issues are multifaceted." Explain what this means.

   c) Why are issues difficult to solve?

Thinking

2. a) The social and economic attitudes of people are often classified according to five categories. Describe these five categories.

   b) Into which category do your social and economic attitudes most closely fit?

   c) What influences helped you develop these attitudes?

3. a) How can you evaluate the validity of information from TV and radio, written sources, the Internet, or from someone you speak to?

   b) Is it important to validate information from a source? Explain.

4. How can you tell that your sources of information may be biased?

5. "With scarce resources available to tackle the problems of the world, prioritization of the problems is necessary." Do you agree with this statement? Explain.

6. What issue or issues do you feel should have been included in the Copenhagen Consensus list of 32 challenges facing humanity? Explain.

Communication

7. Some countries continue to use DDT despite the toxic effects of the chemical on the environment. Find another example of people continuing to behave in a certain manner despite knowing the negative implications of their actions. Write a short report on this topic.

Application

8. a) What are the differences between opinions and facts?

   b) Examine a recent article from a newspaper or magazine. Make a list of facts and opinions, explaining your reasons for your choices.

9. Explore the statement "An individual's perspective influences how he or she sees the world and solves problems."

   a) If a developer and an environmentalist were looking at a wetland area, how would each perceive it?

   b) If a Canadian labour-union official and a shopper were thinking about a clothing factory in China, how would each perceive it?

   c) Pick an issue that was identified in this chapter. Show how three different individuals or groups with differing perspectives might suggest the issue be handled.

CHAPTER 2

Globalization and Sustainability: Two Themes for World Issues

Key Terms

globalization

sustainability

expansionist world view

ecological world view

conceptual models

Spaceship Earth concept

Gaia hypothesis

limits-to-growth thesis

carrying capacity

cornucopian thesis

total stock

resource

renewable resource

nonrenewable resource

Tiger Woods tees off in Dubai from the heliport on top of the world's tallest hotel. Is this the face of globalization and sustainability in the world today?

Key Questions

By the end of this chapter you will be able to answer the following questions.

■ Why are globalization and sustainability useful themes for the study of world issues?

■ In what ways is the world becoming more globalized?

■ What implications does globalization have for the world and for our future?

■ Why is sustainability such an important goal for the future but so difficult to achieve?

■ How are natural resources viewed differently at different times and in different places?

Globalization:
The Example of Dubai

The first of our themes in the study of world issues is **globalization**. Globalization is the trend toward greater interconnectedness of the world's financial, economic, technological, political, cultural, sociological, ecological, and geographical systems. You will encounter this concept throughout this course and, indeed, during the rest of your life.

We will start our study of globalization far from Canada, in a city called Dubai. Dubai may be the most globalized place in the world. In less than 40 years it has transformed itself from a sleepy port city to a major global business and tourism centre. Tiger Woods played golf there for a US$1 million appearance fee. As a result, Dubai received a massive amount of worldwide media exposure.

But how does the concept of globalization apply to Dubai? What can we learn from the example of Dubai, and how can we apply this learning to our study of world issues?

Dubai is part of the United Arab Emirates (UAE) (see Figure 2–1). The city has existed for almost 1000 years, but its modern history as part of the UAE is much shorter. The UAE was created in 1971, when seven previously separate *emirates* (Arab states ruled by an emir, a sheikh [as in Dubai], or other ruler) joined together. This occurred after the United Kingdom, the area's colonial power, left the Persian Gulf.

Unlike its six partners in the UAE and its neighbours, including Saudi Arabia and Iran, Dubai had relatively small oil reserves on which to build its future. In 2006, oil made up only about 6 percent of Dubai's gross domestic product. In fact, some estimates suggested that most of its oil would run out as early as 2010. Dubai needed to take a different route to ensure its future prosperity.

Here are some important facts about Dubai that have played a role in its globalization.

- One family has ruled Dubai for many years. Sheikh Rashid II ibn Said Al Maktoum was the emirate's ruler from 1958 until his death in 1990. Two sons succeeded him in turn. They and their advisors have skillfully plotted the course that led to Dubai's role as a globalized centre of business and tourism.

- The emirate of Dubai consists of the city of Dubai and a small surrounding area extending southward into the desert. The area of Dubai is 3885 square kilometres. (The Greater Toronto Area [GTA]—Toronto, Durham, York, Peel, and Halton regions—is 7125 square kilometres.) Dubai has only 72 kilometres of shoreline along the Persian Gulf.

- Dubai's population was about one million in 2007, but is growing rapidly. The majority of the population is made up of *expatriates* (people who go to another country to work).

- Only 19 percent of Dubai's population was born in the UAE; 23 percent are from Iran or from Arab countries, and 50 percent are from South Asia (most commonly Pakistan and India), most of whom work in construction and basic services. The remaining 8 percent of foreign workers are from Europe, North America, or East Asia. Most of these workers are in professional, managerial, and technical fields.

- Dubai has a subtropical desert climate. In winter, night temperatures drop as low as 10°C; in summer, daytime temperatures can reach a scorching 48°C. On average, rain falls only five days a year. Average precipitation for the UAE is 42 mm per year. Almost no rain falls between May and November. In comparison, Toronto averages 834 mm. Regina, one of Canada's drier cities, averages 388 mm per year.

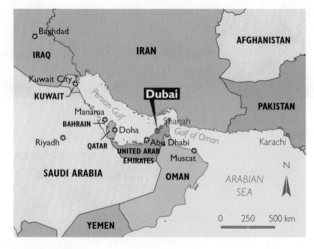

Figure 2–1 Location of Dubai

What Dubai Has Done and Is Doing

Dubai's leaders decided to take advantage of the spread of globalization to allow the emirate to become prosperous. In the beginning, their goal was to become the dominant service centre for the Middle East and the Arab world in general. Now that this goal has been achieved, they are trying to expand Dubai's global influence. When you read the following descriptions, remember Dubai is a city of about one million in a country of less than four million people.

Tourism

Creating a successful tourism-based economy involves two components. First, people have to want to visit—there must be a significant attraction present. Second, there must be an effective and attractive infrastructure in place for when people do visit—hotels, restaurants, transportation facilities, and so on. Dubai has focused on providing both of these.

Dubai's climate makes it an attractive destination for winter visitors from Europe and Japan. In addition, it offers a wide range of activities for visitors. There are championship golf courses, water parks, and even skiing and snowboarding. Yes, that's right—Dubai offers indoor skiing, even on days when the temperature outside is 48°C (see Figure 2–2). A second ski facility being built has a "mountain" that moves while the skier stays relatively in place.

Each year, a European PGA golf tournament is held in Dubai, as are tennis tournaments that attract the world's top players. The Dubai World Cup, a horse-racing event with a purse of US$6 million, is also a favourite event on the annual calendar. Not all attractions are sports events, though. For example, each year, two huge shopping festivals attract millions of visitors to the emirate. This event is advertised as having "The world's best brands at the world's best prices." Soon Dubai will have the world's largest shopping mall, too.

Dubai offers many hotel options for visitors. The Burj Al Arab hotel (see page 21) is called the world's only seven-star hotel, and rates start at $1500 a night. A plan was announced in 2005 to increase the number of hotel rooms in Dubai to 29 000. This plan includes the construction of the world's largest hotel, with 6500 rooms. Dubai has hundreds of restaurants of all types, as well. Also, a new Metro system is being built. When completed, it will be 166 km long and will operate both above and below ground. By 2010, it is anticipated that Dubai will welcome about 15 million tourists a year.

Figure 2–2 Ski Dubai offers five runs up to 400 m long and 60 m high. The facility has a quad chairlift, and can accommodate 1500 people at a time. Temperatures are kept at −1°C to −2°C at all times.

Air Travel

In addition to providing access to the UAE for tourists, Dubai International Airport has become the main hub for travel between many destinations in Europe, Africa, and Asia. In 2006, it handled almost 30 million passengers (just slightly fewer than Toronto's Pearson Airport). A second airport being built, the Dubai World Central International Airport, will be the largest in the world. (Part of the process of "selling" Dubai is to focus on having the "biggest" things.)

Emirates Airlines is based in Dubai and was created in 1985 with only two leased aircraft. It has grown explosively since then, at a time when many airlines worldwide have been struggling financially. Emirates Airlines now flies to 59 countries as far away as New Zealand, Brazil, and Canada. In 2007, the airline was awaiting the delivery of more than 100 new aircraft worth more than US$33 billion. Emirates Post, the UAE's postal system, is expanding its international freight-handling abilities and in 2007 announced the purchase of 50 additional aircraft to help them achieve their goal of competing with FedEx and DHL.

Finance and Business

Dubai is also investing billions of dollars to become the business centre of the Arab world and a major player in world commerce. To promote this goal, the emirate has a number of free-trade zones in which companies can operate free of import and export duties. An example of this is TECOM (Technology, Electronic Commerce and Media Free Zone). This business district has attracted important companies like Oracle, Microsoft, IBM, CNN, Reuters, and Associated Press. To provide skilled workers for these and other companies, Dubai has created a "Knowledge Village" with several universities and colleges. Dubai is also the home of a stock exchange and hosts the head offices of several banks and other corporations.

How Dubai Is Doing It

Having the desire to grow and innovate was the beginning of Dubai's plan to use globalization to achieve prosperity. A secure environment and bold political and economic leadership have allowed Dubai to forge ahead.

Creating a Globalization-Friendly Environment

The leaders of the emirate have worked very hard to make Dubai an attractive place in which to live, do business, invest, or visit. In a region infamous for political instability, Dubai provides a high degree of stability both for investors and for visitors. In addition, most residents speak English, which has become the *de facto* (Latin expression that means *actual*) language of globalization.

Dubai is a dominantly, and officially, Islamic entity, but it is tolerant toward the beliefs of most non-Muslims. For example, alcohol is served to non-Muslims (expats and visitors) in hotels, restaurants, and clubs, and dress restrictions are not as severe for women as in many neighbouring countries. The government has provided land for the construction of Hindu and Sikh temples and churches for several Christian faiths. The exception is that there is no acceptance of Judaism.

The emirate is trying its best to provide a balance between respect for traditional Islamic beliefs and the realities of the modern globalized world. A good example of this can be seen at Dubai's Wild Wadi water park. One day a week is set aside as a women-only day with only female staff present. On these days, no photography is allowed in the park.

Selling the Brand

As you have seen already, one of the most important reasons for Dubai's growth is its ability to attract attention. Another way to do this is to build an extravagant, ultra-modern city in the desert with the biggest mall,

biggest airport, biggest hotel, etc. Dubai is building the Burj Dubai, the world's largest building, which should be open by 2009. This combined office building/condominium will loom over every other building in the world.

Another feature of Dubai's development is the building of new land in the Persian Gulf. A striking example of this are The Palm Islands (see Figure 2–3), the world's largest human-made islands. Each island will have thousands of exclusive homes and apartments along with hotels, marinas, and health and tennis clubs. For those wanting even more privacy, another island development called The World will offer between 250 and 300 private islands on which private estates and commercial resorts can be built.

Learn more about Dubai's human-made islands on the link at our Web site.

Figure 2–3 This satellite image of part of Dubai's coastline shows two of the Palm Islands, and the World Island under construction. This image was taken in September of 2006.

Investment

The remarkable growth of Dubai could have occurred only with enormous amounts of foreign investment, both by foreigners in Dubai and by Dubai interests outside the UAE. Vast sums of money have been invested in building the physical and economic infrastructure of Dubai. This money has come from several sources: the European Union (EU), the United States, Japan, and, in particular, from the Islamic world. The reasons for this investment are obvious. Dubai offers the attractive combination of political security and stability (rare in the Middle East) along with the potential for making a good profit. At the same time, banks and state-owned and private firms in Dubai are active investors in other countries. For example, Dubai is one of the most important sources of foreign investment in countries such as Pakistan and Indonesia.

Negative Reactions to Globalization

You will learn in this course that the move toward globalization can be very controversial. This has been the case with Dubai. Reactions against what the emirate is trying to do have occurred both at home and abroad. Within Dubai, there have been ongoing concerns about bringing the "moral laxity" of the Western world into what had initally been a conservative Islamic society. This influence can be seen in everything from the serving of alcoholic beverages to the wearing of skimpy bathing suits on the beach. A significant minority of people in the UAE is not comfortable with the compromises that have been made to attract tourism and international business. Only time will tell whether these negative reactions increase or decrease in the years to come.

> **GLOBALIZATION**
>
> . . . the move toward globalization can be very controversial.
>
> *Why might it be particularly controversial in the centre of the Islamic world?*

Not all of the negative reactions have occurred in Dubai. In 2006, a Dubai state-owned company called Dubai Ports World reached an agreement to purchase the port operations in six cities along the eastern seaboard of the US. The ports involved—New York, Newark, Philadelphia, Baltimore, Miami, and New Orleans—were owned by a British company and are vital for the movement of both freight and cruise-ship passengers. The purchase ignited a firestorm of protest in the US, caused by fears that Arab ownership of the ports might make the ports more susceptible to terrorism. Because of the negative reaction, the deal was abandoned.

So there you have it—a brief visit to the most globalized place on Earth. Who knows—you may even end up working there at some point, if Dubai's wealth and influence continues to grow in an ever-more-globalized world. Now it is time to move on and look at what globalization is in more detail, and see how it is changing the world.

The Nature of Globalization

We have seen what globalization has meant to Dubai. Now let's look at globalization more generally.

To some people, the mention of globalization inspires visions of the global village—a world where every person is linked by the latest high-technology communications systems and where free trade and the efficient operation of the world's economy contribute to growing wealth for all. To others, globalization is the reason a local factory shuts down, only to reopen thousands of kilometres away in a country with cheaper labour, poor labour practices (for example, child labour and no tolerance of labour unions), and weaker environmental laws. To critics, globalization means the destruction of local cultures and the weakening of traditional religious beliefs, only to be replaced by a *homogenized* (blended into a uniform state), largely American-dominated culture.

Why should there be such wildly varying views of the same concept? First, globalization is an ongoing, evolving process. Its ultimate impacts are, as yet, unclear. Second, there is not just one form of globalization; there are at least eight types that can occur separately, or in a wide variety of combinations.

Financial Globalization

The world's financial systems have become intimately interconnected. For example, the world's stock markets are constantly affecting one another like a wave that ripples from east to west around the globe each business day. Trading on the New York stock exchange influences what happens hours later in Tokyo and Hong Kong. In turn, their trading affects that of the European markets. The next day, the wave continues, as European trading influences North American markets.

An interesting characteristic of this kind of globalization is that it does not involve the interconnection of nations. Rather, it reflects what happens in a network of world cities that have significant financial markets (see Figure 2–4).

Economic Globalization

In the past, a corporation tended to be identified with one particular country. For example, when one thought of General Motors, one thought of the US. Now, a growing number of huge companies, including GM, are multinational or transnational in nature, since they have integrated operations across much of the world. Companies like Coca-Cola, Toyota, IKEA, and Shell move their production and capital, and seek markets anywhere in the world that will benefit the company. This type of globalization has been one of the most controversial. Supporters maintain that economic globalization brings efficiency and produces much greater global wealth. Opponents say economic globalization tends only to increase the difference between the world's haves and have-nots and produces a situation in which transnational corporations become more powerful and influential than most countries. (See Chapter 12 for more information.)

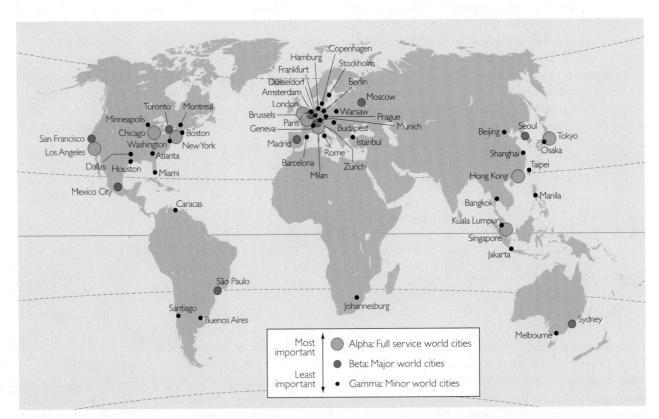

Figure 2–4 One study identified these world cities as "command points in the world economy." The reason why Dubai is not included is that this study focused only on accounting, advertising, banking, finance, and law. Hence, it did not consider fields like transportation and tourism that are so important to Dubai's view of globalization.

Technological Globalization

When we talk about the global village, we are referring primarily to technological globalization. This has occurred because of the remarkable growth of communications and computer technology in the past 50 years. Consider how the impact of this technological revolution affects you almost every day.

It is vital to remember globalization is a process and not a destination. So far, it has been the residents of wealthier countries, who are able to pay for Internet access, cellphones, and other technological advances, who have enjoyed the benefits of technological globalization. However, there is considerable evidence that this is changing. Many developing countries are going directly to cellphone networks (see Figure 2–5) and avoiding the great costs of building conventional, land-line-based phone systems. A non-profit association is developing a crank-powered laptop computer (see Figure 2–6) for children in developing countries that can be produced for less than US$160.

Figure 2–6 This inexpensive laptop is being built to bring the advantages of computers and the Internet to students of the developing world.

Political Globalization

As the world's countries become more economically and technologically interdependent, it is not surprising there are pressures on them to adopt more uniform policies. In the 1990s and early 2000s, the economic pendulum swung toward a neo-liberal agenda. (You can learn more about neo-liberal economics in Chapter 11.)

Canada's move to join with the US and Mexico in a free-trade agreement is typical of this trend toward less national sovereignty and greater emphasis on free trade among nations.

Cultural Globalization

This type of globalization refers to the gradual harmonization of the world's cultures at the expense of distinctly different local cultures. Eventually, most people in the world will watch the same television shows and movies, listen to the same music, eat the same foods, have the same values, and so on. If this makes you think of someone in Argentina (or South Africa or India) eating sushi (or pizza or "shrimp from the barbie") while they watch *The Simpsons* (or *anime* [see Figure 2–7] or Manchester United vs Real Madrid), you are on the right track.

Critics suggest that cultural globalization can happen only with the loss of the world's cultural diversity, and that the world culture that develops will be primarily an American one. For many people, the most important aspect of culture is religion and for significant numbers of these people, globalization is seen as a great threat. A newspaper clipping from a Pakistani newspaper illustrates this well (see Figure 2–8).

Figure 2–5 A worldwide explosion of cell phones use is a major factor in technological globalization.

Figure 2–7 *Anime*, or Japanese animation, is popular around the world.

Ecological Globalization

In recent decades, there has been a growing acceptance of the idea that the planet must be treated as a single ecosystem rather than a collection of separate ecological systems. A good example is the problem of ozone depletion. The world's nations were able to achieve a broad agreement on the nature of this problem and how it could be overcome. This came to be known as the Montreal Protocol, since it was signed in that city.

This treaty has done much to reduce the amount of ozone depletion in the atmosphere. Environmentalists hope the model of international cooperation that proved so successful in this case will act as a model for the even greater risks posed by climate change.

Sociological Globalization

Central to this form of globalization is the increasingly common belief that we are members of a single, world society that has become more significant than distinct national and cultural societies. This idea goes far beyond the elements of popular culture that are part of cultural globalization. It can be seen in the growing belief that certain common attitudes and standards of behaviour should exist in every country. Examples can be found in discussions of the morality of capital punishment, or the role of women in society.

Geographical Globalization

Even the study of geography has been globalized. In the past, geographers tended to look at the world in terms of what happened within one country, or what relationships existed between and among countries. Increasingly, they see a borderless world dominated not by countries, but by worldwide ecological concerns and political, cultural, economic, and other relationships existing among the network of world cities and the regions surrounding them.

HOME
NATIONAL
WORLD
POLITICS
BUSINESS
ARTS & ENTERTAINMENT
TECHNOLOGY

Religious activists, some of whom were wearing masks, also staged a demonstration before the Friday prayers. Burqa-clad girl students of Madressah Hafsa kept a vigil atop the seminary's roof. The activists were chanting "Al Jihad, Al Jihad."

Armed with sticks, a group of religious activists set on fire thousands of video and audio cassettes and computer compact discs "given up" voluntarily by a shop owner who, according to them, had announced [plans] to abandon "this business."

Maulana Aziz reminded the shopkeepers that they had been given a 30-day deadline to close down their "evil" businesses and switch over to some other "decent" venture and said students of the seminary would punish the shopkeepers who did not do so. He asked traders to financially "support" the owners of video and CD shops to enable them to switch over to some other business.

Maulana Aziz urged the authorities and the people concerned to stop dealing in video CDs, putting up billboards with women's photographs, selling liquor, and running "brothels" and drug dens in Islamabad.

Figure 2–8 This report from an English-language newspaper in Pakistan indicates that one-way globalization can be seen as a threat to traditional values.

In the preceding sections, we broke globalization down into a number of types. However, when we are examining a specific issue or situation, it is often the relationship existing between the different types of globalization that proves to be important. When you read the following, consider what the operations of McDonald's restaurants have to tell us about the various forms of globalization.

Big Mac Index

An important British magazine, *The Economist*, uses the price of Big Macs in different countries to compare the accuracy of the exchange rates for different currencies. It is able to do this for two reasons. First, McDonald's operates in over 100 countries, including all the major ones. Second, the Big Mac is virtually uniform in size and content in all countries. The exception is India, where McDonald's does not serve beef out of respect for the religious beliefs of the majority of the population.

Golden Arches Theory of Conflict Prevention

American author Thomas L. Friedman in his Golden Arches Theory of Conflict Prevention has proposed the theory that no two nations that have McDonald's restaurants will ever fight a war. His idea is that globalization allows a country to develop a large enough (and rich enough) middle class to sustain a McDonald's chain. Once this condition is reached, the citizens of the country would realize that they have too much to lose from fighting a war, and that they would prefer to line up for a burger and fries. His theory has stood up surprisingly well. There have been only two exceptions to the theory. One was the American invasion of Panama in 1989; the other, the NATO bombing of Serbia in 1999. Friedman has now created a similar theory—that no two nations who are part of the Dell Computers supply chain would ever fight a war. So far there have been no conflicts that violate this "law."

The Case of MaDonal

In this case, we are not even talking about a real McDonald's. Instead we are looking at a copy of the real thing, called "MaDonal," (see Figure 2–9) that illustrates the *iconic* (symbolic) role played by McDonald's in representing the benefits of prosperity in a globalized world. MaDonal was opened in 2004 by Suleiman Quassab in a Kurdish town in northern Iraq. The owner of the restaurant had fought against the government of Saddam Hussein in the 1970s and had been forced to become a refugee in Vienna. While

there, he had worked in a McDonald's as a cook. When he was able to return to Iraq, he tried to get a franchise from McDonald's but was turned down because of the ongoing instability of the country. In his mind, he did the next best thing: he opened a restaurant that resembled McDonald's, in its appearance and its menu—it even served "Big Macks." At first glance this may seem quite odd, but what he was trying to do was reproduce part of the stable and prosperous world he had experienced in Europe. His ultimate goal was to have a real McDonald's, in spite of the fact that his restaurant has been threatened by suicide bombers.

Figure 2–9 MaDonal in Iraq

Questions

1. **a)** What does the Big Mac Index try to do? What makes these comparisons possible?
    b) Explain, in your own words, the Golden Arches Theory of Conflict Prevention. Do you think this theory and/or the Dell theory make sense?
    c) What is MaDonal? How does the case of MaDonal reflect the relationship between globalization and the post-war American occupation of Iraq?

2. Which types of globalization are reflected in each case?

3. **a)** Why does McDonald's play such an iconic role in globalization?
    b) Name at least two examples of other corporations that play similar iconic roles, but operate in different fields.
    c) In what ways do these corporations play a positive role globally? In what ways do they play a negative role?
    d) Name at least four individuals who are iconic global figures. Do they portray positive or negative roles in globalization?

Concerns About Globalization

Globalization is a controversial topic in the world today because it is a relatively new trend that involves so many aspects of life and has the potential to have truly profound impacts (both positive and negative) on people. The full impact of globalization has not yet been felt. For example, supporters of cultural globalization might say that in time all people of the world will have access to the benefits of the Internet. Opponents might say that time will bring only the loss of unique cultures, and that once the damage has been done, it will be too late. A second concern is that the trend toward globalization emphasizes short-term gains over possible long-term consequences. Opponents say economic globalization places corporate profits before workers' rights and environmental protection. Supporters say that in a globalized world, governments will eventually agree on global labour and environmental standards and laws.

Globalization is not an entirely new phenomenon, especially when we think about politics and economics. By the late 18th century, an intricate pattern of trade moved raw materials and manufactured goods between Europe, the US, China, Africa, Canada, and just about every other part of the world. The great colonial empires that existed before World War II can be seen as an earlier form of globalization.

The organization of these empires was obviously political and their purpose primarily economic, but there were still significant cultural implications. These can be seen in the role played by colonial languages today—English in India, Portuguese in Brazil, French in much of North and Central Africa, and Spanish in most of South and Central America. It can also be seen in other aspects of life, such as the important role that the British sport of cricket plays in former British colonies as diverse as Pakistan, Australia, Jamaica, and South Africa.

What is clear is that the growth of these eight globalizations—financial, economic, technological, political, cultural, ecological, sociological, and geographical—must and will change the way we look at the world.

These eight dimensions [of globalization] are interconnected in many complex ways and are themselves subject to much academic debate and rancour *[bitter ill will]. . . . However, there is one thing that everybody does seem to agree about: some fundamental changes are at large which involve some reforming of the geographical scales through which we live our lives as workers, consumers, investors, voters, viewers, vacationers, and many more of our social activities.* –P.J. Taylor and C. Flint

The divergence in opinion, even among those who oppose globalization, can be confusing. Different groups of people oppose globalization for different reasons. Previously, we considered the case of people in Pakistan who oppose globalization because they see it as a threat to their religious beliefs and morality. Others oppose cultural globalization because of the potential loss of other aspects of their contemporary culture, such as their own movies, television, and popular music. For others, their main complaint against globalization is economic. International meetings of organizations like the G8 or World Trade Organization, that are seen to be promoting globalization, have attracted large demonstrations by globalization opponents who often have different motivations for being there (see Figure 2–10).

At the same demonstration, there might be union members worried about the loss of jobs because of economic globalization, and environmentalists concerned about the demands that globalized development places on Earth's resources. The issues surrounding globalization affect people in so many different ways it is difficult to single out one aspect and determine its impact. Clearly, globalization is an important and complex idea that must be central to our study of world issues.

Figure 2–10 Protestors demonstrating against the WTO, a major force for globalization

A Final Observation About Globalization . . . for Now

We started our examination of globalization in Dubai with Tiger Woods, and we will finish it with him. In a number of ways, Woods is a perfect example of a globalized person. He earns his living from playing golf, a globally popular game, and from endorsements in a worldwide market. More than this, he has become an international icon and role model. In the US, he is seen primarily as a highly successful African-American; but in Asia he is seen as an Asian-American success story. This is not a great surprise, if one considers his ethnic background. His late father, Earl, had mixed African-American, Chinese, and Aboriginal ancestry. His mother, Kultida, has mixed Thai, Chinese, and Dutch ancestry. This means that Tiger Woods' ancestry is half Chinese, an eighth African-American, an eighth Thai, an eighth Aboriginal, and an eighth Dutch. Since Woods' wife, Elin, is Swedish, the next generation of the Woods family will have an even more international ancestry. As well, Earl Woods met Kultida when he was a US Army officer stationed in Thailand. The simple fact of their meeting can be seen as a result of one aspect of globalization—the nearly worldwide influence of the US military. Without globalization, there would likely be no Tiger. In many ways, Woods can be seen as a prototype of the modern global citizen.

Sustainability in Dubai

Dubai has achieved a remarkable amount in quite a short period of time, but at what cost? When we look at Dubai's success, two thoughts come to mind. First, many remarkable achievements have been accomplished very quickly. Second, Dubai's development is being pursued with little regard for environmental **sustainability**.

> ### SUSTAINABILITY
> When we look at Dubai's success, two thoughts come to mind. First, many remarkable achievements have been accomplished very quickly. Second, Dubai's development is being pursued with little regard for environmental sustainability.
>
> *What factors contribute to the lack of sustainability of Dubai's astonishing growth?*

Sustainability, or sustainable development, was defined in 1987 by the World Commission on Environment and Development (also known as the Brundtland Commission, after its chair) as development that "meets the needs of the present without compromising the ability of future generations to meet their own needs." However, this definition has a major problem. Who determines what a *need* is? One person's need may seem an unnecessary luxury to someone else.

To understand how sustainability is *not* happening in Dubai, we need only to focus on two vital aspects of the emirate's development.

As we have seen, rainfall in this region is very low, and yet Dubai enjoys water-intensive activities, such as water parks and golf courses. One source says water usage in the UAE is the highest in the world—503 litres per day per person. This compares to the US at 322 litres per day per person. Other sources say the US and Canada use the most water, with the UAE placing third. No matter which statistics are correct, an important difference exists between the Emirates and North America. Much of North America has abundant natural water resources, while the UAE has very limited water resources.

The UAE uses its natural rainfall resources very carefully. It has built 114 reservoirs to store winter runoff for later use. This provides a total of 118 million cubic metres of water per year throughout the Emirates—but this is only 12 percent of the water used each year. The remaining amount, 950 million cubic metres, comes from the *desalination* (the process of removing salt) of sea water. This brings us to our second measure of sustainability for Dubai—energy.

Dubai uses large amounts of electricity for desalination and other things, such as air conditioning and even snow-making! In 2006, its electricity usage was 14 723 kilowatt hours (kWh) per year per person, and has been growing between 12 and 14 percent per year.

Almost all of Dubai's electricity is generated in modern thermal plants powered by local sources of readily and cheaply available natural gas. An obvious result of this is that huge amounts of greenhouse gases are released to enable people to golf, stay at luxurious resorts, and go skiing in the desert. Between 1990 and 2000 (no newer statistics are available), the UAE's total carbon dioxide (CO_2) emissions increased by 75 percent. Obviously much of this is related to the growing wealth and population of the emirate, but it is interesting to compare this emission growth to that of the two Asian economic giants, both of which grew very rapidly. In one decade, China's CO_2 emissions grew by 32 percent, while India's grew by 41 percent. It would be fair to suggest Dubai's incredible development has been accomplished with too little regard for environmental sustainability.

Closer to Home— the Mountain Pine Beetle

Sustainability, economic development, social problems, and globalization do not exist in isolation from one another. Consider the case of the mountain pine beetle (MPB) in western Canada. The MPB is not new to the forests of British Columbia. In the past, each year, a relatively small number of beetles would attack and kill lodgepole pines—one of the province's most important commercial tree species. During the winter, however, the cold weather would kill most of the beetle's *larvae* (immature insects when they are newly hatched from eggs), thus allowing no increase in the number of adult beetles during the following summer.

Sometimes though, winters are too mild to kill large numbers of larvae. This happened for a ten-year period starting in the early 1980s and again from 1994 to the present. In the latter case, many people blame climate change for the spread of the MPB. The result is an epidemic that threatens not only the health of the forest, but also the economy of much of the interior of British Columbia (see Figure 2–11).

The impact on forest towns, such as Williams Lake and Quesnel, has been profound. In the short term, forest-harvest companies, sawmills, and paper mills are working full out to use the lumber from trees that have been killed by the MPB before it rots or is burned in forest fires. Soon, all the lodgepole pines will be gone, and it will be decades before there are substantial numbers of new trees to harvest. Numerous jobs will be lost when mills are forced to close, and the future of many towns will be threatened. Now many experts fear the MPB epidemic could spread eastward across the country into the Jack pines of the boreal forest as average winter temperatures continue to rise.

The pine forests of British Columbia have been badly damaged and the boreal forest of the rest of Canada is at risk, most likely because of climate change.

As we will see in Chapter 20, climate change is occurring because people and industries are emitting so much carbon dioxide (CO_2) and other greenhouse gases into the atmosphere. Burning natural gas to make electricity and desalinate water to turn Dubai into a global hub releases vast quantities of CO_2. So Dubai's growth is contributing to the destruction of the forests of BC and threatening jobs there. At the same time, greenhouse-gas emissions from Canada are helping to make Dubai even hotter (+50°C anyone?) and drier.

Figure 2–11 The reddish pine trees in this British Columbia forest have been killed by an infestation of the mountain pine beetle. There are fears that mild winters farther east will allow the pine beetles to expand into the boreal forest that covers most of the Canadian Shield.

A Historical Perspective on Sustainability

Throughout most of human history, people survived by hunting animals and gathering plant materials, such as edible nuts and roots. Hunter-gatherers, as people living this way are called, had relatively little impact on the environment because there were so few of them and because they lacked the technology to cause significant environmental damage. Later, as agriculture developed and urban civilizations became more widespread, humans had a greater impact on their environment.

Some early civilizations were aware of the potential for destruction of the environment and, consequently, lived in a way that promoted sustainability. They used manure to maintain soil fertility, created terraced fields on mountain slopes to prevent soil erosion, and instituted religious taboos to protect certain animals and locations. Nevertheless, before the Industrial Revolution in the mid-18th century, when most of Earth was sparsely populated, people generally viewed the land and its resources as unlimited. As a result, there was not much concern for the state of the environment.

By the end of the 1700s, Europeans had explored and colonized parts of the Americas, Australia, and Africa. Colonization resulted in soil erosion and the gradual destruction of vegetation and wildlife, as large-scale commercial agriculture spread to much of the world. For example, the great herds of bison were hunted almost to extinction. Forests fell to loggers' axes to allow for farming and the sale of lumber, and the native grasses and vegetation disappeared under the plough and as a result of grazing by domesticated cattle and sheep.

Expansionist World View

During the 18th century, Europeans had an **expansionist world view**. The Industrial Revolution, which began in England in the middle of the 18th century, gave rise to mechanization, factories, railways, and steamships. New machines and processes meant products could be made more cheaply and much faster. This created many jobs, as more people were needed to run the machines. Rural inhabitants flocked to booming cities near the coalfields that powered new industries. As people lost their direct contact with the land, their knowledge of and respect for nature diminished. Merchants and business owners believed they were justified in exploiting nature and its resources because the ensuing accumulation of wealth was equated with progress.

Why were Europeans so destructive of the lands they used both at home and overseas? They perceived the "new" lands as having limitless natural resources and space, and set about using their technology to exploit the environment. They believed science and technology could control nature for the benefit of humankind.

Ecological World View

An **ecological world view** began developing in the late 18th century in reaction to the destruction of the environment caused by the Industrial Revolution and colonial expansion. Instead of viewing nature as something to be exploited and tamed, the ecological world view placed emphasis on the emotional and spiritual relationships that bind humans and the environment together. Cities were a particular target of those who took this view. Critics thought they were artificial and dehumanizing.

In the US, writers and activists were raising awareness about the destruction of natural resources and argued for the preservation of wild places. The concept of setting aside land for national parks was first proposed in the US in 1832, with the first national park, Yellowstone, being created in 1872 (see Figure 2–12). The first environmental organization, the Sierra Club, was founded in 1892. The expansionist and ecological world views can be compared in Figure 2–13.

Figure 2–12 The Old Faithful geyser faithfully erupts every 30 to 120 minutes. It is one of the reasons why Yellowstone became the world's first national park.

Expansionist World View	Ecological World View
• Nature is a resource to be used, not preserved.	• The universe is a totality, with all parts interrelated and interlocked.
• Conservation must work together with the dominant values of the surrounding society, not against them.	• The biotic community and its processes must be protected.
• The primary value of natural areas lies in their value to modern society.	• Nature is intrinsically valuable—animals, trees, rocks, etc., have value in themselves.
• Conservation should work against the wastefulness and environmentally disruptive excesses of a developing society.	• Human activities must work within the limitations of the planet's ecosystem.
• Conservation is equated with sustainable exploitation.	• Preservation works against the dominant societal values.
	• Nature provides a forum to judge the state of human society.

Figure 2–13 A comparison of early-20th century approaches to conservation

Growth of Modern Environmentalism

In spite of the existence of the ecological world view, the dominant philosophy in the world was, and remains, expansionist. Since World War II, population growth and the expansion of industrialization have dramatically increased pressure on land and resources. New forms of pollution have developed as the chemical industry and other industries expand. Industrial accidents at a chemical plant in Bhopal, India (see Figure 2–14) and a nuclear plant in Chernobyl, USSR (now Ukraine) killed thousands of people. Air pollution in larger cities sometimes reaches toxic levels, and water supplies in some heavily populated areas have become severely contaminated with industrial waste. Oil spills and the careless dumping of toxic wastes threaten the world's oceans and the survival of species that depend on the seas. Synthetic pesticides that were extremely successful in increasing agricultural production have proved to have severely damaging consequences for the environment.

In her 1962 book, *Silent Spring*, Rachel Carson warned about the damage caused by the indiscriminate use of pesticides, such as DDT. Carson's book was at the forefront of a popular environmental protection movement, based on an ecological world view that began to develop in the 1960s. By the end of the decade, environmental awareness of issues related to pollution, resource depletion, nuclear waste, population growth, and oil spills had increased among all segments of society. The first Earth Day took place in the US in April 1970. The Canadian government responded by creating the Department of the Environment in 1971.

Starting in the mid-1980s, a second wave of environmentalism began, in which the issues were frequently international in perspective. Scientists argued that climate change, ozone depletion, rainforest and old-growth forest cutting, and loss of animal and plant species had negative implications for people everywhere in the world. By the 1990s, environmental awareness was widespread throughout the developed countries. Companies, both large and small, were eager to link their corporate image to environmentally friendly behaviour—as long as it did not cost too much. Environmental awareness led to such practices as recycling and other programs to reduce the amount of waste being buried or burned. By the mid-2000s, climate change had come to be the most significant environmental concern. In spite of this rising concern, however, not enough major behavioural changes have occurred to substantially reduce the impact that human beings are making on Earth.

Figure 2–14 Dr. D.K. Satpathy has done more than 20 000 autopsies on people who died, immediately or years later, after a spill of more than 40 tonnes of a deadly chemical in Bhopal, India. This photo shows some of the victims.

Different Views of Our World Today

Many **conceptual models** of Earth have been created in the last 30 years or so. Their purpose is to aid understanding by simplifying the complexity of the real world while focusing on the key concepts the author wants to stress. Often these models are based on easily understood metaphors. Some are based on an expansionist world view, while many are ecologically based. Consider these ideas.

Spaceship Earth Concept

Viewed from space, Earth (see Figure 2–15) resembles a spaceship travelling through the universe. The **Spaceship Earth Concept** regards Earth as a fragile, finite, self-contained sphere with limited resources and a rapidly growing population whose life-support system is in jeopardy. According to this view, we must change the way we live because there is nowhere else we can go if our air, water, and other resources run out or become too polluted to use.

Gaia Hypothesis

Some ecologists felt a better metaphor may be that Earth is a dynamic, self-regulating organism, alive in its own right. Scientists know Earth's temperature has remained relatively constant for over four billion years. In the same period, the sun's temperature has increased by about 25 percent. Something has regulated Earth's greenhouse gases, resulting in temperatures remaining stable enough to allow living organisms to survive. In 1972, chemist James Lovelock concluded that Earth's living organisms have regulated its climate. Through evolution, living organisms have regulated the amount of carbon dioxide and other gases to keep temperature and precipitation at levels suitable for their survival. Lovelock called his theory the **Gaia hypothesis**, named after the Greek goddess of Earth.

In 1988, Lovelock further developed his hypothesis by equating Earth to a single living organism. In this view, the world is a self-regulating, living entity made up of organisms that modify Earth's atmosphere, oceans, climate, and crust to ensure their survival. In other words, there is constant feedback between living and non-living matter to maintain balance among life-giving components. Lovelock now believes human activities are overwhelming these regulatory mechanisms to the extent that human survival on Earth is seriously threatened. (You can read more about Lovelock's view in *The Revenge of Gaia: Earth's Climate Crisis and the Fate of Humanity*.)

Figure 2–15 Earth (shown here with the moon) travels through space like an immense, but limited, spaceship.

Limits-to-Growth Thesis

In 1972, an international group of experts, calling themselves the Club of Rome, wrote a report called *Limits to Growth*. The **limits-to-growth thesis** is based on computer models predicting what might happen if current growth trends continue. These experts started with the premise that there are limits to population growth: finite resources, like oil and metals, will be used up, while renewable resources, like soils and air, can be overused or damaged. They found that if trends in population growth, economic development, resource use, and consumption were to continue, the limits to human growth would be reached within 100 years. In other words, world population would exceed Earth's **carrying capacity,** which is the maximum number of people that can be sustained by Earth's resources.

Cornucopian Thesis

The **cornucopian thesis** is an expansionist model that is an alternative to the limits-to-growth thesis. It is based on the belief that scientific and technological advances will develop new resources to take the place of depleted resources. An example is the belief that solar power could replace oil, natural gas, and coal. Implicit in this thesis is the idea that Earth's resources are not really finite. In essence, there need not be limits to growth as long as technological development continues. The Cornucopians, many of whom are economists, feel the only way to create jobs and wealth is through constant economic growth.

Resources and Resource Use

Resources are not, they become; they are not static but expand and contract in response to human wants and human actions. –Erich W. Zimmermann

All the material components of the environment taken together are called the **total stock**. The total stock includes energy, living organisms, and non-living materials. Any part of the total stock that becomes useful to human beings is called a **resource**. Resources are anything that meets people's needs, including natural resources (water, air), human-made items (labour, technology), or items appreciated for their aesthetic qualities (landscapes, ecosystems).

The quotation at the beginning of this section tells us that something becomes a resource only when humans need it, and therefore something may be considered a resource at one time in history and not at another. For example, a type of mineral called flint was a vital resource to early hunting and gathering societies because it was used to make fire. Today, flint has little value. On the Pacific coast of North America, the Douglas fir and Pacific yew grow in the same environment. The Douglas fir was used for timber, but the Pacific yew had no value for lumber production. In the 1980s, however, a substance in the yew called taxol was found to have cancer-fighting properties. The tree's new value to humans changed it to a valuable resource. If inexpensive means were found to create taxol synthetically, the Pacific yew would return to non-resource status.

Three conditions must exist before something in the total stock becomes a resource:

- The technology must exist to develop the item for human use.

- The return on the investment must be greater than the cost of developing the resource. Deposits of oil sands in Alberta are a perfect example. When oil sold for less than US$20 per barrel, it made no sense to extract the oil here. Since 2004, oil prices have exceeded US$40 (and sometimes US$100) and the oil sands have become perhaps the world's most important oil resource.

- It must be culturally acceptable to develop the resource. Because of cultural and historical differences, commercial whaling is considered acceptable in Norway, Japan, and Iceland, but unacceptable in other advanced Western nations. An exception to this rule exists in Canada. Most Canadians agree with the view that Inuit hunters should be allowed to kill a few whales each year.

Most of the world's resources can be classified as renewable or nonrenewable (see Figure 2–16). **Renewable resources** are infinite; that is, they should exist for as long as humans need them because nature replenishes them. Air, forests, water, and solar energy are examples. But, if humans interfere with the natural processes that produce these resources, many of them can be destroyed or damaged. **Nonrenewable resources** are finite; once we have used up our current reserves, they are gone.

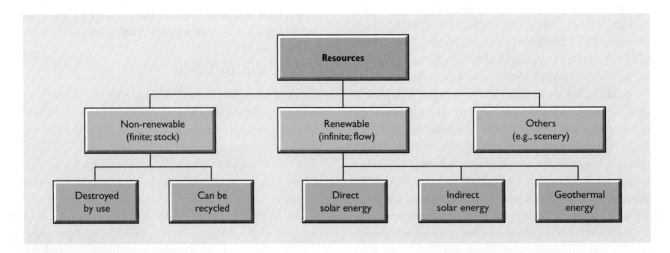

Figure 2–16 Types of resources

The Need for Sustainable Development

Throughout history, societies have collapsed because of imbalances they created in the environment on which they depended. One theory suggests the Mayan civilization of Central America declined around the year 900 CE because of the damage caused by growing only one crop—corn.

The concept of sustainable development was introduced in 1980 in the *World Conservation Strategy*, published by the International Union for the Conservation of Nature and Natural Resources, the United Nations Environment Program, and the World Wildlife Fund. The strategy set out the following three objectives that must be met if development is to be considered sustainable:

- maintenance of essential ecological processes
- sustainable use of resources
- preservation of genetic diversity

SUSTAINABILITY

Throughout history, societies have collapsed because of imbalances they created in the environment on which they depended.

Can you think of an example of this? What was the nature of the imbalance?

Nick Middleton, at Oxford University, has developed a *model* (a simplified analogy used to represent a complex, real situation) to show how human interaction with the environment can bring about sustainable development (see Figure 2–17). This model may be applied locally or globally, and across different timelines. At first glance, the model might be a bit confusing. The best way to understand it is to see how each individual cycle works, and then to consider how a society can move from one cycle to another.

Cycle A represents the global economy of the past, when wealth was accumulated largely through the degradation of the environment. Growing wealth reduced the negative impacts on society by increasing the standard of living. Further efforts to increase wealth led to further inappropriate development and more environmental damage. Cycle A can be repeated many times, as long as the size of the population and the impact of technology is so limited that the environmental damage does not become excessive.

When the damage becomes too great, Middleton suggests that a society moves into Cycle B. A society enters Cycle B when the environment is so degraded that less wealth is generated. Reduced wealth increases stress on society that only encourages even more inappropriate development to occur. An example of this is the stress felt by the management of a mining company with declining profits and share prices. Under great pressure to do better, they may resort to developing a new mineral resource in a country with poor environmental standards. Like Cycle A, Cycle B can occur repeatedly as the environment is degraded more and more in a futile attempt to maintain and improve living standards.

The only way to get out of Cycle B is to enter Cycle C at point Y. This has not happened yet, but many people would suggest it must happen if we are to live on Earth successfully in the long term. Our *parasitic relationship* (when an organism benefits from a host organism by injuring or damaging it) with the environment becomes a *symbiotic relationship* (when two organisms live cooperatively with no damage to either) in Cycle C. Moving into Cycle C requires a permanent long-term strategy to minimize environmental damage, while providing for the needs of the population.

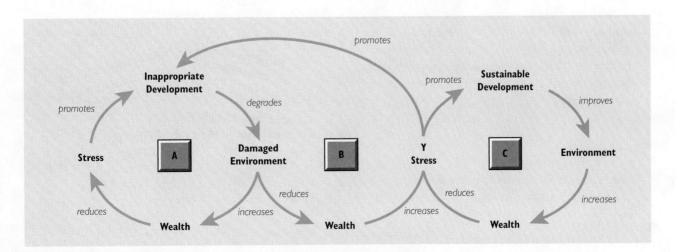

Figure 2–17 This model shows the possible relationships that exist between development and the environment.

Chapter Questions

Knowledge and Understanding

1. a) Why did the leaders of Dubai decide they would use globalization as a tool to build wealth in the emirate?

   b) What advantages did Dubai possess that allowed it to pursue a global perspective in its development?

   c) What risks were there for the emirate in choosing this route?

   d) What risks are there for the future of Dubai?

2. a) In your own words, describe the meaning of each type of globalization.

   b) For each type, give a specific way in which it might be a positive and negative development for the world. Choose any three negative aspects and explain how these disadvantages can be minimized.

   c) Using examples from at least three types of globalization, identify ways in which countries or regions are becoming interdependent.

3. In your own words, compare the expansionist world view with the ecological world view. Use examples from the text.

4. a) Explain the Gaia hypothesis.

   b) What is your opinion about this hypothesis?

5. Compare the limits-to-growth and cornucopian theses.

6. a) What three conditions must exist within a society for it to turn something in the total stock into a resource? Use examples in your explanation.

   b) Explain why the following situation exists: Seal hunting is seen by many people in Canada as a part of the cultural traditions of some rural communities in Atlantic Canada and Inuit communities in the North. It is also seen as a useful way of increasing the incomes of some of our poorest people. In contrast, many people in Europe see the hunt as barbaric and organize boycotts of not only seal products, but many other Canadian exports as well.

Thinking

7. "Resources are not: they become." Explain this statement, using specific examples.

8. Examine Figure 2–16 and answer the following questions:

   a) Explain the difference between a stock resource and a flow resource, using an example of each.

   b) Give an example of a nonrenewable resource that can be recycled and one that cannot.

   c) Explain the difference between direct and indirect solar energy. Give at least two examples of each.

   d) What is geothermal energy? Is geothermal energy a resource where you live? Explain.

   e) How can scenery be seen as a resource? Give a second example of a resource in the "Others" category (for other categories of resources).

9. Using Figure 2–17, explain in your own words how human interaction with the environment can bring about sustainable development.

10. Examine the newspaper headlines in Figure 2–18. Determine whether each one relates to or demonstrates the themes of globalization, sustainability, or both. Briefly explain the relationship between the headline and the theme(s).

Figure 2–18 Types of resources

Communication

11. As a class, organize an informal debate on the statement: "Globalization offers the world our best chance to solve the problems we face." Prepare your arguments on this topic, taking the role of either

• a resident of a wealthy country, such as Canada, Germany, or Japan;

• a resident of a desperately poor country, such as Haiti, Sudan, or Myanmar; or

• a resident of a relatively advanced developing country, such as Mexico, India, or Brazil.

12. Write a short paragraph in which you predict how globalization will make your study of Canadian and world issues different from that undertaken by a student 20 years ago.

13. a) All human activities directly or indirectly have an impact on the natural environment. Write two scenarios, with supporting visuals, about what the global environment will be like by 2025. One should be optimistic and the other pessimistic.

 b) Which scenario do you think will come to pass? Explain. **S**

Application

14. Assume the premier of Ontario has chosen you to give advice on whether the Greater Toronto Area (GTA) could use the example of Dubai to become a leader in globalized business and tourism. You should discuss this with your classmates, friends, or family members before answering this question. You have three tasks:

 a) Identify how Dubai achieved its goal of being a world leader in globalization. This task includes describing the preconditions Dubai faced, and the steps the emirate took to achieve its goal.

 b) Identify the advantages and disadvantages the GTA has in becoming more globalized.

 c) Suggest several initial steps the GTA (and/or the provincial and federal governments) should take to start this process.

15. a) Explain the concept of sustainable development.

 b) What can you do to make your own use of resources more sustainable?

16. In your own words, and using examples, explain the concept presented in Figure 2–17.

17. Search the Internet for a group that promotes sustainable development. Determine such facts as who the group is, what projects it supports, from where it receives funding, and on which type of sustainable development it focuses.

18. Earth Day is celebrated every April. Develop an activity your class (or school) could perform to address the spirit of Earth Day.

19. a) What harmful environmental damage was created for you by previous generations?

 b) What obligations do you have, if any, in preventing environmental damage for the next generation?

 c) How might you address these obligations? **G**

CHAPTER 3

Different Ways of Looking at the World

Key Terms

economic development
social development
political maturity
more globalized core
less globalized periphery
Old Core
New Core
Near-Core Periphery
Far Periphery
North
South
Third World

It's all a matter of perspective. For a *Kiwi* ("Kiwi" is a common nickname for a New Zealander), the world tends to look quite different than it does for a Canadian.

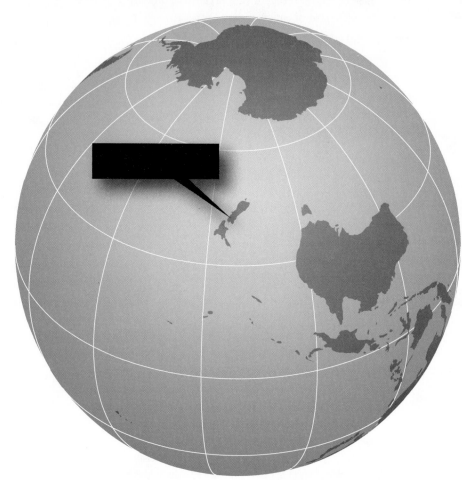

Key Questions

By the end of this chapter you will be able to answer the following questions.

■ How can you group countries to make it easier to understand international differences?

■ What graphical methods can you use to make analysis easier?

■ How can you use nontextual methods to present the results of analysis?

YOUR MENTAL MAP OF THE WORLD

Each of us has a mental map of the world—a virtual atlas that we carry in our head. Some parts of our mental map are quite detailed, while others are almost empty. Why is this not a surprise? One goal of this course is to improve and expand the contents of your mental map.

To see what is in your virtual atlas, take a standard piece of blank paper and turn it sideways. Now sketch a map of the world. On it, label what you regard as important features. These might include, but are not limited to, continents, regions, countries, major cities, and important bodies of water. Try not to look at other people's maps until you have completed your own. Don't be too concerned if your map seems incomplete—remember, your study of world issues is just beginning!

1. Examine your map. Which parts of the world do you know best? Which parts do you know less well? Why?

2. Do you feel it is important to know where places are in the world? Give reasons for your answer.

3. Save your map. It might be a good idea to do a similar map at the end of this course—there should be a considerable difference!

Grouping Countries

Your mental map is just one way that you can look at the countries of the world. But there are other ways, and they will help you organize your knowledge of the more than 190 countries in the world.

Only an international affairs specialist would be able to keep track of the economic, social, and political similarities and differences of so many nations. For the rest of us, however, it is easier to learn the characteristics of countries by grouping them in some way. If you have ever used or heard terms such as "First World," "developing nation," or "North–South split," then you are already familiar with the idea of referring to groups of countries. Such terms, when used properly, are useful forms of shorthand in the discussion of world issues.

One relatively new way of grouping countries is to consider the degree to which each country is an active participant in a globalized world. The level of global involvement can be assessed by examining three major areas. The first is **economic development**—a community's material wealth and trade, which is determined by such measures as per-capita GDP, ratio of cars to people, and per-capita electrical power capacity. The second major area is **social development**, which is the level of education, healthcare, life expectancy, and rate of infant mortality in a society. The third major area is **political maturity**, which is measured by considering factors such as whether a country is democratic, has a low level of corruption, a functioning and established electoral system, and rule of law.

A variety of measures are used to describe a country's progress in each of these areas. Some measures relate directly to only one area, while others relate to more than one area (see Figure 3–1).

Did You Know?

There is no clear agreement about what constitutes a country. One common way of deciding if a political entity is a country is membership in the United Nations. There were 192 UN members in 2008. That did not include Taiwan and Palestinian Territories, which, by many standards, could be considered countries, and Kosovo, which achieved independence from Serbia in 2008.

Measures of Global Involvement	Description	Relates to 1) Primary, 2) Secondary
Freedom House rating	• measure of political rights and civil liberties • values range from 2 (most rights/liberties) to 14 (least rights/liberties)	1) political growth 2) social development
Infant-mortality rate	• measures the number of children (per 1000 births) who die before age one • values range from about 3 to about 100	1) social development 2) economic development
Gross Domestic Product (GDP) per capita on a Purchasing-Power-Parity (PPP) basis	• frequently used measure of a country's wealth • calculation on a PPP basis relates income to the cost of living in a country • values range from about US$600 to US$69 000	1) economic development
Percentage of GDP from agriculture	• richer, more economically advanced countries earn less of their wealth from agriculture • values range from 1% to 65%	1) economic development 2) social development
Visiting tourists as a percentage of population	• values range from near 0% to over 100%	1) economic development 2) social development
Oil consumption per capita (m^3/person/year)	• recognizes the role played by consumption energy • values range from 0.3 to 1.0	1) economic development
Human Development Index (HDI)	• an index that combines measures of wealth, education, and health • values range from 0.350 to 0.960 (high values are better)	1) social development 2) economic development
Number of McDonald's locations per million people	• values range from 0 to 43	1) social development 2) economic development
Corruption-Perception Index (CPI) from Transparency International	• indicates the degree to which corruption is common in a country's public sector • values range from 1.8 to 9.6 (high values are better)	1) political growth 2) social development economic development
Internet users (per 100 000 people)	• indicates access to the information and entertainment of the Internet • values range from 200 to 80 000	1) social development 2) economic development political growth

Figure 3–1 A wide variety of data can be used to measure a country's global involvement.

Notes: The Freedom House rankings measure political rights and civil liberties. Countries with ratings from 2 to 5 are considered to be "Free," those with ratings from 6 to 10 are considered "Partly Free," and those with ratings from 11 to 14 are considered "Not Free."

You can learn more about Freedom House and Transparency International at the link on our Web site.

When considering how to group countries, two key questions need to be answered: How many groups should we use? and What methods should we use to group the countries together? Let's see how this can be done.

Starting at Home

Let's start "at home" and examine something familiar by looking at Canada. We will also compare Canada to Germany—a country that most people would agree has much in common with Canada (see Figure 3–2). When you look at these statistics, you can see that they are, in fact, similar. On this basis, it would be fair to assume that these two countries belong in the same group of countries. You can almost certainly predict other countries that would join Canada and Germany in this group. In terms of global involvement, both these countries can be considered members of the world's **more globalized core** (or *Core* for short). Countries in the Core have contributed significantly to, and benefitted greatly from, globalization.

The statistics in Figure 3–2 suggest that Canadians and Germans share a lifestyle that is the goal of most people who live outside the Core. They are relatively wealthy and have comfortable lifestyles as a result of their countries' advanced economies. They live in a secure environment with good healthcare. They have a high degree of freedom and have governments that are generally free from serious corruption.

Measures of Global Involvement	Canada	Germany
Freedom House rating	2	2
Infant-mortality rate (per 1000)	4.7	4.1
Gross Domestic Product (GDP) per capita on a PPP basis (US$)	35 200	31 400
Percentage of GDP from agriculture	2	1
Visiting tourists (% of population)	57.8	25.8
Oil consumption (m^3/person/year)	4.022	1.876
Human Development Index (HDI)	0.950	0.932
Number of McDonald's locations (per million people)	35.2	13.2
Corruption-Perception Index (CPI)	8.5	8.0
Internet users (per 100 000 people)	60 966	42 702

Figure 3–2 Suggest several countries that would be members of the more globalized core along with Canada and Germany.

Far from Home

Now let's compare Bangladesh and Zambia, countries that are very different—both in terms of distance and characteristics—from Canada and Germany (see Figure 3–3). The differences could not be more striking. For each of the ten measures, Bangladesh and Zambia—countries on different continents with very different geographies and histories—have similar values. These values, however, vary enormously from those of countries in the Core. It would be fair to conclude that Bangladesh and Zambia are not part of the Core and have not significantly benefitted from globalization. Bangladesh, Zambia, and similar countries can be said to belong to a large group of countries called the **less globalized periphery** (or *Periphery* for short). They are much poorer than countries in the Core and their people have much less personal security. They have limited political freedom and civil liberties, and corruption is almost always a serious problem.

Measures of Global Involvement	Canada	Germany	Bangladesh	Zambia
Freedom House rating	2	2	8	7
Infant-mortality rate (per 1000)	4.7	4.1	60.8	86.8
Gross Domestic Product (GDP) per capita on a PPP basis (US$)	35 200	31 400	2200	1000
Percentage of GDP from agriculture	2	1	20	20
Visiting tourists (% of population)	57.8	25.8	0.01	4.5
Oil consumption (m^3/person/year)	4.022	1.876	0.033	0.066
Human Development Index (HDI)	0.950	0.932	0.530	0.407
Number of McDonald's locations (per million people)	35.2	13.2	0	0
Corruption-Perception Index (CPI)	8.5	8.0	2.0	2.6
Internet users (per 100 000 people)	60 966	42 702	208	2051

Figure 3–3 Comparing the measures of global involvement for Canada, Germany, Bangladesh, and Zambia clearly shows some important differences between the more globalized core and the less globalized periphery.

Figure 3–4 Frankfurt, Germany, is typical of the wealthy cities that are found in Core nations.

Figure 3–5 This slum alley of Dhaka, Bangladesh, is a dramatic example of poverty in the poorest parts of the Periphery.

The Countries In Between

We have looked at two extremes: very rich countries, with advanced social development and relatively smooth-running political structures, and very poor countries lacking in social progress, with political systems that do not work well by western standards. Most countries, however, are somewhere in between. Consider the four countries in Figure 3–6: Malaysia, Poland, Iran, and the Philippines. They do not fit readily into either of our first two groups, but does it make sense to consider them to be members of the same group? We end up with a choice. We can divide them into two groups with less variation within each, or leave them in one group with less precision within each. Most observers suggest that it makes more sense to have four groups in all; that is, to divide our in-between countries into two groups.

| Measures of Global Involvement | OLD CORE | | FAR PERIPHERY | | NEW CORE | | NEAR CORE | |
	Canada (1)	Germany (2)	Bangladesh (3)	Zambia (4)	Malaysia (5)	Poland (6)	Iran (7)	Philippines (8)
Freedom House rating	2	2	8	7	8	2	12	6
Infant-mortality rate (per 1000)	4.7	4.1	60.8	86.8	17.2	7.2	40.3	22.8
Gross Domestic Product (GDP) per capita on a PPP basis (US$)	35 200	31 400	2200	1000	12 700	14 100	8900	5000
Percentage of GDP from agriculture	2	1	20	20	8	5	11	14
Visiting tourists (% of pop.)	57.8	25.8	0.01	4.5	64.4	39.9	2.4	2.6
Oil consumption (m^3/person/year)	4.022	1.876	0.033	0.066	1.224	0.672	1.276	0.222
Human Development Index (HDI)	0.950	0.932	0.530	0.407	0.805	0.862	0.746	0.763
Number of McDonald's locations (per million people)	35.2	13.2	0	0	5.7	0.4	0	2.3
Corruption-Perception Index (CPI)	8.5	8.0	2.0	2.6	5.0	3.7	2.7	2.5
Internet users (per 100 000 people)	60 966	42 702	208	2051	41 243	23 341	8096	5008

Figure 3–6 How do the measures of global involvement for Malaysia, Poland, Iran, and the Philippines compare to those of the first four countries we examined? The numbers under the countries are needed for the country grouping exercise (Figure 3–14) on page 49.

Figure 3–7 This scene in Krakow, Poland, suggests that a fairly advanced standard of living exists in New Core countries. What cannot be seen in this photograph are the advances in political and human rights that are also happening in this part of the world.

Figure 3–8 As the name suggests, economic and political conditions in Near Core countries such as Iran (this is Tehran), are dramatically better than in the Far Periphery but not as advanced as in the New Core.

Countries such as Poland (see Figure 3–7) and Malaysia are generally considered to be members of the Core, even though they are not at the level of Canada and Germany. For example, they are not as wealthy and often have governments that are not as democratic. There is a simple reason for this difference. Poland, Malaysia, and similar nations are relatively new members of the Core. As the years pass, members of this second group of Core nations are becoming more like Canada and Germany. Accordingly, it makes sense to divide the Core into two subgroups: the **Old Core** with members like Canada and Germany, and the **New Core** with members like Malaysia and Poland.

GLOBALIZATION
Poland, Malaysia, and similar nations are relatively new members of the Core.

What political and economic changes have contributed to the dramatic growth of the New Core?

Following a similar logic, the Periphery can be subdivided into two subgroups. Countries such as Iran (see Figure 3–8) and the Philippines are clearly much more advanced than countries such as Bangladesh and Zambia. With continued economic, social, and political growth, they have the potential to join the Core within the next few decades. As a result, this group has been called the **Near-Core Periphery** (or for short, the **Near Core**). In contrast, the level of economic, social, and political development of the final subgroup, including Bangladesh and Zambia, is so limited it will be many years until these countries are able to become fully functioning members of the globalized world. This group has been called the **Far Periphery**. Figure 3–9 summarizes how the world's nations can be grouped.

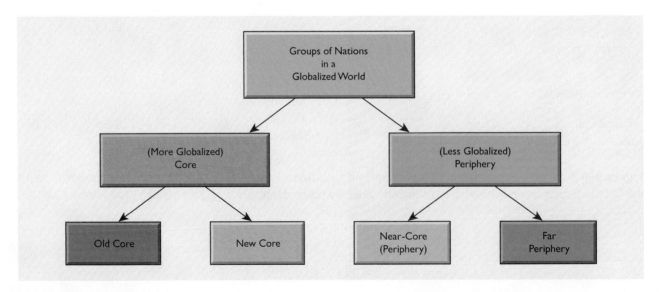

Figure 3–9 Grouping the world's nations

AN EXERCISE IN COUNTRY GROUPING

1. Examine the statistics in Figure 3–10. At first glance, this mass of numbers may be somewhat intimidating and may present no obvious patterns. When you look at them more closely, however, you should start to see similarities between countries; for example, countries B and C seem comparable. Still, trying to divide these countries into our four groups just by examining the table is a formidable task likely to lead to inaccurate results. A much better approach is to look for groupings on a *scatter graph* (a graph used to show the distribution of related pairs of statistical data on an x/y axes graph; also called a scatter plot or scatter diagram) that relates two measures of development. For example,

Figure 3–11 shows the relationship between per-capita GDP and the number of Internet users. Note the location of country B.

2. On a scatter graph like this, it is often relatively easy to identify the countries that have similar characteristics, that is, they belong to the same group. Groupings are not so clear in Figure 3–11, though, because of the mass of countries in the lower-left corner of the graph. In a situation like this, the use of semi-log or log-log graph paper can help. If you are not familiar with the use of logarithmic scales, read section 3. If you are comfortable using log scales, skip to section 4.

Country	Freedom House Rating	Infant-Mortality Rate (per 1000)	GDP Per Capita on a PPP basis ($US)	Percentage of GDP from Agriculture	Visiting Tourists (% of population)	Oil Consumption (m³/person/yr)	Human Development Index (HDI)	McD's Locations (per million people)	Corruption-Perception Index (CPI)	Internet Users (per 100 000 people)
A	11	70.5	2 600	22	0.4	0.113	0.539	0.1	2.2	1 231
B	2	6.4	43 500	1	15.5	4.038	0.948	43.3	7.3	54 655
C	2	4.6	32 900	4	23.5	2.544	0.957	34.9	8.7	64 709
D	11	15.1	12 100	5	13.9	1.015	0.797	0.7	2.5	11 156
E	11	19.5	9 100	10	18.2	0.808	0.784	1.4	3.6	10 862
F	6	51.8	3 000	13	4.5	0.303	0.692	0.0	2.7	3 951
G	13	12.8	13 800	3	33.7	3.959	0.777	3.5	3.3	6 003
H	12	91.5	1 500	33	0.2	1.319	0.368	0.0	2.0	621
I	3	3.2	33 100	2	4.8	2.433	0.949	28.7	7.6	50 354
J	3	6.2	24 200	3	11.9	2.560	0.912	5.0	5.1	64 925
K	4	28.6	8 600	8	2.5	0.677	0.792	0.6	3.3	11 821
L	5	30.9	6 400	9	4.2	0.320	0.767	0.4	3.3	1 153
M	8	97.1	1 400	17	0.7	0.128	0.448	0.0	2.2	1 374
N	5	34.4	3 800	13	2.2	0.256	0.711	0.3	2.4	5 996
O	13	23.1	7 600	12	3.2	0.289	0.768	0.3	3.3	7 196
P	2	2.7	31 600	1	34.3	2.333	0.951	25.2	9.2	75 539

Figure 3–10 You can use these data sets to determine the characteristics and members of each of the four groups.

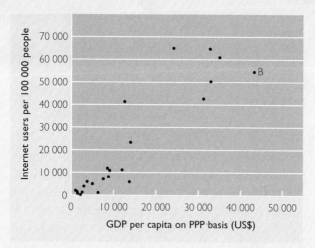

Figure 3–11 Linear scales do not work well with these data sets since there are so many values clustered in the lower-left corner.

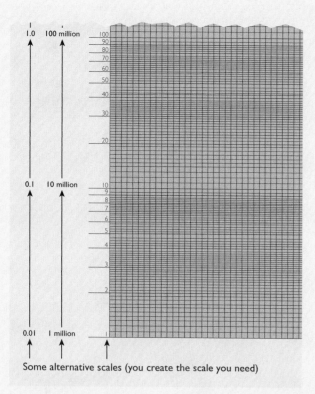

Some alternative scales (you create the scale you need)

Figure 3–12 This logarithmic scale has two cycles, which means it could be used to show two orders of magnitude. The user decides what values to assign to the scale based on the data to be shown.

3. **a)** Logarithmic graphing seems a lot more complex and intimidating than it really is. In fact, the difficult mathematical part (the logarithmic conversion) is done for you when you use special graph paper with a logarithmic

scale (see Figure 3–12). Graph paper that has one logarithmic scale and one linear scale is called *semi-log* paper. Graph paper with log scales on both the *x*- and *y*-axes is called *log-log* paper.

b) You should consider using a logarithmic scale any time you have data that extend over three or more orders of magnitude. For example, if you have numbers in the 10s, 100s, and 1000s, you could use a logarithmic scale with three cycles to display three orders of magnitude. If you have numbers in the millions, tens of millions, hundreds of millions, and billions, you have four orders of magnitude—so you would need to use four-cycle logarithmic graph paper. Generally, if you have only one or two orders of magnitude, you can use conventional, linear graph paper successfully.

c) There are three restrictions on the use of logarithmic scales. Two of those restrictions are that you cannot show negative values, and you cannot show zero. In both cases, this is because there would always be another smaller, positive cycle to the left of (or below) the one currently being shown. For example, if you have a cycle that goes from 1 to 10, the cycle below this would go from 0.1 to 1, and the one below that from 0.01 to 0.1 (and so on). The third restriction is you cannot show both positive and negative values on the same graph.

4. Figure 3–13 shows what the data in Figure 3–11 would look like if we use semi-log graph paper. On this graph, a logarithmic scale has been used for the number of Internet users in each country. This method of graphing spreads out the data and makes it easier to see the differences.

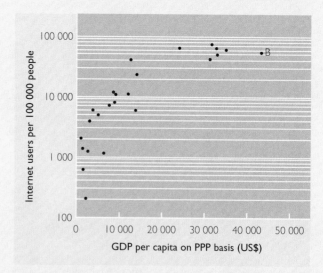

Figure 3–13 A semi-log graph makes the data in Figure 3–11 easier to interpret but there is still tight cluttering (in the *x*-axis direction), particularly on the left side of the graph.

If we now move from semi-log to log-log paper (Figure 3–14), it gets even easier to identify the country groupings, since we have now expanded the GDP per-capita scale.

5. Work in a group of three or four students. Each of you will draw at least two scatter graphs, each showing different pairs of data. You will have to decide which type of graph

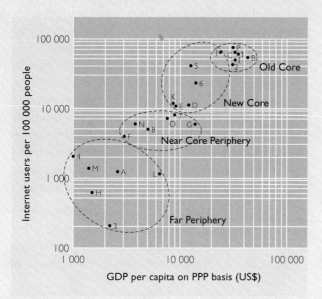

Figure 3–14 Log-log graphing makes country groupings even easier to see. The Far-Periphery group is particularly clear. The Old Core is fairly obvious, although the status of country J is a bit unclear. There is a bit of confusion along the border between the New Core and the Near Core. This situation would be clarified by doing graphs with other data.

paper is appropriate for the data you are using. Each student should do at least one graph that requires either semi-log or log-log graph paper to allow for easier interpretation. From each graph, you should identify which countries you think are in each of the four groups.

6. Here are some hints to help you with this analysis:

a) Include the eight sample countries from Figure 3–6 (Canada, Germany, etc.) on your graph. Since you know which groups these are in, they will help you identify country groups on your graph.

b) There are four countries from each group in Figure 3–10. Hence there are six countries in each group on your graph (two sample countries + four countries from Figure 3–10).

c) On any particular graph, there may be ambiguous results. For example, in Figure 3–14, it is not clear to which group countries D, E, K, and J may belong. To clarify, compare your results with those obtained from other graphs (yours or those done by other members of your group) so you can arrive at a consensus about the correct grouping for each country.

d) When you are done, your teacher will tell you which countries are in each group. How did you do? You can also check Figure 3–15, although it is hard to tell in which group many small countries are at this scale.

As your study of world issues continues, you will have many opportunities to use this four-world model, so be sure to examine Figure 3–15 in detail.

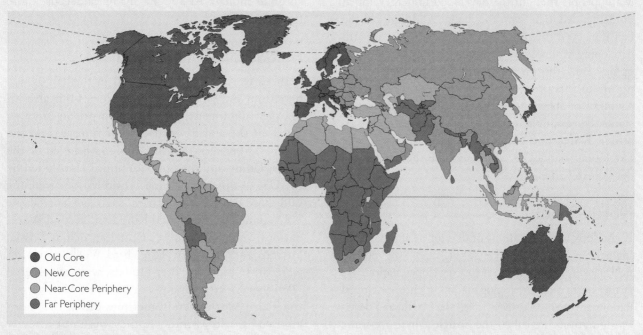

Figure 3–15 The world can be divided into four groups based on their level of global involvement and social, political, and economic status.

Other Ways to Group Countries

Over the years, many methods have been used to group countries in the world. You should be familiar with the more common methods, or models, because the terminology derived from them is often used in the media and in classrooms. Try to look for similarities between the countries in each of the groups described in the models below and in the four groups we identified above.

Using Two Groups

Very often the world has been divided into two groups based on differing levels of economic development. The use of two groups has been popular because of its simplicity, even if having so few groups must inevitably lead to a high degree of imprecision within each group.

Developed/Underdeveloped Worlds

In this relatively old and simple model, the world was divided into economically developed countries (what we have called the Old Core) and underdeveloped countries (everyone else). A major problem with this approach is that there can be confusion between economic and non-economic development. For example, some economically less-developed countries, such as India and China, are highly developed culturally.

Developed/Developing Worlds

Many people thought the developed/underdeveloped model tended to be *static* (unchanging). It ignored the fact that even the most developed countries are still developing in almost every respect. The developed/developing model, though, more fairly reflected the dynamic nature of this process of development. Over time, countries are able to move from developing to developed status. For example, in the years after World War II, South Korea and Singapore were clearly in the developing world. Fifty years later, they had joined the developed world.

North–South

If you look at the locations of developed and developing nations on a world map (see Figure 3–16), you will notice a surprising pattern. Most developed nations are farther north than developing nations. Hence, developed nations are often collectively called the **North,** and developing nations are called the **South**. There are some obvious exceptions, however, to this rule. Australia, New Zealand, and Argentina are quite far south and yet are developed countries. Geographers looking at this pattern might quickly conclude a more accurate description is that developed countries tend to be located in temperate regions, while developing countries tend to be located in tropical areas. They would argue that the terms "temperate" and "tropical" might be more accurate descriptors of two groups of countries. Unfortunately, the simpler, if less accurate, "North" and "South" terminology continues to be commonly used.

South Africa, which has a latitude similar to Australia, New Zealand, and Argentina, is in a unique situation. In spite of the end of the Apartheid system, it continues to have an economy that is partly North (the part that continues to be white-dominated) and partly South (the rest of the economy).

GLOBALIZATION

Geographers looking at this pattern would argue that the terms "temperate" and "tropical" might be more accurate descriptors of two groups of countries.

Why have these more accurate terms not replaced North–South in common usage?

Using Three Groups

Over the years, many geographers decided dividing the countries of the world into only two groups was not accurate enough. As a result, many models use more than two groups.

First/Second/Third World

A three-world model developed in the 1950s was based not only on development levels but also on political alignments. This is not surprising since so much of the world's focus at that time was on the Cold War between the Communist world led by the Soviet Union and the non-Communist world led by the US. In this model, First World nations were the Old Core capitalist countries, such as Canada, the US, Japan, and the United Kingdom. Second World nations were Communist countries, such as Russia, Poland, and Hungary. The Third World countries were those that, in other models, were considered "Periphery", "developing", or "South". Members of the Third World were sometimes called the "nonaligned" world to indicate they were not directly connected to either the First or Second World camps.

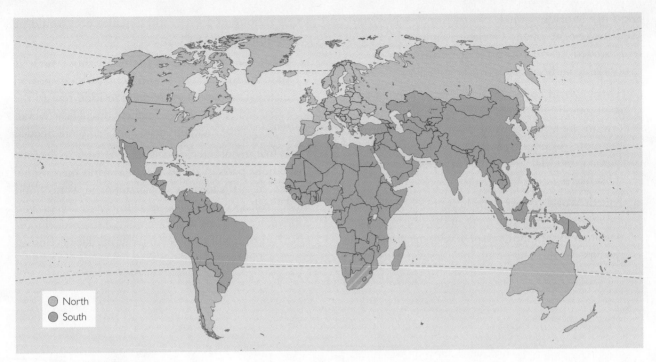

Figure 3–16 While the use of the terms "North" and "South" remains common today, a more accurate description would be "temperate" and "tropical." Note that South Africa is striped on this map to indicate its unique situation.

In this model, non-European Communist countries, such as Cuba, China, and Vietnam, were in an *ambiguous* (able to be seen in more than one different way) situation. They had some characteristics of Second World countries (for example, their form of government and their focus on social development issues such as medical care and education) and some characteristics of Third World countries (for example, poor economic development). As a result, they were sometimes considered Second World, if the discussion was focused on political and military issues; or sometimes Third World, if the discussion was focused on developmental issues. Of these three "worlds," the only term commonly used today is **Third World**.

Developed/Newly Industrialized/ Developing

This model, which is entirely economic in nature, adds a transitional stage for countries moving from an agriculturally based economy to a more advanced industrial- or service-based economy. The reason for the addition was to allow more precision when describing the characteristics of each group. In this model, the newly industrialized states would be spread over what we have called the New Core and Near Core.

Using More Than Three Groups

Several models have more than three groups; for example, some models allow for more transitional stages. Other models have country groups that reflect particular types of economic development. A good example of this would be a model that has a separate group for rich oil-producing countries like Saudi Arabia and Brunei that have little economic development other than oil production.

Five Worlds

An earlier edition of *Global Connections* included a five-world model. Five worlds were chosen as a reasonable compromise between accuracy and simplicity. The First and Second Worlds were as described above, although by the time of publication in 2003, most Second World countries were no longer Communist; they were gradually evolving into capitalist economies at various levels of development. For example, Hungary and Latvia were slowly becoming members of the First World, while Kazakhstan and Armenia were moving into the Third World because they were not as economically developed as Hungary and Latvia. This five-world model divided the enormous range of developing economies into three "worlds" called Third, Fourth, and Fifth Worlds. China, North Korea, Cuba, and Vietnam were exceptions. Of these, China and Vietnam had moved toward capitalist economies while maintaining authoritarian governments.

- Third World countries had levels of social and economic development that were rapidly moving toward the levels found in First World countries. Examples of countries in this group are Brazil, Mexico, and Malaysia. In our model, this would be most like the New Core.

- Fourth World countries had economic and social development levels that were in the early stages of transition toward the levels of development found in the First World. This group includes countries such as Indonesia, Egypt, and Ecuador and would be most like the Near Core.

- Fifth World countries included those such as Bangladesh, Ethiopia, and Haiti, which showed little evidence of starting the transition toward the social and economic development of the First World. What group would this be in our Four-World model?

While any of these models could be used to describe the various parts of the world, in a world increasingly influenced by the forces of globalization, our Four-World model makes a great deal of sense. In *Global Connections: Canadian and World Issues*, we will use this model most often, but you will also encounter terms like developing country and First World.

Knowledge and Understanding

1. Define each of the following terms:

   a) more globalized core

   b) less globalized periphery

   c) Old Core

   d) New Core

   e) Near Core

   f) Far Periphery

2. You were exposed to a great many terms for describing country groups in this chapter—many of which overlap. Listed below are these terms, grouped by the model in which each appears. Pair the Core/Periphery model to each of the other models in the table. For example, the term "Old Core" would be paired with the term "Developed." Use Venn diagrams to identify the matches. Your teacher will give you a handout to help you do this.

Old Core	Developed	
New Core	Developing	
Near Core		
Far Periphery		
South	Developed	
North	Underdeveloped	
Second World	Developing	Fourth World
First World	Newly Industrialized	Fifth World
Third World	Developed	Third World
		First World
		Second World

3. Consider the five-world model. Why was it inevitable that this model would eventually evolve into a four-world model of some sort?

4. a) We have looked at a model for country grouping based on the idea that economic, social, and political development stem from globalization. Why does this idea make sense? In your answer, consider all three aspects of development as described in this chapter.

   b) Even members of the Far Periphery like Bangladesh and Zambia have some degree of globalization. Describe examples of this for each of these countries. If you do not know the answers, you may have to do some Internet research.

Thinking

5. a) Look at the ten measures of global involvement in Figure 3–1. Write a brief description, in your own words, of each measure, indicating why it is a useful measure of economic, social, and/or political development. (Hint: You may wish to refer to the Glossary for an explanation of some of the terms.)

   b) Suggest two additional measures that could be used to describe development in each area.

6. Why might higher levels of development of a country be related to temperate locations?

Communication

7. a) In your notebook, copy and complete the table in Figure 3–17 to show the range of values that is typical within each of the four worlds for each measure of development. Use the data from Figure 3–10.

b) Create a visual summary of these data. You are not limited to showing the data in graphs; you can use drawings, cartoons, collages, or some other medium to do this.

Your teacher will tell you whether you will do this activity on paper or using GIS.

Application

8. Consider the mental map that you completed at the beginning of this chapter.

a) What factors have influenced your knowledge of the world?

b) How might these factors influence how you approach this course and what you will learn about world issues?

c) What did you learn in this chapter that helps to fill in any gaps in the knowledge you had at the beginning of this course? **G**

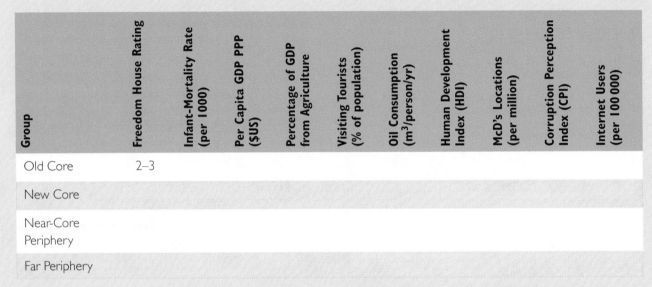

Group	Freedom House Rating	Infant-Mortality Rate (per 1000)	Per Capita GDP PPP ($US)	Percentage of GDP from Agriculture	Visiting Tourists (% of population)	Oil Consumption (m³/person/yr)	Human Development Index (HDI)	McD's Locations (per million)	Corruption Perception Index (CPI)	Internet Users (per 100 000)
Old Core	2–3									
New Core										
Near-Core Periphery										
Far Periphery										

Figure 3–17 Copy and complete the table to show the range of values that is typical within each of the four worlds for each measure of development.

UNIT 2 HUMAN POPULATION

The world is facing two conflicting population problems. In some parts of the world, population growth is the issue—there are too many people. In other regions, the problem is the opposite—increasing population decline.

CHAPTER 4

Demography

Key Terms

demography
carrying capacity
nomadic hunters and gatherers
Agricultural Revolution
Industrial Revolution
birth rate
death rate
natural increase rate
immigration rate
emigration rate
net migration rate
population growth rate
dependency measures
dependency load
age-dependency ratio
infant mortality rate
life expectancy
population pyramid
total fertility rate
replacement rate
rule of 70

How will changes in human populations around the world affect your future?

Key Questions

By the end of this chapter you will be able to answer the following questions.

■ What demographic trends are taking place in the world?

■ How does new technology affect employment and resource management?

■ How do we measure demographic changes?

■ What conclusions, judgments, or predictions can I make using reasoned analysis and supporting evidence?

The world's population growth is summarized in Figure 4–1. Graph these data using semi-log graph paper and then answer the following questions. You will need two-cycle paper to show population growth on the y-axis (logarithmic scale). (A brief introduction to the use of semi-log graph paper can be found in Chapter 3.)

(The beginning of the *Common Era* [CE] is based on the Gregorian Calendar, with years numbered from the birth of Jesus. The BCE [Before the Common Era] and CE systems have the same chronology as the BC [Before Christ] and AD [Anno Domini] systems.)

1. Along the line showing population growth, label the point at which each of the following events occurred. If you are not sure of some dates, you may have to conduct some research at the library or on reliable Web sites.
   - the arrival of the Vikings in North America
   - the invention of the Gutenberg printing press
   - the year Canada became a country
   - the year the first humans landed on the moon
   - the year of your birth
   - today

2. Geographers and other social scientists have estimated world populations in the period before 1 CE. These estimates suggest that the world had 125 000 people one million years ago, 3 000 000 people 35 000 years ago, and 5 000 000 people 10 000 years ago. What do these figures tell you about the rate of population growth during this time?

3. During which time periods did the world's population decrease? Suggest why this might have happened.

4. In what time period did the population explosion begin? Suggest three reasons why this occurred. You may need to do some research.

5. a) How many years did it take for the world's population to increase from
   i) one billion to two billion
   ii) two billion to three billion
   iii) three billion to four billion
   iv) four billion to five billion
   v) five billion to six billion
   b) The projections in Figure 4–1 are from the United Nations. Using these UN projections, calculate the number of years it may take for the world's population to increase from

   i) six billion to seven billion
   ii) seven billion to eight billion
   iii) eight billion to nine billion
   iv) nine billion to ten billion
   c) What change in pattern did you see? When did this change happen?
   d) What does this tell you about the world's population growth rate?

6. a) What advantages are there to using semi-log graph paper for this type of data?
   b) What approach would you use if you wanted to create a world population growth graph that would go back one million years? Why would you choose this approach?

Date (ce)	Population (millions)	Date (ce)	Population (millions)
1	300	1950	2500
200	310	**1960**	**3000**
600	300	1970	3600
1000	400	**1974**	**4000**
1200	500	1980	4400
1400	400	**1987**	**5000**
1500	440	1990	5300
1600	540	**1999**	**6000**
1700	720	2000	6100
1800	980	2007	6600
1804	**1000**	**2013***	**7000**
1900	1600	**2028***	**8000**
1920	1800	**2054***	**9 000**
1927	**2000**	**2183***	**10 000**
1940	2300		

Figure 4–1 World population growth since Common Era

*projected

Trends in Population

Demography, the study of human populations, is an important tool for governments and businesses. They rely on demographic data to help them predict future needs for such essentials as schools, housing, and labour, formulate plans to deal with these changing needs, and determine what types of consumer goods and services will be needed. Demography helps explain the causes and effects of population change within local communities, across Canada, and throughout the rest of the world.

About 90 percent of the human population occupies about 20 percent of Earth's land area. The cartogram of world population in Figure 4–2 shows the size of each country if it were based on population rather than on actual land area.

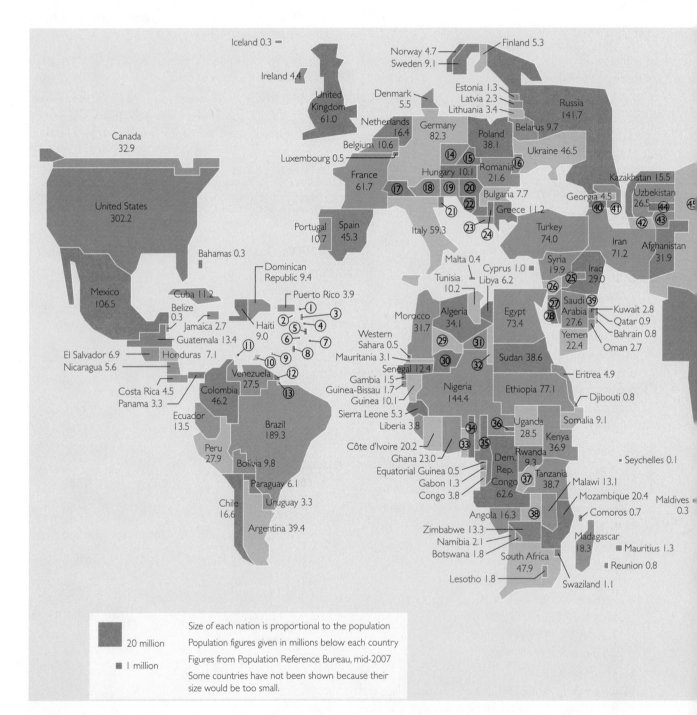

Figure 4–2 This population cartogram shows the size of each country according to its population. The most populous countries are shown as the largest.

By 2007, the total world population was about 6.6 billion. Although this is a significant figure, the rate at which the population was growing is equally significant. The graph you constructed in the World Population Graphing activity gives you some idea of the growth rate of the world's population. A summary of growth rates from 1600 appears in Figure 4–3. The values in this table are simple growth rates based on how much the population grew between the years shown.

In this unit, we will concentrate on two population trends: the first, the population explosion since the 1600s, is shown in Figure 4–1; the second, the decline in the population growth rate since 1980, is shown in Figure 4–3.

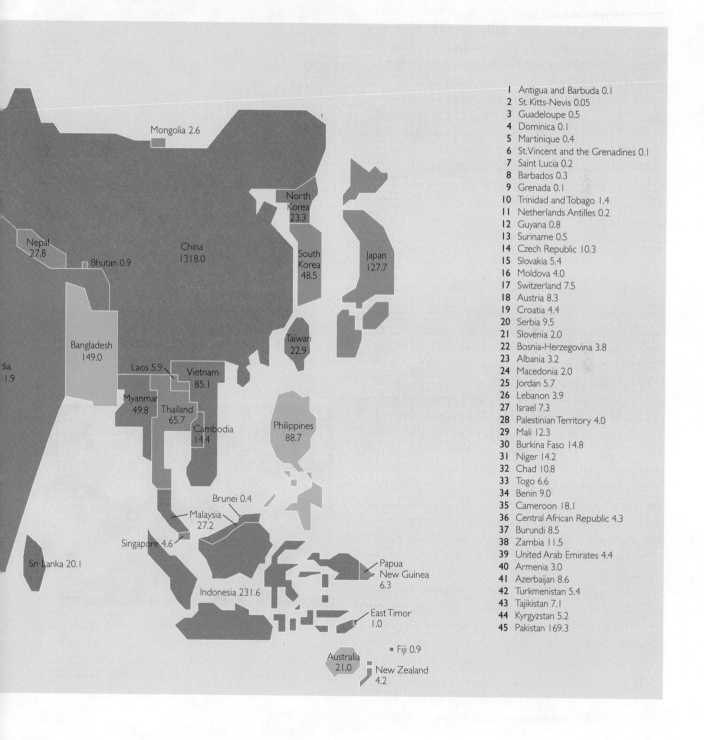

1	Antigua and Barbuda 0.1
2	St. Kitts-Nevis 0.05
3	Guadeloupe 0.5
4	Dominica 0.1
5	Martinique 0.4
6	St. Vincent and the Grenadines 0.1
7	Saint Lucia 0.2
8	Barbados 0.3
9	Grenada 0.1
10	Trinidad and Tobago 1.4
11	Netherlands Antilles 0.2
12	Guyana 0.8
13	Suriname 0.5
14	Czech Republic 10.3
15	Slovakia 5.4
16	Moldova 4.0
17	Switzerland 7.5
18	Austria 8.3
19	Croatia 4.4
20	Serbia 9.5
21	Slovenia 2.0
22	Bosnia-Herzegovina 3.8
23	Albania 3.2
24	Macedonia 2.0
25	Jordan 5.7
26	Lebanon 3.9
27	Israel 7.3
28	Palestinian Territory 4.0
29	Mali 12.3
30	Burkina Faso 14.8
31	Niger 14.2
32	Chad 10.8
33	Togo 6.6
34	Benin 9.0
35	Cameroon 18.1
36	Central African Republic 4.3
37	Burundi 8.5
38	Zambia 11.5
39	United Arab Emirates 4.4
40	Armenia 3.0
41	Azerbaijan 8.6
42	Turkmenistan 5.4
43	Tajikistan 7.1
44	Kyrgyzstan 5.2
45	Pakistan 169.3

Map labels: Mongolia 2.6 · Nepal 27.8 · Bhutan 0.9 · China 1318.0 · North Korea 23.3 · South Korea 48.5 · Japan 127.7 · Bangladesh 149.0 · Taiwan 22.9 · Laos 5.9 · Vietnam 85.1 · Myanmar 49.8 · Thailand 65.7 · Cambodia 14.4 · Philippines 88.7 · India 1.9 · Sri Lanka 20.1 · Brunei 0.4 · Malaysia 27.2 · Singapore 4.6 · Papua New Guinea 6.3 · Indonesia 231.6 · East Timor 1.0 · Fiji 0.9 · Australia 21.0 · New Zealand 4.2

The Population Explosion

The first trend, as seen in Figure 4–1, is the population explosion that began in the latter half of the 1600s and accelerated through the 1900s and into the 21st century. Two statistics illustrate what happened to the world's population during the 1900s. In 1960, the world's population reached three billion. It had taken more than one million years to reach this level. Fewer than 40 years later, in 1999, the population had doubled to six billion. Consider what effect this growth had on people, governments, and economic systems in the latter half of the 20th century. In only 40 years, the world had to provide for twice as many people. This meant, among other things, twice as much food, twice as many homes, and twice as many jobs.

A minority of the world's citizens enjoyed a high standard of living over this period. Most of this privileged minority lived in Old Core countries such as Canada and Sweden. Some lived in New Core countries such as South Korea and Poland, and a few, the wealthy elites, lived in Near Core countries such as the Philippines and Iran. A much larger group of people concentrated in the Near Core and Far Periphery lived in abject poverty at a level most Canadians could not even imagine.

Declining Growth Rate

At first glance, the second trend—the decline in the world's growth rate since 1980—seems relatively insignificant (Figure 4–3). The reduction from 2.31 percent in 1980 to 1.25 percent in 2007 seems small. In fact, 1.25 is, by historical standards a high rate of growth. At the same time, however, it indicates the largest decline in the world population growth rate in human history. The magnitude of the decline is partially hidden by the fact that different countries of the world were experiencing two entirely different population trends. Some were experiencing high growth rates and the problems that these entail; others were experiencing declining growth rates, or at least, would soon experience them. The age composition of countries changed as a result of each of these trends (see Figure 4–4).

Countries that experience declining populations, or negative growth rates face new challenges because their social systems and economies are based on the assumption that populations will continue to grow. Consider the following examples that show the impact that a declining growth rate could have on you.

■ If Canada's population growth rate declines, the percentage of young people entering the labour force would become considerably lower than the

percentage of older people heading into retirement. You, as a young Canadian working in a shrinking labour force, would have to pay more tax than the previous generation to cover the cost of the greater number of services (for example, pensions, health-care, retirement homes) needed by an ever-increasing aging population.

From	To	Average Annual Growth Rate (%) (ignoring compounding)
1600	1700	0.14
1700	1800	0.52
1800	1900	0.71
1900	1920	0.62
1920	1940	1.18
1940	1960	1.61
1960	1980	2.31
1980	2000	1.83
2000	2007	1.25

Figure 4–3 The calculation of a growth rate is as follows: the population in the "To" year, minus the population in the "From" year, is divided by the number of years between the dates. The resulting value is divided by the population in the "From" year. This value is then multiplied by 100 to express it as a percentage.

Figure 4–4 A group of seniors in Yokohama, Japan. Fourteen percent of Japan's people are under the age of 15, while 21 percent are 65 or older. In contrast, 48 percent of the population of the west African country of Guinea-Bissau are under 15, while only 3 percent are 65 and older.

■ Most young Canadians look forward to buying homes that will become more valuable over the years because of constantly growing demand. The enhanced value of their homes could be used to help pay for a more expensive home, or to help provide for a comfortable retirement. But when the population growth rate declines, and there are fewer young people to buy homes, the demand for housing falls. This, in turn, reduces the value of everybody's home. What impact would this have on families' economic progress?

Technological Change and Population Growth

At different times in human history, revolutionary discoveries in technology have produced changes in the way people live and in the carrying capacity of Earth. Earth's **carrying capacity** is the number of people that the world's resources can support using the technology that exists at that time. In this section, you will have an opportunity to learn about the relationships among technology, lifestyle, and population.

Stage 1: Hunting and Gathering

In the earliest stages of human history, people were **nomadic hunters and gatherers**. Hunting and food gathering played an important role in ensuring the survival of the extended family groups that lived together. Two facts stand out about the hunting-and-gathering "lifestyle." The first is that the food supply of these societies was not reliable, and as a consequence, population growth did not increase at a steady rate. When game or edible plants were abundant, survival rates were higher and population increased; if food was scarce, survival rates were lower and populations decreased. The second fact is that because a very large area of land was necessary to support a relatively small number of people, the earth's carrying capacity was low. The world's population was a few tens of millions at the most. Before the population could substantially increase, a more reliable and abundant food supply had to be developed. This would be accomplished by new technology.

Stage 2: The Agricultural Revolution

The development of agriculture is undoubtedly the most important innovation in history. Without it, cultural and technological advances would not have been possible. Agriculture developed independently in many places around the world at different times. We know it was practised more than 10 000 years ago in what is now the Middle East, China, India, Africa, and the Americas (see Figure 4–5).

Once farming became a successful activity, life was never the same. The most important result of farming was the creation of a food surplus, which had some staggering impacts on society (see Figure 4–6). As you might expect, the **Agricultural Revolution** had a profound effect on the world's population. When more food could be obtained from each square kilometre of land, the land's carrying capacity grew. In the centuries that followed the development of farming, agricultural productivity and Earth's carrying capacity increased.

Stage 3: The Industrial Revolution

By the 1700s, agriculture and the production of manufactured goods in the more technologically developed parts of the world (principally western Europe) had become quite advanced, but further progress was being impeded by an "energy crisis" of sorts. The only source of energy was the muscle power of people and domesticated animals such as horses and oxen. The solution to this energy crisis—the invention of machines powered by steam—led to what we now call the **Industrial Revolution**.

The earliest sources of power were ones that we now consider to be desirable because they relied on clean, renewable resources. Examples include the famous windmills of Holland, which were used to pump water, and the *gristmills* (water-powered mills that grind wheat and other grains into flour) and sawmills that were crucial to the development of southern Ontario. More powerful energy sources were developed later: coal, in the late 1700s, and oil in the late 1800s.

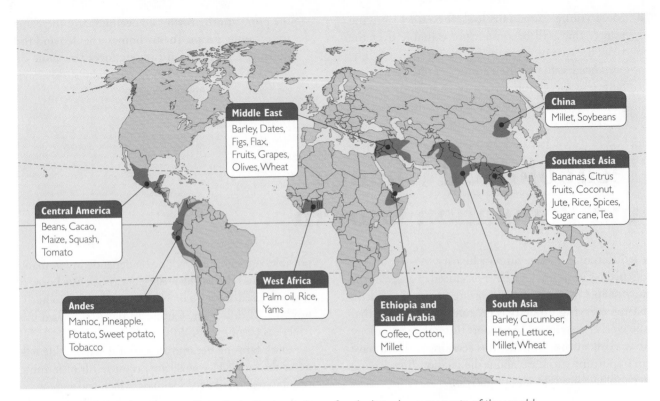

Figure 4–5 Consider how your diet reflects the beginnings of agriculture in many parts of the world.

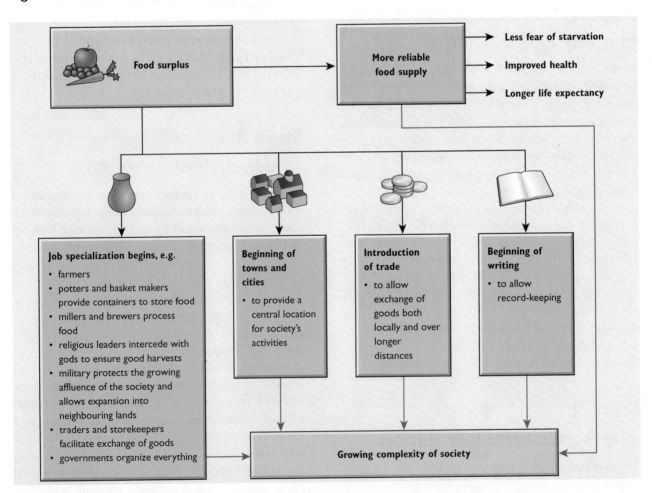

Figure 4–6 When we consider the developments in agriculture, it is not hard to imagine that it was the most profound advancement in human history.

Like the Agricultural Revolution, the Industrial Revolution fundamentally changed the nature of life. Both in the factory and on the farm, a person's physical efforts were multiplied many times by the use of energy from a variety of sources. In fact, one's physical strength became much less important than one's skills and intellect. One of the many impacts of the Industrial Revolution on agriculture was that substantially fewer farm workers were needed to grow food.

Out-of-work agricultural workers migrated to cities or, in some cases, to the new colonies in the Americas or Australia. This migration to cities, which became the great urban boom that continues today in many countries, fundamentally changed the nature of the population in those parts of the world.

Another impact of the Industrial Revolution was that it greatly increased the carrying capacity of Earth. The Industrial Revolution's improved agricultural techniques led to the production of more food per square kilometre.

Measuring Demographics

There are two types of demographic measures: absolute and relative (see Figure 4–7). Absolute measures are simply the number of something. For example, in a given year, Country A has 400 000 births, while Country B has 200 000 births.

These two absolute measures are of limited usefulness because when we compare them, we still don't know if each measure is a large or small number of births for these particular countries. On the other hand, relative measures relate one number to another. For example, if Country A has a population of 40 million, then with 400 000 births, it has 0.01 births for every person in the country. We related the absolute number of the population to the absolute number of births to create a relative birth rate. We usually express the measure 0.01 as 10 births for every 1000 people. If Country B has a population of ten million, then with 200 000 births, it has 20 births for every 1000 people. With relative values like these, a comparison becomes much easier. Accordingly, in this chapter we will focus on relative measures in the form of rates.

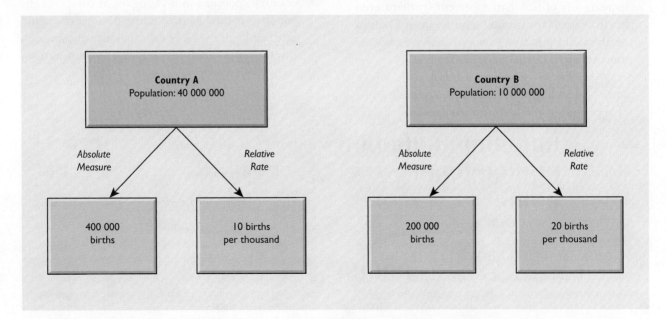

Figure 4–7 Statistics have more meaning and are easier to analyze when relative measurements are used.

A Primer of Demographic Terms

In this section, you will have the chance to learn some of the terminology that will help your study of world populations. You will notice that these terms are used frequently in all parts of the book. They should become part of your working vocabulary.

■ **Birth rate** is the number of births in a country for every thousand people in the population. For example, if 150 000 children are born in a given year in a country with a population of 5 000 000, the birth rate would be 30 per thousand (150 000 / 5 000 000 × 1000 = 30). A birth rate over 30 is considered high, and less than 15 is considered low. In 2007, Canada's birth rate was 11 per thousand.

■ **Death rate** is calculated in a fashion similar to birth rate. For example, if our sample country of 5 000 000 people had 100 000 deaths in a year, the death rate would be 20 per thousand (100 000 / 5 000 000 × 1000 = 20). High and low death rates are over 30 and under 15 per thousand, respectively. Canada's death rate was only 8 per thousand in 2007.

■ **Natural increase rate** is the difference between a country's birth rate and death rate. In our sample country, with a birth rate of 30 and a death rate of 20, the natural increase would be 10 per thousand, or 1 percent. A less developed country might have a natural increase rate of over 2 percent, while a more developed country might have a natural increase rate of less than 1 percent (perhaps even less than zero). For Canada, a birth rate of 11 and a death rate of 8 meant a natural increase of 3 per thousand, or 0.3 percent, in 2007.

■ **Immigration rate** measures the number of people who permanently move to a country. It is calculated in a fashion similar to the birth rate. For example, if 15 000 people move to our sample country, it will have an immigration rate of 3 per thousand (15 000 / 5 000 000 × 1000). Between July 1, 2006 and June 30, 2007, Canada's immigration rate was 7.2 per thousand.

■ **Emigration rate** deals with the number of people who permanently leave a country. It is calculated like the birth rate. For example, if 10 000 people leave our sample country of 5 000 000 in a given year, the emigration rate would be 2 per thousand (10 000 / 5 000 000 × 1000). Canada's emigration rate between July 1, 2006 and June 30, 2007 was 1.3 per thousand.

■ **Net migration rate** is the difference between the immigration rate and the emigration rate. In our example, with an immigration rate of 3 per thousand and an emigration rate of 2 per thousand, the net migration rate is 1 per thousand, or 0.1 percent. Only a few countries (Canada, the US, and Australia are good examples) have large positive net migration rates; that is, more people move into the country than out of it. Most countries have small negative net migration rates, that is, more people move out of the country than into it. For Canada, an immigration rate of 7.2 per thousand and an emigration rate of 1.3 per thousand mean a net migration rate of 5.9 per thousand, or about 0.6 percent.

■ **Population growth rate** is the rate at which a country's population is changing. It combines the country's natural increase rate and its net migration rate (see Figure 4–8). For the majority of countries, migration is much less important than natural

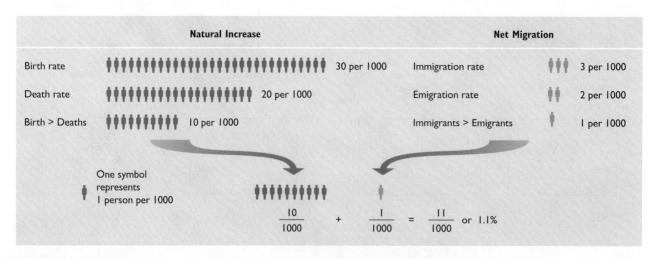

Figure 4–8 Our sample country's population increase has two parts: natural increase and net migration.

increase as a determinant of population growth (or decline). Population growth rates are most commonly given as percentages. A high rate of growth would be anything in excess of 2 percent. For 2007, Canada's natural increase of 3 per thousand and net migration rate of 6 per thousand give a population growth rate of 9 per thousand, or about 0.9 percent. A few countries are experiencing negative growth rates.

■ **Dependency measures** are used to compare the population in the "dependent ages" (those who need to be housed, fed, educated, etc., for example, those 14 and under and 65 and older) to those in the "working ages" of 15 to 64. Even though some people in the dependent ages do work and some in the working ages do not, these ages have been selected by population-measuring organizations to make global comparisons possible.

Some countries have a large number of dependent children, while others have a large number of dependent older people. Too many dependent people can put great stress on a country's economy. There is no single value that can be used to determine when the dependent population is too large. Many factors complicate this judgment. For example, a wealthy country has more resources to meet the needs of its dependent population. On the other hand, the dependent people in such countries may have high expectations for things such as advanced medical care and comfortable housing. Two measures of dependency are commonly used.

■ The **dependency load** is the percentage of a country's population that is 14 and under and 65 and older that must be supported by the independent, working population. In 2007, about 17 percent of Canadians were 14 and under, while another 14 percent were 65 or older, so the dependency load was 31 percent.

■ The **age-dependency ratio** is the ratio of people in the "dependent" ages to those in the "working" ages. It is calculated using the following formula:

$$\frac{\text{population 14 and under + population 65 and older}}{\text{population 15 to 64}} \times 100$$

In 2007, Canada's age-dependency ratio was

$$\frac{5\ 605\ 920 + 4\ 616\ 640}{22\ 753\ 440} \times 100 = 44.9.$$

This means there were 45 people in the dependent ages for every 100 persons in the working ages.

■ **Infant mortality rate** is the number of children in a country who die in the first year of life for each 1000 births. It is commonly used as a measure of economic and social development. An infant mortality rate of over 80 is considered high. A rate of less than 15 is considered low. Canada's infant mortality rate in 2006 was 5.3 per thousand.

■ **Life expectancy** is the average lifespan, at birth, of a human being. A short lifespan is less than 50 years, while a long lifespan is over 75 years. The life expectancy for Canada's population in 2006 was 80 years.

■ **Population pyramid** is a special type of graph that summarizes the age and gender structure of a population (see Figure 4–9). Each bar graph in the pyramid indicates the number or percentage of people of a

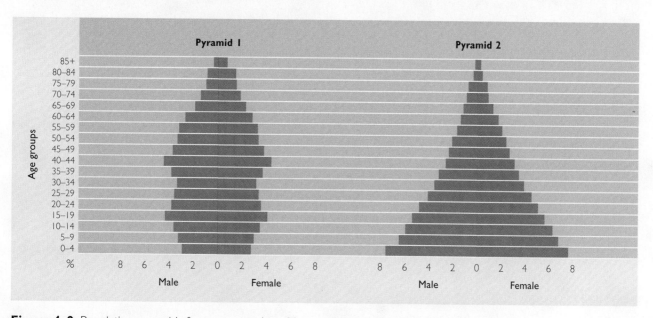

Figure 4–9 Population pyramids for two countries with very different population characteristics

particular gender in a specific age group; for example, males aged 15 to 19 are shown in green and females aged 15 to 19 in brown. Sometimes you will be most interested in some detail of the pyramid, for example, the impact of a world war on the balance of men and women. More often, though, you will want to look at the overall shape of the pyramid. With practice, you will be able to tell a great deal about a country from this shape. Figure 4–10 summarizes some of the characteristics of the two countries whose pyramids are shown in Figure 4–9.

■ **Total fertility rate** is the average number of children that each woman will have in her fertile years. The fertile years are assumed to be between the ages of 15 and 45. A high fertility rate is greater than 5, while a low fertility rate is below the replacement rate of 2.1 (see next definition). Canada's total fertility rate was about 1.61 in 2007.

■ **Replacement rate** is the total fertility rate that produces a natural increase rate of zero. If we do not take migration (which is of little importance in most countries) into consideration, a natural increase rate of zero means the country's population remains the same. The standard replacement rate is 2.1. At first glance it might appear that this fertility rate should be 2.0, since each woman would bear two children who would eventually replace her and her partner. However, the extra 0.1 is required to make up for women who choose not to or are unable to have children, or who die before having children.

■ **Rule of 70** is a simple way to estimate how long it would take for a country's population to double. To estimate this, you divide 70 by the country's population growth rate (as a percentage). For example, a population that is growing at 2.3 percent per year will double in about 30 years (70 / 2.3 = 30). If the 2006 population growth rate of 1 percent were maintained, Canada's population would double in about 70 years.

	Pyramid 1	Pyramid 2
Country group	Old Core	Far Periphery
Infant mortality	Low	High
Fertility rate	Low	High
Life expectancy	High	Low
Nature of dependency load	Many older people	Mainly young people

Figure 4–10 A description of population pyramids 1 and 2

Chapter Questions

Knowledge and Understanding

1. Examine Figure 4–6. Briefly describe how any three of the innovations mentioned depended on the creation of a food surplus.

Thinking

Research the answers to the following questions at the beginning of this chapter.

2. **a)** Technological development has not occurred in all parts of the world at the same rate. Give at least two examples of hunting-and-gathering societies that still exist today.

   b) Traditional agricultural societies keep livestock or grow crops in shifting locations. Name two regions where agricultural societies still exist.

3. **a)** Figure 4–10 lists some of the things that can be learned from analyzing a population pyramid. What can the shape of a pyramid tell you about each of these things? Use the two pyramids in Figure 4–9 as a guide.

   b) Examine the population pyramid shown in Figure 4–11. Give a brief overview of the population characteristics of this country.

4. **a)** Most experts would say that we are now moving into a post-industrial age. What is meant by this term?

   b) What influence do the attitudes of people living in a post-industrial age have on the world's population size and structure? Why?

Communication

5. Write a "word equation" for each of the following terms.
   Example: Birth Rate = Births / Population × 1000
   a) death rate
   b) natural increase rate
   c) immigration rate
   d) emigration rate
   e) net migration rate
   f) population growth rate
   g) dependency load
   h) age-dependency ratio
   i) infant mortality rate

6. **a)** Use the special graph paper provided by your teacher to create a population pyramid for the data provided in Figure 4–12 on page 68.

   b) What population characteristics are revealed about this country?

7. Suppose a country had a population of 31 850 000 at the beginning of 2001. During the year, the following changes occurred in the population:
   - 1 038 000 babies were born
   - 594 000 people died
   - 86 000 people emigrated
   - 53 000 people immigrated
   - 93 000 babies died during the year
   - 9 159 000 women were aged from 15 to 45

   Calculate the following values:
   a) the population at the end of the year
   b) the birth rate
   c) the death rate
   d) the emigration rate
   e) the immigration rate
   f) the natural increase rate
   g) the net migration rate
   h) the population growth rate
   i) the infant mortality rate
   j) the total fertility rate

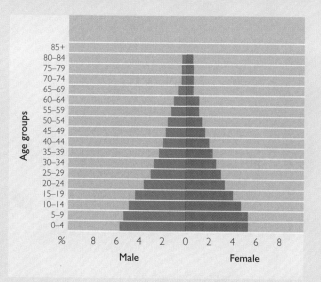

Figure 4–11

8. The US Census Bureau has a Web site called the International Data Base (IDB) that can generate population pyramids for countries around the world. In addition to static population pyramids for specific years, the Web site can generate dynamic pyramids that show changes in population structure over a period of years.

a) i) Go to the IDB Web site link on our Web site. In the "Single Country Data" box, select "Population Pyramids." Select a country from the list. Under "type of output" choose "selected years." Under "graph size" select "medium." After you submit your request, a list of years will appear. Select a year and submit your request.
   ii) What population characteristics does this pyramid reveal?

b) i) Repeat the process, except change the "type of output" to "Summary (2000, 2025, 2050)."
   ii) What happens to this country's population structure over these three time periods?

c) i) Repeat the process, except select "Dynamic" for the "type of output."
   ii) What changes take place over the course of the animation?

Application

9. Explain how a declining population might affect Canada's economy and lifestyles. Consider such areas as government priorities, consumer spending, the role played by economic growth in our society, and environmental demands.

10. a) Being dependent is defined by the government as being under the age of 15, or 65 and over. Is this definition realistic in modern Canadian terms? Why or why not?
    b) If it is not realistic, why is this definition used? What ages do you think would be realistic and why?

11. Examine Figure 4–12.
    a) i) Which areas were experiencing the fastest growth?
       ii) What do these areas have in common?
    b) i) Which areas were experiencing the slowest growth?
       ii) What do these areas have in common?

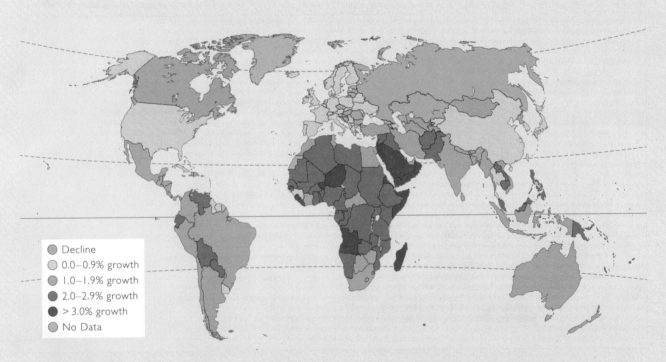

- Decline
- 0.0–0.9% growth
- 1.0–1.9% growth
- 2.0–2.9% growth
- > 3.0% growth
- No Data

Figure 4–12 Annual population growth, 1995–2000. Note the regional patterns of population growth.

CHAPTER 5

Population Theories

Key Terms

demographic transition

pre-transition

early transition

germ theory

late transition

birth control

post-transition

cornucopians

theory of demographic
regulation

Malthusian

phantom carrying capacity

Changes in birth and death rates
are the result of worldwide
developments in science,
economics, and society.

Key Questions

By the end of this chapter you will be able to answer the
following questions.

■ What is the theory of demographic transition and what are its
global implications?

■ What are the characteristics of the four stages of demographic
transition?

■ What factors cause countries to move from one stage of
demographic transition to another?

■ What arguments support the view that large families and a
growing population are desirable?

■ What arguments support the view that ever-increasing population
levels are unsustainable?

■ What are the United Nations' population projections
for the future?

CHANGING FAMILY SIZES

Would you like to have as many children as the parents in the picture on page 69? Although this is a personal question, your answer likely reflects the changes in social and economic conditions and attitudes that have occurred over recent generations. Complete the following activity on the number of children in your family and your friends' families to gain an understanding of the changes in family size that have occurred over several generations.

1. Calculate the average number of children that each person in your class would like to have.

2. Based on the total number of children in all the families of students in your class, calculate the average number of children per family.

3. Ask your parents for the number of children in each of their families when they were children. Calculate the average number of children per family.

4. Now repeat the exercise using information about your grandparents. Find out how many children were in each of their families when they themselves were children. Calculate the average number of children per family.

5. a) Graph the average number of children over the three generations.

   b) What changes in family size do you see?

   c) What factors might have contributed to these changes?

6. In 2007, Canada's total fertility rate was 1.61. Is there a significant difference between this value and your answer to question 1? (A significant difference is more than 20 percent.) If so, what might explain this difference?

7. Give at least three reasons why there is considerable economic and social pressure to have fewer children than your parents or grandparents had.

The Theory of Demographic Transition

In the previous activity, you undoubtedly found that family sizes have decreased significantly over recent generations. This pattern is being repeated in every country in the world. In fact, in about 60 countries, the total fertility rate has fallen to below the replacement rate of 2.1 children. Canada is one of these countries, with a fertility rate of only 1.61 in 2007. This trend has not occurred by accident. As you will see in this chapter, this change is predictable and the result of a range of economic, social, and scientific developments that continue to occur in various parts of the world. The term **demographic transition** describes the phenomenon of a country's high birth and death rates changing over time to low birth and death rates.

Stage 1: Pre-transition

The best way to understand what happens to a country's population over time is to compare birth rates and death rates at various points in its history. Because Sweden has kept adequate records since about 1740, it is often used as an example of demographic transition. Consider Sweden's situation between 1740 and 1840 (Figure 5–1).

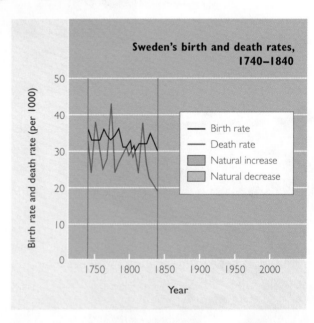

Figure 5–1 Before 1830, Sweden's population stayed relatively stable. The birth rate was relatively constant, while the death rate fluctuated in response to particular events such as good harvests, famines, and wars.

As you can see from the graph, the birth rate was relatively stable, while the death rate went up and down in response to specific events such as wars and famines. The result of this combination of rates was that at some times the population grew, while at other times it decreased. Over many centuries, though, Sweden's population remained relatively stable.

A similar pattern can be seen 150 years later in Mexico (Figure 5–2). Mexico has been selected for comparison because it is a developing country going through a demographic change just as Sweden did 150 years ago, and because Mexican data is available for the various stages. A **pre-transition** country has a distinctively shaped population pyramid (see Figure 5–3).

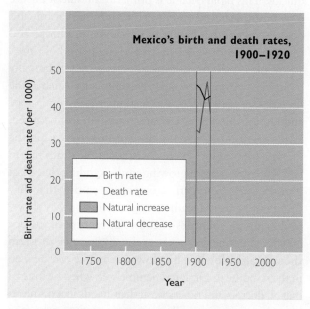

Figure 5–2 Mexico's population before 1920 demonstrates a pattern of alternating increases and decreases similar to those of Sweden.

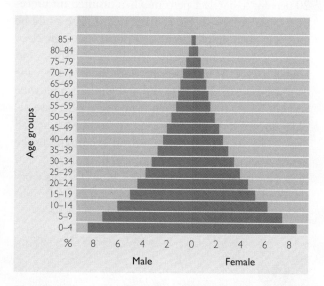

Figure 5–3 A pre-transition population pyramid

The very wide base that rapidly narrows reflects both a very high birth rate and high infant mortality. The number of people in each age group is noticeably less than in the previous one. This characteristic indicates that life is precarious and that death rates are high in every age group. Old age in such a society was 45 or 50. Life in a pre-transition society was difficult and uncertain.

For example, in Sweden in 1750, the life expectancy was barely 35 years. Food supplies were erratic, and diseases such as smallpox, whooping cough, and measles could sweep through the population with devastating results. Most children died before reaching adulthood. A couple might have ten or more children to ensure that they had at least one son to take care of them in their old age. Daughters would generally marry, leave home, and help care for their in-laws.

Not all countries have similar rates in the pre-transition stage, as seen in the comparison between Sweden and Mexico. In Sweden, birth and death rates tended to be in the low to middle 30s, and in Mexico they were in the upper 30s to upper 40s. The important factor in identifying pre-transition in each of these countries is that both birth rates and death rates were high and at relatively the same level.

Stage 2: Early Transition

No country in the world is still at the pre-transition stage; every country has progressed to at least the early transition stage. There may not even be any isolated societies remaining at the pre-transition stage. In **early transition**, a dramatic drop occurs in the death rate. Some people have described this as the beginning of "death control." Consider what happened in Sweden (Figure 5–4) and Mexico (Figure 5–5).

In each country, the death rate dropped while the birth rate remained high. It remained high because many children were still needed to help raise food and to ensure there was at least one caregiver for aging parents. Religious teachings also restricted the use of

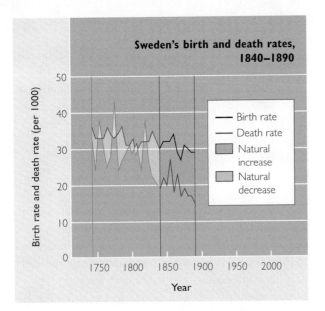

Figure 5–4 Early transition in Sweden occurred when a growing understanding of the causes and prevention of disease, along with improvements in sanitation, caused the death rate to decrease.

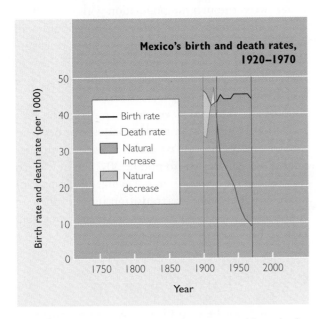

Figure 5–5 Early transition occurs more rapidly today in developing countries like Mexico, than it did in countries like Sweden that were developing a century earlier.

birth control. As a result, a period of significant natural increase began. At first, the rate of natural increase was small, but before long it grew. The result was the beginning of the remarkable population explosion that caused Earth's population to rise from one billion in 1804 to almost seven billion by 2008.

Although the early transition pattern is similar for nations that were developing over a century ago and those developing today (a declining death rate coupled

with a high birth rate), there is one significant difference. Countries like Mexico that experienced early transition more recently have death rates that declined much more quickly. This rapid decline is primarily a result of the use of various means of water purification, sanitation, and disease control that had been developed in Europe and the rest of North America over a long period of time.

While deaths from some diseases were substantially reduced by advances in medical technology, (such as the invention of the smallpox vaccination in 1796), in Europe and North America, where early transition first occurred, lower death rates were usually not linked to a specific medical innovation. Then what caused the death rate to fall? The reason was a growing understanding that most diseases came from germs, organisms so tiny that they could not be seen. Death rates declined relatively slowly in developing countries of the 19th century in Europe and North America because the acceptance of **germ theory** came slowly. This slow acceptance can be seen in the response to Dr. Ignaz Semmelweis when he insisted that all doctors and nurses wash their hands in a disinfecting solution before tending to patients. Semmelweis, a doctor in Vienna's maternity hospital in the 1840s, saw the death rate among new mothers decline rapidly from 20 percent to barely 1 percent when disinfectant procedures were followed. He realized that disease could be fought by such simple means as personal sanitation, clean drinking water, and proper handling of human and animal sewage. This pioneering work should have made Semmelweis a medical hero and brought him worldwide acclaim. Instead, he left Vienna in disgrace because the older doctors did not understand or accept what he had done. The struggle for recognition eventually broke Semmelweis; he ended up in a mental institution, and died soon after from an infection. However, his work inspired others, such as Joseph Lister, who fought disease by applying Semmelweis' methods.

 You can learn more about Dr. Ignaz Semmelweis and his work on our Web site.

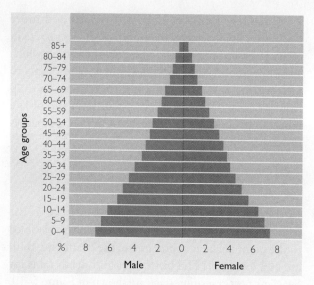

Figure 5–6 The population pyramid for early transition starts to fill out as more children survive into adulthood.

The population pyramid of an early transition country can be seen as a progression from that of pre-transition (see Figure 5–6). The graph shows that there are still relatively few older people, but a growing number of children are surviving beyond infancy. The graph shows that this latter fact has two impacts. First, farming families, which are the majority in early transition, become larger and as a result have more labourers available to help support the family. Furthermore, there is a greater chance that one or more children will survive to support their parents in their old age. Second, more surviving children means that the child dependency load increases. Societies at the early transition stage must meet increasing demands for such facilities as schools and maternity hospitals.

If you want to identify an early transition country, you must look for a birth rate that remains at the high level of pre-transition, and a death rate that drops and remains below the birth rate.

Stage 3: Late Transition

Soon, citizens of European countries in early transition realized that life had fundamentally changed. Women continued to have ten or twelve children, but were finding that seven or eight were surviving instead of two or three. This caused some novel problems. For example, under European inheritance laws, the eldest son inherited all the family property. This meant that younger sons had to leave and find other ways to support themselves. For some, this meant moving to new areas to farm. For others, it meant moving to the growing cities that were developing in response to the Industrial

Revolution. Keep in mind that for the countries that are now developed, **late transition** occurred at the same time as the beginning of mass intercontinental migrations in the 1800s and early 1900s.

If early transition was marked by "death control," then late transition was characterized by **birth control**. This trend is shown clearly in the graphs for Sweden (Figure 5–7) and Mexico (Figure 5–8).

Like early transition, late transition occurred faster in Mexico than in Sweden. Countries in late transition have a relatively high birth rate to begin with, but it eventually drops and approaches the death rate. As they

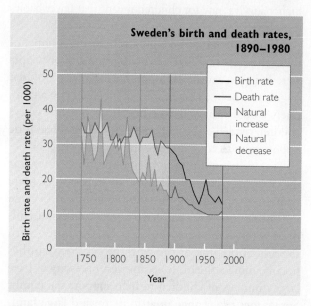

Figure 5–7 Sweden's late transition is characterized by a falling birth rate in conjunction with a declining death rate that began in early transition.

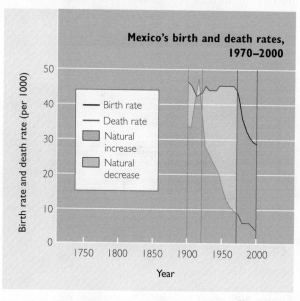

Figure 5–8 Mexico's late transition is very rapid.

enter the late transition stage, these countries continue to experience a population explosion because of the initial gap between high birth rates and low death rates. As this gap closes and the birth rate approaches the death rate, population growth slows.

When we discuss birth control here, we are not talking about the technological means used to prevent births. For example, oral contraceptives were not introduced until the early 1960s, long after birth rates had significantly decreased in developed countries. Rather, we are talking about the desire of couples to limit the size of their families in response to several factors. Most important of these factors was the simple fact that a higher survival rate for children meant that fewer babies were needed.

Another reason for couples to limit the number of their children was that a growing number of people were living in cities. Although having many children might have been a benefit for a family living on a farm, rarely would it have been a benefit in the city, where children tended to be a financial burden and had little opportunity to contribute to their family's support.

An additional reason for falling birth rates was the changing character of family life. In particular, more women were working outside the home. It became unfeasible for women to have large numbers of children when they were working. Furthermore, with the added income of the working mother, families became more affluent. It became less necessary to have large numbers of children to help support the family. Sometimes the change in attitude toward large families occurred very quickly. For example, Thailand's total fertility rate dropped from six children to two in only two decades. The population pyramid for a late-transition nation looks less pyramidal (see Figure 5–9).

Since fewer children are being born and more people are living longer, the numbers of the people in each age group are similar. To identify the time at which a country moves into late transition, you need only to look for the point when the birth rate starts to drop from its early transition levels. Toward the end of late transition, you will notice that the birth rate approaches the death rate.

Stage 4: Post-Transition

In the **post-transition** stage, the final stage of the demographic transition model, the birth rate has declined to the point where it approximates the death rate. Both are at a low level. The birth rates and death rates for Sweden's post-transition stage are shown in Figure 5–10. We cannot show a graph for Mexico because the post-transition stage has not yet been reached.

If the birth rate equals the death rate, the natural increase will be zero and the population will stabilize. Life in a post-transition country such as Sweden, Spain, or Italy is highly urbanized and people generally have small families. There is a high dependency load, particularly of older people. The population pyramid for a post-transition country has a characteristic bullet shape (see Figure 5–11).

Since a growing population will have more people entering childbearing years than leaving them (remember the shape of a late-transition pyramid), it will take years for the population to stabilize after the birth rate and death rate are the same.

The world has had abundant experience with the first three stages of the demographic transition model,

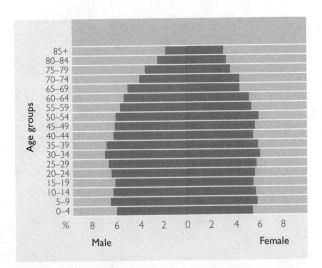

Figure 5–9 In late transition, the population pyramid becomes more block-like.

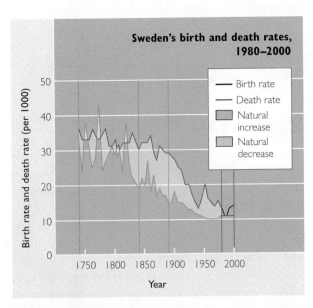

Figure 5–10 Sweden's population has stabilized in the post-transition stage.

so we know that they are valid predictors of how the population will change as a country develops. The post-transition stage is new: countries began to reach this stage only in the 1970s. There is a certain intellectual "neatness" in suggesting that the birth rate and the death rate in such countries will become equal, but there is no particular reason why this should happen. In fact, in most countries that have reached post-transition, the total fertility rate has dropped substantially below the replacement rate of 2.1 for developed countries. Lowest of all is Taiwan with a total fertility rate of only 1.1 in 2007. Some experts have suggested that this low fertility rate is a temporary phenomenon, and that family size will increase in the future to something approximating the replacement level. Other experts think that average family sizes will remain small, with the fertility rate substantially below 2. If this does happen, the population will decline. Some suggest that the demographic transition model should have a fifth stage to account for this decline.

Summary

If we combine all stages of demographic transition for both Sweden and Mexico (Figure 5–12), we get a similar pattern for each with minor variances due to differences in each country's history. For example, you can see the impact of World War II on Sweden.

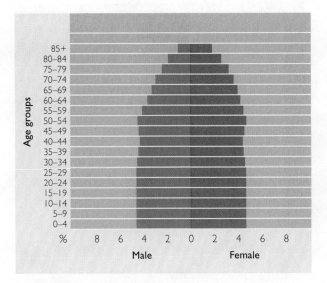

Figure 5–11 A post-transition population pyramid has a characteristic bullet shape.

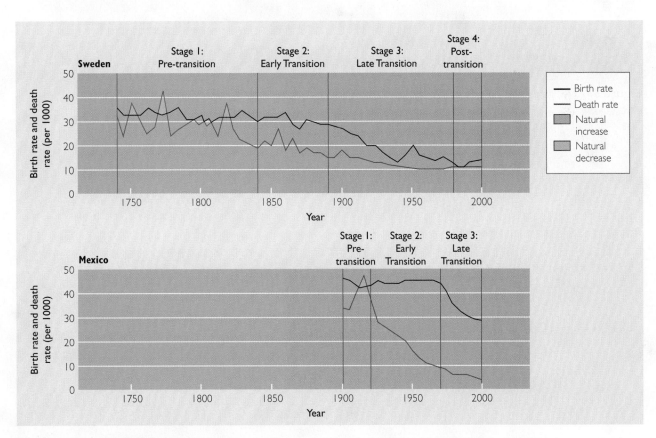

Figure 5–12 Overall look at demographic transition for Sweden and Mexico. With all stages combined, it becomes easier to see the pattern of demographic transition for each country.

The population patterns of any country in the world will show similar variances based on their history. Nevertheless, if we generalize these transitional patterns, we get a theoretical pattern of demographic transition (Figure 5–13). This theoretical model illustrates a country's population changes, and tells you that the country's economic and social development is progressing.

Demographic transition can also be shown by a sequence of population pyramids (Figure 5–14). These pyramids can be classified as either stable or changing. Pyramids for the pre-transition and post-transition stages can be regarded as stable. That is, they represent populations that are not growing. All the other shapes show populations that are either growing or shrinking.

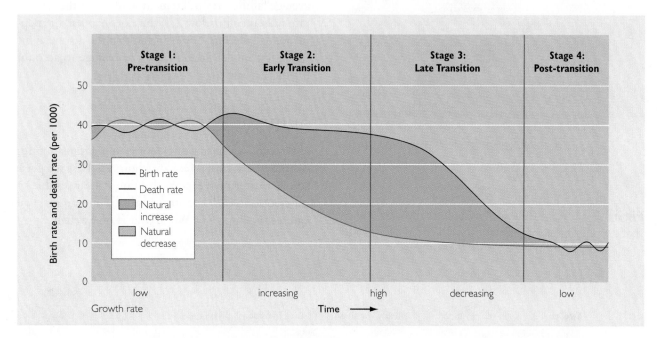

Figure 5–13 A generalized model of demographic transition. No one is entirely sure whether there should be a fifth stage.

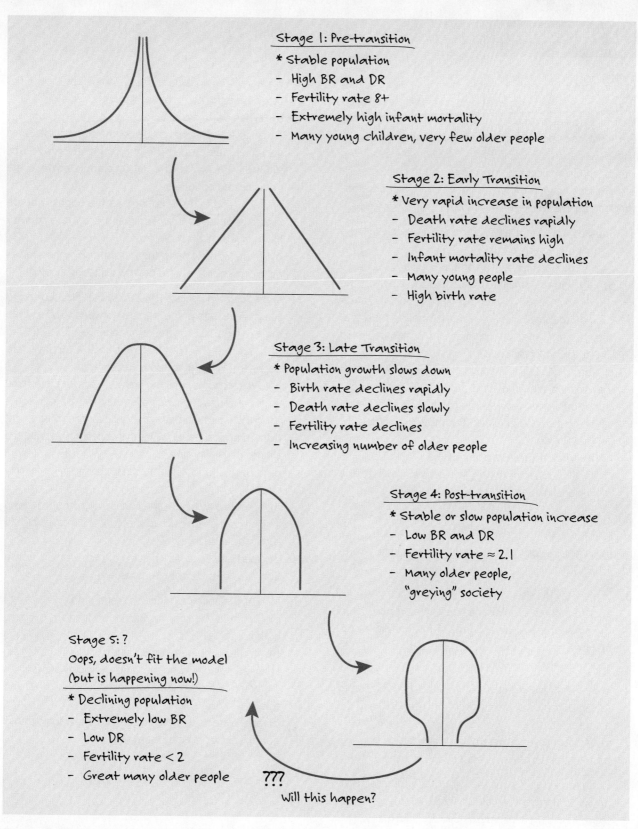

Stage 1: Pre-transition

* Stable population
- High BR and DR
- Fertility rate 8+
- Extremely high infant mortality
- Many young children, very few older people

Stage 2: Early Transition

* Very rapid increase in population
- Death rate declines rapidly
- Fertility rate remains high
- Infant mortality rate declines
- Many young people
- High birth rate

Stage 3: Late Transition

* Population growth slows down
- Birth rate declines rapidly
- Death rate declines slowly
- Fertility rate declines
- Increasing number of older people

Stage 4: Post-transition

* Stable or slow population increase
- Low BR and DR
- Fertility rate ≈ 2.1
- Many older people, "greying" society

Stage 5: ?
Oops, doesn't fit the model (but is happening now!)

* Declining population
- Extremely low BR
- Low DR
- Fertility rate < 2
- Great many older people

??? Will this happen?

Figure 5–14 This sequence of population pyramids provides an alternative way of looking at demographic transition.

In this chapter you have looked at demographic transition from a theoretical perspective with two well-researched examples (Sweden and Mexico), going back many years. But what does demographic transition look like if we go back fewer than 50 years? To do this, we will use a Web site called Gapminder. This site allows you to create a variety of animated graphs based on a wide range of development data. (We will return to Gapminder in Chapter 13.)

1. Start by looking at all of the many countries in the Gapminder database.
    a) Find the Gapminder link on the Pearson Web site.
    b) Click on the small arrow beside the label on the y-axis and choose "Children per woman (fertility rate)." Click on the small arrow beside the label on the x-axis and choose "Time." Be sure that both scales are set to "lin," meaning "linear scale."
    c) To show the distribution in a particular year, click on that year in the "Play" line. Select 1960. Place your cursor on a circle to make the country name appear.
        i)   Which countries had the three highest fertility rates in 1960?
        ii) Which three regions of the world had high fertility rates in 1960? (The colours refer to the regional map in the upper right corner.)

2. a) Which countries had the three lowest fertility rates in 1960?
    b) Which regions of the world had low fertility rates in 1960?

3. In the "Play" line, select the most recent date.
    a) Which three countries had the highest fertility rates?
    b) Which three regions had the highest fertility rates?
    c) How do the answers in 3. a) and 3. b) compare to your answers for 1960?

4. In the "play" line, select 1960. Press the "Play" button to see an animation of the changes between 1960 and the most recent date.
    a) What changes in patterns and values to do you see?
    b) What patterns remain essentially unchanged?

5. Find the "Select" box to the right of the Chart screen.
    a) Select the eight sample countries representing our four "worlds" (Bangladesh, Canada, Germany, Iran,

Malaysia, Philippines, Poland, and Zambia) by clicking the box beside the name of each country.
    b) When you have selected one or more countries, a triangular slider appears below the country list. Once you have selected the eight countries, move this slider all the way to the left to completely hide the non-selected countries.
    c) If you find that the country names appear one on top of another, you can "drag and drop" the country name labels so all are visible.
    d) If you want to hide the "zoom box" in the lower right corner, click on the downward facing arrow.

6. In the "play" line, select 1960. Press the "Play" button to see an animation of the changes between 1960 and the most recent date for the eight countries.
    a) Describe the general trend in the fertility rate between 1960 and the most recent date.
    b) Which country had the greatest change? Determine this by moving your cursor over the circle for each country in 1960 and then over the circle for the most recent date. Subtract the two values that appear to calculate the change in fertility rate.
    c) Which country had the least change in its fertility rate?
    d) Speculate as to why the country in part b) had such a significant change while the country in part c) had such a small change.
    e) Speculate as to which stage of demographic transition each of the eight countries is in.

7. Repeat the animation for China and India.
    a) Describe the changes in the fertility rate for each country.
    b) What might explain the fact that India's fertility rate changed steadily over the time period, while China's increased and decreased markedly between 1960 and the late 1970s?
    c) Speculate as to which stage of demographic transition these two countries are now in.

Differing Ideas About Population Growth

For more than two centuries, authors have written about why and how population growth occurs. Optimists have concentrated on the human ability to adapt to the demands of population growth, while pessimists have written about the problems that population growth has caused or may cause.

Optimistic Views

Throughout most of human history, there has been general agreement that large families and a growing population are highly desirable. Such opinions have been expressed by religious leaders because large families theoretically contribute more adherents to the faith. Large numbers of adherents make a religion both socially and politically powerful. Similar thoughts have been expressed by *secular* (not religious in nature) leaders who need large and growing populations to support their economic and military expansionist desires.

Cornucopians

The question of whether or not Earth can support a growing population is a crucial one. Many people have faith in the human ability to find technological innovations that will produce increases in Earth's carrying capacity. People who hold these beliefs are called **cornucopians**. As evidence, they would point to the Agricultural and Industrial Revolutions, which led to unprecedented increases in world population. The obvious question is, "What might be the nature of the next revolution?" Cornucopians would respond that it is impossible to predict. If pressed, a cornucopian might say that the next revolution would have to solve the most serious threats we face. For example, an innovation allowing us to use solar or wind energy (Figure 5–15) very cheaply would address both a future energy shortage and the environmental damage caused by our current energy use.

Bogue

Writing in the 1960s, D.J. Bogue described what he called the **theory of demographic regulation**. By this he meant that, over an extended period of time, a society naturally limits its own population. The population will grow only in response to Earth's ability to support it. Supporters of demographic regulation would say it is just a matter of time before the world's population naturally stops growing, that the Industrial Revolution dramatically raised Earth's carrying capacity, and that the world's population has been growing in response.

Figure 5–15 Cornucopians believe that breakthroughs in energy production, like these wind turbine generators, could support a much larger population.

They would also say that in developed countries such as Sweden, the population has already naturally limited itself, while in developing countries such as Mexico, population growth is continuing. Bogue's theory appears to be supported by the demographic transition model. We can also find support for demographic regulation in the fact that many countries have tried to limit their population growth in recent years. The best example of this is China's one-child policy, examined in Chapter 6.

Pessimistic Views

Although most people throughout history have been optimistic about ever-increasing population levels, there have been critics of this optimism, particularly since population levels have exploded in recent decades. The critics have all made basically the same point: Earth is of finite size and has an ability to support only a certain level of population. They feel that, ultimately, we will reach a point where the size of the population will be unsustainable because it exceeds the world's ability to support it.

Malthus

Thomas Malthus is one of those remarkable thinkers whose ideas were so powerful and revolutionary that his name became part of the language. Any idea described as **Malthusian**, or *neo*-Malthusian ("neo" means something is new, recent, or a revival of the older form), is pessimistic about population growth. People today who share Malthus' views are often called neo-Malthusians. Malthus began writing about the danger of increasing population in 1798, far earlier than others. He theorized that population would grow in a geometric sequence (1, 2, 4, 8, 16...) while food could only increase arithmetically (1, 2, 3, 4 . . .); in other words, food production cannot be increased as rapidly as a population can grow—obviously not a sustainable situation. To Malthus, the only possible result would be the onset of what he called "misery," which included famine, disease, and warfare, all of which would produce a terrible collapse of the population and great suffering for millions.

Catton

William Catton, writing in the 1980s, did much to modernize and expand the views of Malthus. He introduced the concept of Earth's carrying capacity, which he states can be exceeded only at the expense of environmental damage. This concept is closely related to the idea of the ecological footprint (see Chapter 29). Catton suggests that Earth's population has been exceeding its carrying capacity for many years. This excess has been possible only because we are using up the world's fixed stock of non-renewable resources. For example, our immense population and high standard of living require us to burn the oil and coal that our descendants will need. Using non-renewable resources in this way produces a **phantom carrying capacity** that, while

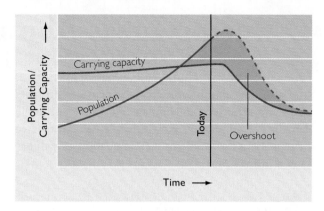

Figure 5–16 Supporters of Catton's ideas believe that we are living in an "overshoot" condition—the population exceeds Earth's true carrying capacity. This has been achieved by relying on the phantom carrying capacity provided by the overuse of non-renewable resources.

allowing a higher population, is ultimately non-sustainable. Sooner or later, our economic and ecological systems must collapse (see Figure 5–16). When this collapse occurs, we will find that the true carrying capacity has been diminished because so much of our stock of non-renewable resources is gone.

Population Projections

It is crucial that we learn to predict the world's population for the years to come. If we do not know how many people there will be, it will be impossible to plan in such vital areas as food supply, healthcare, education, and environmental management. (Population projections will be looked at in more detail in Chapter 7.)

The UN has made three projections for the world's population, ranging from low to high (Figure 5–17).

These projections vary greatly—the difference between the high and low projections for 2050 is almost three billion. Each projection is based on a different set of possible circumstances. The low projection assumes that demographic transition will occur more quickly than expected in developing countries and that fertility rates in developed countries will remain lower than anticipated.

Recent population projections have been somewhat lower than those made in previous years. This trend indicates that, on a worldwide basis, demographic transition is occurring more quickly than anticipated. Clearly, one of the most important questions that we must answer is where the size of the world's population is heading. As well, we must be able to determine how to support this population in a sustainable fashion.

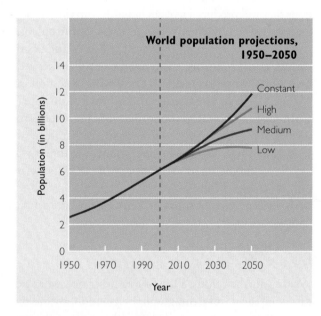

Figure 5–17 World population projections, 1950–2050. All three of the UN's population projections assume a decline in today's population growth rate. The term "constant" means that fertility remains constant at the level estimated for 2000–2005.

Chapter Questions

Knowledge and Understanding

1. In your notebook, complete the table in Figure 5–18 to summarize the characteristics of each stage of demographic transition.

2. Briefly summarize the two reasons why the onset of early transition and late transition occurred later and faster in developing countries.

3. Contrast the factors responsible for "death control" (the decline in the death rate) with birth control during demographic transition. Consider such factors as improved infant nutrition and the care of aging parents.

Thinking

4. Acceptance of the germ theory has made infection control a major health goal worldwide. Provide one example of each of the following

   • a household product named after a pioneer in the fight against germs

   • a major Canadian public-health tragedy caused by inattention to infection risk

   • something you might do to protect yourself against infection

   • a major concern of international travellers

   • a major concern in Canadian hospitals

5. In 2006, the death rate in Mexico was 5/1000 and the death rate in Sweden was 10/1000. Explain why Mexico's current death rate is lower than Sweden's in spite of the fact that Sweden is more highly developed and has more advanced healthcare.

6. a) Do you think Earth has an ultimate carrying capacity? Explain.

   b) What natural and human factors would influence the magnitude of Earth's carrying capacity?

   c) Coal, oil, and natural gas can be used as fuels or as industrial raw materials. What is the difference between these two possible uses? How is the difference related to the idea of a phantom carrying capacity?

7. In a short commentary, describe the implications of the three population projections made by the UN. Consider the environmental implications, economic impacts, and resource demands.

Indicator	Pre-transition	Early Transition	Late Transition	Post-transition
Typical birth rate				
Typical death rate				
Typical natural increase				
Major population figure				
Dominant economic activity				
Population is primarily urban or rural?				
When occurring (developed countries)				
When occurring (developing countries)				

Figure 5–18

8. Some people argue that the size of the world's population is not the true problem. As they see it, the real problem is the rate of consumption of Earth's resources by people in Old and New Core countries.

   a) What do they mean by this?

   b) Who might hold this view?

   c) What is your opinion of this perspective on the "population problem?"

Communication

9. Construct a map to show the demographic transition stage of a selection of countries that your teacher will provide. This can be done in two different ways: by hand on a base map, or by using ArcView GIS software. Your teacher will suggest which method to use and will provide you with full instructions. What patterns are evident?

Application

10. The table in Figure 5–19 summarizes Canada's birth rate and death rate since 1921. Graph these data, and describe Canada's demographic transition by labelling the stages.

11. Describe the relationship, if any, between the theory of demographic transition and each of the four divergent views of population growth discussed on pages 79 to 80.

12. a) Select a country in each of the following "worlds": Old Core, Near Core, New Core, and Far Periphery.

 You can check out the IDB site at the link on our Web site.

Year	Birth Rate	Death Rate
1921	29.3	11.6
1926	24.7	11.4
1931	23.2	10.2
1936	20.3	9.9
1941	22.4	10.1
1946	27.2	9.4
1951	27.2	9.0
1956	28.0	8.2
1961	26.1	7.7
1966	19.4	7.5
1971	16.8	7.3
1976	15.7	7.1
1981	15.3	7.0
1986	14.2	7.0
1991	14.3	7.0
1996	12.2	7.1
2001	10.5	7.1
2006	10.6	7.3

Figure 5–19 Birth and death rates, Canada 1921–2006

b) Research the birth rates and death rates for each country you selected. A good place to find data is the US Census Bureau International Data Base (IDB).

c) **i)** Graph the birth rates and death rates from the earliest data available to the present.

ii) On the graph, show the different stages of the demographic transition that the country has experienced. See the general model of the demographic transition in Figure 5–13.

d) **i)** At the IDB Web site, select "population pyramids." For each of the four countries, have the site construct a population pyramid for the current year.

ii) Compare the shape of each pyramid to the models in Figure 5–14.

e) **i)** Use the two graphs to determine the latest stage reached by each country.

ii) Explain the pattern that you see.

iii) Did any of the results surprise you? Explain.

13. Webquest: Population Growth Theorists

a) Introduction: In this chapter you have read the views of several population theorists. Some have optimistic views about population growth and others have pessimistic views. Is any one position correct, or is there a middle ground?

b) Task: You will role-play a population theorist. Your task is to convey your point of view in such a way that members of your class will accept your point of view over those of others.

c) Process:

i) Select a population theorist from the following list, or one suggested by your teacher. You will be role-playing this person during the presentation phase of this activity. (Note: The actual selection process will be determined by your teacher.)

- D.J. Bogue
- Esther Boserup
- William Catton
- Paul Ehrlich
- Ann Ehrlich
- Betsy Hartmann
- Thomas Homer-Dixon
- Robert Kaplan
- Thomas Malthus
- Julian Simon

ii) You will research

- your character's background
- the articles/books your character has written
- your character's point of view on population growth
- the arguments your character has used against the views of other population theorists

iii) You will prepare a presentation that you will use to persuade your classmates that your views are the most valid.

iv) You will present, in character, your views to the class and respond to any questions or criticism.

v) Based on the information from the presentations, the class will discuss the various points of view with the goal of answering the following question: "To achieve a sustainable future, should the global population grow, decline, or remain stable?"

d) Resources: Use several Internet search engines (and reliable Web sources) and key words from this chapter to find the information necessary to meet the task criteria.

e) Evaluation: Your teacher will explain the evaluation process and criteria.

CHAPTER 6

Population Explosion and Control

Key Terms

demographic trap

overpopulation

feedback loop

population control

Great Leap Forward

one-child policy

structural change model

change by diffusion model

International Conference on
Population and Development
(ICPD)

A family planning poster in
Singapore, 1972; India's billionth
baby. What might be the dangers
for a country experiencing a rising birth rate coupled with a
falling death rate?

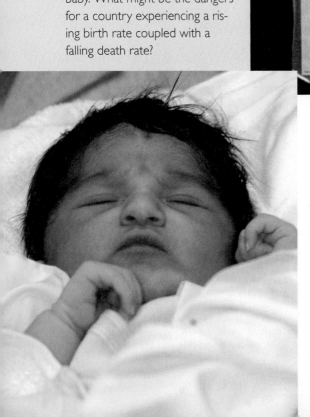

Key Questions

By the end of this chapter you will be able to answer
the following questions.

■ What is the demographic trap? What problems does it cause?

■ What measures have India and China used to try to control their
population growth?

■ What are the impacts of population control measures on the
societies of India and China?

■ How do economics and culture influence a country's population
policies?

■ Did the Indian state of Kerala find a better way to reach
post-transition?

The Population Explosion

The final stage of the demographic transition model is known as post-transition. In post-transition, a country's birth rate equals, or may even fall below, its death rate. As a result, the population stabilizes or begins to decline.

Countries shift into post-transition as they experience the benefits of economic and social growth. These can include urbanization, the changed role of women within the society, a rich resource base, and accessibility to education, healthcare, and advanced technology. This growth, albeit at different rates, is responsible for the completion of demographic transition in countries as varied as Canada, Sweden, and Singapore. But what happens if a country does not achieve the level of economic and social development that leads to post-transition?

Too Many People: The Demographic Trap

Some demographic experts think that some nations of the Near Core and Far Periphery may not reach post-transition. They fear that these developing countries may fall into a situation known as the **demographic trap** (Figure 6–1). This is a situation in which these countries continue to experience a high birth rate instead of the declining birth rate of the late transition stage. A high birth rate coupled with the declining death rate typical of late transition results in an increase in population. The increasing population places great demands on the country for an increased food supply and for all kinds of services, including medical and educational services. As a consequence, the country does not have enough revenue to promote the economic and social development necessary to proceed to post-transition. Furthermore, if the country's birth rate does not eventually decline, the population explosion will continue until a Malthusian collapse becomes inevitable. This devastating collapse would occur because the population had grown to the point where it exceeded the carrying capacity of the country.

Each year, India's population grows by an amount almost equal to the populations of Ontario and Quebec combined. This means that annually, the Indian economy must provide food, housing, healthcare, education, and everything else that 19 million more people need—before being able to improve the standard of living of the existing population. China is experiencing a similar situation—its population is growing annually by

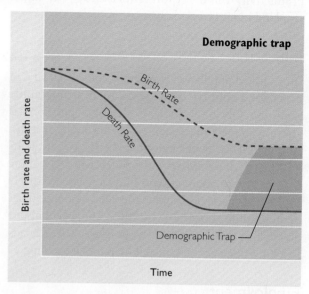

Figure 6–1 The demographic trap

seven million, an amount almost equal to the population of Quebec. Ultimately, the demands of these growing populations will exceed their countries' carrying capacity. This circumstance is called **overpopulation**.

Food

The provision of enough food is the most basic problem associated with overpopulation. In recent decades, however, India has been able to provide enough food for most of its people because it was a major beneficiary of the Green Revolution. The Green Revolution sprang from a series of agricultural innovations that began in the late 1940s and became widely used in many developing countries throughout the 1970s. New crop varieties and agricultural methods caused major improvements in crop yields. (The Green Revolution is discussed in more detail in Chapter 10.)

Between 1950 and 2000, India doubled its production of rice and wheat. The country achieved this remarkable feat not by increasing the amount of its cropland, but by using modern agricultural technology. By the late 1990s, however, rapid gains in agricultural productivity had slowed because no new innovations were occurring.

As India's population increases, its per-capita amount of cropland diminishes. In 1960, cropland use for wheat and rice stood at 0.21 hectares per capita; by 2006, it had declined to about 0.06 hectares per capita. During the Green Revolution, increased agricultural productivity made up for this decline, but whether that productivity will offset further declines in per-capita cropland use is not yet known.

Education

An educated population is generally considered vital in order for a country to move through demographic transition. Obviously, India's exploding population has a serious impact on its ability to educate its citizens. Although it has made enormous efforts to educate its people since the country's independence in 1947, more than half of its adults remain illiterate. This relatively low level of educational advancement has hindered India's demographic transition. In 2007, India had about 360 million children under 15 years of age, while Canada had only about six million children in that age range.

Employment

Countries with booming populations have difficulty providing jobs for the great number of people entering the workforce each year—in India's case, about ten million people annually. Traditionally, most people have worked in agriculture, but agricultural jobs are now harder to find. Although the number of farms in India increased from 48 million in 1960 to 116 million in 2006, the average farm size decreased from 2.7 hectares to 1.4 hectares. These tiny farms do not provide many new jobs. It is worth noting, however, that although the individual small farm in India does not provide employment for many people, together these farms are a large source of employment. In 2007, the labour force in India was 516.4 million, with 60 percent in the agricultural sector. Compare this to Canada's workforce of 17.9 million, of which only 2 percent are involved in agriculture.

Because India's agricultural economy cannot support the ever-growing population, increasing numbers of people are moving to cities. Unfortunately, most of these people lack the education to take advantage of the opportunities offered by India's growing urban economy. For example, India's large and growing software and service industries (Figure 6–2) offer no prospect to an illiterate person who has just moved from a depressed agricultural region. (You will learn more about migration to the cities of the developing world in Chapter 8.) At the same time, however, the growth of these industries is being hindered by a shortage of workers with the necessary skills. This is a good example of a **feedback loop** (see Figure 6–3).

Figure 6–2 Many high-tech companies are taking advantage of India's low labour costs and are expanding production operations in cities like Bangalore. When you call a company about a computer software problem you may be experiencing, it is not unusual to end up talking to someone in India.

Population Control

The world's two most populous countries, China and India, together have about 37 percent of the world's population. In 2006, China's population was approximately 1.3 billion and India's was approximately 1.1 billion. Although China's fertility rate began declining about two decades ago, India's fertility rate started declining more recently. Between 2020 and 2030, it is expected that India's population will become larger than China's; this will make India the world's most populous country (see Figures 6–4 and 6–5). Both countries have reduced their fertility rates through government-driven **population control** measures, but China's approach has been more strict.

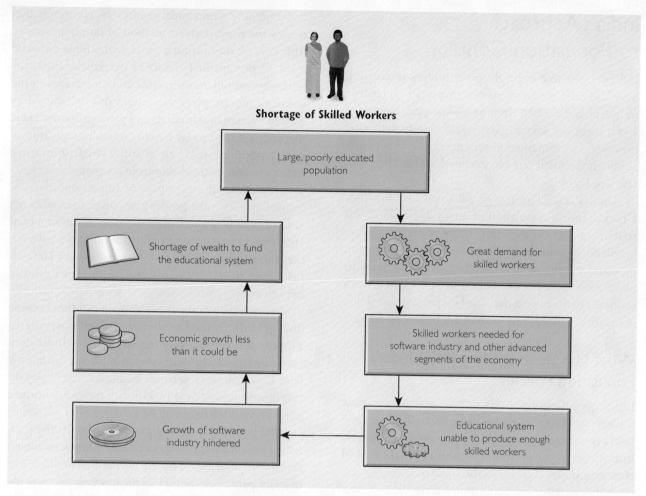

Shortage of Skilled Workers

Large, poorly educated population

Shortage of wealth to fund the educational system

Great demand for skilled workers

Economic growth less than it could be

Skilled workers needed for software industry and other advanced segments of the economy

Growth of software industry hindered

Educational system unable to produce enough skilled workers

Figure 6–3 This is one of several feedback loops that are involved in the demographic trap.

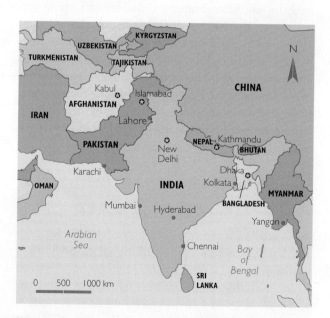

Figure 6–4 India and surrounding countries

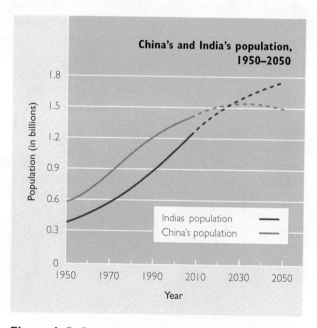

China's and India's population, 1950–2050

Population (in billions)

Indias population
China's population

Year

Figure 6–5 China and India's population

India's Approach to Population Control

India's efforts to control the growth of its population have had only moderate success. Since 1950, fertility in India has decreased from six children per woman to about three per woman. The population growth rate, however, has remained almost unchanged because, although the birth rate has declined, so has the death rate (see Figure 6–6).

Until 1921, "The Year of the Great Demographic Divide," India's population of about 251 million was relatively stable. At this time, however, its population began to increase steadily as a result of sanitation programs and famine- and epidemic-control measures. Its population exceeded one billion in 2000, and growth continues to the present day. The UN projects that India's population will reach more than 1.5 billion by 2030.

What Has Been the Impact of India's Population Policies?

India's population policies and programs have gone through six phases, as shown in Figure 6–7. These have not been successful everywhere, partly because they were insensitive to the enormous cultural, religious, and economic differences within the country.

India's target-driven population policies did not focus on sustainable birth-rate reductions. No attention was paid to factors such as the role of women in society, education levels, economic development, and health, all of which are important in reducing fertility rates. Because of the abuses associated with male sterilization in the past, this procedure is unpopular in India; female sterilization is now the most popular method of family planning. Although the use of contraceptive methods has increased from 13 percent in 1970 to 53 percent in 2004, the birth-control pill and the *IUD* (a device placed in the uterus to prevent pregnancy) are widely mistrusted by women because of side effects and previous abuses. These methods are used today by only a small proportion of India's population. There is still a need to improve services to deliver these choices to couples.

One conspicuous impact of India's population-control policies is the gender gap—an abnormally high ratio of male births to female. In most countries, about 105 boys are born for every 100 girls. In India, however, the ratio ranges from 113 to 129 boys for every 100 girls from state to state. What is causing this high ratio of boys to girls?

Many Indian families prefer male children because boys remain in the family home after marrying to support and care for their aging parents. (India does not have an old-age security system.) Boys also supply farm labour, or work in family businesses. They carry on the family name, and in Hindu families, conduct religious rites when parents die.

The gender gap in India is widening. In the past, female *infanticide* (the practice of killing newborn babies) and the withholding of healthcare resulted in the deaths of infant girls. Since the mid-1980s, however, the focus has changed to aborting female fetuses. This change has occurred because of the development of ultrasound machines that can detect the gender of a fetus. A 2006 study by researchers from the University of Toronto estimated that the number of female fetuses aborted from 1978 to 1998 was about ten million. The study also found that the "girl deficit" was more prevalent among educated urban women, who have access to ultrasounds and money to pay for the scans. Furthermore, because these women generally have small families, the gender of their children is more important to them than it is to less-educated rural women, who generally have more children.

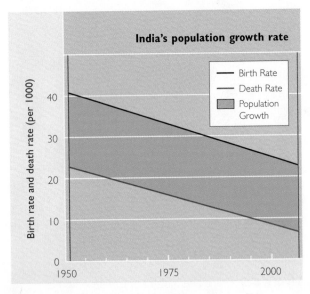

Figure 6–6 Why didn't India's population growth rate decline between 1950 and 2007?

Did You Know?

In India's parliament, the number of seats for each state is based on the size of the state's population. Some states, particularly those in the north, gained seats as their birth rates increased. Other states saw this as a reward for failure to lower birth rates. A constitutional amendment was passed in 1976 that froze the number of seats for each state at the 1971 level. In 2001, this freeze was extended to 2026.

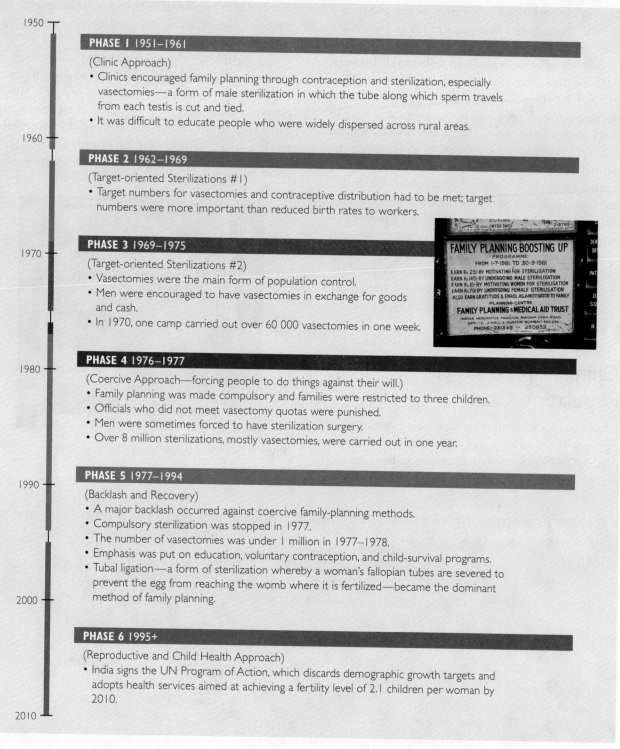

Figure 6–7 India's policies on population control

In 1994, in an attempt to eliminate the practice of aborting female fetuses, the Indian government passed a law making it illegal for ultrasound operators to tell families the gender of a fetus. However, the use of ultrasounds to determine gender is still widespread. National campaigns such as "Save a Girl Child" have been introduced to improve the status of women, to encourage parents to value female children, and to highlight the achievements of young girls. To enhance the value of girls, the government chose a baby girl as India's "billionth baby," on May 11, 2000, (see page 84). Some states even implemented their own campaigns. Delhi developed a "Girl Child Protection Scheme," in which money is deposited into an account for every girl born in a government hospital or maternity home. The money and the accrued interest is given to the girl when she turns 18 and has achieved a certain level of education.

A study of over one million households between 2002 and 2004 estimated that India has about 882 girls for every 1000 boys. The consequences of this gender gap are profound. Men wishing to marry may have to travel farther from their villages, marry women from different socio-economic groups, or look outside the country for a wife. There is evidence that some poor families are selling or trading their daughters into forced marriages to sons of richer families. In some cases, the tradition of the bride's family providing a *dowry* (property or money given by the woman's family to the man's family) has been reversed: the groom's family now pays the wedding price to the bride's family. Perhaps the shortage of women will increase women's status, and society will pay more attention to women's education, economic development, and health.

China's Approach to Population Control

China has an enormous population problem (see Figure 6–8). In 1950, it had a population of 550 million. By 2006, in spite of drastic efforts to limit population growth, China had 1.3 billion citizens in a land area that is a little smaller than Canada's. Imagine what life would be like in Canada if we had to support more than 40 times as many people as we do.

By the mid-1950s, the communist government of China decided to take dramatic steps to control population growth. The policies enacted by the Chinese government at that time as part of the **Great Leap Forward**—and later in the form of the **one-child policy**—had profound effects on the country's population, as shown in the timeline in Figure 6–10.

Figure 6–8 This poster promotes China's one-child policy.

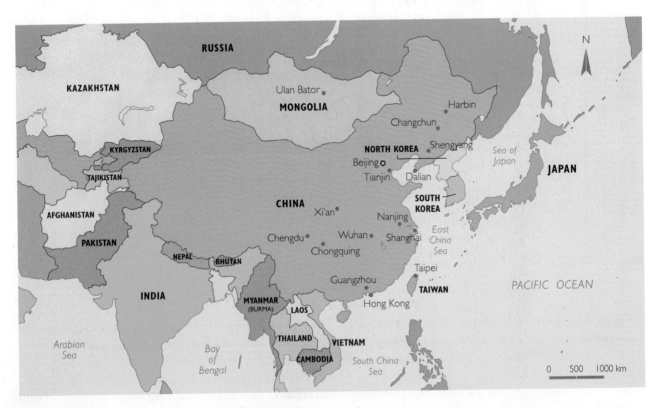

Figure 6–9 China and surrounding countries

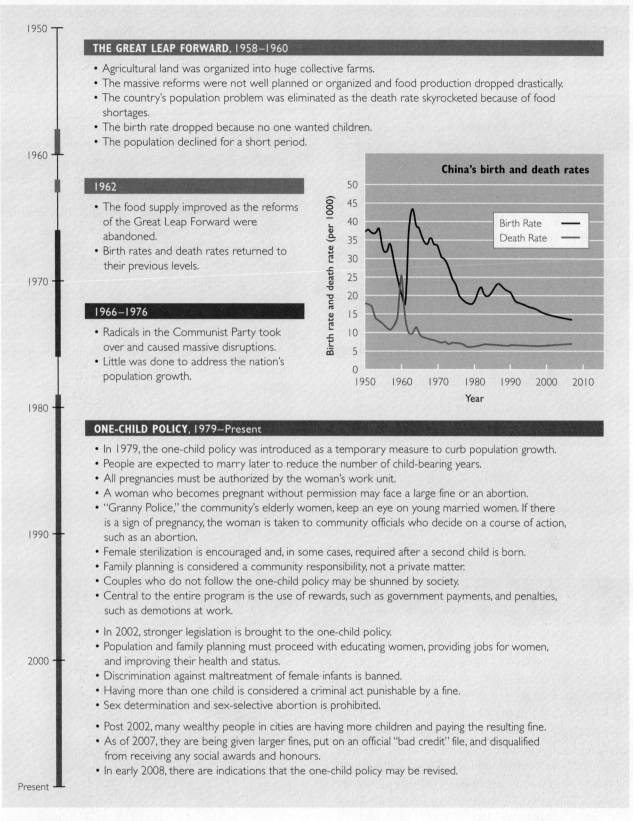

THE GREAT LEAP FORWARD, 1958–1960

- Agricultural land was organized into huge collective farms.
- The massive reforms were not well planned or organized and food production dropped drastically.
- The country's population problem was eliminated as the death rate skyrocketed because of food shortages.
- The birth rate dropped because no one wanted children.
- The population declined for a short period.

1962

- The food supply improved as the reforms of the Great Leap Forward were abandoned.
- Birth rates and death rates returned to their previous levels.

1966–1976

- Radicals in the Communist Party took over and caused massive disruptions.
- Little was done to address the nation's population growth.

China's birth and death rates

Birth rate and death rate (per 1000)

Birth Rate
Death Rate

Year

ONE-CHILD POLICY, 1979–Present

- In 1979, the one-child policy was introduced as a temporary measure to curb population growth.
- People are expected to marry later to reduce the number of child-bearing years.
- All pregnancies must be authorized by the woman's work unit.
- A woman who becomes pregnant without permission may face a large fine or an abortion.
- "Granny Police," the community's elderly women, keep an eye on young married women. If there is a sign of pregnancy, the woman is taken to community officials who decide on a course of action, such as an abortion.
- Female sterilization is encouraged and, in some cases, required after a second child is born.
- Family planning is considered a community responsibility, not a private matter.
- Couples who do not follow the one-child policy may be shunned by society.
- Central to the entire program is the use of rewards, such as government payments, and penalties, such as demotions at work.

- In 2002, stronger legislation is brought to the one-child policy.
- Population and family planning must proceed with educating women, providing jobs for women, and improving their health and status.
- Discrimination against maltreatment of female infants is banned.
- Having more than one child is considered a criminal act punishable by a fine.
- Sex determination and sex-selective abortion is prohibited.

- Post 2002, many wealthy people in cities are having more children and paying the resulting fine.
- As of 2007, they are being given larger fines, put on an official "bad credit" file, and disqualified from receiving any social awards and honours.
- In early 2008, there are indications that the one-child policy may be revised.

Figure 6–10 China's policies on population control

What Has Been the Impact of China's Population Policies?

Chinese officials claim that the one-child policy has prevented 400 million births. One study shows that the country's fertility rate has decreased from 5.8 children per woman in the 1970s to 1.8 children per woman in 2007. On the surface, the one-child policy seems to have been successful, but the cost has been great. A number of major issues are tied to China's population-control policies.

- As in India, the gender gap is increasing. The ratio of boys to girls in 1982 was 108:100; in 2005 it was 118:100. One authority has estimated that as many as 3.5 million girls were killed in China over a ten-year period.

- Policies to ensure the equality of women and to improve the education of girls have been implemented in an effort to rectify the gender imbalance. It is ironic but perhaps not surprising that the shortage of women is now causing parents to value their female babies more than in the past.

- By 2020, about 40 million Chinese men will be unable to marry because not enough women will be available. Some experts believe that this could lead to kidnapping and trafficking in women. It is said the government is considering drafting bachelors to keep them occupied and quell possible social unrest.

How Successful Are the Population Policies of India and China?

The goal of family-planning measures is to reduce population pressure and allow improvement in people's standard of living. By most objective measures, in India and China there has been considerable success in both these directions. Both countries have had some success in bringing about a reduction in fertility by using government-driven population-control measures, although the success has been less dramatic and less widespread in India. China's population-control measures have been much more successful than those of India. In 2007, India's population growth rate of 1.6 percent was almost three times as high as China's, which was only 0.6 percent. By comparison, Canada's, growth rate (including migration) was 0.9 percent.

UN demographers estimate India's population will surpass that of China by 2025. By 2050, India's population will have continued to grow, but China's will have started to decline. Chinese demographers are already starting to consider the problems the country will face as it moves into post-transition, among them labour shortages and a higher dependency load of older people (see Figure 6–5, page 87, the graph of each country's population growth).

CASE STUDY Kerala: Population Control

So far, we have considered the approaches of two countries to controlling population. India's program includes measures that are used in many other countries in the world, but its quota-based plans and coercive practices have met with resistance. Furthermore, it remains unknown if the Program of Action suggested by the **International Conference on Population and Development (ICPD)** and incorporated into Phase 6 of India's population policy has begun to take effect. China's program has proven to be effective, but it has serious implications for human rights.

Is there a better way to control population growth? Can poor countries reach post-transition quickly without achieving wealthy economies or coercing their citizens to adopt unpopular birth-control methods? Kerala, an Indian state (see Figure 6–11), may have discovered a way.

Figure 6–11 The Indian state of Kerala

Compare Kerala's demographic characteristics in 1947 and 1997, as shown in Figure 6–12. The 1947 birth rate of 47 per thousand and death rate of 25 per thousand clearly indicate that Kerala was in early transition.

Now compare the 1997 data for Kerala, and the 2005 data for the whole of India, and the United States in 2005. Kerala's demographic charateristics are more like those of the US than those of India as a whole. They suggest that Kerala is now in the post-transition stage.

Factors in Kerala's Transition

The data show that Kerala has reached post-transition while the rest of India is lagging behind. You might conclude that Kerala's successful transition must have been because the state was wealthier, more industrialized, and more urbanized than the rest of the country. Your conclusion would make sense based on what we know about demographic transition elsewhere. But this was not the case.

Kerala did not fit the demographic transition model when it entered post-transition during the 1990s. It had an agricultural economy with limited manufacturing and serv-ice sectors. It had a very high population density, with more than 70 percent of its people living in rural areas. Kerala was poor even by Indian standards. In the early 1990s, its per-capita income was 70 percent of that of the entire country. Not only was Kerala poor, its economy was stagnating while that of most of India was growing steadily. By 2001, however, Kerala was still more than 70 percent rural, but its per-capita income was 16 percent higher than that of the rest of India. What has contributed to Kerala's successful demographic transition?

Education

Levels of education in Kerala have been significantly higher than in India as a whole for a long time. In 1951, for exam-ple, the literacy rate in Kerala was 47 percent, versus India's rate of 18 percent. The Kerala literacy level for men in 2001 was 94 percent; for women it was almost 88 percent. In contrast, India's literacy rates in 2001 were 76 percent for men and 54 percent for women. Essentially, almost all Keralese of child-bearing age are literate.

The importance placed on education in Kerala is signif-icant because, everywhere in the world, people with more education tend to have fewer children than those with less education.

Status of Women

Elevated female literacy levels indicate the high standing of women in Kerala. High status is also shown by the fact that Kerala is the only Indian state in which there are more females than males. (This difference is partly because many of the men of Kerala work overseas and send money home to raise the standard of living of their families). A well-edu-cated, empowered female population (see Figure 6–13) is very likely to take control of its fertility levels.

Since 1947, the mean age of marriage in Kerala for women has increased from 15 to 22 years (the mean age for marriage in India for woman is 19.7). Since women who marry at a younger age have more years to bear children, this delay in marriage has reduced the total fertility rate. The mean age for marriage in Kerala for men is 28.7 years, compared to all of India at 24.9. In Canada and the US, the median age for first marriages is just over 24 for women and nearly 27 for men.

Indicator	Kerala (1947)	Kerala (1997)	US (2005)	India (2005)
Birth rate (per 1000 people)	47	17	14	24
Death rate (per 1000 people)	25	6	8	8
Natural increase (%)	2.2	1.1	0.6	1.7
Life expectancy (years)	N/A	72	78	64
Infant mortality rate (per 1000 births)	150	13	7	58
Total fertility rate (number of children)	6.0	1.7	2.0	2.9

Figure 6–12 Demographics for Kerala, India, and the US

Figure 6–13 Kerala has a long tradition of educating girls, and its female literacy rate is much higher than in the rest of India.

Healthcare

Kerala has a long tradition of advanced healthcare. Healthcare was and is readily available and relatively inexpensive. Mass immunization against disease is common, and most births occur in hospitals.

Improved healthcare has the effect of reducing fertility levels. Couples have fewer children when the availability of good healthcare ensures that offspring will survive into adulthood. Furthermore, fewer children are born when an effective system of clinics and hospitals offers couples better access to birth control.

Land Reform

In many developing countries, the majority of the agricultural land is owned by a relatively small number of people. Most families are poor tenants who rent farmland from wealthy landowners. Kerala took steps to avoid this situation. It instituted a series of land-reform policies that limited farm size during the late 1950s and early 1960s. The size of the landholding varied with the size of the household, but could not exceed ten hectares. This limitation on farm size ensured that every farmer would gain ownership of some land. Owning their land encouraged farmers to work even more diligently once they were working for themselves. The improved economic and social conditions of the rural population gave rise to a better understanding of the benefits of family planning.

Government

The policies of Kerala's governments have contributed significantly to the state's demographic transition. Starting in the early 1800s, a series of progressive-thinking monarchs decided that the state should assume the cost of educating its people. Similar decisions would not be made in more so-called "advanced" societies—such as Canada—until many years later.

Since India's independence in 1947, the citizens of Kerala have frequently elected governments that have been dominated by one or another of India's two communist parties. These governments have effectively provided for social progress for women, as well as education and healthcare for the state's population.

Expatriate Workers

Since the mid-1970s, Kerala has been a major source of expatriate workers for the oil-rich countries of the Persian Gulf, including Kuwait, Saudi Arabia, and the United Arab Emirates. These workers, who fill many of the menial jobs such as dishwashers, farm workers, and unskilled construction labourers in the Gulf, bring two things back to Kerala with them. One is money, and the other is the experience of living in a modern society, where the advantages of having a small family are evident. (The importance of money sent home by expatriate workers is covered in more detail in Chapter 13.)

Change by Diffusion

Geographers refer to two different models to describe how significant change occurs in a society. The first is the **structural change model**. In this model, governments adopt measures to force, or at least strongly encourage, people to change their behaviour. This is what happened in China and India when the government urged, and often forced, people to adopt birth control measures that may, in many cases, have gone against societal norms.

The second is the **change by diffusion model**. In this model, the spread or diffusion of new ideas and social norms occurs through various forms of social interaction and the influence of mass media. Kerala's citizens adopted birth control methods through informal discussions with friends, and as a result of formal educational programs and health services that provided information and access to birth control. The mass media (television, radio, print) also changed people's attitudes by depicting smaller families as desirable and modern. Gradually, an understanding of the benefits of having fewer children spread throughout the state. Figure 6–14 illustrates the change by diffusion model.

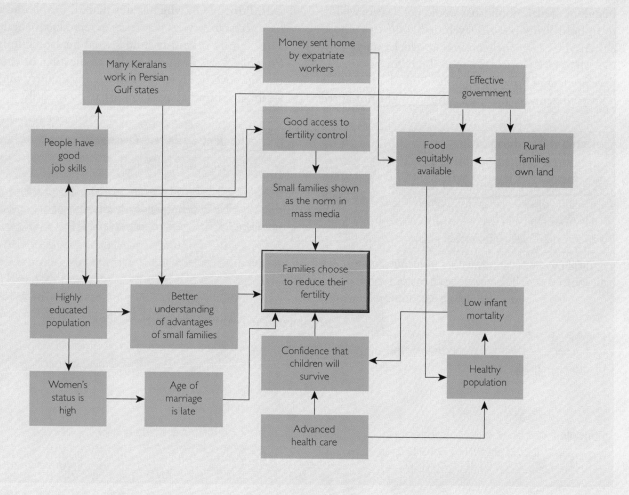

Figure 6–14 Fertility control in Kerala has a complex origin. What is clear is that the trend to smaller families occurred as a result of a series of individual choices rather than a program of government measures.

The Future of Population Control

What is next for the countries of the world that face the possibility of being caught in the demographic trap? The UN addressed this question at the International Conference on Population and Development (ICPD) in Cairo in 1994. Its aim was to come up with a series of policies that would help countries complete demographic transition while also developing their economies. These policies, however, would have to be politically and morally acceptable to the nations that adopted them.

The ICPD knew that trying to curb population growth simply by applying methods of fertility control was doomed to failure. It realized that countries would have more success controlling population growth if they adopted certain principles that lead to cultural, economic, and social development. These principles would provide a framework within which countries could develop specific plans for social and economic development that would then lead to lower fertility rates (see Figure 6–15). The ICPD states that population-related policies are integral parts of economic and social development.

The different cultural, economic, and religious characteristics of the world's countries have made it difficult for all nations to accept and carry out the principles proposed by the ICPD. For example, developing countries that have strong cultural and religious traditions of male dominance would not be very willing to uphold Principle 4. Developed countries whose citizens drive large fuel-consuming vehicles might find the call to take particular responsibility for sustainable development in Principle 15 difficult to adopt. Nations whose citizens are mainly Catholic might not agree with Principle 8, which states that all people should have access to services that relate to reproductive health-care, family planning, and sexual health. Though Principle 7 sets forth the goal of eradicating, or eliminating, poverty, an ideal to which any country might aspire, no country has the ability to do so easily.

Selected ICPD Principles	Millennium Development Goals and Targets
Principle 4 calls for advanced gender equality and equity and the empowerment of women, and the elimination of violence against women. The human rights of women and girls are an inalienable, integral, and indivisible part of universal human rights.	**Goal 3:** Promote gender equality and the empowerment of women Target: *Eliminate gender disparity in primary and secondary education in all levels of education no later than 2015*
Principle 6 identifies sustainable development as a means to ensure human well-being. States should reduce and eliminate unsustainable patterns of production and consumption and promote appropriate policies in order to meet the needs of current generations without compromising the ability of future generations to meet their own needs.	**Goal 7:** Ensure environmental sustainability Target: *Integrate the principles of sustainable development into country policies and programs and reverse the loss of environmental resources* Target: *By 2015, reduce by half the proportion of people without sustainable access to safe drinking water and basic sanitation* Target: *Achieve, by 2020, a significant improvement in the lives of at least 100 million slum-dwellers*
Principle 7 calls on all states to cooperate in the essential task of eradicating poverty as an indispensable requirement for sustainable development.	**Goal 1:** Eradicate extreme poverty and hunger Target: *By 2015, reduce by half the proportion of people whose income is less than one dollar a day* Target: *By 2015, reduce by half the proportion of people who suffer from hunger*
Principle 8 says that everyone has the right to the enjoyment of the highest attainable standard of physical and mental health, and that states should take all appropriate measures to ensure universal access to healthcare services, including those related to reproductive healthcare, family planning, and sexual health.	**Goal 5:** Improve maternal health Target: *Reduce by three-quarters, by 2015, the maternal mortality ratio* **Goal 6:** Combat HIV/AIDS, malaria, and other diseases Target: *By 2015, have halted and begun to reverse the spread of HIV/AIDS* Target: *By 2015, have halted and begun to reverse the incidence of malaria and other major diseases*
Principle 10 says that everyone has the right to education, which shall be directed to the full development of human resources, and human dignity and potential, with particular attention to women and girls.	**Goal 2:** Achieve universal primary education Target: *Ensure that, by 2015, children everywhere, boys and girls alike, will be able to complete a full course of primary schooling*
Principle 11 calls on states and families to give the highest priority to children. The child has the right to the highest attainable standards of health, and the right to education.	**Goal 4:** Reduce mortality rate of children under five years Target: *Reduce by two-thirds, by 2015, the maternal mortality rate*

Figure 6–15 Many of the ICPD goals and targets were incorporated into the Millennium Development Goals, which were adopted at the Millennium Summit in 2000.

Selected ICPD Principles	Millennium Development Goals and Targets
Principle 15 requires that in the context of sustainable development and social progress, sustained economic growth be broadly based, offering equal opportunities to all people. All countries should recognize their common but differentiated responsibilities, and the developed countries should acknowledge the responsibility they bear in the international pursuit of sustainable development.	**Goal 8:** Develop a global partnership for development Target: *Further develop an open, rule-based, predictable, non-discriminatory trading and financial system* Target: *Address the special needs of the least-developed countries. These needs include tariff- and quota-free access for the least-developed countries' exports, an enhanced program of debt relief for heavily indebted poor countries, and the cancellation of official bilateral debt.* Target: *Address the special needs of landlocked countries and small island developing states* Target: *Deal with the debt problems of developing countries through national and international measures in order to make debt sustainable in the long term* Target: *In cooperation with developing countries, develop and implement strategies for decent and productive work for youth* Target: *In cooperation with pharmaceutical companies, provide access to affordable, essential drugs in developing countries* Target: *In cooperation with the private sector, make available the benefits of new technologies, especially information and communications*

At the ICPD in 1994, 179 countries adopted a 20-year Program of Action. At various times during this 20-year period, the Program calls for progress to be evaluated and specific targets to be established or refined. For example, in 1999, the UN General Assembly convened a Special Session (known as the ICPD+5) to examine the progress made after Cairo. In 2000, the UN hosted the Millennium Summit, many of the ICPD goals and targets were incorporated into the Millennium Development Goals (MDGs). The ICPD Program of Action focuses on population-related efforts, and meeting its targets is seen as prerequisite to the achievement of the larger development goals of the MDGs (see Figure 6–15).

As this action plan was reaching its mid-point in 2004, the United Nations Population Fund (UNPFA) conducted a global survey of 169 countries—151 developing countries and 18 developed (aid donor) countries—to assess the progress that had been made in achieving the Cairo goals. This review provided a wake-up call to countries so that those not meeting their commitments could accelerate the implementation of policies to meet the end of the 20-year time frame in 2015.

- 96 percent of responding countries have taken measures to improve access to education.
- 99 percent reported that they had adopted measures to protect the rights of girls and women and have taken measures to empower women economically and politically.
- 88 percent have taken measures to integrate reproductive health-service components into the primary healthcare system.
- 88 percent reported taking action to provide access to information on birth control to adolescents.

Although the survey indicated that many countries are making progress in meeting the ICPD goals, over 80 percent of countries reported that available resources did not meet their country's reproductive-health needs. Since the survey did not focus on the quality or impact of the programs, or on their effects on the lives of vulnerable groups, a more exhaustive survey in 2015 will be required to determine the success of the ICPD 20-year Program of Action.

Chapter Questions

Knowledge and Understanding

1. What is the demographic trap, and why is it a threat for developing countries?

2. **a)** A number of factors that contribute to the completion of demographic transition were mentioned in this chapter. List these, and explain one way in which each contributes to transition.

   b) Explain why an educated population is vital in helping a country move through demographic transition.

3. **a)** What population policies has India followed since the middle of the 20th century?

   b) What coercive tactics were used to implement some of these policies?

   c) What effects did these coercive tactics have?

4. **a)** What are the reasons for the abnormally high ratio of boys to girls in India and China?

   b) What are the implications of the gender gap?

   c) What is being done about this gender gap?

   d) The Indian and Chinese governments have told their people that it is the responsibility of every child (not just male children) to look after his or her parents. What is the purpose of this move? Is it likely to work? Explain.

5. **a)** Why is the status of women a critical factor in demographic transition?

   b) Why is it so difficult to make changes in regard to the status of women?

6. Examine Figure 6–14. Demonstrate how the trend to smaller families in Kerala occurred as a result of a series of individual choices rather than due to a program of government measures.

Thinking

7. **a)** Per-capita grain production in India is expected to decline between now and 2050. Keeping in mind the population growth of India, briefly describe the human, economic, and political impacts that this decline might have on the nation.

   b) India's population is projected to be at least 1.7 billion in 2050. Give two reasons why this might *not* occur.

8. How would you feel if you had to face a committee at your workplace to ask for permission to have a child?

According to the UN Declaration of Human Rights, this interferes with your human rights. The Chinese government, however, might argue that the one-child policy is a lesser violation of individual rights than would be the case if the population were allowed to continue to grow. What is your opinion?

9. **a)** Do you find Kerala's experience surprising? Why or why not?

   b) Does the experience of Kerala point the way to demographic transition for the poorest developing countries?

   c) Compare the efforts of Kerala and China to control population growth. Which of these approaches do you think will have the most desirable long-term results?

10. You have seen the approaches that India and China have taken to deal with their population growth challenges. What should other countries of the world do to deal with similar challenges?

11. Some people have argued that Canada has too many people for the amount of arable land that it has. What should Canada do, if anything, to rectify this situation?

12. Examine Principle 4 of the ICPD on page 96. Some countries deny rights to women and girls. How can the world community ensure that the rights set out in Principle 4 are being met?

13. Statistics show that Canada's Aboriginal population has some demographic characteristics, namely high birth and death rates, similar to those of developing countries. Explain. What can or should be done to deal with this situation?

Communication

14. Use a table or other organizer to relate the principles, of the ICPD to the demographic transition experience of

    • India   • China   • Kerala

15. If you have lived in a country with enforced population policies, make a short presentation to the class describing the policies, how they are enforced, how the general population feels about them, if people follow the policies, and your opinion of the impact of the policies.

Application

16. a) What is a feedback loop?

b) Show how a feedback loop can hinder demographic transition, using an example different from the one given in this chapter.

17. Examine the population pyramids in Figure 6–16. What evidence is given here about the relative success of China's and India's attempts to control fertility? Give specific references to the pyramids in your answer.

18. Write a paragraph to suggest how you think each group has been reacting to or might react to the directions implicit in the ICPD principles.

- Old Core countries
- Countries outside the Old Core **G**

19. There are several ways in which a country can move toward the completion of demographic transition. Consider the examples of Canada, India, China, and the Indian state of Kerala. Research two countries in the world to see which approach they followed. Give evidence to support your choice. **S**

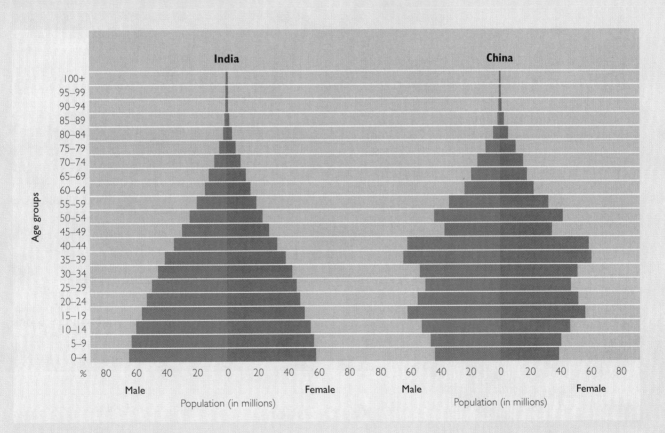

Figure 6–16 Population pyramids for India and China

CHAPTER 7

Population Futures

Key Terms

population implosion

medium variant

high variant

low variant

birth dearth

DINKs

pension plans

labour shortage

pronatalist strategies

Bologna, Italy (right), has the world's lowest fertility rates. Fertility rates are also declining in most other parts of the Old Core, many parts of the New Core, and some parts of the Far Periphery. One of the implications of this is an increasingly elderly population.

Key Questions

By the end of this chapter you will be able to answer the following questions.

■ How are changes in fertility related to changing roles of women and men in Core countries?

■ How are population predictions made? Why are accurate predictions hard to make?

■ What are the implications of low fertility rates in developed countries?

■ What does this all mean to you, as a young Canadian?

The people of Bologna live a very good life indeed. Situated in northern Italy, this wealthy, cultured city was settled more than 2500 years ago. Its famous university (100 000 students) opened in 1088. It is the hometown for Lamborghini sports cars and Ducati motorcycles. The city has been called the food capital of Italy, which is high praise indeed in a country that values eating so highly. *Bolognesi* love to sit in cafés to talk about politics and the fortunes of the city's two great rival basketball teams, *Virtus* and *Fortitudo*.

Finding a babysitter in Bologna is rarely a problem. Bologna has the world's lowest fertility rate, only 0.80 children per woman. If this trend continues until 2020, Bologna will have 25 people over the age of 50 for every child under five. What is happening so dramatically in Bologna is happening more slowly in most other parts of the Old Core, many parts of the New Core, and even some parts of the Periphery. This chapter examines the implications of this **population implosion**. (In the absence of significant net in-migration, a country that maintains a total fertility rate significantly below 2.1 for many years will experience a population implosion—a dramatic collapse in numbers, and aging of the population.)

1. **a)** Claudia is a high-school student in Bologna. She has always wanted to be a kindergarten teacher. What options does she have if she would like to pursue this goal?

   b) Name three other careers that will become less common as populations age.

2. It is not all bad news, though. An aging population offers many opportunities as well. Name three jobs that will become more common.

3. Some companies will benefit from an aging population while others will face challenges. Identify which of these companies is likely to gain and which will lose because of demographic change. If you have not heard of these companies, you may want to do some quick Internet searches.

i) Extendicare	v) Clublink
ii) Nike	vi) McDonald's
iii) Princess Cruises	vii) Intrawest
iv) Arbor Memorial	viii) Manulife

4. Companies that face serious demographic challenges cannot just give up—they must adapt. Explain what this means for the business focus of any two of the companies listed above.

Different Assumptions → Different Predictions → Different Futures

Three fundamental factors affect the size of any population:

- The total fertility rate (TFR)—more births mean a higher population.
- The life expectancy of people—if they live longer, the population will be greater.
- The impact that migration has on population—more immigrants than emigrants will increase the population.

Each of these factors is influenced by such a complex combination of economic and social conditions that population prediction is a tricky business. A wrong assumption about future fertility trends or immigration policies can dramatically affect the accuracy of a population projection. In spite of the risks, a number of international organizations, including the United Nations and the World Bank, produce world population projections—because they must have some idea of how many people there will be in the future if appropriate planning is to be done.

Consider that, to make such projections, a demographer must be able to predict how many children you (and others your age) will have and how many children your children and their children will have.

Typically, population projections include a range of possibilities based on different assumptions about the total fertility rate, life expectancy, and, where appropriate, migration. For example, one projection may be based on what experts think is the lowest realistic estimate for total fertility rate, a second on the highest realistic TFR, and a third on their "best guess" for the TFR. Similar assumptions are made about possible increases in life expectancies and migration patterns. A range of projections is produced rather than a single number. The most likely future population is called the **medium variant**, while the others are called the **high variant** and the **low variant**. Unless the experts were very wrong about their assumptions, the future population should almost certainly be between the high and low variants, and is most likely to be close to the medium variant. Why does a range of projections make better sense than one best-guess projection?

In 2006, the UN projected a world population in 2050 of between 7.8 billion (low variant) and 10.8 billion (high variant), with a medium variant of 9.2 billion. Even in the case of the low variant there is considerable growth from the current population of 6.3 billion. The projections are quite different for the Core countries, though. The UN predicted a 2050 population for Europe of between 566 and 777 million (medium variant 664 million) compared to a population in 2006 of 731 million. Similar stagnant or declining populations are also likely in Old Core countries such as Japan, Russia, and even Canada if our immigration levels decline significantly.

Population Futures in the Old Core and Eastern Europe

We will examine some detailed population projections made by the International Institute for Applied Systems Analysis (IIASA), so that you will better understand how Core populations are changing and how this will affect you in the decades to come. Let's look at the population projections for the areas defined by IIASA as developed nations:

- North America (Canada, the United States, Puerto Rico, Guam, the Virgin Islands)
- Europe and the European parts of the former Soviet Union
- Japan, Australia, New Zealand

The implications of very low total fertility rates will be felt soonest and most by a few countries. In particular, Russia, the countries of eastern Europe, and Japan are facing the worst population-implosion problems. Countries outside the Old Core and eastern Europe are not immune to the impact of low total fertility rates. (In fact, some of these countries already have declining populations.) Some New Core members such as China, Chile, and South Africa will also be affected by declining birth rates.

Did You Know?

The International Institute for Applied Systems Analysis (IIASA) is a non-governmental research organization located in Austria. Since its inception in 1972, the Institute has conducted interdisciplinary studies on the human components of environmental, economic, technological, and social change.

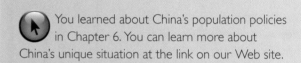

You learned about China's population policies in Chapter 6. You can learn more about China's unique situation at the link on our Web site.

What Are IIASA Projections for the Developed World?

The IIASA made a set of nine population projections for the developed world based on varying combinations of fertility and life expectancy. (Since fertility assumptions ranged from high to medium to low, as did life expectancy assumptions, there are nine [3 × 3] possible combinations.) The populations of many countries in the Old Core are also increasing due to in-migration. In-migration, however, is less important than fertility and life expectancy. We will focus on two projections (see Figure 7–1): the lowest projection based on the assumptions of a low fertility rate and a

	1995	2020	2050	2100
Lowest projection	1251	1250	1032	607
Moderate projection	1251	1340	1319	1216

Figure 7–1 IIASA Population Projections for Developed Countries (in millions). The IIASA's lowest projection suggests a massive decline in the developed world's population. Its moderate projection is for a slight decline.

small increase of life expectancy; a moderate projection based on the assumptions of a moderate fertility rate and a moderate increase in life expectancy. These assumptions are summarized in Figure 7–2 and explained below.

Fertility Rate

Examine Figure 7–2. Total fertility rates (TFRs) in 2000 in the developed world were already very low in relation to the values used for future projections—even at the moderate level. In 2000, only one Old Core country, the US, had a TFR over 2.00, and 20 major countries, including Germany, Poland, Russia, Japan, Italy, and

Spain, had TFRs less than 1.40. Moreover, in many of these countries, the decline in total fertility has not stopped. (These comments ignore very small countries and territories such as Guam and San Marino that have TFRs over 2.00). We can see that the fertility rates of the developed world could easily result in the lowest population projection coming true.

Life Expectancy

Advances in medical science may prolong life. However, we cannot predict how quickly these advances might occur. At the same time, it is difficult to make predictions about the impact on life expectancies of healthier (or less healthy) lifestyles or more (or less) pollution in the future since we do not really know what the trends for these will be. The experts at the IIASA expect there to be slow but steady increases in life expectancy by at least ten years over the 21st century.

Where Is the Population of the Core Headed?

North America

If we accept the lowest projections, we can anticipate that by 2100, within the life span of your children (or more likely your *child*), the population of the developed countries could drop by more than 50 percent to barely 600 million. The distribution of this population is shown in Figure 7–3. North America's

	Life Expectancy Increase per Decade (years)	Total Fertility Rate 2000 (actual)	Total Fertility Rate 2030–2035 (projected)	Total Fertility Rate 2080–2085 (projected)
Lowest projection	1*	1.13–2.06**	1.20–1.58	1.39–1.59
Moderate projection	2	1.13–2.06**	1.50–1.94	1.89–2.09

Figure 7–2 These are the assumptions used by the IIASA for population projections.

*Except for males in the former Soviet Union, which is 0

**Other than the US at 2.06, the highest value is 1.81

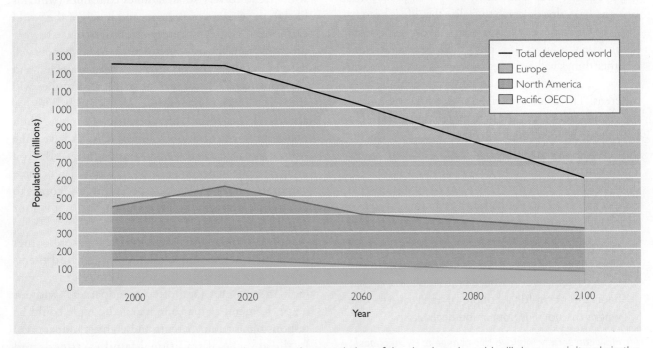

Figure 7–3 If the IIASA's lowest projection is correct, the population of the developed world will drop precipitously in the 21st century.

population will rise slightly and then decline to about 250 million from the current 330 million. A disproportionate share of this decline is likely to occur in Canada because our total fertility rate is significantly lower than that of the US.

SUSTAINABILITY

If we accept the lowest projections, we can anticipate that by 2100, within the life span of your children (or more likely your *child*), the population of the developed countries could drop by more than 50 percent to barely 600 million.

On balance, will this be a desirable trend or not?

Japan, Australia, and New Zealand

The population of this part of the Core will start out fairly stable at around 150 million before declining to about 70 million 2100. Most of this decline will occur in Japan, which has a much lower total fertility rate than Australia and New Zealand.

Europe and the European Parts of Russia

Europe, and in particular eastern Europe and adjacent parts of Russia, will be most affected by this low total fertility rate, which is often called the **birth dearth**. Europe's population has already started to decline slightly. This decline will accelerate throughout the century as the children of today's smaller families have small families of their own. Europe's projected population of about 290 million for the year 2100 is only about the same number of people who live in Russia, Germany, and France combined today.

What Are the Implications of the Birth Dearth?

Only since the 1990s have serious concerns over a possible population implosion surfaced. Social scientists are working diligently to understand the likely effects that these declining populations will have, while political leaders, at best, have barely begun to consider the problems that will occur. People in places like Bologna have already come to realize that life is becoming very different than it was even 40 years ago, when family size was larger. It is not primarily a question of whether things will be better or worse—just that it will be socially, economically, and environmentally very different. The challenge will come in how we handle the change from a world where population growth has been the norm for a couple of centuries to one where the norm is population decline—at least in the parts of the world where we live. If we handle this transition well, there can be benefits, certainly from an environmental perspective. If we do not handle it well, there could be social and economic chaos.

SUSTAINABILITY

The challenge will come in how we handle the change from a world where population growth has been the norm for a couple of centuries to one where the norm is population decline ...

How can society manage this change to avoid chaos?

Five of the major implications of the birth dearth are described below.

1. Family Structures

If the trend to very small families continues (which is likely), the citizens of Bologna and much of the world can look forward to family structures that are very different from those we are used to. Many people will have no brothers and sisters, no aunts and uncles, and few cousins. The existence of such tiny families will alter the character of family life as we know it. This has already happened in China because of the one-child policy. In one generation, Chinese families have gone from very large to very small (see Figure 7–4). As a result, the phenomenon of "little emperors" has become common. The single child, especially a boy, comes to be spoiled not only by his parents, but by his four grandparents as well.

If we look many years into the future, other problems emerge. Single children might find themselves overwhelmed by the responsibility of trying to look after parents (and often grandparents) without help. (Remember that one married couple could be responsible for four parents and eight grandparents.) In the absence of traditional families, friends and

Figure 7–4 A one-child family in Anhui, China. Could this be a typical 21st-century family?

co-workers may come to play family-like roles for many people. A characteristic of declining fertility rates has been an explosion in the number of **DINKs** (Double Income, No Kids) couples.

2. Aging Populations

Perhaps the most profound effect of the birth dearth will be a dramatic change in the age structure of the population. As a result of the post–World War II baby boom, countries such as Canada have spent a half-century with a culture dominated by young people. The next century is likely to be dominated by the elderly. Figure 7–5 shows a sequence of projected population pyramids for Spain until 2050. Spain, which had one of the lowest total fertility rates in the world in 2007, shows the direction in which dozens of countries are going. In fact, if predicted trends continue to 2100, *half* of all Europeans will be over age 60. Between 1990 and 2030, the World Bank expects the number of people over age 60 to go from 500 million to 1.5 billion.

The most obvious impact of an increasingly elderly population will be the need to spend vast amounts of money to meet the special needs of older citizens—in particular, for pensions and healthcare. All developed countries have government and private **pension plans** to provide incomes for older people. In the past, pension plans were relatively affordable for government and society because the working population was much larger than the retired population. For example, in 1955 there were nine working Americans for each person receiving government Social Security payments. By 2030, there will be only two workers for each retired person.

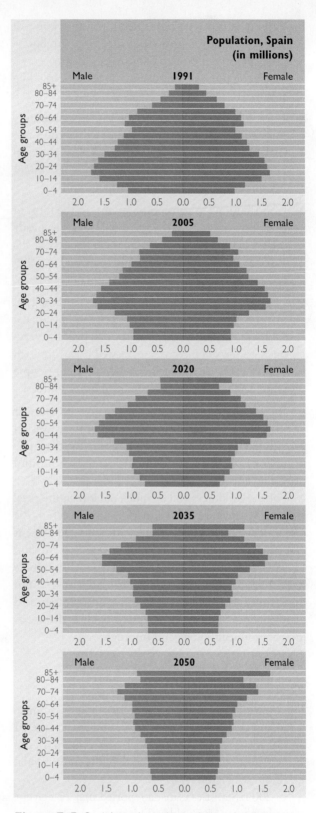

Figure 7–5 Spain's projected population development may be typical of that of developed countries in the 21st century: a sharply declining population and, by 2050, women over 85 making up the largest population group. What implications does this have for Spain and other countries experiencing similar demographic changes?

Perhaps it is not surprising that a major issue in American politics is how to ensure that the Social Security system will not go bankrupt.

Three solutions are possible in the face of exploding older populations:

- Pension benefits for each person can be significantly lowered. Reducing benefits can be achieved in two different ways—by paying out lower pension amounts, or by requiring people to work longer before they are eligible for their pensions.

- Contributions to pension programs, in the form of premiums or taxes, can be increased. This has already started in Canada. Contribution rates for the Canada Pension Plan were substantially increased in 1999 because of fears that the plan would run out of money.

- Eligibility for pensions can be restricted based on income. This too has already happened in Canada. Old Age Pensions, which used to be paid to everyone regardless of income, are "clawed back," through higher taxes or reduced payments, from people who have significant income from other sources.

Inter-generational conflict is possible as younger people rebel against focusing so much of their lives on providing financial and moral support for the huge number of older people. Similar issues exist around providing adequate healthcare for older people.

Future workforces will be much older than the present one. A preview of this situation can be seen in the case of Italy's high school teachers. In 2001, 90 percent of senior secondary school teachers were over 40, and only 0.1 percent were under 30. Having a workforce with many older workers has both advantages and disadvantages. What might these advantages and disadvantages be in teaching and in fields as diverse as information technology and mining?

3. Labour Shortages

The expression "Freedom 55" started as an insurance company's advertising slogan. Soon, however, it entered the Canadian *vernacular* (informal speech) as a powerful image—the desire to retire earlier than the conventional age of 65 (see Figure 7–6).

In 2005, Statistics Canada reported that 22 percent of workers were 55 or older. This was more than twice the number in the same age group in 1986. The large number of potential retirees was emerging at a time of already low unemployment and shortages of many types of skilled labour.

In fact, for many Canadians and residents of other developed countries, early retirement has become a reality. This trend to earlier retirements may be short-lived,

Figure 7–6 Older people are generally healthier and more active than they were in the past. This allows them to have longer careers than their parents, but most people in this age group prefer to retire and spend their time pursuing other activities.

however, and may benefit only people of your grandparents' generation. The reason is that, as our population ages, there will be too few people to do all the work society needs done. The shortage of workers is made even worse because most people spend more years in school than was the norm.

How bad might this **labour shortage** be? The IIASA has looked at the percentage of the population that will be 60 or older at various points in the future, and the projections are startling (see Figure 7–7). Two important conclusions can be drawn from these data. First, Freedom 55 may have to be replaced by Freedom 70+ if we are to have enough workers to power our economy. Note that in the "worst case" (but entirely possible) projection, more than half the population of Europe will be over 60 by 2100. Second, while a greying population may be a problem for some Core countries in the early decades of the 21st century, by 2050 it will be seen as a global problem.

There is some evidence that labour shortages are already starting to happen in Core countries. For example, there have been ongoing shortages in fields such as computer engineering, nursing, manual labour, and skilled trades. Germany's robust economy has been maintained only because, over the years, the country has been able to import millions of "guest workers" from countries such as Turkey and Iran. The legal situation for foreign workers in the US is different, but the

Region	1995 (actual)	2020 (predicted)	2050 (predicted)	2100 (predicted)
Africa	5.0%	5.5–6.5%	7.5–14.3%	13.9–35.8%
Asia-East	9.4	14.0–7.0	17.4–34.5	18.0–46.6
Asia-West	6.5	9.0–10.4	12.2–21.3	18.2–43.0
Europe	17.8	22.6–26.8	26.3–44.9	22.0–51.1
Latin America	7.5	10.9–13.0	15.5–27.8	17.8–42.8
North America	16.4	21.9–25.9	22.8–38.9	20.6–45.0
Less developed	7.2	9.9–11.7	13.0–23.8	17.3–41.6
More developed	17.7	23.1–27.3	25.7–43.6	21.9–49.1
World	9.5	12.2–14.4	14.7–26.6	17.8–42.5

Figure 7–7 Regional projections for the percentage of the population over age 60. The numbers shown are the low and high variants supposing various assumptions about fertility rates and changes in life expectancies. The medium variant in each case is approximately the average of each pair of values.

economic impact of the labour shortage is similar. The US has about 12 million people who are in the country illegally. They are an essential, if not officially acknowledged, part of the economy. Illegal workers, primarily from Mexico and other Latin American countries, fill poorly paid service, manufacturing, and agricultural jobs in many parts of the US. If illegal workers were forced to leave, there would be nobody to take their jobs because the US economy is at near full employment levels.

Over the next century, developed countries will need to accept hundreds of millions of immigrant workers in order to maintain their economies. This may cause major problems in Japan and some countries of Europe. Unlike Canada, they do not have the tradition of accepting large numbers of immigrants and integrating them into society. In countries like France and the United Kingdom, which have taken in many immigrants, intolerance of different cultures is a significant problem. Germany, France, Austria, and other countries have political parties that advocate strong anti-immigrant policies.

Another problem is that there may be a shortage of skilled immigrants available in the world. Canada's most important immigrant source is China. Each year we accept thousands of Chinese immigrants who bring with them a wide variety of technical and professional skills. Will these immigrants still be available for Canada as labour shortages emerge in China because of its birth dearth and rapidly growing economy? In Chapter 8 you will learn more about why migration between countries happens and why it might stop, or at least slow down dramatically.

4. Economic Effects

The foundation of our economy is the concept of never-ending growth. This growth occurs for two reasons:

- People are getting wealthier and want/need (and are able to pay for) more "stuff" (goods and services).

- For centuries, world and national populations have been growing continuously, so there have been more people, each of whom wants/needs "stuff."

If there is a population implosion, the second component could disappear, and there would be fewer consumers in the world. While this may have certain environmental advantages (discussed below), it does have serious implications for the health of the world's economy. This should not emerge as a serious problem in the first half of the 21st century because the world's population will continue to increase—according to the lowest estimates, by more than one billion. Further, most people in the New Core and Near Core will become increasingly affluent. Economic problems will

Did You Know?

In 2007, the US Congress considered, but did not pass, a bill to legalize a system of guest workers.

become more noticeable in the second half of the century, as the population significantly declines, and the possibility arises that growth in material wealth may be limited by environmental and resource constraints.

5. Shift in World Power

The Security Council is the UN's most powerful body. It has 15 member countries, of whom five are permanently on the Council. As well as being permanent, these five (the US, Russia, China, the UK, and France) have veto power over any resolution voted on by the Security Council. They were given this extraordinary power when the UN was formed at the end of World War II because they were clearly the most powerful nations in the world at that time. But how should world power be distributed in 2050, when all the permanent Security Council members are likely to have declining populations, and only 12 percent of the world's population live in the developed world? Will countries like India, Indonesia, and Pakistan come to be seen as major world powers, replacing Russia, the UK, and France (see Figure 7–8)? Along with the shift in population, there will be a significant growth in the economic and military power of nations outside the Old Core.

Benefits of the Birth Dearth for the World

While the impending population implosion presents challenges for the world, there is considerable good environmental news attached to the idea of a smaller-than-anticipated world population. Fewer people mean less resource use and fewer waste products like carbon emissions, solid waste, and air and water pollution. Also, since population declines will occur in the world's wealthiest countries, there will be fewer people who use the most resources and produce the most waste. We can understand the impact of these changes by looking at the demographic assumptions that underlie predictions about climate change in the future. These predictions were based on an assumed population of 11.3 billion in 2050. If there are instead seven to nine billion people, there will be an obvious difference in the amount of global warming. Of course, it does not help nearly as much if the world's population, of whatever size, chooses to live in a wasteful and unsustainable way.

Predicted Rank (2050)	Country	Population (millions)
1	India	1628
2	China*	1437
3	US*	420
4	Indonesia	308
5	Pakistan	295
6	Brazil	260
7	Nigeria	258
8	Bangladesh	231
9	Ethiopia	170
10	Philippines	142
11	Mexico	139

Predicted Rank (2050)	Country	Population (millions)
12	Egypt	126
13	Vietnam	115
14	Russia*	111
15	Iran	102
16	Turkey	101
17	Japan	101
18	Sudan	84
19	Afghanistan	82
20	Germany	75
22	UK*	67
25	France*	64

Figure 7–8 The world's 20 most populous nations in 2050. The UK and France are included since they are permanent members* of the UN Security Council.

Why Is the Birth Dearth Happening?

There are many reasons why birth rates have declined sharply in dozens of countries. You should be familiar with most of these reasons since they are simply the explanations for demographic transition that you studied earlier. There is more to the birth dearth than this, however.

What is most critical in the ongoing decline of birth rates is the changing role of women in society. There are many aspects to this.

- Young women today are better educated than young women in previous generations. Numerous studies, in both Core and Periphery nations, have shown that women with more education typically have fewer children.

- More women are choosing to have a career outside the home.

- They also choose to work for more years.

- They have more control over their lives than in traditional societies.

- They marry later.

- They are more likely to divorce.

- Increasingly, they may choose not to marry at all.

- They have greater access to effective birth control.

The birth dearth is occurring as a result of the decisions made by individuals about the direction they want their lives to take. You are likely at the point in your life when you are starting to make decisions that will affect your future career and family life. Consider the example of Laura Forbes, aged 35, who had to make these decisions.

After graduating from university, Laura worked as a teacher. At age 32, she returned to school to get a Master's degree for her new career in educational administration. Upon finishing her Master's degree, Laura got a contract job (temporary) with the provincial ministry. Her employer told her that a permanent job, with paid maternity leave and a guaranteed position upon her return, would not be available for a couple of years. Her doctor, however, told her that if she and her partner wanted a child, it would be better not to wait much longer.

Laura now faced a conflict between her career goals and her desire for a family. This conflict is typical for many women in Core countries. Laura is now likely to have only one child (or perhaps none at all), and as a consequence, will contribute to Canada's birth dearth. Laura's situation is very common, not just in Canada, but in countries where women are trying to combine having a family with having a career. After considering Laura's experience, what questions come to your mind about the relationships between individuals' desires to have children, the responsibility of employers and society in this regard, and the impact this is having on populations in developed countries? Try to identify at least four such questions.

Can We Prevent a Population Implosion?

It is difficult to answer this question because declining populations are such a new problem. Obviously, to prevent a population implosion, people in developed countries would need to be encouraged to have more children. Policies designed to do this are called "pronatalist." There are many possible **pronatalist strategies**. Some governments provide cash payments or offer tax benefits to parents. Following World War II, Canada provided monthly grants called "baby bonuses" to families with children. Now, lower-income families receive "child tax credits." These relatively small payments have had no demonstrable impact on birth rates in Canada. New pronatalist strategies are being considered or attempted in many parts of the world. For example

- Mario Dumont, head of the Action démocratique du Québec (ADQ) party, proposed in the 2007 Quebec provincial election to give a $100-per-week family allowance for each child not enrolled in the province's $7-a-day daycare program (itself a costly pronatalist policy). These policies reflect the fact that Quebec has the lowest fertility rate and oldest population in Canada and that its population is expected to start to decline by about 2020.

- South Korea, which has the lowest total fertility rate in the world—1.12 in 2007—is embarking on a US$35 billion program of pronatalist policies.

Pronatalist strategies are typically designed to address the economic and non-economic pressures that parents and prospective parents feel. For example, more generous short-term and long-term parental leaves could be provided. Employers could provide more on-site daycare and/or allow more employees to work from home. Even reducing the cost of higher education might have an impact.

There is little evidence that pronatalist strategies encourage higher fertility rates—though they tend to be popular politically. For example, the Swedish government has a proud tradition of providing the highest level of family support in the world. In 1990, Sweden had the highest birth rate in western Europe, with a TFR of 2.12. However, by 1998, in spite of its pronatalist policies, Sweden's TFR had fallen to 1.42. This decline began during the early 1990s, when economic conditions were poor, and continued through the late 1990s, when the economy had recovered.

The other solution to a population implosion is immigration. Considerable evidence suggests that this may be at best a temporary solution. In Canada and in other developed nations, the fertility rates of most immigrant women quickly decline to mirror that of all women in the nation. For example, in Canada the overall fertility rate for immigrant women is 1.4, which is slightly lower than those of all women in Canada. In France, the large number of immigrants from North Africa has helped to increase the country's TFR to 1.98 in 2007 from 1.70 in 1996, but there is no way of knowing if this increase will be maintained.

What Will Happen?

No one knows how long the current birth dearth will continue. We lack the expertise to make a dependable prediction because nothing like this has ever happened. Some authorities feel that society has fundamentally changed and that larger families are a thing of the past.

To know what will happen in the decades to come, we would have to be able to anticipate the decisions that people like you will make. The possibility of a population implosion in some parts of the world does not mean that we need no longer fear the impact of a population boom. Rather, both events will happen in different parts of the world at the same time. The result is likely to be demographic tension between countries with rising populations and those with falling populations. International organizations will be faced with meeting the often conflicting needs of nations fighting to limit their populations, as well as those needing to increase theirs. How well this can be done will be critical to human progress in the 21st century.

SUSTAINABILITY

Some authorities feel that society has fundamentally changed and that larger families are a thing of the past.

How do smaller families reflect the realities of modern life? Consider both economic and social realities.

Chapter Questions

Knowledge and Understanding

1. **a)** In this chapter you learned a great deal about how the population of Canada and other Core countries will change in this century. How might what you have learned affect your career choice? Why?

    b) Give specific examples of jobs that will become more common and others that will become less common because of demographic change.

2. Describe how your career choice may affect your family choices and how your family choices may affect your career.

3. **a)** Describe how the healthcare needs of countries like Canada will change as the population implosion occurs.

    b) What evidence is there that this change is already happening?

4. **a)** In recent years, there has been a tendency toward earlier retirements. In the future, this is likely not to be the case. Give two different reasons why working until an older age will make sense (or indeed be necessary) in the future.

    b) Describe how pension payments are related to the ratio of active and retired workers. Why are pensions being threatened by population changes?

5. Describe one social and one economic influence of each of the three factors that affect the size of a population and the accuracy of population projections.

Thinking

6. Discuss the statement, "The birth dearth is essentially a women's issue." Note that, in your answer, you should consider both the ways that this statement might be true and those in which it might not be true.

7. What changes in the organization of the work world would be necessary to meet the needs of women and men who want children?

8. Explain why solving the demographic issues of the next century is not as simple as moving people from overpopulated regions of the world to underpopulated regions.

9. **a)** Imagine that you have been asked to write a plan for the recreational needs of your community or the province of Ontario for the next 25 years. Your plan should consider which recreational demands are likely to grow and which are likely to decline. Suggest additional facilities and programs that should be added and existing ones that may not be needed.

    b) Part (a) of this question looked at how demographic change will have an impact on one area of human life— recreational needs. Suggest three other major aspects of life not discussed in this chapter that will be affected by demographic change and give one example of an impact in each area.

10. **a)** Our economy has been based on the fundamental idea of growth. In what two ways does this growth occur? How might this change in the future?

    b) Why does this have both positive and negative implications?

    c) Suggest ways that the impact of this change could be reduced—other than by increasing birth rates.

Communication

11. **a)** Graph the TFR data in Figure 7–9 on page 112. Hints:

    • Use solid lines to show the trend from 1960 to 2007 and dashed lines to show the projection to 2050.

    • Label each country's line.

    • Add a line to show the global TFR replacement value. Label this line. You will have to do some research to find this figure.

    • Give the graph an appropriate title.

    b) Describe the patterns you see. What do these patterns suggest about the world's future population, both in total and in the different "worlds"?

    c) Why might the TFR projections for some countries increase between 2007 and 2050?

12. How old will you be in 2050? Assume that you will have an eight-year-old grandchild by then (this might be the first time in your life you have considered your grandchildren!). Write him or her a letter explaining how life is different today (2050) than it was when you were in high school because of changes in demography. **S**

	1960	1980	2007	2050 (projected)
Old Core				
Canada	3.80	1.70	1.61	1.70
Japan	2.00	1.80	1.23	1.70
New Core				
China	5.70	2.90	1.75	1.80
Chile	5.30	2.80	1.97	1.70
Near Core				
Ecuador	6.70	5.10	2.63	2.03
Indonesia	5.50	4.40	2.38	1.75
Far Periphery				
Ethiopia	6.90	6.90	5.10	2.78
Haiti	6.30	5.30	4.86	2.04

Figure 7–9 Historical, current, and projected TFRs for selected countries

Application

13. Not all areas of the Core will be affected by the population implosion in the same way. Discuss the impact on each of the following regions.

   • Canada
   • US
   • Russia and eastern Europe
   • Western Europe and Japan
   • China

CHAPTER 8

Population Migration

Key Terms

push factors

pull factors

voluntary migration

involuntary migration

environmental migration

guest workers

legal migration

illegal migration

internal migration

brain gain

brain drain

remittance

replacement migration

refugees

internally displaced persons (IDPs)

Each year since 2000, Canada has welcomed more than 220 000 immigrants. At right, members of a family, originally from Bangladesh, are being sworn in as Canadian citizens. Immigrants often send money to family members in their homeland, through banks and companies like Western Union.

Key Questions

By the end of this chapter you will be able to answer the following questions.

■ What impact does human migration have on natural and human systems?

■ How has the pattern of Canada's immigration changed? Why?

■ What types of migration occur globally?

■ What problems does migration solve? What problems does it cause?

■ What causes people to become refugees and internally displaced persons?

SOURCES OF CANADIAN IMMIGRANTS

Depending on where you live in Canada, chances are some of your classmates have recently moved to Canada from another country, like the family on page 113.

Few countries in the world have been, or are being, more affected by immigration than Canada. Only 2 percent of Canadians are of Aboriginal descent. This means that 98 percent of us are immigrants or descendants of immigrants. Immigration has been critical to Canada's development for 400 years; the sources of this immigration, however, have changed over time. Complete the following activity to see the changing pattern of where Canada's immigrants have come from.

1. Using the information in Figure 8–1, construct a multiple bar graph for each time period. Place time along the x-axis and the percentage of immigrants on the y-axis. The first part of the graph is shown in Figure 8–2.

2. a) What changes do you see in terms of the sources of Canada's immigrants since 1921?

   b) Which sources contributed the most immigrants to Canada in 2001?

   c) Give reasons why the sources of Canada's immigration have changed.

3. Why do people migrate to Canada? Consider conditions in the source region compared to those in Canada.

4. How might Canada be affected if immigration stopped today?

Hint: What exactly do the numbers show? Any numerical data that you encounter have an implied degree of accuracy. The numbers in this table have been rounded to the nearest 0.1 percent. For example, this means that the actual percentage of European-born residents in Canada in 1921 was somewhere between a lower limit equal to or greater than 75.85 percent and an upper limit less than 75.95 percent. In math class terms, this could be written as $75.85 \leq n < 75.95$.

Values of 0.0 percent do not mean that there were zero residents of Canada from 1921 to 1961 born in Latin America or Africa—instead the number was so small that it rounded to zero rather than to 0.1 percent. If you think about it, this means the actual number would be less than 0.05 percent ($n < 0.05$) since anything higher would round up.

Did You Know?

Origin of foreign-born residents of Canada, 2005

• 21% Europe

• < 4% US

• > 50% Asia Pacific

• 20% Africa and the Middle East

Place of Birth	1921	1941	1961	1981	2001
Europe	75.9	79.9	85.7	66.8	42.0
US	19.1	15.5	10.0	8.1	4.4
Asia	2.7	2.2	2.0	14.0	36.5
Caribbean	0.2	0.2	0.4	3.5	5.4
Latin America	0.0	0.0	0.0	2.8	5.6
Africa	0.0	0.0	0.0	2.7	5.2

Figure 8–1 Sources of foreign-born residents of Canada, 1921–2001, expressed as a percentage. This change in trends continues today.

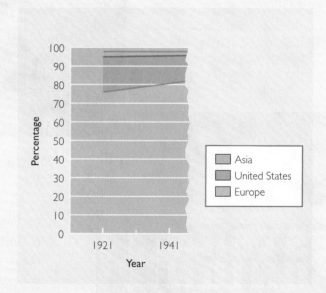

Figure 8–2 The multiple bar graph for 1921 and 1941 should look something like this.

Nature of Migration

What makes people migrate? Certain conditions, known as **push factors**, cause people to leave the places where they live. Push factors may include low wages, shortages of food, overcrowded living conditions, political persecution, high crime rates, wartime conditions, lack of economic opportunity, degradation of agricultural land, or the depletion of forests or water. Other conditions, known as **pull factors**, attract people to new places. Pull factors may include high wages, good educational opportunities, havens from political or religious persecution, high standards of living, or plentiful resources such as fresh water, forests, wildlife, or agricultural land.

People who move *from* a country are known as *emigrants*. People who move *to* a country are known as *immigrants* (see Figure 8–3). Each year, more than two million people migrate and settle permanently in other countries; millions more migrate, but settle only temporarily. Many people migrate within their own country. Much migration tends to be between adjacent countries and regions—for example, from Mexico to the US, and from North Africa to Europe. Convenient, relatively inexpensive air transport has allowed migrants to travel great distances. Today, virtually all of Canada's immigrants arrive by plane from distant countries such as China and India.

SUSTAINABILITY

Each year, more than two million people migrate and settle permanently in other countries; millions more migrate, but settle only temporarily.

Do you think these numbers are likely to grow or decline in the future? Why?

There are four questions we should ask about any migration:

- Is the migration *voluntary* or *involuntary*?
- Is the migration *permanent* or *temporary*?
- Is the migration *legal* or *illegal*?
- Is the migration *international* or *internal*?

Did You Know?

Much of the in-migration to Eastern Africa in Figure 8–3 reflects the return of people to Rwanda after security there was re-established in the middle of the 1990s.

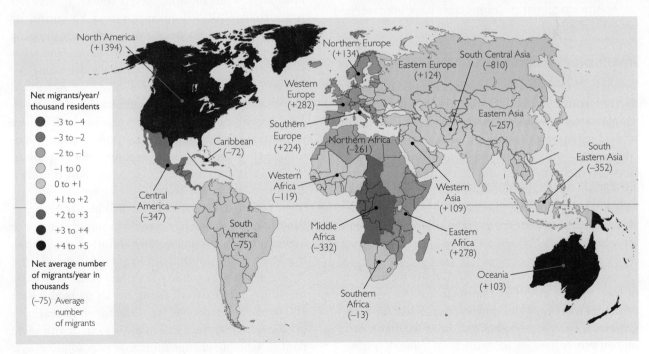

Figure 8–3 World migration patterns in 2000. The map shows both the number of migrants to or from each region and the rate of migration to or from each region. Note that the map shows nothing of the migration patterns within any region (for example, between Canada and the US or between Brazil and Argentina).

When you consider the possible combinations of the answers to these four questions, you will see that migration takes many forms. For example, migration may be *voluntary, permanent, legal,* and *internal* or it may be *involuntary, temporary, illegal,* and *international.* Let's look at each of these forms in more detail.

Is the Migration Voluntary or Involuntary?

Voluntary Migration

Between 1800 and 1914, approximately 70 million people left Europe and migrated, by choice, to Canada, the United States, Australia, Argentina, and other countries. This is an example of **voluntary migration**, that is, the movement by people, by their own free will, from one place to another. As a result of this voluntary migration, Europe was able to alleviate serious population pressures, and the emigrants were able to establish themselves in countries with security, more abundant resources, and better opportunities for financial success. This type of migration could be regarded as "good" migration since people are able to pursue a better future for themselves and their families.

Generally, when Canadians talk about immigration, it is voluntary migration they are considering. Each year since 2000, Canada has welcomed more than 220 000 permanent, international immigrants, most of whom are voluntary migrants. Immigrants have become an *integral* (essential) part of Canada.

Involuntary Migration

Involuntary migration has occurred throughout history, and unfortunately, occurs far too often today. Stated in simple terms, **involuntary migration** is the movement of people, against their will, to a different location. Involuntary migration is not a new phenomenon. Between the years 1500 and 1810, between 11 and 15 million people were forcefully taken out of Africa to be sold as slaves in the Americas. In general, there are two causes of involuntary migration: geopolitical and environmental.

Geopolitical. One of the saddest outcomes of the invasion of Iraq, and the civil strife that followed, has been the enormous number of involuntary migrants that has been generated. This migration has had two parts. About two million people have felt so unsafe in Iraq that they have left the country entirely and become refugees (see Figure 8–4). Most of these people have fled to Syria and Jordan. In addition to these international, involuntary migrants, the Iraq War has also meant the internal displacement

Figure 8–4 These refugees were forced to flee Iraq following the American invasion.

of another two million people. Conflicts among the country's three main religious/ethnic groups, the Shias, Sunnis, and Kurds, have meant that many people have felt unsafe living in areas dominated by a group other than their own. The result has been that they have moved to parts of the country (or the city of Baghdad) that are dominated by their own group (see Figure 8–5). This type of migration could be regarded as "bad" migration since individuals are forced to move by often horrendous circumstances.

Environmental. South of the Sahara Desert is the *Sahel* (an Arabic word meaning desert shore). It stretches more than 4000 kilometres across 15 countries (see Figure 8–6). Successive droughts since the early 1970s, plus the overuse of grasslands, forests, and water resources are lowering the water table, degrading the soil, and causing the vegetation to disappear. As a result, the Sahara Desert is spreading southward into the Sahel. This desertification is forcing the people who live there to move away. Involuntary migration forced by environmental change is called **environmental migration**.

In the future, climate change could cause the greatest human migration ever. People living on low-lying islands or coastal plains may see their homes disappear beneath rising sea levels and could be forced to move to higher land. A number of tiny nations, for example, the Maldives in the Indian Ocean and Tuvalu in the Pacific, face the possibility that their entire land mass may disappear beneath rising sea levels in the next 100 years. Other people, from areas with increasingly dry climates, may be forced to move to areas with more rainfall. Climate-change migration may soon be seen as the "ugly" migration since so many people will be affected—and they will have to move to other areas that are havin g to face their own climate-change challenges.

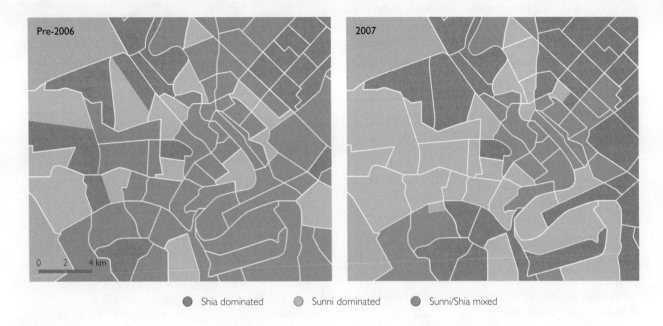

Shia dominated Sunni dominated Sunni/Shia mixed

Figure 8–5 Population of Baghdad neighbourhoods by religion. Canadians often move from one part of a city to another to buy a nicer house or to shorten a commute. This is voluntary migration. In Iraq, many people have moved because of suicide bombers and random kidnappings and killings. These maps show how the population distribution of districts of Baghdad has changed as a result of this involuntary migration.

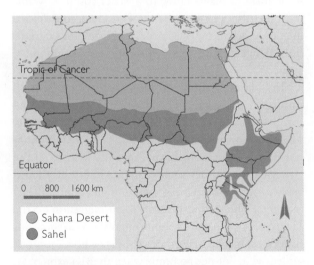

Figure 8–6 The Sahel Region of Africa

Is the Migration Permanent or Temporary?

In years gone by, most migration tended to be permanent. When Ukrainian families left for Saskatchewan in 1910, chances were that they would never see their homeland again. To a large extent, this reflected the difficulty, high cost, and danger of travelling long distances. Temporary migration, however, is more common now. Air travel has become widespread and relatively inexpensive, so people can migrate to one place and then move on to another.

Frequently, people who intend to migrate permanently, only migrate temporarily; the reverse is also common. Consider the following:

■ A group of six Chinese immigrants to Canada met for dinner in 1995. They shared several characteristics: they were recent arrivals, highly educated, and ambitious. A dozen years later, they had all become successful in business or high-tech jobs. However, only two of the six still lived in Canada. Two had moved to the US, while two had returned to China. This example shows how "permanent" immigration frequently becomes temporary.

■ Many countries need immigrants to fill jobs in a growing economy, but do not want permanent immigrants. Instead, they admit **guest workers** (temporary migrants). Some guest workers in Germany, though, have been there for more than 40 years! Although many have German-born children and grandchildren, they still do not have "permanent" status. Sometimes guest workers fill an overall shortage of labour. In other cases, they take poorly paid or unpleasant work.

- Refugees fleeing from conflicts are usually considered temporary migrants, the assumption being that when conditions at home improve, the refugees will go home. Frequently, however, conditions in home countries don't improve and temporary migrants become permanent immigrants. For example, Palestinian refugees have been living in Jordan and other countries for six decades.

Is It Legal or Illegal Migration?

Legal Migration

Countries that accept immigrants control **legal migration** by establishing clear rules that determine who will be accepted or rejected. The particular set of rules that a country chooses reflect that country's economic and social needs.

- Canada, for example, focuses on attracting highly skilled and/or wealthy permanent immigrants. This reflects what the government sees as Canada's economic needs. It accepts immigrants of several types within these categories (see Figure 8–7).

- Germany, on the other hand, follows a different route: it accepts few permanent immigrants, but allows many temporary guest workers to fill jobs in manufacturing and service industries.

- Rich countries in the Middle East, like Saudi Arabia and the United Arab Emirates, have guest worker programs that focus on both low-level jobs in services and construction and high-level jobs in finance, transportation, and the oil industry. (You read about Dubai, part of the UAE, in Chapter 2.)

Illegal Migration

Many people in the Near Core and Far Periphery and in many parts of the New Core see the nations of the Old Core as lands of unlimited opportunity. Whether this impression is accurate is largely irrelevant to desperately poor people who see little likelihood of getting ahead in their home country. Many of these people are poorly educated and unlikely to qualify as legal immigrants to countries that, like Canada, want only the "best and brightest" from the developing world. With the possibility of legal migration unavailable to them, they pursue

 You can learn more about the categories of immigrants shown in Figure 8–7 on our Web site.

Category	Description
Skilled workers	Canada accepts well-educated people who can contribute to our economy. Immediate family members also qualify.
Investors, entrepreneurs, and self-employed people	This category is for those able to invest in Canada or start a business.
Family reunification	Permanent residents of Canada can sponsor close relatives.
Provincial sponsorship	Provinces can agree to sponsor immigrants who can contribute directly to meeting that province's labour needs.
Refugees	Refugees are those forced to flee their home countries.

Figure 8–7 There are five ways that legal immigrants can come to Canada.

some form of illegal entry to a richer country. While most illegal migration is to the Old Core, some illegal migration occurs between other countries, for example, from Bangladesh to India where job opportunities are greater.

In general, there are two ways that **illegal immigration** occurs. The simplest of these is illegal entry—sneaking into the target country by land or water. The best-known example of this is the hundreds of thousands of people from Latin America who cross the US–Mexican border each year (see Figure 8–8) and become part of the US's growing population of illegal migrants. The second type of illegal migration occurs when a person violates a country's terms of legal entry. For example, someone may enter a country with a tourist or student visa, but not go home when the visa expires.

Illegal migration is a huge and growing problem for much of the Old Core. The number of illegal immigrants has been estimated at five million in Western Europe and 12 million in the US. In spite of many attempts to stop, or at least curtail, illegal migration into the US and western Europe, the problem continues. It is thought that between 700 000 and 850 000 people enter the US illegally each year. About 50 000 Africans enter southern Europe each year; thousands more perish in the attempt when their boats prove unseaworthy. Approximately 500 000 illegal migrants from eastern Europe and the former Soviet Union enter western Europe by land each year.

Figure 8–8 A member of the US Border Patrol monitors the border between the US and Mexico in Calexico, California.

Is It International or Internal Migration?

When we talk about migration, we are usually referring to migration between countries. Migration, however, often takes place within a country's borders as well. This is known as **internal migration**. There are two types. The first, and most significant, is the movement of people from rural to urban areas. This trend started more than 200 year ago in England and France when the Industrial Revolution eliminated many jobs on farms but created more jobs in mines and in factories in cities.

Today, the rural–urban shift has virtually ended in the countries of the Old Core. In Canada, for example, the proportion of the population living in cities and towns has stabilized at about 80 percent. In the New Core, Near Core, and Far Periphery, though, the movement to the cities continues. In fact, 2007 marked an important milestone in this process: for the first time, more of the world's people lived in urban areas than in rural areas. You can learn more about rural–urban migration in Chapter 9.

The second type of internal migration is the movement of people from one region of a country to another. Within Canada, there is considerable internal migration from province to province. This interprovincial migration typically has been a significant contributor to the population growth of Ontario, British Columbia, and Alberta, and to the decline of populations in Newfoundland, Saskatchewan, and Manitoba.

Did You Know?

Even though the proportion of Canadians living in urban places has stabilized, migration is continuing from smaller urban places to larger ones. Many smaller urban communities are declining in size while the largest cities, in particular Toronto, Calgary, and Vancouver, are growing explosively.

An Overview of Important Migration Issues

Even a *cursory* (rapid or superficial) glance at the newspapers or the Internet reveals that immigration is a subject that provokes constant discussion and controversy. You may have had discussions about the benefits and drawbacks of certain immigration issues in your own family. Some of the more important immigration issues are discussed below.

Brain Drain

In general, the receiving countries of the Old Core and wealthy nations in the Persian Gulf do very well from immigration. They are able to "cherry-pick" the kind of immigrants they want. In particular, receiving countries are looking for workers with advanced skills in fields like medicine, engineering, education, and computers. Of all legal immigrants to the 30 OECD (Organization for Economic Cooperation and Development) nations, 88 percent have at least a high-school education. Because of the way Canada chooses immigrants, the overwhelming majority of its independent immigrants have post-secondary education or technical training. In rich countries, this trend has been called the "**brain gain**." In some cases, it can also be a "*brawn* gain" since migrants fill many heavy-labour jobs.

The arrival of educated workers contributes enormously to the economies of rich countries, but what does it do to the sending nations? The **brain drain** can be devastating. A 2003 study by the World Bank discovered that 25 percent to 50 percent of all the college graduates from countries like Ghana, Mozambique, and El Salvador now live in OECD nations. The situation is much worse for Haiti and Jamaica. More than 80 percent of their college graduates now live in OECD nations. The brain drain occurs in many other parts of the world as well—for example, many highly educated people from eastern Europe move to western Europe where they can earn more money. This migration is made easier within the European Union.

The impact of the brain drain can be illustrated by a specific example from one tiny, impoverished country. Lesotho, in southern Africa, has a small university that graduates a handful of registered nurses (RNs) each year. The skills of these RNs are desperately needed in Lesotho, a country that has the third-highest incidence of HIV/AIDS in the world. Since their qualifications are recognized in OECD countries, nearly every RN graduate leaves Lesotho for a more lucrative opportunity, usually in South Africa or the United Kingdom. The qualifications of Lesotho's nursing assistants, however, are not recognized elsewhere, and hence most of them stay home—often taking over the roles of RNs and even doctors in this poor country.

There is no obvious solution to the brain drain that does not involve restricting the freedom of individuals to pursue the future of their choice. A couple of proposals, however, have been made. The first is that receiving nations should "pay" in some form for each educated person that immigrates. Perhaps this could be in the form of additional targeted foreign aid that could be used to expand the capacity of higher-education facilities in the sending countries. A second proposal is that skilled workers be admitted to receiving countries as temporary migrants only for a fixed number of years with the understanding that they will return home at the end of the term. If this process were followed, the sending nation would gain since the skilled worker would return home with additional skills learned while working away. Which of these proposals do you think would be a more acceptable solution to the receiving country?

Importance of Remittances

A **remittance** is an amount of money sent by a migrant to family members living in the migrant's homeland. Remittances are surprisingly important to the economies of many countries. Perhaps the most studied example of remittances is that of workers from the Philippines. In 1974, the Philippine government established the Overseas Employment Program to tackle chronic unemployment within the country and the need to bring in scarce foreign currencies. In 1975, the program sent 36 000 workers to other countries; by 2007 more than one million Filipinos were working outside the country. These workers sent more than US$12 billion home in 2007, an amount equal to more than 10 percent of the Philippine's annual GDP. Remittances are even more important to many smaller countries (see Figure 8–9).

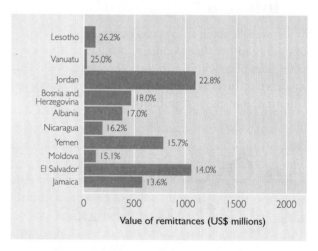

Figure 8–9 Remittances are vitally important to many smaller countries. In this graph, the horizontal bars reflect the dollar value of remittances. The height of each bar reflects the percentage of each country's GDP from remittances.

The Organization for Economic Cooperation and Development (OECD) is an international group made up of the 30 wealthiest nations. You can learn more at the link on our Web site.

In 2006, official remittances to all developing countries amounted to a remarkable US$221 billion. To put this figure in context, the total amount of official development assistance (foreign aid) from all 30 members of the OECD to the developing world in 2006 was US$105.3 billion. In reality, total remittances may be much higher since this figure does not include money brought home in person by migrant workers. Also, it might underestimate remittances from illegal workers, who are less inclined to use official monetary transfer mechanisms such as banks and companies like Western Union.

Remittances play several important roles in the economies of the countries receiving the money. First, the remittances help alleviate the poverty faced by the migrant worker's family. Second, the money spent by the family helps stimulate the local economy and provides a much-needed source of investment capital. For example, El Salvador's remittances are almost seven times greater than the amount of foreign direct investment. Third, remittances are earned in a variety of foreign currencies that are usually exchanged for the local currency. This exchange helps to increase the value of the currency in the countries receiving the remittances. People receiving the remittances are able to buy imported goods that are generally more expensive than they could afford.

Challenge of Integrating Immigrants in Receiving Countries

Countries receiving migrants benefit in many ways. First, immigrants often have skills that are in great demand in their new country (see Figure 8–10). These immigrants will become more important in the years to come as labour shortages become more common in Core nations. Second, immigrants act as a ready market for goods and services produced in their new country. Third, as taxpayers, they help pay for governmental programs in their new country.

It is not always easy, however, for immigrants to integrate effectively into the culture of their new country. For example, in western Europe and Japan, where a multicultural *ambience* (mood or feeling) is not considered desirable, immigrants (who are frequently guest workers since permanent immigration is hard to achieve in those areas) are often not welcomed and have difficulty integrating. This is unlike Canada, Australia, and the US, where a cultural mix within society is generally seen as positive, and immigrants' values and customs are generally viewed as worthwhile. In these

Figure 8–10 A country that has a shortage of people with specialized skills is interested in receiving people like this healthcare worker.

countries, the integration of immigrants, while not without problems, is much easier.

An interesting comparison in this regard can be made between Toronto and Paris. The vast numbers of immigrants who have come to the Greater Toronto Area (GTA) have fundamentally changed the nature of the city and its suburbs. Before World War II, Toronto was an overwhelmingly British city. Its sarcastic nickname, "Toronto the Good," was reflected in laws that kept movie theatres closed and professional sports banned on Sundays. This situation has changed dramatically, partly because of immigration. The laws were changed as the values, religions, and customs of immigrants became part of the social fabric of the city. In addition to the great economic benefits, immigration has meant an explosion in the city's cultural diversity with an enormous range of entertainment, restaurants, and shopping from all over the world. A multicultural group of high school students may start a Saturday with a visit to a huge Chinese mall, followed by dinner at a Portuguese restaurant and the latest Bollywood movie.

The impact of immigration on Paris has been dramatic. The beautiful city that tourists enjoy is not the Paris of the city's immigrants. Significant immigration to Paris from North Africa began almost 100 years ago, but became more common starting in the 1950s. Many immigrants live in dreary, high-rise apartments in poor suburbs of Paris with populations highly segregated by race and poverty. Unemployment rates are as much as 50 percent. Residents of these *ghettos* (parts of a city in which members of a minority group live, especially because of social, legal, or economic pressure) have found out that when they apply for a job, it has been "filled" when they give an African name or when the employer hears their accent. Discrimination in hiring continues. In 2007, a division of L'Oréal, the world's largest cosmetic company, was convicted of discriminatory hiring of hostesses who were to demonstrate shampoo in supermarkets. The company stipulated that they wanted young "BBR" women. (BBR stands for *bleu, blanc, et rouge*—the colours of the French flag.) This expression is a code word for "white and French-born" within right-wing groups in France. The main difference between L'Oréal and many other employers is that L'Oréal got caught.

GLOBALIZATION

The beautiful city that tourists enjoy is not the Paris of the city's immigrants.

What is meant by this statement?

Social alienation and despair in 2005 resulted in riots in a Paris suburb after two North African teenagers being chased by police were electrocuted when they tried to hide in an electrical substation. Rioting spread through several suburbs of Paris and then jumped to other parts of France (see Figure 8–11). Before it was over, one person was dead and almost 9000 vehicles had been burned. Property damage was almost 200 million euros and almost 3000 people were arrested. In a three-week period, rioting occurred in 274 towns and cities.

Countries that welcome newcomers often find that their immigration policies cause fear among citizens who object to the perceived loss of job opportunities caused by increased competition from immigrants. This has been one reason why illegal immigration to the US is so controversial. In some cases, this job loss may be real. Immigrants, however, do not generally take desirable jobs. Instead, they take the jobs that others do not want because the jobs are hard, dangerous, unpleasant, and often poorly paid. Immigrants are often treated as scapegoats when complex economic or social problems develop. Citizens

Figure 8–11 In a seventh night of rioting, French police advance during clashes with youths in the Paris suburb of Aulnay-sous-Bois.

may also object to the costs of integrating immigrants into their society. These costs that provide healthcare, temporary shelter, language instruction, and other social services are borne by taxpayers. Although newly arrived immigrants may initially require considerable support as workers, in time they contribute more in tax dollars than they ever took in the form of benefits in the first place. Their spending also *creates* jobs.

Many immigrants find it hard to be successful in their new country because of cultural and professional difficulties. Foreign professionals sometimes find that their degrees and other forms of certification are not recognized in the receiving country, or that they would have to take additional training that may be difficult or expensive to access. This has been a common complaint in Canada, and the Canadian government is trying to institute a policy that would let potential immigrants to the country know, before they came, whether their qualifications would be accepted here. Foreign workers often find working in their new country difficult because of their weak language skills or lack of familiarity with how institutions (for example, businesses, hospitals, or schools) operate.

The reality of modern terrorism also makes the integration of immigrants more difficult. Major terrorist attacks in the US (2001), Spain (2004), and Britain (2005) have made many residents of Old Core countries less accepting of immigrants. This attitudinal change has occurred in spite of the fact that only a very tiny percentage of immigrants are potential terrorists. In fact, many immigrants leave their home countries to get away from the destructive beliefs that are central to terrorist activities. (You can learn more about terrorism in Chapter 23.)

Problem of Illegal Immigration

Illegal Immigration in the US

The US has the largest and best-known problem with illegal migration. Surveys indicate that a significant majority of American citizens not only want to stop illegal immigration, but would also like existing "undocumented aliens," as they are officially known, to be sent home. Illegal migrants, however, are a vital part of the US economy. If they were forced to leave the US, the economy would be left in a shambles. Consequently, the American government faces a "damned if it does, damned if it doesn't" situation. It has tried to stem the tide of economic migration by building a high fence along long sections of its southern border, by equipping its 11 000 border-patrol officers with high-tech equipment such as night-vision goggles and ground sensors, and by using aircraft, four-wheel-drive vehicles, and dogs to apprehend potential illegal migrants. Although the border patrols catch hundreds of illegal migrants each day, the migrants suffer no punishment when they are caught. Many then try to cross again on a different night and at a different location.

In 2007, President George W. Bush led the fight for a comprehensive bill to deal with illegal immigrants. His plan had several facets: tougher border enforcement to stop the entry of more illegal migrants, a guest-worker program, penalties for employers who hire illegal migrants, and an amnesty process by which illegal residents could move toward legal status and eventually citizenship. Congress soundly rejected his plan—in particular, because of opposition to any form of amnesty. Opposition to Bush's plan came from both Democrats and Republicans.

Smuggling of Illegal Immigrants

Organized crime syndicates around the world are involved in human smuggling. These syndicates offer "package deals" that include counterfeit documents, airline tickets, spaces in cargo containers, contacts, and the use of safe houses at various points en route. The fee per individual varies from $500 to $50 000, depending on the package and the destination country. For these large sums of money, illegal migrants put themselves in the hands of criminals who smuggle them across borders, sometimes in very dangerous ways (see Figure 8–12). In 2000, for example, 58 migrants from the Chinese province of Fujian were found suffocated in a container truck that arrived in the UK.

The smuggling of illegal migrants is big business, and is growing. The Fujian smugglers, known as "snakeheads," not only charge large sums of money for passage and documents, they also charge high interest until the amount is paid off. This financial burden forces "illegals" to work long hours under very poor conditions—usually in restaurants or garment factories, on farms, or sometimes as prostitutes. The snakeheads often threaten the migrants or their loved ones in China if the money is not paid.

Need for Replacement Migration

As you learned in Chapter 7, it is projected that over the next 50 years, the populations of most developed countries will diminish while the median age will dramatically increase. Even if fertility rates increase, there won't be enough people to make up for the loss of working-age people unless developed countries adopt a policy of **replacement migration**, that is migration that occurs to make up for an aging and potentially declining population.

Developed countries with declining populations will have to decide in the near future how much replacement immigration they should allow. Germany, for example, would have to accept 24 million migrants (487 000 per year on average) by 2050 to maintain the working age population that it had in 2000. Having so many new residents in addition to its current

Figure 8–12 Chinese police, shown here, arrested more than 20 illegal immigrants, including five women, inside a container at the Huangpu container port. They were being smuggled to an unidentified Western country.

Figure 8–13 Maslakh refugee camp is the largest refugee camp in the world. It is located outside Herat, Afghanistan. Maslakh, which means "slaughterhouse," was named after a slaughterhouse nearby that no longer functions because there are no animals to process.

guest-worker numbers could challenge a country that has not shown a strong ability to integrate immigrants effectively. Many other European countries and Japan will find themselves in a similar situation. Canada will need replacement migrants as well, but we are already used to accepting and integrating large numbers of immigrants. The question may be whether we will be able to maintain the tough qualifications that we now use for immigrants at a time when so many countries will be competing for the best migrants.

If governments decide that replacement immigration is not an option, they will have to change many policies regarding the appropriate age for retirement, the level of healthcare for the elderly, and the amount of tax imposed on workers. Otherwise, there will not be enough people to fill the jobs that are necessary for the proper functioning of some countries' economies, or money to help maintain services for the aging, shrinking population.

The Ongoing Global Refugee Crisis

The following fictitious account is based on various refugee reports.

The camp in which we are staying has tents row upon row. The continuous rain has turned the ground into a muddy field, making it difficult to walk. There is a shortage of wood, so we are often cold, and it is not always possible to have hot meals even if we can get food. The international aid agencies send food, but there is never enough, and we have to fight for our share.

Our lives were not always like this. Before war came to my country, I went to school, played with friends, and looked forward to the future. But all that seems so far in the past. Soldiers took my father, grandfather, and older brother one night and we haven't seen them since. My mother was raped when enemy soldiers came through town. As soon as the soldiers left, we fled our home and left all our possessions behind. We travelled at night to avoid the patrols until we came to this refugee camp.

Do I have a future? I am so tired and sad that I almost don't care anymore....

Each year, thousands of people in the world face a prospect similar to what is shown in Figure 8–13. They may have been forced from their homes by any of the following: threats of violence from civil war or terrorism; authoritarian government controls; religious, racial, or ethnic persecution; environmental problems; and declining socio-economic conditions.

We tend to label all those who flee their homes for any of these reasons as **refugees**. The UN, however, is more specific and defines people who are displaced from their homes in different ways. Refugees are those who are forced to flee their homes for another country; **internally displaced persons** (IDPs) are those who are forced to leave their homes, but who stay within the borders of their own country.

At the end of 2004, the United Nations High Commissioner for Refugees (UNHCR) estimated that there were approximately 9.2 million refugees (see Figure 8–14) and 5.4 million IDPs in the world.

The UNHCR tries to assist refugees and IDPs by offering three possible "durable solutions" to their problems.

Refugees Received		Internally Displaced Persons	
Iran	1 046 000	Colombia	2 000 000
Pakistan	961 000	Sudan	662 000
Germany	877 000	Azerbaijan	578 000
Tanzania	602 000	Liberia	494 000
US	421 000	Sri Lanka	352 000
China	299 000	Russia	335 000
UK	289 000	Bosnia and Herzegovina	309 000

Figure 8–14 People in the Old Core often think that they bear most of the load for supporting displaced persons. As these 2004 statistics show, this is not the case. Most of the countries receiving refugees and that have many IDPs are poor Periphery nations. When you look at these statistics, try to relate them to the populations of the countries to get a better sense of the true load.

- The preferred solution is *voluntary repatriation*. If conditions in the home country improve to the point that refugees believe their lives or liberty are no longer in danger, they may safely return home.

- The second solution is *local integration* of refugees into countries of first asylum. The country of first asylum is the first country to which refugees flee and usually borders on the refugees' home country. The UNHCR tries to link refugees with kinship groups or other populations with whom they have linguistic or other cultural ties. This solution of course depends on the agreement of the country of first asylum.

- The third solution is *third-country resettlement*. When repatriation to the refugees' home country is not possible and the first-asylum country refuses local integration (or is overwhelmed by numbers), the final option is to find a third country willing to accept the refugees. Third-country resettlement was the case in the 1970s after the war in Vietnam. Thousands of refugees from Vietnam, Laos, and Cambodia were settled in the US and Canada.

 You can learn more about refugees at the link on our Web site.

GLOBALIZATION

Unfortunately, most of the world's refugees do not find a durable solution to their problems.

Why is this unfortunate and not a surprise?

Unfortunately, most of the world's refugees do not find a final solution to their problems. The majority have been granted temporary asylum in neighbouring countries but have not been able to integrate into those societies. Instead, millions live in refugee camps, generally in squalid conditions, with poor job prospects and educational opportunities, and with limited chances to move somewhere else.

Most countries are willing to offer asylum to refugees whose survival has truly been threatened by war, terrorism, or ethnic or political persecution. It is sometimes difficult, however, to distinguish between genuine refugees and "economic" refugees; that is, those people who have immigrated solely for the purpose of improving their standard of living. For example, although most of Canada's refugee claimants are from countries in turmoil, such as Afghanistan and Sri Lanka, we also receive refugee applications from citizens of the US and the UK. Canadian immigration officials are often suspicious of the true motives of those claiming refugee status. In a typical year, less than half of refugee claimants to Canada are accepted.

Chapter Questions

Knowledge and Understanding

1. Describe, with specific examples, the four categories of migration.

2. a) Define "push factor." Give two examples of push factors that might encourage a Canadian to migrate to another country.

   b) Define "pull factor." Give two examples of pull factors that might encourage someone to migrate to Canada.

3. a) Explain the difference between "brain drain" and "brain gain."

   b) Describe a current situation where these two events are occurring.

4. a) What are remittances?

   b) Demonstrate how remittances are important to the economies of many countries.

   c) Select a country and show how remittances are important to its economic well-being.

5. Differentiate, using specific examples, between the terms "refugee" and "internally displaced person."

6. a) What are the three "durable solutions" offered by the UNHCR?

   b) Describe the role played by the UNHCR in a current refugee situation.

Thinking

7. Individuals who migrate tend to fall into specific categories and show these characteristics.

   • Age: Most migrants are younger adults.

   • Skills: People with higher-level rather than lower-level skills tend to migrate.

   • Ambition level: More ambitious people tend to migrate.

   • Marital status: Most immigrants are single.

   • Gender: More males than females tend to migrate between countries, although this is slowly changing as more women are developing the skills that make them desirable immigrants, and as traditional restrictions on females are eased in many countries.

Explain the reasons for each of these characteristics. Consider this question from the perspective of both the migrant and the receiving nation.

8. "The most significant consequence of immigration is the alteration of the cultural, ethnic, racial, and political make-up of the receiving country." Use specific examples to support or refute this statement.

9. In 1986, Canada was awarded the Nansen Refugee Award by the UNHCR. Why do you think Canada received it? Research information about this award.

10. Research the activities of an NGO involved in refugee assistance. Determine such aspects as

    • the location of their offices

    • the guiding principles of the organization

    • the countries in which they operate

    • the types of activities in which they are involved

    • their source of funding

    • where the workers/volunteers come from

    You may look at the work of one of the following organizations or another NGO of your choice:

    • *Amnesty International*

    • *Canadian Council for Refugees*

    • *Canadian Centre for Victims of Torture*

    • *National Network on Immigrant and Refugee Rights (in the US)*

    • *European Network on the Integration of Refugees*

    • *Refugee Council of Australia*

    • *Les Sans-papiers (in France)*

    Your report should be based on research from at least three sources and include appropriate text written in your own words, as well as maps and other materials. Ⓖ

11. Based on your knowledge of world affairs, suggest two trouble spots in the world that are generating (or are likely to generate) substantial numbers of refugees. If some of these refugees came to Canada, would they find it easy or difficult to integrate into Canadian life? Explain.

12. Investigate ways to prevent illegal migration. Start your research at the Web site of the International Organization for Migration.

13. Research the media to find one or more recent incidents of illegal migration into Canada, the US, Australia, or western Europe. Examine such aspects as

- where the migrants were coming from
- why they left their home country
- why they selected their country of destination
- conditions en route
- what happened to them when they arrived at their destination

Communication

14. Create two maps to show the sending and receiving countries of refugees. This may be done by hand, or by using the GIS application ArcView. Your teacher will suggest which approach to use and provide you with the appropriate data.

15. Construct a chart to show the pros and cons of immigration for receiving and sending countries.

    a) What are Canada's current immigration policies?

    b) Do you think these policies are fair
    - to Canadians?
    - to prospective immigrants to Canada?

    Explain your responses.

    c) If given the opportunity, would you change these policies? Explain

Application

16. Should governments offer amnesty to illegal immigrants? Evaluate the pros and cons as a class, and try to reach a concensus on this question.

17. In 2001, *TIME* magazine published a report in which it posed the following question: The Canadian border separates the US from 33 million people; the Mexican border divides the US from 109 million—or 500 million, if you count all the way to Chile. Which border is more important, and which has more impact?

    a) How would you answer this question? Explain your point of view.

    b) How might a US citizen answer this question?

CHAPTER 9

Rural to Urban Migration

Key Terms

rural to urban migration

mega-cities

decentralization

recentralization

gentrification

infrastructure

overurbanization

squatter settlements

fiscal squeeze

slums of hope

slums of despair

busways

hedonics

The Kibera slum in Nairobi, Kenya, was the scene of much of the violence in 2008 in the aftermath of disputed presidential elections.

Key Questions

By the end of this chapter you will be able to answer the following questions.

■ What causes rural to urban migration?

■ What are the effects of rural to urban migration in New Core, Near Core, and Far Periphery countries?

■ How will the size of rural and urban populations change in the future?

■ What changes are taking place in the cities of Old Core, New Core, Near Core, and Far Periphery countries?

■ What problems do cities in the Old Core, New Core, Near Core, and Far Periphery countries face? What are possible solutions to these problems?

■ What does the future hold for urban areas throughout the world?

Global Patterns of Urbanization

Two hundred years ago, less than 5 percent of the world's 980 million people lived in urban communities. In 2007 the world reached a significant milestone—for the first time ever, more people were living in urban areas than rural ones. But what caused (and is causing) this enormous migration from the countryside to cities—the largest migration in history?

Rural to Urban Migration in Developing Countries

The migration of population from rural to urban areas began first in Britain during the mid-18th century. It was the gradual, but direct, result of industrialization and the mechanization of agriculture. Farmers migrated from rural areas to find work in factories (that had been built during the Industrial Revolution) and to provide services for the growing urban population. Rural depopulation was also caused by new agricultural machinery that reduced the need for manual labour on the farms. This pattern of **rural to urban migration** has spread worldwide as industrialization has become a global phenomenon.

Today, the process of urbanization in New Core, Near Core, and Far Periphery countries occurs at what seems like lightning speed compared to what took place in Old Core countries. What took 200 years during the 18th and 19th centuries has taken just over half a century in many of today's developing countries. One result for this is the creation of informal urban areas like Kibera in Kenya. As is the case with international migration, there are push and pull factors at work as rural populations in developing countries migrate to cities (see Figures 9–1 and 9–2).

The effects of rural to urban migration are many and far-reaching. For example, it is generally the better-educated, more ambitious, wealthier people in rural

Push	Pull
Subsistence farms do not provide enough food or income to support grown children, who must migrate to the city to find work.	Urban areas offer more employment opportunities, in a wider range of economic activities that are often growing very rapidly so that new jobs are constantly being created.
Government policies may favour urban over rural areas. For example, a government may protect goods manufactured in city factories by imposing import taxes on foreign goods. But, to maintain social stability in the cities, it may keep the price of agricultural products low so that city dwellers have cheap food.	Living in a city can provide significant economic and social empowerment for women compared to traditional lifestyles in rural areas.
Rural areas of most developing countries offer a poor living. The UN estimates that 60 percent of the developing world's poorest people live in rural areas.	In developing countries, educational opportunities and medical care in cities are better than what is available in most rural areas.
Government policies, both at home and in other countries, may create problems for farmers. In the 1980s, Brazil encouraged farmers to resettle in cleared areas of the tropical rainforest. After a few harvests, the soil was so depleted that the settlers had to abandon the land and move to the city. Agricultural subsidies in Old Core countries often mean that farmers in poor countries cannot compete in unfair world markets. This greatly increases rural poverty. (See Chapter 10.)	Urban areas offer a wider range of opportunities and lifestyles and may be seen as more "exciting" than life in rural areas. This is often particularly attractive to young people.

Figure 9–1 Factors in rural to urban migration. Similar push and pull factors that encourage migration to the cities are at work across the New Core and Periphery.

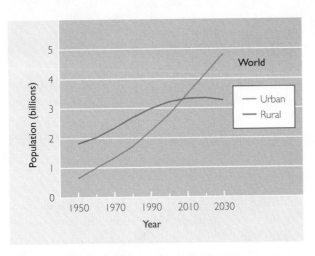

Figure 9–2 Changes in the world's urban and rural populations, 1950 to 2030

men are moving to urban areas. This trend seems to be occurring in China as well. The growth of labour-intensive industrialization and the development of service industries in cities are providing many job opportunities that did not exist in the past for women. The money they earn from these new jobs gives them the potential (not always realized) of an increased level of independence. The downside of the migration of women to cities is that many of the jobs are temporary, unsafe, poorly paid, and provide little security. Some women may be sexually harassed in the workplace or even forced into prostitution. Despite these negative aspects, migration has generally provided greater opportunities and some empowerment for women.

communities who tend to migrate to cities. They are in a better position to learn about opportunities and to be able to recover the costs of moving. If they have friends or family in the city, they are more likely to be supported until they are settled.

Over the past 50 years, the number of women migrating to the cities has been increasing. In countries such as the Philippines and Thailand, more women than

CASE STUDY   A Life of Urban Poverty

The photographs on page 128 show part of a slum area of Nairobi, Kenya, called Kibera. Remarkably, more than 600 000 people live in this area of only 256 hectares. To get a sense of how crowded this is—if Kibera were a square block, the sides would be only 1.6 kilometres long! Similar districts exist in and around most cities of the Periphery and many cities in the New Core.

1. A variety of names are used for areas like Kibera. These include "informal settlement," "shanty town," "spontaneous settlement," "squatter settlement," "mushroom city," "community built after dark and before dawn," and "uncontrolled settlement." From these names, and by viewing these images, describe

   a) how areas like Kibera come into existence

   b) what life would be like for residents (Consider both positive and negative aspects of life.)

   c) why it is not a surprise that such areas have grown enormously in recent years

2. What is the most obvious difference in appearance between Kibera and neighbouring districts? What characteristics of Kibera account for this difference?

3. What do you see in the foreground of this picture? Why, by the standards of the Old Core, is it strange to find this feature next to a slum area?

4. What kinds of jobs would residents of Kibera be most likely to take?

5. Old Core cities also have significant numbers of poor people. Are there areas like Kibera in the Old Core? Why or why not?

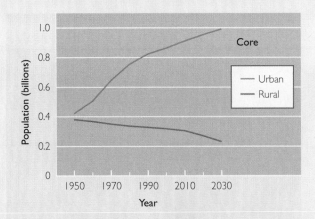

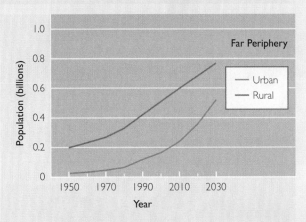

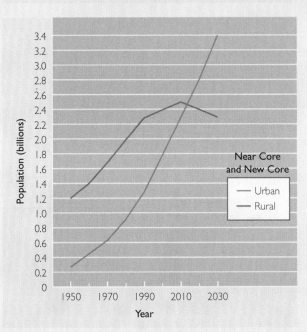

- What percentage of the world's population today is rural and what percentage is urban?

- What are the trends for the future?

Complete the following activity to discover the answers to these two questions. In this exercise you will be analyzing a number of simple graphs. If you think back a few years, you will remember the concept of "slope" in math class. The slope of a line on this graph is the rate of change of population. You could do a *slope* (rate of change) calculation, but it is not really necessary. It is enough to think about whether the slope is getting *steeper* (faster growth) or *flatter* (slower growth).

1. Figure 9–2 shows global trends in rural and urban population growth.

    a) What will happen to the world's rural population between 2000 and 2030?

    b) Why do you think this is happening?

    c) What will happen to the rate of change of the urban population?

    d) What does this suggest about the number and size of cities in the future?

    e) What percentage of the world's population lived in cities in 1950? What percentage will live in cities in 2030?

2. Figure 9–3 includes three graphs that show rural–urban population changes in the Old Core, New Core, Near Core, and Far Periphery.

    a) What will happen to the rural populations of each region between 2000 and 2030?

    b) Why do you think this is happening?

    c) What will happen to the urban populations of each region between 2000 and 2030?

    d) What does this suggest about the distribution of large cities in the future?

    e) For each region, calculate the percentage of the population that lived in cities in 1950 and the percentage that will live in them in 2030.

Figure 9–3 Rural to urban migration patterns vary in different parts of the world. These graphs are based on UN-delimited regions that correspond with the "worlds" used in this book: a) Old Core (plus adjacent areas in eastern Europe), b) Far Periphery, c) New Core (minus adjacent areas of eastern Europe) and Near Core.

As you might expect after completing the previous activity, regions around the world are urbanizing at different rates. Examine Figure 9–4. Between 1950 and 2000, the percentage of the population of North America living in urban areas rose 13 percentage points. Latin America and the Caribbean, on the other hand, experienced a rise of 34 percentage points. Now look at Africa and Asia in the year 2000 and calculate the projected percentage increases in urbanization for these two regions for the year 2030.

Another urban trend is demonstrated in Figure 9–5. Not only are more people living in cities, but these cities are also becoming larger and larger. Large cities do have some advantages. There is considerable evidence that they are, on a per-capita basis, environmentally more sensible. For example, greenhouse-gas emissions are lower than for people at a similar socio-economic level who live in rural areas or smaller urban areas. Why do you think this would be so? As you will learn later in the chapter, there are a number of significant challenges that face people (and governments) in large cities.

You may be under the impression that Old Core countries, because they have well-developed economies, efficient transportation systems, high levels of education and health, and modern services and conveniences, must have great numbers of large cities. In fact, this is not the case. Figure 9–6 shows the number of cities with more than one million residents in Old Core countries compared to the rest of the world.

Included in the global number of cities with over one million people are a number of special urban

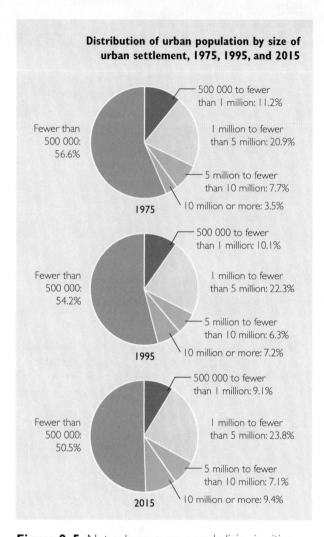

Figure 9–5 Not only are more people living in cities, but they are typically living in larger cities.

	1950 (%)	1975 (%)	2000 (%)	2030 (est. %)
North America	64	74	77	84
Latin America and the Caribbean	41	61	75	83
Europe	52	67	75	83
Oceania	62	72	70	72
Africa	15	25	38	55
Asia	17	25	37	53

Figure 9–4 Urban populations as a percentage of total population. What regional trends can you identify from the table?

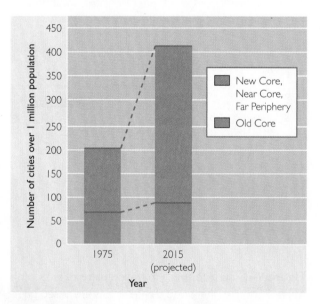

Figure 9–6 The years from 1975 to 2015 are a time of explosive growth in the number of cities with over one million people. This growth is focused in areas outside the Old Core.

settlements known as **mega-cities** (such as Tokyo, in Figure 9–7). These cities have at least ten million residents. Until the 20th century, cities this large were almost unimaginable. In fact, 100 years ago, London was the only city in the world with a population of even five million. By 2005, there were 20 cities with more than ten million people (see Figure 9–8).

Figure 9–7 The population projection for Tokyo, Japan, indicates that it will continue to be the largest mega-city in 2015.

1950 Population (millions)	1975 Population (millions)		2005 Population (millions)		2015 Projected Populations (millions)	
1. New York, OC 12.3	1. Tokyo, OC	19.8	1. Tokyo, OC	35.2	1. Tokyo, OC	35.5
	2. New York, OC	15.9	2. Mexico City, NwC	19.4	2. Mumbai, NwC	21.9
	3. Shanghai, NwC	11.4	3. New York, OC	18.7	3. Mexico City, NwC	21.6
	4. Mexico City, NwC	11.2	4. São Paulo, NwC	18.3	4. São Paulo, NwC	20.5
			5. Mumbai, NwC	18.2	5. New York, OC	19.9
			6. Delhi, NwC	15.0	6. Delhi, NwC	18.6
			7. Shanghai, NwC	14.5	7. Shanghai, NwC	17.2
			8. Kolkata, NwC	14.3	8. Kolkata, NwC	17.0
			9. Jakarta, NrC	13.2	9. (tie) Dhaka, FP	16.8
			10. Buenos Aires, NwC	12.6	Jakarta, NrC	16.8
			11. Dhaka, FP	12.4	11. Lagos, FP	16.1
			12. Los Angeles, OC	12.3	12. Karachi, FP	15.2
			13. Karachi, FP	11.6	13. Buenos Aires, NwC	13.4
			14. Rio de Janeiro, NwC	11.5	14. (tie) Los Angeles, OC	13.1
			15. Osaka, OC	11.3	Cairo, NrC	13.1
			16. Cairo, NrC	11.1	16. (tie) Manila, NwC	12.9
			17. Lagos, FP	10.9	Beijing, NwC	12.9
			18. (tie) Manila, NwC	10.7	18. Rio de Janeiro, NwC	12.8
			Beijing, NwC	10.7	19. Osaka, OC	11.3
			Moscow, NwC	10.7	20. Istanbul, NwC	11.2
					21. Moscow, NwC	11.0
					22. Guangzhou, NwC	10.4

Country Grouping	Abbreviation	Example
Old Core	OC	New York
New Core	NwC	Shanghai
Near Core	NrC	Jakarta
Far Periphery	FP	Dhaka

Figure 9–8 Not only has the number of mega-cities grown, but so has their population size. Note the concentration and growth of mega-cities outside the Old Core.

Urban Changes Worldwide

Changes in the Cities of the Old Core

Before World War II, cities in developed countries such as Canada, France, and Japan tended to be fairly compact since house lots were small and many people lived in low-rise apartments. This land-use pattern made sense as ownership of private automobiles was limited, and most people travelled to work and other destinations by public transit—buses, streetcars, and, in the largest cities, subway systems. The high population density resulting from small lots and many apartments meant that more people were within easy walking distance of public transit lines.

The years after World War II marked the beginning of a revolutionary change in how urban dwellers lived. The middle class grew in size. Car ownership became common. Families grew during the "baby boom." People who could afford to buy new houses, particularly in North America, moved from the central areas of cities into the suburbs. In the United States in 1950, for example, 70 percent of the urban population lived in central areas of cities. By 1990, however, less than 40 percent lived in central areas. Many who lived in downtown cores would have preferred to move to the suburbs but could not afford to.

This **decentralization** occurred for a variety of social, political, and economic reasons, including the widespread ownership of motor vehicles. Racial tensions in inner-city areas in the US, as well as the promise of newer housing and better educational and recreational facilities, propelled many in the middle-class to the suburbs. Shopping opportunities expanded with the building of large outdoor, and later indoor, shopping malls and "big box" stores. Industries and offices also moved to the suburbs. Spacious industrial parks with easy access to highways, plus cheaper costs for land were attractive to old and new businesses alike.

After 1990, however, decentralization slowed down in much of the Old Core. In many cities, problems that were once associated with downtown areas, such as traffic congestion, overcrowded schools, and the rise of crime, became common in the suburbs. It wasn't long before people began to consider inner-city addresses desirable once more. People began moving back into central parts of cities in a process of **recentralization**. They could see that many of the most livable cities (or neighbourhoods within cities) are those with higher concentrations of people—hence better public transportation facilities, more convenient shopping, and more recreational activities. A process of **gentrification** began as people bought and renovated attractive, but often rundown, older houses in less desirable neighbourhoods for a good price. At the same time, developers converted obsolete factories and warehouses into condominiums. As more "gentrifiers" moved into a neighbourhood, businesses opened to meet their needs as well (see Figure 9–9).

Recentralization has also occurred as a result of demographic changes. When young couples have fewer children (or even none), they feel less pressure to move into detached, suburban houses. At the same time, many aging baby boomers have decided that their large suburban houses are too costly and bothersome to maintain. Many have moved from the suburbs to high-rise condos or apartments in city centres.

What makes some cities successful—that is, desirable places in which to live (see Figure 9–10)? Experts suggest that a variety of factors are involved.

Figure 9–9 A gentrified house in downtown Toronto

Ranking	City
1.	Vancouver
2. (tie)	Melbourne
	Vienna
	Geneva
5. (tie)	Perth
	Adelaide
	Sydney
	Zurich
	Toronto
	Calgary
11.	Stockholm
16. (tie)	Montreal
	Tokyo
	Paris
33. (tie)	Honolulu
	Miami
41 (tie)	Hong Kong
	Detroit
47 (tie)	London
	Los Angeles

Figure 9–10 Ranking of the world's cities on the basis of their livability in 2005. Top ten cities and a selection of other cities on the list of the top 50 are shown.

- **A strong economy**. A strong economy ensures more available tax money for services and relief of poverty. Urban residents who feel confident about their finances spend more on better housing and activities in the city.

- **Good government**. Beneficial effects of good government can be seen at all levels of society, and include a fair and respected legal system and a well-educated population, which increases prosperity.

- **An active democratic process**. People feel that they are involved in making the decisions that affect them every day.

- **Openness to, and effective communication with, the world**. One aspect of this factor is having a population with a wide ethnic and religious mix. (This may help explain why there are so many Canadian and Australian cities on the list of most livable cities. Both of these countries have shown a willingness and ability to absorb immigrants.)

Changes in New Core, Near Core, and Far Periphery Cities

Urban change occurs in different ways in New Core, Near Core, and Far Periphery countries than it does in Old Core countries. Outside the Old Core, urban population growth often takes place at a faster rate than economic development and the building of necessary **infrastructure**, which is a society's basic support system. (This disparity happens in the Old Core too, but to a much smaller extent.) In some cases, rural migrants flock to cities because they are desperate for a better standard of living, but find that there are not enough jobs available when they get there. In other cases, there may be jobs but no decent housing, and migrants end up living in a slum like Kibera. Rapid migration to cities causes overwhelming problems that local and national governments just can't cope with—just as water and sewage lines are being built for 10 000 people in one neighbourhood, 20 000 people are moving into another. When a city's population grows faster than its ability to sustain itself, the result is **overurbanization** (see Figure 9–11). Too many people, large-scale unemployment, and lack of housing lead to sprawling **squatter settlements** on the outskirts of cities. These urban settlements lack proper sanitation facilities, decent shelter, schools, and hospitals, as well as basic social services.

Urban change in developing countries is extremely diverse. It takes place for many different reasons, and trends are difficult to define. In Central and South America, domestic industries, in an effort to compete on an international scale, have moved to the outskirts of cities in search of cheaper labour and land on which to expand. This trend has caused massive urban growth or "sprawl," not to mention the loss of farmland. In sub-Saharan Africa, cities such as Kinshasa and Freetown have fallen into serious states of disrepair due to civil war, government mismanagement, and the stress of rapid population growth.

COMMON GLOBAL URBAN PROBLEMS

1. Identify the most serious urban problems that you think cities face in all parts of the world.

2. Imagine that you are the mayor of the community in which you live. The UN has asked you to rank the top 14 urban problems in your community in order of their severity, from the most to the least severe. Compare your list with those of your classmates.

3. The United Nations Development Program asked mayors around the world to rank the top 14 urban problems in their communities. The percentage of mayors who identified each problem as severe in their city is shown in Figure 9–19 on page 143.

   a) How does your list compare to that of the world mayors?

   b) Which problems did you not identify? Why might you have missed these?

   c) Did you identify problems not on this list?

4. a) Now imagine that you are the mayor of a large city in a Near Core or Far Periphery country. Re-rank these 14 problems in order of their severity.

   b) How does your list differ from the list you made in question 2? Explain any differences.

Figure 9–11 The cities of the world face a wide range of seemingly insoluble challenges ranging from gridlocked traffic to urban decay.

Urban Problems in Old Core Countries

Urban problems anywhere in the world cannot be studied in isolation. Unemployment, poverty, problems associated with the elderly, inadequate tax base, decaying neighbourhoods, decentralization, lack of affordable housing, air pollution, traffic, solid waste disposal, and all the other problems that beset urban areas are interconnected in an intricate web of cause and effect.

Economic Problems

One of the major problems facing Old Core cities has been called the **fiscal squeeze**. This means that there is never enough tax money to pay for all the services that cities need to run efficiently. Why is this so?

The problem stems from the fact that, over the last half century, developed countries have moved from industrial to post-industrial economies in which most people work in businesses that provide services. (See Chapter 11 to learn more about this.) As this has happened, Old Core cities have undergone tremendous change. Traditional manufacturing industries—and their related activities, such as warehousing and transportation—have moved away from inner cities to the suburbs, or disappeared entirely as manufacturing activities have moved to China and other countries.

As a result, the tax base in the central city has decreased and city governments now have less money to maintain and repair older roads, out-of-date water and sewage lines, and crumbling public buildings. Add the costs involved in paying for social assistance, providing increasing levels of service to an aging population and to new immigrants, and cities really begin to feel the squeeze! A problem for many cities, such as those in Ontario, is that they are able to tax only the value of properties and not the incomes of residents. This limits their ability to raise money.

What is the solution to this dilemma? Starting in the 1990s, the US federal government came to the rescue of many of the country's largest cities by spending billions of dollars on infrastructure improvements. In Ontario, Toronto's municipal government was given special taxation powers in 2006 that allow it to impose taxes on things like real-estate sales and car registrations. Some observers have suggested that a more permanent solution would be for cities to become the equivalent of provinces or states. This would mean that they would have taxation powers that would better match their governmental responsibilities.

Social Problems

Another serious urban problem in developed countries is poverty. A study of poverty in Canada in 2000 by the Canadian Council on Social Development found that 20 percent of urban dwellers were living below the poverty line. According to a study done in the US during the 1990s, people living in the inner city are more than twice as likely to be poor than people living in the suburbs. Urban decay, lack of employment opportunities, poor housing, and overcrowded conditions usually lead to a cycle in which one generation after another remains locked in poverty. Overcrowded living conditions and poor diet contribute to absenteeism at school and work, which in turn leads to lower educational achievement and lower incomes. An environment of high unemployment, low wages, lack of successful role models, and general despair creates a continuous cycle of poverty.

SUSTAINABILITY

Urban decay, lack of employment opportunities, poor housing, and overcrowded conditions usually lead to a cycle in which one generation after another remains locked in poverty.

How can this cycle of poverty be broken?

Even when recentralization occurs and the economies of inner cities improve, problems can arise for residents. Redevelopment can push up rents faster than wages increase. The combination of low incomes and high rents causes many families to lose their homes. The number of homeless people has also increased since the mid-1980s because of cutbacks in welfare programs. The homeless are now much more visible in the cities of Canada, the US, Japan, Australia, and Western Europe, and include men and women of all ages, as well as an increasing number of children (see Figure 9–12). In fact, it is estimated that about one-quarter of Canada's homeless are children.

A major problem in many cities is the shortage of affordable housing. Budgeting experts say that people should not spend more than about 30 percent of their income on housing costs. People working for low wages find that 30 percent of their salary is not enough to cover housing costs. Their choice is either to spend more on housing (leaving them less for other essentials like food), or to end up homeless. Lack of affordable housing has contributed to homelessness in many cities.

Social activists have made a number of suggestions to solve (or at least reduce) the homelessness problem. One suggestion has been that minimum wage levels should be substantially increased—one common suggestion is to $10 per hour. To help alleviate the problem of affordable housing in Canada, the Toronto Disaster Relief Committee has proposed a "1 percent solution." All levels of government would spend 1 percent more of their existing total budgets on housing than they do now. Since the three levels of government spent about 1 percent of their current budgets on housing and support services for people who needed housing in 2001, an increase of 1 percent would double the amount they spent.

Figure 9–12 Homeless people often sleep on the street year round. Some city officials feel this tarnishes the city's image and negatively affects tourism.

Environmental Problems

The concentration of so many people in cities leads to numerous environmental problems.

- Since many cities in North America have not developed effective rapid transit systems, people take their cars to work. When the number of vehicles on a highway exceeds its capacity, gridlock and excessively long travel times are the result.

- The large amounts of pollutants produced by traffic congestion are a threat to young and old alike, especially to those with respiratory difficulties.

- The "heat island effect" created by large cities in the summer only exacerbates the problem: large expanses of buildings and paved streets heat up, increasing the temperature. As the heated air rises, it carries the pollutants upward to form a smoggy haze over the city.

- Greenhouse gases produced in cities by vehicles, by electrical generating stations that burn fossil fuels, and by heating and air-conditioning systems are a major contributor to climate change in the world.

- Our throwaway society produces huge amounts of garbage, and most cities today are facing a garbage-disposal crisis. Most North American cities have landfill sites in rural locations nearby, but rural residents don't like having someone else's garbage "in their backyard." Some cities incinerate their garbage, but this produces greenhouse gases and, if not done correctly, dangerous air pollutants. Many cities recycle bottles, cans, paper, and plastic and compost organic materials, but these programs are not yet extensive enough. A combination of landfill, incineration, and recycling is probably the best that most cities can achieve for the present.

Urban Problems in the New Core, Near Core, and Far Periphery

New Core, Near Core, and Far Periphery cities typically have fewer resources to deal with problems that are much more severe than those found in the Old Core. The result is that the residents of most cities in the developing world face appalling living conditions.

Economic Problems

Cities in developing countries offer relatively few jobs that pay well. Rural migrants who come to the cities looking for a better life often find themselves working in the informal sector of the economy (see Figure 9–13). This sector encompasses a wide range of jobs that includes such activities as shining shoes, selling souvenirs, working in roadside repair shops, and running "phone centres." The informal sector also includes prostitution, begging, and scavenging in garbage dumps. It is estimated that more than a billion people worldwide make their living from such occupations. The poor wages and unreliable nature of these jobs lead to chronic poverty for the people who undertake them.

Many children work in the informal economy. Very often, industries in the formal sector, such as clothing manufacturers, subcontract work to families who carry out the work in their homes. Here, the children routinely work with other family members because everyone is needed to contribute to the family's income. In situations like this, education obviously suffers—especially in the many countries where school fees must be paid. Lack of education makes it much more likely that poverty will continue into the next generation.

Figure 9–13 This man's income comes from collecting scrap on the street and selling anything of value that he finds.

Did You Know?

In poor countries, running a phone centre means owning a cellphone that you allow other people to use for a fee.

Often a huge gap exists between the rich and the poor. There is usually a very small wealthy population, a huge poor population, and a relatively small middle class. A few very wealthy people live in exclusive enclaves in the most desirable areas of cities, but not very far away is the overwhelming number of poor people living in slums. (The fanciest residential areas of Nairobi are only a few kilometres away from Kibera.)

In cities with low levels of economic development, it is difficult to build a tax base that is large enough to offer services to city dwellers, especially those living in poverty. An inadequate tax base cannot finance the building of schools, hospitals, transportation systems, and roads, or fund social services for the poor. Furthermore, it is difficult—if not impossible—to tax the many people working in the informal sector of the economy.

Social Problems

As in the Old Core, the social problems of cities in poorer countries are associated with too many people living in poverty. There are two important differences. One is in the much higher number of poor people. The other is that the poor often live in squatter settlements. Squatter housing is built on the cheapest land in the city (see Figure 9–14), for example, on steep slopes, in swamps, next to railways, garbage dumps, or in the case of Cairo, in cemeteries. It consists of the most rudimentary type of shelter: hovels made of corrugated steel, cardboard, discarded plastic sheeting, wooden boards, and in some cases, even mud. Squatter settlements have been known to spring up on vacant lots or in vacant buildings overnight. At best, there is an inadequate infrastructure—including sewers, running water, electricity, streets, and policing—in place.

Because of its large population, Kibera is an extreme example of a squatter settlement. Any visitor to this district would immediately notice two things. It smells very unpleasant, and plastic bags litter the ground. These two facts are closely related. Few homes in Kibera have toilets (in the form of pit latrines) and the latrines that do exist are shallow and tend to overflow when it rains. As well, many residents, particularly women, are afraid to walk through darkened alleys at night to the nearest latrine.

Figure 9–14 Compare the housing situation in this squatter settlement of a developing country to that of the high rise apartments in the background.

The result is that many people rely on "flying toilets." They defecate into plastic bags that they dispose of by pitching into the street since there is nowhere else to put them. The UN estimates that there is only one latrine for every 150 people in Kibera. Communal latrines are privately owned and charge four cents per use—a significant sum for people who may earn less than one dollar per day.

The water supply situation in Kibera is just as bad. People have to carry water from central, privately owned supply points. Depending on the season, this water costs between US$3.50 and US$7.00 per cubic metre. In contrast, the cost of government-provided water piped into the homes of richer people in Nairobi is only about US$0.50 per cubic metre—which is similar to the cost of water in large cities in Ontario. The result is that on average, residents of Kibera pay more than 20 percent of their income for water.

Efforts to eradicate slums and squatter settlements have resulted in even more misery for poor urban dwellers. In the past, cities like Manila, Caracas, and Bangkok forcibly removed hundreds of thousands of people from their slum and shantytown dwellings and destroyed their homes. Since the displaced residents had nowhere to go except to new squatter settlements elsewhere in the city, it became evident to governments that this practice was pointless—people still need places in which to live, even if conditions are wretched.

Governments have tried to build high-rise apartment projects to house those forced out of squatter settlements, but these have often not worked out well. In India, for example, new apartments become "vertical slums" almost instantly. Consequently, the government is looking for new approaches to solve this problem.

The Dharavi slum, in Mumbai, India (see Figure 9–15) is a place of great contrasts. It is grossly overcrowded with a population of at least 600 000 in a small area and lacks necessary infrastructure. For example, there are an estimated 1440 people for each toilet. At the same time, it occupies a prime piece of real estate in a city that is built on a peninsula, where land is not available for outward expansion. In addition, it is close to the airport, a major business district, and three commuter railways. These facts make Dharavi a prime candidate for redevelopment. A privately financed $2.3 billion plan is moving forward that will completely change the character of the district through the construction of markets, schools, parks, and much high-density housing (see Figure 9–16).

The intent of this plan is to avoid the creation of vertical slums. The housing will be mixed income. Part of the plan is to accommodate 57 000 families who already live there. Based on their experience with previous redevelopments of squatter settlements, many current residents are suspicious of this plan. They know that not everyone will be accommodated in the new development and they fear that their need to operate informal businesses out of their homes will be impossible in the new apartments. Since 60 percent of the residents must agree to the project before it can go ahead, the government and developers must convince them that it will benefit them. If this project is built and proves successful, it may provide a model for slum clearance—at least in countries like India that have rapidly growing economies.

1. Summarize the factors that contribute to this sort of plan being feasible in this part of Mumbai.

2. Why are the residents of Dharavi suspicious of this plan? Are their concerns valid?

3. Use the Internet to research the current status of this redevelopment project.

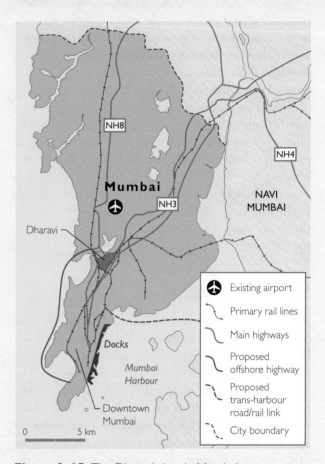

Figure 9–15 The Dharavi slum in Mumbai

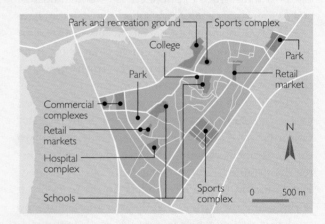

Figure 9–16 The plan for Dharavi's redevelopment

Not everyone agrees that squatter neighbourhoods should be cleared. Some people point out that these communities act as reception areas for newly arrived migrants, who can usually find some support from experienced residents. Low-income squatter communities that provide affordable shelter, community support, and informal jobs are called "**slums of hope**." In time, some of these settlements acquire services such as electricity and communal water supplies that residents have helped install by providing the labour. In some of Brazil's *favelas* (the Brazilian term for squatter settlements), residents have been trained as builders to repair damaged buildings and to construct makeshift electrical and water systems. Activists suggest that locally controlled projects to improve living conditions offer the best and cheapest hope for such areas.

Many social problems are rooted in extreme poverty. Even with attempts to provide medical care and sanitation, incidences of the diseases of poverty—such as malnutrition—are increasing. Poor urban dwellers are also exposed to dangerous traffic conditions or deviant social behaviour associated with living in overcrowded, degraded living conditions. There are no community organizations to help residents, no access to birth control, and no government welfare services. The rates of illness and infant death are high. Often referred to as "**slums of despair**," these areas of urban poverty offer few opportunities for escape.

A World Bank project, "Cities Without Slums," helps to upgrade living conditions in slums by providing education and healthcare for residents and by supporting local small-scale businesses. The aim is to improve the lives of 100 million people throughout the developing world by 2020.

Environmental Problems

When natural disasters are reported on television, it most often seems as if the poorest people in the world are the victims. There is often much truth to this observation. Not only do the poorest people live in badly constructed dwellings offering little shelter, but they also live in the most undesirable sites in the city. Rickety hovels perched on steep hillsides collapse under mudslides during heavy rains; houses built of materials salvaged from the dump blow away in hurricanes; squatter settlements are flattened during earthquakes; homes in low-lying areas are carried away in floods; and thousands of people are poisoned in flimsy shelters next to industrial sites. Underlying all environmental problems that plague urban areas in developing countries is the fact that governments simply do not have the money to solve the problems of so many urban poor.

Figure 9–17 In 2008, Tata began selling a car for about US$2500. It is sure to be a hit among the growing middle class of India and other New Core countries—but at what environmental cost?

Air pollution in cities in the New Core, Near Core, and Far Periphery is almost always worse than in Old Core countries. Rapid population growth results in tens of thousands of poorly maintained trucks, cars, and buses pumping pollution into the air. Added to that are the unregulated emissions from millions of people cooking with inefficient coal, charcoal, or kerosene stoves, as well as from coal-fired electrical power stations and petrochemical industries. The situation is worsened by the heat island effect. The combination of lead, carbon monoxide, nitrogen oxides, and other toxic chemicals in the air causes severe respiratory disease and takes a toll on human health and productivity. Cars made for sale outside the Old Core are built without the pollution-control devices that we take for granted (see Figure 9–17). This is done to make the cars as cheap as possible.

SUSTAINABILITY

Air pollution in cities in the New Core, Near Core, and Far Periphery is almost always worse than in Old Core countries.

Why is this not surprising? Is it avoidable?

The UN determined in 2000 that about 91 percent of the urban populations in Africa, Asia, Latin America, and the Caribbean had access to clean water, but that this amount was 1.2 percent lower than it had been in 1990. This decline reflects the inability of city governments to keep up with demands of growing urban populations. The 9 percent who must rely on questionable water represents something like 170 million urban

 You can learn more about the Cities Without Slums project at the link on our Web site.

residents—about five times the population of Canada. Also, access to safe water is defined by many governments as having a water source within 100 metres of each dwelling. Often, the tap runs for only a few hours a day; residents may have to stand in line for long hours for a small quantity of treated water. Women and children bear the burden of carrying water home from the tap or well (see Figure 9–18). The lack of safe water in cities in developing countries is a leading cause of disease and infant mortality.

The same UN study concluded that only 80 percent of urban dwellers in these areas had appropriate sanitation facilities in 2000 (again not remotely close to the sanitation standard that we take for granted). This was an increase of 9 percent from 1990, but it still meant that about 380 million people (more than ten times Canada's population) had to rely on pit toilets or similar unacceptable methods for people living in densely populated cities. Much of the sewage in poor urban districts still runs into drainage ditches beside the roads, and then flows untreated into rivers and streams that people use for drinking water. Even if there are sewers to collect human waste, most of the sewage is not treated before being pumped into nearby rivers, lakes, or the ocean.

Figure 9–18 Obtaining water is very time-consuming.

The Urban Future—Is There a Better Way?

Can we make our cities—in all parts of the world—better places in which to live? The experience of the city of Bogotá, Colombia, would suggest so. In the 1990s, Bogotá would have been no one's model of an urban paradise. It was the capital city of a country in the midst of a protracted civil war, and the centre of the worst *narco-terrorism* (terrorist activities funded by profits earned from illegal drug trading) in the world. In 1995, Bogotá had 3363 murders and almost 1400 traffic deaths. In comparison, Toronto had about 60 murders and 60 traffic deaths. In addition, Bogotá's air pollution rivalled Mexico City's as the worst in the world. Traffic was appalling and dangerous. Drivers routinely drove on sidewalks when the roads were blocked—which was most of the time. Poor workers from squatter settlements in the south side of the city spent up to four hours a day commuting to their jobs in the wealthy northern part of the city. Clearly a crisis was at hand, and something major had to be done to improve things.

A study paid for by Japanese foreign aid funds suggested that the building of a multi-billion-dollar network of elevated expressways might solve the problem somewhat. The mayor, Enrique Peñalosa, elected in 1998, rejected this plan for his city. He believed that a city could be friendly to the car or friendly to the people—but not to both. Further, he believed that the way to solve the city's problems was to focus on making people happier rather than making them richer. He decreed that the money that would not be spent on expressways would be spent on making people happier. To do this he concentrated on six things that would make people happier:

1. **"Hot" transit.** Surveys showed that long commutes went a long way to making Bogotá's citizens miserable. The solution was to restrict the use of private automobiles (by increasing gas taxes and allowing people to drive into the city core only three times a week at most) and to improve public transit. Subways cost a great deal. Instead Bogotá uses **busways**—separate roads that are reserved for buses. (Busways are used in Ottawa and are being considered by other Canadian communities. In some places, busways are called transitways.) These can be built much quicker than subways and for a fraction of the cost. Faster commutes give people more time to enjoy their lives.

2. **Happy spaces.** When people have the opportunity to meet in pleasant open spaces—like parks, wide sidewalks, bike paths, greenbelts, and public squares—they feel less threatened and more trusting.

3. **Equitable design.** In Bogotá, the rich had fenced off parks to prevent the entry of the poor. The new government focused on opening these parks, and

building new parks, libraries, and community centres in poor neighbourhoods. The result was that people felt more equal.

4. **Participatory government.** Cities can make their citizens feel like they matter by paying more attention to them. Ordinary people must be made to feel that they are part of the planning process and that what they view as important will end up being considered in the city's growth. Bogotá's government made it a priority to involve citizens in its planning processes.

5. **Safe streets.** A happy and successful city values its people above its automobiles. Priority must be given to transit, bicycles, and pedestrians to make people feel valued.

6. **Encouraging crowds.** Streets filled with people are safer than empty streets. Hence, encouraging people to be on the streets makes everyone feel safer.

The idea of planning to maximize collective personal happiness rather than monetary gain is called **hedonics**, which is short for "happiness economics." This approach to planning is quite new but is rapidly gaining support in poorer countries, and even some richer ones.

1.	Unemployment (52%)
2.	Insufficient solid waste disposal (42%)
3.	Urban poverty (42%)
4.	Inadequate housing stock (34%)
5.	Insufficient solid waste collection (31%)
6.	Inadequate water/sanitation facilities (28%)
7.	Inadequate public transportation (26%)
8.	Traffic congestion (22%)
9.	Poor health services (22%)
10.	Insufficient civil society participation (21%)
11.	Inadequate education services (19%)
12.	Air pollution (17%)
13.	Urban violence/crime/personal safety (14%)
14.	Discrimination—against women, ethnic groups, poor people (7%)

Figure 9–19 These are the results of the UN Development Program survey of world mayors asked to rank the top 14 urban problems. The percentage of world mayors who identified the problems as severe in their cities is shown in parentheses. (They were allowed more than one choice.) Seventy percent of the mayors who ranked unemployment as a severe problem also ranked poverty as severe.

Chapter Questions

Knowledge and Understanding

1. What is the problem in defining the term "urban"?

2. a) List the push and pull factors that persuade rural populations in developing countries to migrate to cities.

   b) Are similar factors at work in the Old Core?

3. Describe the effects of rural to urban migration in developing countries.

4. Why are the largest and fastest-growing cities located outside the Old Core?

5. Describe the urban changes that are taking place

   a) in Old Core countries

   b) in New Core, Near Core, and Far Periphery countries

6. a) Summarize the economic, social, and environmental problems facing cities in Old Core countries.

   b) Summarize the same types of problems for cities in New Core, Near Core, and Far Periphery countries.

7. a) Describe the living conditions in squatter settlements.

   b) This chapter referred to "slums of hope" and "slums of despair." What is meant by these terms? Could a particular neighbourhood be both at the same time?

Thinking

8. a) Examine Figure 9–8. On the world map that your teacher gives you, lightly shade, in different colours, the Old Core, New Core, Near Core, and Far Periphery.

   b) Using a different colour for each of the four years shown in Figure 9–8, locate with a small circle and indicate when each of the mega-cities reached (or will reach) 10 million. Label the name of each city on your map. If some areas of the map are too crowded to do this, you may have to use some type of short form and a legend.

   c) What patterns do you see on your map?

9. Spending money on infrastructure improvements is necessary for a city to keep up with new growth and aging infrastructure components. Find out what the Canadian federal government is doing. Do you think these initiatives are enough? Explain.

10. Investigate a major economic, social, or environmental problem in your community or one nearby.

a) What are the causes of the problem?

b) What is being done to solve the problem? Do you predict that these actions will be successful? Explain.

11. In some developing countries, the movement from rural to urban environments is mainly male; in others, it is mainly female. What are the social implications of this?

12. a) What does the term "hedonics" mean? What initiatives did the mayor of Bogotá take to incorporate this concept into the city-planning process?

   b) Do you think this concept has merit? Explain.

   c) If you were the mayor of your city or one near you, what initiatives would you take to incorporate this concept into your city-planning process?

13. a) The number of homeless people is increasing in Canadian cities. Why?

   b) What can or should be done about this problem?

Communication

14. Construct a flow chart to show how the 14 issues in Figure 9–19 are interrelated. If you were a mayor of one of these cities and were given a large sum of money to help alleviate these problems, which ones would you deal with first to make the best use of the money? Explain your choices. Ⓢ

Application

15. a) Conduct an Internet search for urban problems in developed and developing countries.

   b) Make a list of the problems for cities in both developed and developing countries.

   c) For each type of country, categorize the problems according to the 14 listed in Figure 9–19.

   d) Which problems received the most coverage for each type of country?

   e) Does the amount of coverage of these problems on the Internet match your rankings in the activity on page 136? Explain.

   f) Select a problem and research its solutions. Ⓢ

ECONOMIC ISSUES

Lower Manhattan can rightfully be described as the financial capital of an increasingly globalized world. What happens here on a daily basis is influenced by events in financial centres in Europe and Asia and has a profound impact on the economic well-being of billions of people.

CHAPTER 10

Food and Agricultural Issues

Key Terms

famine

starvation

malnutrition

undernutrition

chronic hunger

Green Revolution

high-yield variety (HYV)

loss of genetic diversity

biotechnology

genetically modified organism (GMO)

land reform

agricultural support policies

monoculture

economies of scale

corporate farming

factory farms

vertical integration

organic farming

food miles

biofuel

Compare these two photos. Why is there hunger in a world of plenty?

Key Questions

By the end of this chapter you will be able to answer the following questions.

■ What are the different forms of hunger?

■ What are the successes and failures of the Green Revolution?

■ Will biotechnology solve the world's food problems?

■ Can alternative farming methods make sustainable agriculture a reality?

■ What is the future of the global agricultural system?

The Nature of Hunger—A Vocabulary

Many people in Old Core countries do not really understand what hunger is. They view hunger problems as *synonymous with* (the same as) famine. In fact, fewer than 10 percent of hunger deaths are caused by famine.

Famine is a severe short-term shortage of food caused by a temporary failure of food production or food distribution that leads to starvation. Famine may result from natural causes, for example a drought that causes crop failure such as in Ethiopia, or from human causes, for example, a civil war that interrupts food distribution such as in the Darfur region of southern Sudan.

Starvation is extreme hunger that occurs over an extended period of time. When people fail to receive essential nutrients from food (minerals, vitamins, protein, fats, carbohydrates), they lose energy. To find energy, the body begins to break down its own tissue. As a result, the body mass of people who are starving declines.

The relationship between food availability and health over a period of time is shown in Figure 10–1. In countries where food shortages occur, starvation is frequently the result. In countries where food is readily available, overnutrition is often the result.

	Level of Nutrients	Shorter-term Effects	Longer-term Effects	
NUTRITION AVAILABILITY — *Shortage*	Severe shortage of nutrients to the extent that the body breaks down its own tissues	Starvation and death	None (people cannot live in starvation conditions for very long)	This family is among the thousands suffering from starvation in the Sudan.
	Significant shortage of nutrients in the diet	Undernutrition (shortage of one or more important nutrients in the diet) can cause the development of one or more of 50 malnutrition-related diseases	Chronic hunger resulting in reduced life expectancy and quality of life	Kwashiorkor is a form of malnutrition.
Adequate	"Just right" amounts of all nutrients	Healthy lifestyle	Extended life expectancy and high quality of life	A balance of nutrients is part of a healthy lifestyle.
Excess	Too many calories and/or too much fat in the diet	Overnutrition (can cause high blood pressure, high cholesterol, and diabetes)	Reduced life expectancy and quality of life	Obesity can be thought of as a form of malnutrition.

Figure 10–1 Both undernutrition and overnutrition can contribute to a shorter life expectancy and poorer quality of life. The challenge for every person on Earth is to consume "just the right amount" of necessary nutrients.

Malnutrition is a medical condition of poor health caused by a diet that includes too much, or too little, of one or more essential nutrients. By this definition, obesity and high blood pressure could be considered diseases of malnutrition since they are sometimes caused by excesses in diet. Generally, though, malnutrition is the result of diets that lack nutrients. Malnutrition from a lack of nutrients is called undernutrition. There are more than 50 diseases of undernutrition. Some of the more well-known diseases of undernutrition are summarized in Figure 10–2.

Did You Know?

The Food and Agricultural Organization (FAO) of the United Nations estimates that every year almost six million children under five years of age die from hunger-related causes.

Chronic hunger results from an insecure supply of food. It affects more than 850 million people around the world. People suffer from chronic hunger because they lack the opportunity or the ability to earn enough money to grow or buy food. They are undernourished and are unable to lead healthy lives. When hunger occurs at a specific time of year because of the agricultural or weather cycle (for example, times of drought), it is known as seasonal hunger. Several major factors contribute to chronic hunger (see Figure 10–3).

Chronic hunger kills indirectly. It is responsible for more than 90 percent of hunger-related deaths in developing countries. Some effects of chronic hunger include

- high infant-mortality rates
- increased vulnerability to common illnesses
- acute vulnerability in times of natural disasters such as earthquakes and floods
- poor physical and mental development of children
- poor economic growth of society

Name of Disease	Caused by Deficiency of	Characteristics of Disease
Kwashiorkor	Protein	• Loss of muscle mass • Damaged immune system • Edema (swelling), particularly of belly
Scurvy	Vitamin C	• Anemia • Weakness • Gum disease • Bleeding skin sores
Pellagra	Niacin and tryptophan (an amino acid)	• Scaly skin sores • Diarrhea • Mental illness
Anemia	Iron	• Lack of energy • Weakened immune system
Keratomalacia	Vitamin A	• Blindness
Beriberi	Vitamin B_1	• Damage to heart and nervous system
Marasmus	Calories and protein	• Starvation

Figure 10–2 These are just a few of the many diseases resulting from undernutrition.

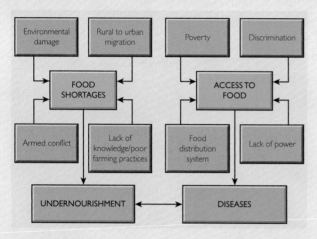

1. Explain how each input affects "Food Shortages" and "Accessibility to Food."

2. List the diseases associated with undernourishment.

Figure 10–3 The causes of chronic hunger are complex and interrelated.

The Geography of Hunger

The International Food Policy Research Institute (IFPRI), an NGO based in the United States, has developed the "Global Hunger Index" to rank countries on the basis of several variables. The Index shows the severity of hunger in countries in the Near Core and Far Periphery (see Figure 10–4).

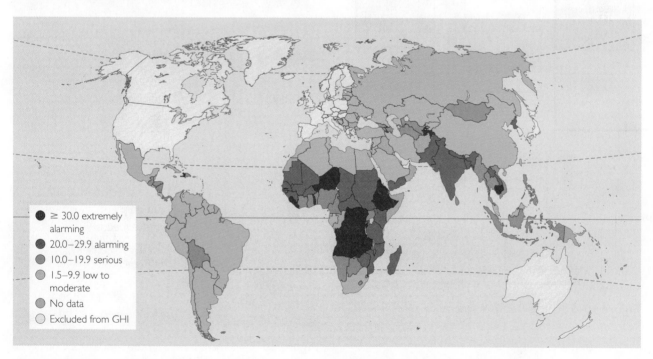

≥ 30.0 extremely alarming

20.0–29.9 alarming

10.0–19.9 serious

1.5–9.9 low to moderate

No data

Excluded from GHI

Figure 10–4 The Global Hunger Index (GHI) includes three equally weighted indicators: the proportion of people who are food-energy deficient, the prevalence of underweight children under the age of five, and the under-five mortality rate. The Index ranks countries on a 100-point scale, with zero being the best score (no hunger) and 100 being the worst.

The Nature of Agriculture

In Canada, we take having a reliable and relatively inexpensive supply of food for granted. This is not surprising. Since the farming population is less than 2.5 percent of the total population, very few of us have direct experience with farming. Let's look at what natural inputs are necessary for agricultural success (see Figure 10–5).

Few places in the world have the perfect combination of conditions for agricultural success: a long growing season, not too much and not too little moisture, rich soils, level land, and the right mix of biological conditions. Unfortunately, most areas suffer from one or more deficiencies. For each deficiency, farmers have been able to make adjustments (see Figure 10–6).

Agricultural Deficiency	Human Adjustment
Growing season too short or too cool	• Grow a crop with a shorter growing season • Develop varieties that mature more quickly • Provide additional energy input (e.g., use a greenhouse)
Insufficient moisture	• Provide irrigation • Use growing methods that preserve moisture (reduce evaporation) • Develop crops that require less water
Infertile soils	• Add natural fertilizers (e.g., manure, compost) • Add chemical fertilizers • Use appropriate plant rotations
Hilly terrain	• Build terraces • Use cropping practices that minimize erosion
Low-lying, wet terrain	• Choose crops that tolerate or need abundant water (e.g., paddy rice) • Tile (drain) soils
Shortage of beneficial insects	• Introduce beneficial insects (e.g., ladybugs and bees)
Excess of harmful insects	• Use chemical insecticides • Introduce predator insects • Use cropping methods that limit insects • Grow genetically modified, insect-resistant crop varieties
Excess of weeds	• Use chemical herbicides • Manually and mechanically remove weeds • Grow genetically modified plant varieties that tolerate herbicides • Use cropping methods that minimize weeds

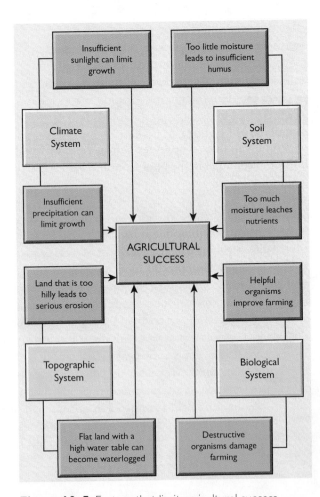

Figure 10–5 Factors that limit agricultural success

Figure 10–6 Humans have adjusted agricultural practices to deal with deficiencies. Have all the agricultural practices been positive? Explain.

Types of Agriculture

Agricultural activities can be categorized in two ways. The first category includes *subsistence farming* and *cash-crop farming*. Subsistence farming is the dominant form of agriculture in much of the Periphery and even some parts of the New Core. Subsistence farmers grow crops and raise livestock to meet the immediate food needs of their families. They usually produce many different agricultural products on small acreages. Any surplus products are sold or traded to meet other needs of the family. In contrast, cash-crop farmers specialize in producing only one or two products even if they have very large farms. Their products are sold on open world and local markets. These farmers might not consume any of the products they produce. For example, a dairy farmer who produces hundreds of litres of milk a day might buy milk at the local supermarket.

The second category of agriculture includes *intensive farming* and *extensive farming*. Intensive farming takes place on a relatively small amount of land that is worked with a great deal of labour, machinery, and high inputs of such things as fertilizers, pesticides, and water. The results are high yields of product per hectare. Typical forms of intensive farming in Canada include fruit and vegetable growing, and vineyards in such places as the Okanagan Valley in central British Columbia, the Annapolis Valley of Nova Scotia, and the Niagara Escarpment region and Holland Marsh in Ontario. Intensive farming also includes hog factory farms, and livestock feedlots where animals are penned and fattened in small fields.

Extensive farming, in contrast, takes place on a relatively large amount of land that is worked with a limited amount of labour and smaller inputs of fertilizers, pesticides, and water. The results are lower yields of product per hectare, but because farm sizes are so large, the farmer can still make a profit. Examples in Canada include grain and oilseed farming, and ranching in the West, and most forms of *mixed farming* (growing crops and raising animals) in eastern Canada. Although we have talked about four distinct types of farming here, in reality, farming exists on a continuum between subsistence and cash cropping and between intensive and extensive farming (see Figure 10–7).

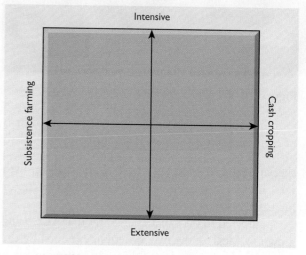

Figure 10–7 Every type of agriculture in the world can be located somewhere on this diagram.

Did You Know?

- Nomads still travel from place to place with their herds of camels, goats, sheep, cattle, and horses in parts of North Africa, the Middle East, and Central Asia. This type of agriculture is declining as governments, in an effort to control the nomads, force them into settlements.
- Most farmers living in East, South, and Southeast Asia practise intensive subsistence agriculture. Small plots are worked primarily with human labour to produce high yields, particularly of rice.

The Green Revolution

The **Green Revolution** began in 1943 when the Rockefeller Foundation, at the request of the Mexican government, established an agricultural research station in Mexico to develop more productive varieties of wheat that could be used to feed the rapidly growing population of the country. The basic idea behind this initiative was that the selective breeding methods that had greatly improved agricultural productivity in the developed world could be used with equal success in developing countries.

Dr. Norman Borlaug, who won the 1970 Nobel Peace Prize for his efforts, was head of the research station. Borlaug and his colleagues wanted to produce **high-yield varieties (HYVs)** of wheat that could be used to increase food production in Mexico and eventually throughout the developing world. HYVs are crops

Figure 10–8 In northern India, dwarf wheat crops like this one increased grain supplies and helped save millions of people from malnutrition.

specially bred or selected to have an increased growth rate, increased percentage of usable plant parts, or increased resistance to crop diseases.

Compared to the varieties of wheat that were being grown in Mexico, the new varieties developed by the researchers had a number of things in common:

- They were smaller (see Figure 10–8). Dwarf plants focus more of their energy on growing their seeds (the part of the plant that we eat) and less on growing their stems, which are useless as food.

- They responded better to the use of farming inputs like fertilizer, pesticides, and irrigation.

- They grew faster. In suitable areas, a variety that grows faster allows the same land to be used for more than one crop per year.

The success of the wheat project in Mexico encouraged other researchers to develop high-yield varieties of rice at the International Rice Research Institute (IRRI) in the Philippines. Ultimately, 15 research institutes were set up, each specializing in some crop or aspect of food production in the developing world.

Successes of the Green Revolution

In the decades after World War II, experts predicted massive famines as the world's population exploded. The Green Revolution helped prevent this. In the countries of the developing world especially, the Green Revolution reduced food-supply problems. With more food available to feed their growing populations, developing countries were able to use more of their limited resources to develop social and economic programs (for instance, family-planning education and better

healthcare systems). These programs allowed countries to take control of their burgeoning populations. In effect, the Green Revolution helped countries in the New Core and Periphery work through demographic transition (see Chapter 5).

Between 1950 and 1999, global grain production increased by 170 percent on the same amount of land. If conventional farming techniques had been used, millions of hectares of forest and natural grassland would have been used to increase the cropland required to produce enough food to meet the growing population.

Worldwide, food production increased 20 percent more quickly than did the population. On average, prices for wheat and rice declined by 70 percent. This meant that all but the poorest people had better diets than before the Green Revolution.

GLOBALIZATION

Worldwide, food production increased 20 percent more quickly than did the population.

Why didn't this increased food production solve the world's hunger problem?

Concerns About the Green Revolution

While no one disputes its role in boosting world food production, critics have expressed some concerns about the Green Revolution.

- It used a modern Western model for agriculture that involves costly inputs such as chemical fertilizers, pesticides, and irrigation. Many poor farmers on small plots could not afford these inputs. The Green Revolution actually benefitted wealthy farmers, but often harmed the poorest (see Figure 10–9).

- The Green Revolution led to a dramatic **loss of genetic diversity**, which, in turn, threatened the global food supply. Some varieties of the same crop are susceptible to weed and insect damage, while others are not. Consequently, it's a good idea to plant as many varieties as possible. If one or two varieties fail as a result of disease or a pest invasion, the many other varieties that survive will provide the food that is needed. However, if only one or two highly developed varieties are planted, and both are wiped out, then there is no other crop to fall back on. The Green Revolution promoted only a few highly developed varieties of wheat, rice, and corn, and these came to replace the hundreds of native varieties that had been previously grown in developing countries.

	Before the Green Revolution		After the Green Revolution	
	Poor Farmer	Wealthier Farmer	Poor Farmer	Wealthier Farmer
Yield (units per hectare)	20 ×	20 ×	20 ×	50 ×
Price (per unit)	10 =	10 =	7 =	7 =
Income per hectare	200	200	140	350

Figure 10–9 The Green Revolution actually harmed the poorest farmers, since they could not afford to take advantage of new varieties of crops.

■ The Green Revolution produced a system of agriculture that is not as environmentally sustainable as traditional agriculture. Although traditional mixed cropping provided relatively stable yields for centuries, yields from HYV crops declined significantly in only a few decades. These decreasing yields occurred because of losses due to insect and plant pests, and because HYVs caused a decline in soil fertility that cannot be made up entirely by the addition of chemical fertilizers.

SUSTAINABILITY

The Green Revolution produced a system of agriculture that is not as environmentally sustainable as traditional agriculture.

Do the high yields that are produced by HYV crops for a few decades outweigh the environmental impacts that occur from their use?

■ Some critics suggest that self-interest prompted the developed countries to fund research that supported the Green Revolution. The creation of Western-style agriculture opened huge new markets for the makers of fertilizers, pesticides, farm equipment, and other products, almost all of which came from companies in developed countries.

■ The Green Revolution focused initially on research related to farming in areas with the most fertile soils and reliable rainfall. This research was of little help to people who lived in arid and semi-arid regions. Africans, for example, benefitted very little from the

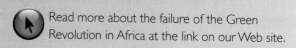

Read more about the failure of the Green Revolution in Africa at the link on our Web site.

Green Revolution. Here, most of the soil is infertile because of excessive leaching, and 71 percent of the continent consists of arid and semi-arid areas.

■ The Green Revolution focused on developing varieties of wheat, rice, and maize (corn). It did not benefit the poor in Africa and other countries who relied on diets whose staples were millet, sorghum, cassava, and yams.

■ The mechanization promoted by the Green Revolution reduced the number of agricultural jobs in developing countries.

■ Women farmers, who grow much of the food in developing countries, did not have the money or access to financing to purchase equipment and the seeds of newly developed varieties of crops.

Upon receiving the Nobel Peace Prize in 1970, Dr. Borlaug stated that the Green Revolution was only a "temporary success" because boosting yields on existing cropland is only part of the solution to world hunger; slowing population growth is the other part. He further stated that the Green Revolution would provide the world with "breathing space" until population growth came under control. In recent years, the world's population has increased annually at 2.2 percent, while global food production has increased at an annual rate of only 1.3 percent. How can the *disparity* (difference or gap) between food production and population growth be addressed when the amount of land suitable for growing crops is *finite* (limited)?

In 2006, the director of the Food and Agriculture Organization (FAO) addressed the problem by calling for a second Green Revolution. His vision was to feed the world's growing population while preserving natural resources and the environment. He realized, however,

In the News

Find out more about **Dr. Norman Borlaug** by creating a profile on him that focuses on his role in the Green Revolution. Use the example on page 14 to guide you.

that the extra yearly one billion tonnes of cereals that would have to be produced by 2050 would have to be grown in an environment threatened by climate change.

What would a second Green Revolution look like? Would farmers use fewer high-performance crop varieties and concentrate more on the efficient use of natural resources? Would they plant genetically modified crops, or adopt organic farming techniques? These and other issues are examined in the next section, "Food Production Issues."

CASE STUDY   Alliance for a Green Revolution in Africa

In 2006, the Bill and Melinda Gates Foundation and the Rockefeller Foundation formed an alliance that would develop a "Green Revolution" in Africa, where the original Green Revolution had had little impact. The Alliance aims to dramatically increase the productivity of small African farms.

The use of traditional seeds and farming techniques has not been particularly effective in increasing the African food supply. In the 15 years prior to 2007, the number of Africans living below the poverty line (US$1/day) increased by 50 percent. To alleviate this poverty and low agricultural productivity, new seeds and new agricultural techniques will be given to millions of small-scale farmers—the majority of them women working on farms smaller than one hectare—in order that they may grow enough food to feed their families (see Figure 10–10).

The initial investment of US$150 million (US$100 million from the Bill and Melinda Gates Foundation; the remainder from the Rockefeller Foundation) will support the Program for Africa's Seed Systems (PASS). PASS endeavours to improve the availability and variety of seeds that produce higher yields in sub-Saharan Africa. It has five goals:

- To develop improved varieties of African crops that provide higher yields for small farmers by using conventional methods of plant breeding. PASS's research programs take into consideration the differences in local pests, diseases, rainfall patterns, soil properties, and the needs of local small farm communities.
- To train a new generation of African crop scientists who will become the crop breeders and agricultural scientists on which the seed system will depend for growth and productivity.
- To ensure that improved seeds reach small farmers. In the past, the lack of an effective seed delivery program, poor rural transportation, and a lack of money limited the small farmer's access to improved seeds. PASS will ensure that the improved crop varieties are produced and distributed through private and public channels so farmers can adopt them.

- To develop a network of African agro-dealers that will act as a conduit for seeds, fertilizers, chemicals, and knowledge for small farmers.
- To monitor, evaluate, and manage the projects to ensure that they are carried out effectively.

In 2007, former UN Secretary-General Kofi Annan became the first chairperson of AGRA. His task is to build broad political and economic support across Africa for this new approach to a Green Revolution.

Questions

1. a) What organizations founded the Alliance for a Green Revolution in Africa (AGRA)?
   b) What is AGRA's main goal?
   c) What steps is it taking to achieve this goal?

2. Do you think the five-point program of PASS is an effective way of improving the availability and variety of seeds in sub-Saharan Africa? Explain.

Figure 10–10 AGRA's goal is to replace traditional seeds and farming techniques. New seeds, such as those provided by these Kenyan agro-dealers, will increase Africa's food supply.

Food Production Issues

The Green Revolution peaked in the mid-1980s. At this time, the per capita world production of grain slowly but steadily began to decline (see Figure 10–11). This decline is just one of a number of concerns about the production of the world's food.

Biotechnology and Farming

Some diets, especially those in which rice is the staple, tend to be deficient in two important nutrients: iron and vitamin A. Nearly two billion people in the world suffer from iron deficiency, and almost two million children each year are at risk of going blind because of vitamin A deficiency. A more varied diet, or vitamin supplement, would eliminate such deficiencies, but these are not options for millions of poor people. Recent breakthroughs in **biotechnology**—the application of biological processes to agricultural and industrial purposes—may go a long way toward eliminating these problems.

Biotechnology in Food Production

Swiss scientists spent more than ten years and US$150 million to produce new varieties of rice that would provide sufficient amounts of vitamin A and iron. Vitamin A-rich "golden rice" was produced by modifying the genetic material of rice with the addition of two genes from a type of daffodil and one from a bacterium. The resulting variety is high in beta-carotene, a nutrient that the body can convert to vitamin A and thus prevent blindness. A similar approach was used to produce an iron-rich variety of rice.

The methods of biotechnologists are completely different from those used by scientists in the Green Revolution. Biotechnologists move desirable genes from one organism to another; in fact, they can move genes, and the characteristics they carry, between entirely different plant species, and even between animals and plants. The Green Revolution scientists used traditional crossbreeding between two varieties of plants, hoping to pass the genes for certain desirable qualities from parent plants to offspring.

The new species created as a result of biotechnology are called transgenic organisms or **genetically modified organisms (GMOs)**. Some observers suggest that we may be entering a second Green Revolution, but one that is driven by biotechnology.

Crops of GMOs are already widely grown, particularly in the Americas (see Figure 10–12). Varieties of soybeans, corn, cotton, and canola, in particular, were created to not be affected by certain herbicides, and/or to be resistant to insects. In 2006, there were 102 million hectares (about the size of Ontario) of transgenic crops grown in the world by 10.3 million farmers in 22 countries (see Figure 10–12).

Some herbicides have to be applied several times during the growing cycle, and may be effective only against certain types of weeds. This means that costly applications of different herbicides might be necessary

Country	Millions of Hectares	Crops
USA	54.6	Soybeans, Corn, Cotton, Canola, Squash, Papaya, Alfalfa
Argentina	18.0	Soybeans, Corn, Cotton
Brazil	11.5	Soybeans, Cotton
Canada	6.1	Canola, Corn, Soybeans
India	3.8	Cotton
China	3.5	Cotton
Paraguay	2.0	Soybeans
South Africa	1.4	Corn, Soybeans, Cotton

Figure 10–12 Cultivation areas for GM crops by major producers (over 1 million hectares), 2006. The GMO area in the US is about the same as the total land area of Manitoba.

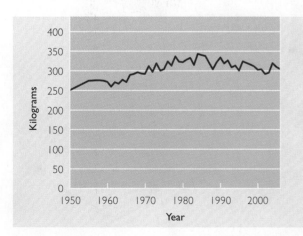

Figure 10–11 The trend in global per-capita grain production has been slowly downward since the mid-1980s.

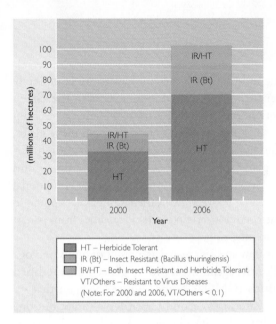

Figure 10–13 Transgenic crops by trait. Since 2000, the area of cultivation of genetically modified plants has more than doubled.

during the growing season. Multiple applications cause an increased risk of damage to the environment and to people's health because of the toxicity of so many chemicals. Chemical companies had also developed broad-spectrum herbicides that could kill just about every weed—but of course these were of little use to farmers once the crop had started to grow.

SUSTAINABILITY

Multiple applications of herbicides cause an increased risk of damage to the environment and to people's health.

Does this increased risk from multiple applications of herbicides justify the use of transgenic crops?

Biotechnological research had a solution. Scientists took a gene from the relatively rare plants that were resistant to two of these broad-spectrum herbicides. Then they introduced it into soybeans and other crops. The results were crops that could be safely sprayed with these herbicides as needed. Furthermore, since the herbicides were broad-spectrum, they could kill virtually every weed that threatened the crop. This reduced the need for applications of many different herbicides, each of which could kill only one specific weed. And this,

In 2004, the UN food agency, the FAO, came out in favour of biotech crops because it believed that they help small farmers financially, have no ill effects on health, and have some environmental benefits. Read more at the link on our Web site.

in turn, cut down on the amount of toxic chemicals entering the environment.

To create crops that were resistant to insect infestations, scientists took a gene from a soil bacterium called *Bacillus thuringiensis* (Bt, for short), modified it, and introduced it into the plant (see Figure 10–13). The new gene allows the Bt-modified plant to produce a toxin that kills specific types of insects and yet is harmless to non-target insects and to people or animals that might eat the plant or its fruit. The use of Bt-modified plants has allowed farmers to reduce their use of insecticides drastically.

Concerns about Biotechnology in Food Production

Although GMOs have had some impressive benefits and promise more for the future, few subjects have proven as controversial in recent years (see Figure 10–14). Opponents have dubbed GMOs "Frankenfoods." This controversy has arisen for many reasons, ranging from the scientific to the ethical. It also has a strong regional bias, as concerns about transgenic crops and animals are much greater in Europe than in North America. GMO opponents have many concerns:

- The use of Bt-modified crops may result in the creation of "super bugs" that are resistant to pesticides. There will always be a tiny number of individual insects that are immune to the toxic effects of Bt crops. These resistant insects would normally make up only a tiny percentage of the total insect population, but without competition, they will flourish and their numbers will explode.

Figure 10–14 GMOs have become the subject of lively debate in the editorial pages of the world's newspapers.

- "Super weeds" that would be resistant to potent herbicides could develop in the same manner as "super bugs."

- Who owns the agricultural advances that have been developed? Charitable groups funded the Green Revolution to benefit the poor, but private companies are carrying out most GMO research.

- Traditionally, farmers saved a portion of seeds from each year's crop to plant the following year. Seeds from transgenic plants or plants developed by traditional cross-breeding can also be saved and replanted the following year, but over several years, the plants gradually lose their desirable qualities. At this point, the farmer has to buy more seed. Critics view this as forcing farmers to buy new seeds so that seed companies may increase their profits.

- Some seed companies have developed "terminator technology." This term refers to plants that are genetically modified to produce *sterile seeds* (seeds that cannot grow). Seed companies know that huge profits would be made if farmers could not save seeds from a previous year's crop and were forced to buy new seeds every year. The world's three largest multi-national seed companies pledged in 2007, in the face of global opposition to terminator seeds, not to pursue this technology. One major company that owns three US patents on terminator technology declared, however, that it will proceed to develop commercial terminator seeds. (In March 2007, the UN Convention on Biological Diversity supported the six-year *moratorium* [suspension] on terminator technology. Canada, the US, New Zealand, and Australia would like to eliminate the moratorium.)

- Critics say that there is danger in introducing genetic material that is programmed not to reproduce. They fear that the terminator gene could escape into the gene pool with potentially catastrophic results. Supporters of terminator plants feel that it would be impossible for terminator genes to enter the gene pool since they cannot reproduce.

- Not enough research has been done to prove the safety of transgenic food products; health problems may affect consumers in the future.

- Consumers in North America usually do not know if they are eating genetically modified foods. Almost 70 percent of the products we buy at the supermarket contain genetically engineered food! Unlike most countries in Europe, Canada and the US do not have labelling rules that make producers state whether products contain GMOs. Public opinion polls in British Columbia and Quebec show that 85 percent of the population support mandatory labelling of GMOs.

Loss of Genetic Diversity

The loss of genetic diversity in agriculture is a serious concern. Thousands of varieties of crops and domestic animals have disappeared as scientists and plant and animal breeders have developed and promoted new hybrid varieties. These hybrids have been developed to have characteristics that are commercially lucrative, for example, a tomato that will not bruise when shipped, or a cow that gives huge amounts of milk. When farmers stop raising the old varieties in favour of the new, the seeds and animal breeding lines are lost forever. The Food and Agricultural Organization of the United Nations estimates that 75 percent of the genetic diversity of agricultural crops was lost in the 20th century.

The maintenance of the largest possible genetic stock is important for the ongoing success of selective breeding programs and genetic engineering initiatives. Both rely on the widest possible range of characteristics from which the most desirable may be selected when breeding or genetic engineering takes place.

Individuals, interest groups, and agricultural colleges have developed programs to protect endangered varieties of agricultural plants and animals. They collect and store seeds, share seeds with others, and raise animals that have become obsolete because they have lost their commercial value. They also provide information about the loss of genetic diversity to the public, farmers, and governments.

Land Reform

In Chapter 6, you learned about the remarkable success of population control in the Indian state of Kerala. A critical factor in this success is that Kerala was able to institute effective **land reform** many years ago. Land reform is the re-distribution of land from large landowners to landless farm workers, *sharecroppers* (farmers who farm land owned by someone else), and small landowners whose holdings may not be large enough to support their families. Land reform has not been the norm in most developing countries, and land ownership issues have often resulted in conflict. In 1954, attempts to introduce land reform in Guatemala led to the overthrow of the government in a violent revolt. In Bolivia, however, recent land reform has been more orderly. By the end of his term in 2011, Bolivian President Evo Morales hopes to have redistributed 20 million hectares of farmland to approximately three million landless farmers. Needless to say, land reform is very popular with the poor, and intensely unpopular with the rich landowners.

Role of Women in Agriculture

In the regions where food shortages are worst, for example, in sub-Saharan Africa and South Asia, women are responsible for the majority of food production (see Figure 10–15). Yet they often have little, if any, control over this important part of their lives.

It has been suggested that part of the solution to food problems in developing countries lies in acknowledging the role that women play in food production. Steps should be taken to ensure that they have the knowledge and power they need to be more successful. Greater access to education and healthcare would give them more control over decision making. Credit, or the ability to borrow money, should be extended to women so that they may purchase land, seed, machinery, and fertilizers. If women are empowered, the food supply in developing countries will increase.

Agricultural Support Policies

Agricultural support policies are designed by governments to manage domestic agriculture and regulate imports of agricultural products. They are put in place to protect the country's agricultural economy. Support policies include such things as price controls that set the prices that farmers must receive for their products; tariffs, which are taxes that food importers must pay to get their products into the country; and cash payments, or subsidies, given to farmers to help them remain competitive with farmers in other countries.

Did You Know?

In 2006, members of the G8 agreed to eliminate export subsidies by 2013. No date, however, was established for the elimination of trade distorting domestic subsidies that favoured one country's producers over another.

Figure 10–15 In many countries, especially those in the developing world, women provide most of the labour in agriculture but have little control over decision making.

Subsidies are the most significant form of agricultural support. In 2004, Canada gave $4.9 billion in subsidies to its farmers, up from $2.8 billion in 2000. In 2005, the European Union gave its farmers $134 billion and the US gave $43 billion to its farmers. Subsidies can be seen as beneficial or as damaging (see Figure 10–16).

At a time when free markets have become so prevalent in the world, why are agricultural markets controlled by so many governmental policies? Although the governments of the European Union nations and the US might wish to reduce, or even eliminate, the support they give farmers, they lack the political will to take on the powerful agricultural lobbies in their countries. In France, attempts to reduce subsidies have been met with national strikes by farmers, who tied up the country's transportation systems by blocking roads and railways, often with large piles of manure.

The poor Periphery countries suffer the most from subsidies in Old Core countries. The US, for example, subsidizes cotton more than any other nation. In 2004, the 25 000 US cotton farmers collected US$4.5 billion in subsidies. This allowed US cotton farmers to export three-quarters of their crop and control 40 percent of world trade. Meanwhile, about ten million small-scale cotton growers in the poor countries in West and Central Africa suffered from low world prices caused by the dumping of large amounts of subsidized cotton from the US on the world market. Even though the World Trade Organization(WTO) has labelled these cotton subsidies illegal, the US has yet to remove them.

Canadian farmers have been harmed by subsidies in other countries because the Canadian government has tended to be less generous with its support than the European and US governments. In 2007, the Canadian government requested that the WTO examine US subsidies. Under WTO regulations, the US is allowed to use subsidies up to US$19 billion annually. Canada contends that the US has exceeded this value in six of the previous seven years.

Monoculture

Think of the vast wheat fields of Canada's Prairie provinces or the hillsides covered with vineyards in southern France. This type of agriculture in which a single crop is planted over a large area is called **monoculture**. It is widely practised around the world because growing a single crop over a large area is a more efficient way to plant, maintain, and harvest. Yields are higher because there is no competition from other plants. This type of agriculture, however, has several drawbacks. Planting the same crop year after year depletes the soil of nutrients and increases the need for fertilizers. Monoculture relies heavily on pesticides to deal with the large number of pests attracted to such a large food supply. Genetic diversity is reduced because a limited number of varieties is grown. The loss of natural habitat reduces the ability of wild animals to survive. Habitat destruction is perhaps the most important cause of species extinction worldwide.

Corporate Farming

The family farm is the traditional model for farming. It is an economic and social unit that involves one family's farming and living off the products of a modest amount of land. Frequently, the family farm is passed down from one generation to another. However, family farming is proving to be less profitable than in the past. As a result, a centuries-old lifestyle is being lost as family farming is replaced by large-scale corporate farming.

Larger farms have a considerable number of economic advantages compared to smaller farms. The term **economies of scale** means that an increase in the scale of the operation causes a decrease in the cost of production. Large-scale corporate farming has developed to take advantage of this fact. **Corporate farming** is the large-scale production of food on farms owned by corporations. Corporate farming encompasses the operation of the farm and often the operation of farm-related

Beneficial Aspects of Subsidies	Damaging Aspects of Subsidies
• Supplement farmers' incomes, thus giving them a higher standard of living	• The majority do not go to small farmers. The largest 10 percent of farm businesses receive almost three-quarters of the subsidies.
• Provide income that enables farmers to continue farming	• Cover some crops and not others; farmers growing non-subsidized crops do not benefit. For example, over 90 percent of federal subsidies in the US go to corn, wheat, soybean, rice, and cotton farmers.
• Help farmers produce the food the country needs, thus making the country less dependent on foreign food	• Artificially increase the price of all agricultural inputs, including land. This makes it more difficult for younger people to become farmers.
• Encourage farmers to grow a crop they might not otherwise grow	• Foster a dependency on government assistance by farmers. Poor farm management may result because decisions are based on how to obtain the greatest financial support rather than on sound commercial or ecological practices.
• Increase agricultural production, thus causing food prices to drop. The more product on the market, the lower the cost to buy it.	• In developed countries, subsidies create overproduction that lowers world food prices. Farmers in developing countries cannot compete against this cheap food and lose markets in their own countries.
• Help create food surpluses that can be used as food aid	• Have led to international trade wars among countries in the Old Core

Figure 10–16 The good and the bad of subsidies

businesses such as the production of seeds, chemical fertilizers, pesticides, herbicides, and farm machinery; food processing; and the marketing of food products. The term "agribusiness" is a general term for many businesses involved in different aspects of agriculture. Critics of large-scale farming use this term in a negative sense to mean corporate farming.

Some farms, either family- or corporate-owned, employ methods that are similar to those used in factories. These **factory farms** are large-scale operations that produce the highest output of livestock, poultry, and even fish at the lowest cost. Huge hog farms in Manitoba and southwestern Ontario are good examples of factory farms. Here, thousands of animals are raised indoors and are fed and watered with quantities exactly measured to produce the greatest weight gain in the shortest time. To maintain the health of the animals, farmers routinely administer antibiotics and vitamins. The discovery of vitamins A and D in the 1920s allowed animals to be raised indoors. The development of antibiotics in the 1940s stopped the spread of disease among many animals living in close contact. Both discoveries facilitated the development of factory farms. Processing of the animals is performed on an assembly-line basis. Factory farming now dominates pork production, and most of the meat, poultry, eggs, and milk in our supermarkets are produced in this intensive manner (see Figure 10–17).

Factory farming increases fears about the contamination of groundwater through the dumping of massive amounts of animal waste. Further, the unpleasant odours and excessive use of antibiotics and hormones associated with factory farming are highly unappealing to many people.

Factory farming also raises questions about the ethical treatment of animals. For example, billions of broiler chickens are raised annually in North America. These chickens are selectively bred and genetically altered to produce more meat in a shorter period of time. Their brief life takes place in overcrowded rooms instead of cages because the birds can get bruised on cage walls. To prevent them from fighting and injuring one another, their beaks and nails are cut off or they are raised in the dark. These kinds of conditions have become a focus for animal rights groups.

Some farmers in the US have joined the fight against farm subsidies. For more information see the link on our Web site.

Figure 10–17 In the crowded conditions of many factory farms, antibiotics are used to prevent the spread of disease. The crowded conditions raise questions about the ethical treatment of the animals.

World food production is being corporatized in other ways. Huge companies that supply inputs to farming (such as seeds, fertilizers, and pesticides) and that market agricultural products have expanded their influence. Large corporations control much of the food system. For example, Monsanto and DuPont control seed markets for corn (65 percent) and soybeans (44 percent), and Cargill, Archer Daniels Midland, and Bunge control about 90 percent of the global grain trade. Some transnational companies (see Chapter 12 for information about transnational corporations) are good examples of **vertical integration** because they control all aspects of the food-production business: seed development, agrichemicals, farm machinery, transportation, storage, food processing, marketing, and retail distribution. Critics point out that such concentrated ownership restricts competition and puts too much control of our food supply in the hands of a few companies.

The influence of huge commercial entities on farming is not new. The best known are the powerful companies that began to operate in Africa, Asia, and Latin America in the late 1800s. Most notorious, perhaps, was a banana company called United Fruit Company, which had immense political power in Guatemala and Costa Rica. In 1954, United Fruit was even involved with the US Central Intelligence Agency (CIA) in the overthrow of an elected Guatemalan government. United Fruit felt that the government threatened its dominance in the country. Today, huge agribusinesses continue to exercise immense and growing economic and political power.

The Search for Sustainable Agriculture

Although there is no single solution that would make our agricultural system more sustainable, organic farming moves us closer to this goal.

Organic Farming

Organic farming has developed largely as a response to consumers' concerns about the safety of the products of conventional agriculture. Consumers worry about pesticide residues on crops and about the routine use of antibiotics on livestock. They fear that GMO products have not been adequately tested. To answer these concerns, a small but growing number of farmers in developed countries have decided to grow their crops in a more natural fashion.

Although there are no commonly accepted definitions of what **organic farming** is, organic farmers avoid the use of chemical fertilizers and pesticides, growth hormones and other livestock feed additives, and GMOs. They try to rely on more natural practices such as cage-free poultry, crop rotation to maintain soil fertility, planting two or more crops in the same field to deter pests and promote biodiversity, leaving crop residues on the land to prevent erosion, and the use of animal manures and *green manures* to enhance the texture and nutritional quality of the soil. (Green manure is a cover crop that is grown to add nutrients and organic matter to the soil. An example of this is clover, which adds nitrogen.)

Organic farming is not without its drawbacks. Some botanical pesticides are toxic to a number of insects, and the application of too much manure can lead to water contamination. If organic food production were to increase globally, more land would have to be brought under cultivation because the yield per hectare is lower than in conventional farming. The cost of organic produce is generally higher than products from conventional farms because of the lower yields.

For the past 15 years, the world market for organic food has grown steadily. In North America, retail sales are predicted to grow by 15 to 20 percent per year. The retail organic food market in 2005 was estimated to be $1.3 billion in Canada and US$15 billion in the US. In that year, there were 3618 certified organic farmers in Canada. They represent, however, only 1.5 percent of the total number of farmers in Canada.

Food Miles

The distance food travels from field to table is referred to as **food miles** (Figure 10–18). This distance has a negative impact on the environment because of the use of, and emissions from, fossil fuels. Another aspect of food miles is how far and how many times people use automobiles to shop for food. Numerous trips in a vehicle to a shopping centre use more energy than similar visits to a local store within walking distance. The distance your food has to travel and the number of car trips you make to the shopping centre have an impact on the environment. When you buy food from faraway places, your *carbon footprint* (the amount of greenhouse gases created by your various activities) is higher than if you purchased locally produced foods.

In 2005, the Waterloo Region Health Department conducted a study of 58 commonly eaten food products imported into the region. It discovered that these products travelled an average distance of 4 497 kilometres and accounted for 51 709 tonnes of greenhouse gas emissions annually. If all of these food items were replaced with products from southwestern Ontario, there would be a reduction in greenhouse gas emissions of approximately 49 500 tonnes, the equivalent of taking 16 000 cars off our roads.

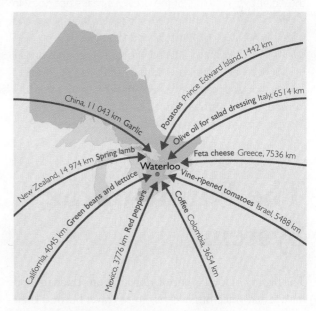

Figure 10–18 A meal can travel a long way from the field to your table. Estimate how far the ingredients in one of your meals has travelled (use a distance calculator on the Internet).

Critics of food miles argue that transportation is only one component of food production and distribution. Food produced on an energy-efficient factory farm far away may use less energy per unit than food produced on a less energy-efficient local farm. In addition, organic food in your supermarket may have a large number of food miles if it was grown and shipped from a distant location.

MacKinnon and Smith wrote a book about their experiences called *The 100-Mile Diet: A Year of Local Eating*, published in 2007. Check out information about the 100-mile diet at the link on our Web site.

CASE STUDY   The 100-Mile Diet

Could you live only on food that was produced within a 100-mile (160-kilometre) radius of where you live? In 2005, this became the goal of James MacKinnon and Alisa Smith, vegetarians and environmentalists living in Vancouver. Their goal was based on the realization that the food eaten by the average North American travels a large number of food miles—2400 to 4000 kilometres (1500 to 2500 miles)—from the farm to the table. MacKinnon and Smith selected 160 kilometres, or 100 miles, as the radius of the land on which their food was produced because that is the distance between the Pacific Ocean and the Coast Mountains. This region comprises the agricultural lands of the Fraser River Delta.

MacKinnon and Smith began their one-year experiment on the first day of spring in March 2005. Since local food wasn't available in farmers' markets until May, they started their diet by eating lots of the previous year's potatoes! In order to have food for the following winter, they picked and froze berries and corn, and canned tomatoes.

As a result of media attention from as far away as Britain, MacKinnon and Smith formed the 100-Mile Diet Society. Several thousand members joined within the first few months. In recognition of their efforts to promote local eating, *Maclean's* magazine named them on its 2006 Honour Roll.

The main criticism of the 100-mile diet is that advocates are taking only one factor into consideration when selecting their food. Critics say they should also take into account how much energy was used in the food's production. For example, food produced in a Near Core or Periphery country may use up less energy than food produced in an Old Core country, despite the distance it has to be shipped to reach the market.

Could you live without chocolate, peanut butter, orange juice, bananas, coffee, rice, sugar, or any other foods you enjoy that are produced more than 100 miles from where you live?

Questions

1. Why is the diet in which food travels 2400 kilometres (1500 miles) from farm to table called the "SUV diet"?

2. Buying food locally may mean fresher food, but it doesn't necessarily mean you are creating a smaller environmental impact. Explain.

3. Would you like to live on the 100-mile diet? Explain.

The Future of the Global Agricultural System

The history of food is one of globalization. Trade in food has existed since humans began to travel beyond their own horizon. In the first century BCE, trade between China and the Middle East along the Silk Road saw the exchange of noodles for wine. Potatoes from South America ware taken to Europe by returning explorers. Food that moved from one part of the world to another was a globalized commodity, and so it remains today.

Can Global Agriculture Continue to Run on Fossil Fuels?

Today, global trade in food is conducted by corporations that produce food on large-scale farming operations. Distribution is accomplished by long-distance transportation systems—hence the expression "lettuce express" that refers to the train that carries lettuce from California to the east coast of Canada and the US. This food-distribution system depends on the use of nonrenewable fossil fuels. Even the food production itself depends on the use of nonrenewable energy; it takes a great deal of energy to produce fertilizers and pesticides, to irrigate and harvest, and to package and refrigerate goods. The dependence of food distribution and production on fossil fuels makes food costs vulnerable to fluctuations in the prices of oil and gas.

Biofuels: Positive or Negative?

The production of biofuels, such as ethanol and biodiesel, is increasing worldwide. A **biofuel** is made from a grain like corn, or another biomass like sugar cane. The crops from which biofuels are made are increasing in price. The rising price of these crops, dubbed "agflation," is caused by growing demand for limited quantities. In the US, annual corn-based ethanol production could double between 2006 and 2016.

What Is the Relationship Between Agriculture and Climate Change?

It is estimated that the amount of CO_2 emissions attributable to producing, processing, packaging, and distributing the food consumed by a family of four is about eight tonnes per year. As the global climate changes because of the burning of fossil fuels, the amount of arable land may be reduced which, in turn, may lead to higher food prices.

Can We Feed Ourselves Without Hurting Poor Farmers in Developing Countries?

Each year, farmers and governments in North America and western Europe face depressed commodity prices that result from overproduction. Prices are so low for some commodities that their producers must rely on subsidies from their governments to survive. These subsidies, in turn, make it impossible for farmers in developing countries to compete. The practice of "fair trade," in which producers in developing countries receive a price for their products that is above the market price, may help alleviate some of their poverty. Fair trade, however, is still limited in scope and applies to only a few, but growing number, of products, such as coffee, bananas, cocoa, spices, and sugar. (See Chapter 28.)

Despite the overproduction of food in Old Core countries, millions of people face death from hunger-related causes in New Core/Periphery countries. To many, this contradiction illustrates that the world does not have a food shortage, but an economic system that does not allow a vital commodity to move from producers to those who desperately need it.

Should We Buy Canadian?

We are often told to "buy Canadian." This helps Canadian farmers, but what about poor farmers in developing countries? Should we always buy locally and deprive developing countries of markets for their products? In climates where we can't produce food in the winter, can we always purchase local foods?

Solutions?

The solution to the global food problem is that we must reform the way in which food is produced and sold in the world market. It is not so easy to suggest exactly how such a vital goal might be accomplished. In reality, each of the problem areas described in this chapter needs to be addressed separately. We must find the solutions at individual, regional, national, and international levels. The problems of food production did not develop overnight, and they will likely take many years to solve.

What can you do? Here are some suggestions:

- buy locally produced goods in season
- buy from local farmers if possible
- support poor farmers around the world by purchasing "fair trade" products whenever possible
- buy more frozen, dried, or canned food in winter
- walk to the local supermarket, or buy in bulk to reduce the number of car trips you take to buy food
- purchase organic food products whenever possible
- speak to your local grocer about increasing the shelf space for organic foods
- buy products in bulk or with limited packaging
- support NGOs that build wells, supply food aid, or provide other assistance to the world's poor

Chapter Questions

Knowledge and Understanding

1. Explain the differences and similarities in meaning of the following terms: famine, starvation, malnutrition, undernutrition, and chronic hunger.

2. Examine Figure 10–4 that shows the Global Hunger Index (GHI).

   a) What three indicators are used to create the GHI?

   b) What parts of the world have the greatest hunger problems?

3. Successful agriculture depends on the interactions among a number of natural systems (see Figure 10–5).

   a) What are these systems?

   b) Give two factors in each system that can affect the success of agriculture.

4. Why are herbicide-resistant crops so popular?

5. a) What is meant by "terminator technology"?

   b) What danger is associated with this technology?

6. Why is it important to maintain genetic diversity?

7. "The history of food is one of globalization." Explain.

8. Research an area of the world currently suffering from a food shortage or famine. Examine

   a) causes

   b) impacts

   c) actions taken by
   - local governments/agencies
   - international governments/agencies

   d) success or failure of these actions

Thinking

9. In 1996, the Food and Agriculture Organization (FAO) called on world leaders to halve the number of hungry people in the world by 2015. In that year there were some 800 million people who were hungry. By 2003, that number had risen to over 850 million. Why do you think the number has risen despite the pledge of world leaders to address this problem?

10. a) Consider the dietary deficiency diseases listed in Figure 10–2. How are these avoided (for the most part) in countries like Canada?

   b) Why are these solutions not practical in most developing countries?

11. Make a diagram like Figure 10–7 in your notebook. On this graph, locate each of the following types of farming operations with a small "x." Label each point.

   a) a 1000-hectare cattle ranch in Alberta

   b) nomadic goat and sheep herding in North Africa

   c) a 0.2-hectare family farm in Bangladesh

   d) a vineyard in southern France

   e) a 75-hectare dairy farm in southern Ontario

   f) a 300-hectare corn and soybean farm in Iowa

12. a) What are the characteristics of the high-yield varieties of wheat (and rice) that were developed during the Green Revolution?

   b) What successes did the Green Revolution have?

   c) What are the concerns about the Green Revolution?

   d) How would you respond to each of the concerns about the Green Revolution? Give reasons for your responses.

   e) Do you feel the Green Revolution was successful or unsuccessful? Explain.

   f) Dr. Borlaug did not see the Green Revolution as the solution to the world's food problems. Rather, he saw it as providing breathing space to allow the world's population growth to be controlled. What do you think of his assessment? Explain.

13. a) How are transgenic crops and animals created?

   b) Create a summary of the advantages of and concerns about GMOs by completing Figure 10–19.

   c) On balance, do you personally feel comfortable eating GMO products? Do you think you have enough information to make an informed choice? Explain.

Advantages of GMO Revolution	Concerns About GMO Revolution

Figure 10–19 Advantages of and concerns about the GMO Revolution

14. Some forms of factory farming raise questions about the ethical treatment of animals.

    a) Give some examples of how animals are mistreated.

    b) What steps should be taken to eliminate this maltreatment?

    c) Do you think the "commando tactics," such as breaking into labs to free animals or blowing up labs, adopted by some animal-rights groups are justified? Explain.

15. Some people argue that organic farming is detrimental to the world's rainforest. Because organic-farming methods rely on less intensive agriculture, more land is required to produce the same amount of food that more intensive methods of farming produce. The argument goes, "If we switch to organic farming, there wouldn't be much room left for the rainforest." What do you think about the accuracy of this idea?

16. The countries of the Old Core are major suppliers of food to the rest of the world. What do you think will happen as more and more food crops are used to produce biofuels in the Old Core countries? What do you think should be done about this situation?

17. When the Canadian International Development Agency (CIDA) and NGOs assist people in famine-ravaged areas, they try to purchase foods from local or nearby suppliers. Why don't they ship in food produced in Canada?

18. Research the roles performed by the United Nations Food and Agricultural Organization. How successful has it been?

19. Sometimes called the "doomsday vault," it is in fact a repository for seeds from major agricultural crops from around the world. It received its first 100 million seeds—from 268 000 varieties of crops—in early 2008. Conduct research on the Svalbard Global Seed Vault and answer the following questions.

    a) Where is the global seed vault located?

    b) What is the purpose of the global seed vault?

    c) Describe the characteristics of the vault.

    d) How are the seeds stored?

    e) Who paid for and maintains the storage facility?

    f) Under what conditions will the seeds leave the facility?

    g) If Canada sends seeds to the vault, who owns the seeds?

h) Some seeds cannot be stored in the vault. Explain.

i) Not everyone agrees that the seed vault is a good idea. What criticisms have been made about this storage facility? What do you think?

Communication

20. a) Most agricultural areas of the world suffer from one or more deficiencies in the natural systems that support farming. List these deficiencies (see Figure 10–6).

    b) Work with three or four classmates to investigate some of these deficiencies. Each of you should choose one of the deficiencies to research. In your investigation, look for examples of both traditional and modern methods of addressing the deficiency. Share your findings with the members of your group.

21. One way to measure the adequacy of the food supply in a country is to compare the amount of food energy available to the amount needed for good health. To examine the world pattern of food adequacy, you will create and analyze either a hand-coloured or ArcView map. (Your teacher will suggest which approach you will use and provide full instructions.)

22. Investigate eight food production issues, using a jigsaw approach. Research one of the topics below and present your findings to other members of the class who have studied other issues and who will present their findings to you. Your teacher will give you details about how to do this.

    a) loss of genetic diversity

    b) land reform

    c) role of women in agriculture

    d) agricultural support policies (for example, subsidies)

    e) corporate farming

    f) organic farming

    g) the 100-mile diet

    h) integrated crop and pest management

Application

23. Philanthropy still plays a role in world development. Using the Internet, investigate how one of the following very rich people has contributed to making the world a better place in which to live.

   a) Ted Turner

   b) George Soros

   c) Bill Gates

   d) another very wealthy person of your choice

24. The production of most food crops depends on honey bees for pollination. However, in North America, Europe and Asia, bees are disappearing. This sudden disappearance may be a result of Colony Collapse Disorder. Do some research on this phenomenon, and answer the following questions:

   a) What is Colony Collapse Disorder?

   b) Give some possible reasons for Colony Collapse Disorder.

   c) What is the current state of finding a cure for CCD?

   d) What has been the impact of CCD on agriculture?

25. The food in our supermarkets comes from all over the world. Work with three or four classmates to investigate where the food you generally eat originates. Canada's Food Guide lists four main food groups:

   • vegetables and fruit

   • grain products

   • milk and alternatives

   • meat and alternatives

   It also mentions

   • oils and fats

   • beverages

   a) Each group member is to visit a supermarket and examine the place of origin for five items in each food group.

   b) Compare your findings with those of other group members. What patterns, if any, did you find? For example, did certain types of foods come from particular countries/regions? (Note: the place of origin for some products may vary with the seasons.)

   c) In each food group, determine which two products travelled the shortest distances and which two travelled the longest distances.

   d) Draw a diagram showing the food miles of the two products in each food group that travelled the longest distances. (Note: Refer to Figure 10–18 to see how your diagram should look.)

   e) Are there alternative places of origin or substitute foods for those products that have a high number of food miles? Explain.

26. The UN has given you the task of making recommendations to solve the following situation: The Core countries have an excess of food, and the Periphery countries have a shortage of food. What do you think can or should be done? Explain your recommendations. **G**

CHAPTER II

Geographic Models of Development and Change

Key Terms

colonialism

mercantile system

concession companies

land tenure

plantations

cash crops

neo-colonialism

free market economy

command economy

mixed economy

economic liberalism

Keynesian economics

progressive thought

neo-liberalism

economic globalization

non-tariff barriers

Trading at the New York Stock Exchange (right), an activity associated with Stage 5 of Rostow's model of economic development compared to traditional farming in China (below), an activity associated with Stage 1 of the model.

Key Questions

By the end of this chapter you will be able to answer the following questions.

■ What five stages do countries go through as their economies develop?

■ How have colonialism and neo-colonialism affected poor countries?

■ What are the differences between progressive government and neo-liberal government policies?

Primary industries are resource-based activities such as agriculture, mining, and fishing. Secondary industries include manufacturing and construction activities. Tertiary industries include services such as government, financial services, and education.

The percentage of a country's gross domestic product (GDP) contributed by primary, secondary, or tertiary industries changes as a country develops. The following activity shows you how these changing values may be used to determine a country's level of economic development.

1. For this exercise, you will be using standard x/y graph paper. However, instead of dealing with two values as you have usually done on standard paper, you will be dealing with three. It is possible to show three values on a two-dimensional graph as long as the three values always add up to the same total—in this case to 100 percent.

   • Remember that the percentage of the GDP from primary industries is shown on the (horizontal) x-axis, while the percentage of the GDP from secondary industries is shown on the (vertical) y-axis.

   • At any point (for example, A, B, or C) along the red line, the combined value of primary and secondary GDP always equals 100 percent (see Figure 11–1). This means that the value of the tertiary GDP equals 0 percent.

   • At any point (for example, D or E) along the green line, the combined value of primary and secondary GDP always equals 50 percent. This means that the value of the tertiary GDP equals 50 percent.

   • At any point (for example, F or G) along the blue line, the combined value of primary and secondary GDP always equals 20 percent. This means that the value of the tertiary GDP equals 80 percent.

   • In simplest terms, as you move toward the graph's origin (0, 0), the percentage of the tertiary GDP value increases. You can see how this works for Canada and Bangladesh in Figure 11–2.

2. Figure 11–3 summarizes the changes in GDP in each economic sector for the countries of our Four-World model. On a full page of graph paper, plot the economic changes for each country in a manner similar to that used for Canada and Bangladesh in Figure 11–2. Plot the members of each "world" in a different colour.

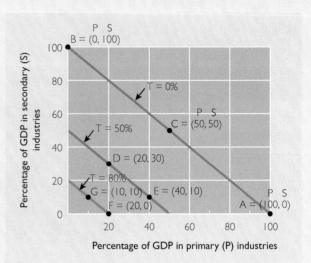

Figure 11–1 Graph of economic development: Percentage of GDP in primary (P), secondary (S), and tertiary (T) industries.

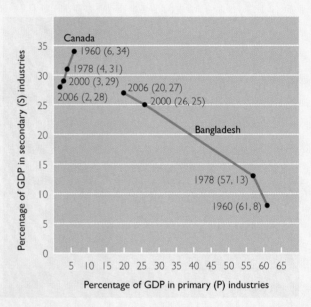

Figure 11–2 Changes in the economies of Canada and Bangladesh. What happens to the GDP value of each industry as a country's economy develops? Note that the scales on this graph are different from those in Figure 11–1.

3. Examine the graph you have created. What economic changes do you see as a country progresses from Far Periphery to Old Core?

4. How might economic planners in less developed countries use knowledge of these changes?

	% of GDP from Primary Industries				% of GDP from Secondary Industries				% of GDP from Tertiary Industries			
	1960	1978	2000	2006	1960	1978	2000	2006	1960	1978	2000	2006
OLD CORE												
Canada	6	4	3	2	34	31	29	28	60	65	69	70
Germany	6	3	1	1	53	48	28	29	41	49	71	70
NEW CORE												
Poland	26	16	3	5	57	64	32	31	17	20	66	64
Malaysia	37	25	12	8	18	32	40	48	45	43	48	43
NEAR CORE												
Iran	54	33*	20	11	9	29*	37	42	37	38*	43	47
Philippines	35	26	17	14	27	28	30	32	38	46	53	54
FAR PERIPHERY												
Bangladesh	61	57	26	20	8	13	25	27	31	30	49	60
Zambia	63	39	24	20	11	17	25	29	26	44	51	51

Figure 11–3 Percentage of GDP from primary, secondary, and tertiary industries of selected countries.

*For 1977, not 1978

Stages of Economic Development

You now have a better understanding of how the three sectors of a country's economy change as the country develops. What might cause one country's economy to grow while another's stagnates? Many models have been developed to explain this. Perhaps the best known is the model for economic growth proposed by Walt Rostow in the 1960s. Rostow suggested that a country goes through five stages as its economy develops (see Figure 11–4).

His model, however, presents only one explanation for variations in the economic development of different countries (see Figure 11–5). It describes development as Rostow saw it in Europe and North America. Elsewhere, economic development may not occur in the same way.

 For a more detailed description of Rostow's five-stage model, go to the link on our Web site.

Figure 11–4 Economic growth, from the stage of the traditional society to the stage of high mass consumption, fundamentally changes the way in which people live.

Stage	Characteristics	Examples
Stage 1: Traditional Society	• Economy is based on subsistence agriculture • Population growth and social and economic progress are limited by natural controls, e.g., droughts, outbreaks of disease • As in the past, some governments today are dictatorships or absolute monarchies • Society changes very slowly	Great Britain before 1750; Canada before 1850; some of the countries in the Far Periphery such as the African countries of Burundi and Malawi today
Stage 2: Establishing Conditions for Takeoff	• Society achieves a surplus of wealth, or "savings" • Savings are invested in vital economic sectors, e.g., transportation, communications, natural resource exploitation • A sense of national purpose evolves • More effective, responsive, central government develops	Many western European nations in the early 1800s; Canada after the 1850s; some Far Periphery countries such as the South American country of Suriname and the African country of Togo today
Stage 3: Economic Takeoff	• Economy begins to change in response to important technological innovations, e.g., improved transportation infrastructure • Agriculture changes from primarily subsistence to primarily commercial • Manufacturing becomes an important part of the economy • Tertiary sector expands as cities grow and number of customers for services increases	Great Britain in the late 1700s; France and the US by 1860; Canada by 1900; some Near Core countries such as Bolivia in South America and Vietnam in Asia; and many New Core countries such as Argentina and Bulgaria today
Stage 4: Drive to Maturity	• An extended period of sustained economic growth • Per-capita wealth increases as economic growth outpaces population growth • Economy becomes diversified with expansion of manufacturing and services • Efficient production methods used in primary and secondary industries • Increasing percentage of the country's wealth invested in the economy • Country reaches maturity about 50 to 60 years after takeoff	Great Britain in the 1850s; France and the US by 1910; Canada by 1950; New Core countries such as Malaysia and Poland today. These New Core countries reached maturity more quickly than was the norm before World War II.
Stage 5: High Mass Consumption	• Many people have incomes that are greater than necessary for buying essentials such as shelter, food, and clothing • A growing demand for additional consumer goods and services • Society is also wealthy enough to invest in social programs, e.g., improved healthcare, education	United States in the 1920s; Canada from the 1950s to the present; Western Europe and Japan following World War II; today many New Core countries such as Singapore, South Korea, and urban parts of China and India

Figure 11–5 Stages of economic development

Colonialism Past and Present

When one country rules another and develops trade with that country for its own benefit, it is following a policy of **colonialism**. Colonialism dominated the world's economic system for more than four centuries until the second half of the 20th century. The effects of colonialism have had a profound impact on the economic, social, and political systems of many countries.

The beginning of the colonial period can be tied to the desires of European countries to establish trade routes to East Asia. In the late 1400s, Europeans began to explore sea routes to South Africa, India, Japan, and China in the hope of finding spices and other exotic goods. Spain and Portugal quickly became dominant in these explorations. As they expanded their trade, rivalry between these two countries threatened to lead to war.

The Treaty of Tordesillas, which was brokered by Pope Alexander VI in 1494, defused the rivalry by dividing the non-Christian world between Spain and Portugal at a north–south line about 2100 kilometres west of the Cape Verde Islands. The fact that this treaty totally ignored the rights of all the people affected by it indicates the central belief of colonialism—that the colonies existed only to meet the needs of colonizers.

GLOBALIZATION

Colonies existed only to meet the needs of colonizers.

Why didn't colonial powers care about the needs of people living in the countries that were colonized?

Many other European countries established their own colonies. Sweden, Belgium, and the Netherlands had only a few colonies, while France and Great Britain developed immense empires (see Figure 11–6).

Did You Know?

Under the Treaty of Tordesillas, Spain got the area to the west of the north–south line, which opened the door for it to develop its immense empire in the Americas. Portugal got the eastern part of the world, which led to the development of its colonies in Africa, India, and China. An anomaly to this pattern is that Portugal colonized Brazil, since Brazil's easternmost point crossed the "magic" line. This is why Brazil is the only country in Latin America with Portuguese as its official language.

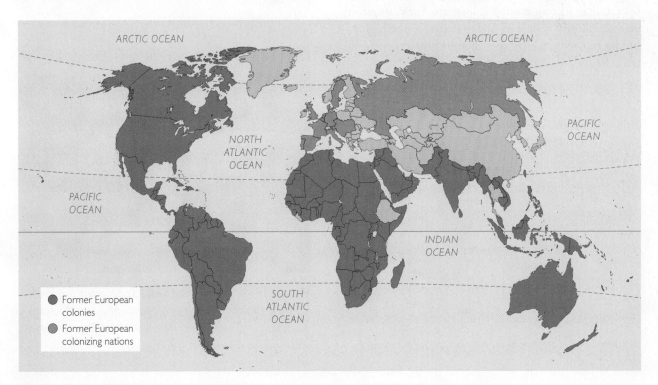

Figure 11–6 Many of today's independent nations were once colonies of the European powers.

Even the United States and Japan developed empires in the late 19th and early 20th centuries. The US took control of Cuba and the Philippines, and Japan expanded its control into areas of Korea and China.

Many observers believe that World War II occurred as a result of the colonial desires of Germany and Japan. Germany invaded the Soviet Union because it said it needed "living space." Japan's attack on Pearl Harbor in 1941 was an attempt to destroy the US Pacific Fleet in order to take control of the oil fields of the Dutch East Indies (now Indonesia) without interference.

The colonial period can be divided into two distinct periods: pre- and post-Industrial Revolution (see Figure 11–7). In the earlier period, colonies were sources of products not available at home. For example, Canada supplied Great Britain with furs, while the southern US provided cotton and tobacco. Colonies also provided novel products such as coffee, tea, spices, and even potatoes. In the post–Industrial Revolution period, raw materials for the mills and factories of Europe came from colonies in exchange for manufactured goods produced on steam-powered machines.

Under the **mercantile system,** also known as mercantilism, of the 17th and early 18th centuries, colonies were considered to exist solely for the economic benefit of the mother country. Not only was the colony a source of raw materials, but it was also a captive market for the manufactured goods produced in the mother country. This rigid system prevented the colony from operating in its own economic interests. For example, it was not allowed to sell its raw materials to the highest bidder or to buy the cheapest manufactured goods; all trade had to be with the colonial master.

The colony was also prevented from competing with the mother country. This was the case with India's cotton industry. India had been a major producer and exporter of hand-woven cotton cloth before the Industrial Revolution. To prevent competition, Britain forced the destruction of India's cotton industry. By the middle of the 1800s, India no longer exported cotton textiles and, in fact, imported one-quarter of all the cotton clothing produced in Britain.

Concession Companies

One important way that European countries developed their empires was by establishing **concession companies**. These companies were created to trade in particular regions of the world, or to trade in particular products. Many actually governed remote parts of the empire. Today, most are little more than minor historical footnotes, for example, the Anglo-Belgian India Rubber Company. But some, like the Hudson's Bay Company, are remembered as vital parts of the history of the countries where they operated (see Figure 11–8). The Hudson's Bay Company (HBC), founded in 1670, is the oldest company in North America and one of the oldest in the world. In 2006, HBC was purchased by Jerry Zucker, a South Carolina billionaire.

Figure 11–8 Inuit women haul a sled loaded with pelts from the wharf in Pangnirtung, Nunavut, to the Hudson's Bay Company warehouse in August, 1946. This concession company, now known as The Bay, is the same company whose store you may visit at your local mall.

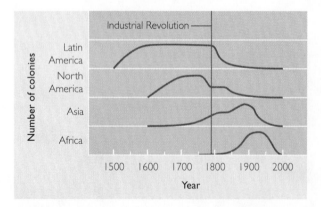

Figure 11–7 Timeline of European colonialism in different countries

You can learn more about the British East India Company at the link on our Web site.

The British East India Company was perhaps the most famous concession company of all. (There were also Danish, Dutch, French, Portuguese, and Swedish East India companies.) Founded in 1600, its charter gave it a monopoly to trade in India, Southeast Asia, and China until 1833. The British East India Company had tremendous power. It operated its own fleet of armed transport ships and fortified trading posts. Its political activities did much to expand the British Empire. At home, its financial success provided much of the wealth that spurred Britain's early economic takeoff.

Impacts of Colonialism

The great colonial empires are gone, but many of their effects endure. Some are positive; for example, Canada's government and legal system are modelled along British lines. Most effects, however, are negative.

- Traditional **land tenure** (owning or occupying property) practices were destroyed. In many pre-colonial countries, land resources were shared. Colonial powers introduced the European system of private ownership: only a few people owned a great deal of land, some had hardly enough to support themselves, and others had none at all.

- Frequently the best land came to be owned by concession companies or European settlers, often in the form of large estates or farms called **plantations**. The local populations were pushed off this land. These dispossessed farmers were then used as cheap labour on the farms and in a variety of industries. Plantations were usually found in tropical or semi-tropical countries where cotton, sugar cane, coffee, and trees (for example, rubber or oil palm trees) were cultivated.

- People who were once self-sufficient became dependent upon imported goods, especially food. The colonial powers planted **cash crops** (for example, tea, coffee, sugar, bananas, cacao, jute, cotton, and silk) on land where local people traditionally produced their own food. Today, the best land is still used for cash crops that are exported, and farmers are often restricted to growing food for local needs on less productive land.

GLOBALIZATION
The colonial powers planted cash crops on land where local people traditionally produced their own food.

Why is the best land still used today for cash crops rather than for growing food for local populations?

- Trade and manufacturing restrictions imposed on colonies delayed the growth of, or destroyed, local manufacturing (for example, textile manufacturing in what is now India and Bangladesh) and often led to armed conflict. The artificial trade and taxation policies imposed by England on the Thirteen Colonies led directly to the American Revolution in 1776.

- Colonial mining, forestry, agriculture, and manufacturing paid little attention to environmental protection. Environmental problems continue in many countries long after independence.

SUSTAINABILITY
Colonial mining, forestry, agriculture, and manufacturing paid little attention to environmental protection.

Why have environmental problems continued in many countries long after independence?

- Colonial powers imposed foreign political systems that did not respect the traditional governing systems of their colonies. In Canada, this has had lingering effects. There is a long history of conflict between the federal government and Aboriginal groups about whether these groups should be accorded self-government. Recently, Canada's government has started to work with Aboriginal groups to accept the validity of their legal traditions, for example, healing circles (see Figure 11–9).

- Colonial powers trained local residents to take less important administrative jobs or to enlist in the army because they were unable to supply enough of their own people to fill these jobs. After independence, these trained local residents ended up running the former colony, whether elected or not. For example, in 1994, in the former Belgian colony of Rwanda, the ruling-elite Tutsi minority was attacked by militias of the majority Hutu population. Within 100 days, over 800 000 people, mainly Tutsis, were killed. This mass killing of ethnic Tutsis and moderate Hutus is called "The Rwandan Genocide." The UN peacekeeping force

Figure 11–9 The Aboriginal healing circle brings together all those concerned about the wrongdoer involved in the offence. Community elders, the families affected, police, and a judge attempt to reach an agreement on the most appropriate consequences for a wrongful act.

under Canadian Lieutenant-General Roméo Dallaire did not have enough troops to stop the genocide. You can read about Dallaire's experiences in his 2003 book *Shake Hands with the Devil*. (The movie of the same title, based on the book, was released in 2007.)

■ Colonial powers created new countries that did not take into account tribal or cultural boundaries. National boundaries were arbitrarily drawn on maps to meet the needs of competing colonizers. For example, the Yoruba, a large, politically well-organized ethnic group, lived in many small kingdoms scattered over a large region of West Africa. When the countries of Nigeria and Benin were created by colonial masters, some Yoruba ended up living in English-speaking Nigeria, while others found themselves living in neighbouring, French-speaking Benin.

■ Colonizers imposed their language on people in new colonies. Sometimes this had positive effects. The colonial language provided a common form of communication in a country with many languages (for example, India has 14 major languages and over 1000 minor languages and dialects). It frequently became an official language after independence because it was often the only common language in the new country.

■ Colonial culture introduced such things as cricket, now an important sport in places as diverse as the West Indies, India, Australia, and South Africa, that share only one thing—they were all British colonies at one time. Colonial culture, however, often had negative effects. The dominant colonial culture often considered local cultures inferior. This led to the loss of native dialects and traditions.

■ Colonizers built transportation infrastructures that served their commercial needs rather than the needs of the local people. They built roads, railways, and ports to ship the colony's raw materials and to assist industries in exporting their products. The transportation system, however, frequently did not serve the most populated areas.

Current Economic Colonialism

The old form of overtly political colonialism has been eliminated, but new forms of economic colonialism have replaced it. This new form of dominance in the post-colonial period is called **neo-colonialism** because it has some things in common with colonialism. Instead of dominating weak countries through direct political control, strong, wealthy nations now use economic policies, trade policies, and cultural influences. For example, a wealthy country may grant foreign aid to a poor country, provided the poor country buy its manufactured products, or, it may *subtly* (not in an obvious way) dominate a country through the gradual imposition of its culture, for example, by its entertainment, language, and access to news and other sources of information (see Figure 11–10).

In some important ways, however, neo-colonialism is different from traditional colonialism. These features are summarized in Figure 11–11.

Some people also argue that neo-colonialism occurs when international conservation organizations give money to governments in poor countries to create national parks, or when the World Bank reduces the national debt of poor countries in exchange for creating wildlife-protected areas. For example, the World Bank reduced Madagascar's national debt in exchange for its setting up and maintaining wilderness areas.

Figure 11–10 The media determine to a large extent what opinions and events people will be exposed to. They also influence patterns of human behaviour and perceptions of such things as beauty and success.

Colonies' Role	Colonial Period	Post-Colonial Period
Source of raw materials	Yes	Yes
Source of manufactured products	No—colonial power did not want competition from its colony	Yes—the former colony can supply low-cost labour
Market for manufactured goods	Yes	Yes
Chief beneficiary	Colonial power	Transnational corporation

Figure 11–11 In the post-colonial period, the chief beneficiaries of economic activities in the former colonies are not the colonial powers, but often transnational corporations.

Economic Systems

Over the past century, economic decision making by the world's nations has occurred along a continuum between two extremes (see Figure 11–12). At one extreme is a **free market economy**. In a perfect free market, the price of all goods and services is determined by the relationship between supply and demand. In a **command economy**, the price of goods and services, as well as the supply, are determined by the government as part of a planned economy.

In reality, there have never been countries that have had a free market economy or a command economy in their purest forms. Governments of all types have learned that, in spite of their political philosophies, they will end up with a **mixed economy** that combines

elements, to a greater or lesser degree, of both free enterprise and government intervention.

The governments of Canada and the US, whose economies are nominally free market, have found that the market cannot be relied on to provide all goods and services. Some activities, such as operating the military, running the post office, and protecting endangered species, are best provided by governments. The fundamental question about mixed economies is how large a role government should play. Adam Smith, the founder of modern economics, published a famous book in 1776 called *The Wealth of Nations*, which advocated the idea of **economic liberalism**. This meant that mercantilism should be abolished, and the economic system

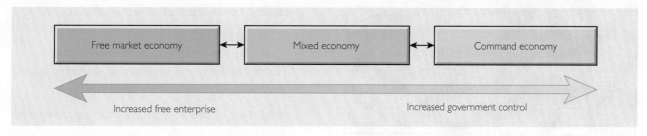

Free market economy ↔ Mixed economy ↔ Command economy

Increased free enterprise   Increased government control

Figure 11–12 World economies fall somewhere between free enterprise and government control.

should be allowed to operate without government intervention. Smith's economic ideas remained dominant in the Western world until the early 1900s.

Keynesian Economics

During the economic collapse of the Great Depression in the 1930s, unemployment reached record levels. John Maynard Keynes, a British economist, proposed that goverment had a key role to play in preventing unemployment. He believed that government should increase its spending during periods of high unemployment, and this in turn would provide jobs for people. With higher employment, the economy would improve.

Keynesian economics became central to the policies of many governments as they fought against the hardships of the Depression. Perhaps the best known of these efforts was the New Deal, which President Franklin D. Roosevelt instituted in the US (see Figure 11–13). The New Deal provided jobs by spending billions of dollars on projects like dam building and highway construction. Similar policies were adopted in Canada and

elsewhere. During and after World War II, the influence of Keynesian economics expanded and led to a changed understanding of the role of government.

Progressive Thought Versus Neo-Liberal Thought

Governments frequently adopt different economic systems in response to changing economic conditions. In the 18th century, the economic liberalism of Adam Smith made its appearance in the Western world. By the 1930s, however, Keynesian policies had become the dominant political/economic system as a result of the Depression. Keynesian thought, now known as **progressive thought**, was popular in developed countries until the 1980s. At this time, a newer form of the ideas of Adam Smith, called **neo-liberalism**, became popular because many people wanted to return to a freer market economy and a reduced role for government. Examine Figure 11–14 to discover some of the differences between progressive and neo-liberal thought and the economic policies each represented.

International Impact of Neo-Liberal Policies

Internationally, the most significant impact of the neo-liberal revolution has been the move toward **economic globalization**. In the past, economic restrictions, such as tariffs and **non-tariff barriers**, reduced the amount of economic integration among nations. (Non-tariff barriers are ways, other than tariffs, used to protect domestic industry and discourage imports, for example quotas and import bans.) Today, the world can be seen as having one economic system with an increasingly easy movement of goods, production, capital, and resources. You can see this economic globalization in the things that you buy each day such as clothing, sporting goods, and food products. Finally, you can see it in newspaper articles about factories closing in Canada when their production is moved to other countries.

Figure 11–13 US President Roosevelt priming the New Deal pump. Does this cartoon represent a free-market or progressive slant?

GLOBALIZATION

Central to the trend toward economic globalization is the elimination of economic barriers among nations.

Why is the elimination of trade restrictions so central to economic globalization?

Central to the trend toward economic globalization is the elimination of economic barriers among nations, and the most important barriers are restrictions on trade.

Progressive Thought	Neo-Liberal Thought
When? Prevalent from 1930s to 1980s	**When?** Prevalent from 1980s to present
Who? • In the US, the Democratic Party, and in Canada, the Liberal Party and New Democratic Party support greater government intervention in regulating the economy and in providing a social safety net to varying degrees • During the 1990s, the usually progressive thinking Liberal government of Canada adopted some neo-liberal thinking and scaled back its support for social and economic development programs	**Who?** The name has led to considerable confusion since the political parties most supportive of these policies have been conservative in nature (Republican Party in the US) and, in some countries, in name as well (Conservative Party in Canada and the Conservative Party in the UK)
Why? Concern that private industry could not jumpstart the economy, that there was no safety net for citizens during economic downturns, and that only a Keynesian philosophy of government intervention in regulating the economy would keep it growing	**Why?** Concern that progressive governments were spending more than they collected in taxes, thus creating huge national debts, that trade practices and subsidies supported non-competitive industries, and that the taxes used for social services were reducing economic growth

What?
 	
• Governments act as agents of social and economic change
 	
• Taxation has two main roles:
 	
  — to pay for publicly funded services, e.g., education, transportation infrastructure, the military
 	
  — to redistribute incomes from richer to poorer citizens; e.g., since 1957, Canada has had a system of equalization payments in which money is transferred from the richer provinces of Ontario, Alberta, and British Columbia to the rest of the provinces
	What?
	
	• Promote a freer market economy that reduces the role of government (started in the UK and followed by the US)
	
	• Privatize government-owned public utilities such as electricity
	
	• Allow private companies to build highways and charge tolls for their use
	
	• Reduce government involvement in providing public housing for the poor

Figure 11–14 Comparing progressive and neo-liberal thought.

(See Chapter 12 for more information on economic globalization.) Accordingly, the last few decades have been marked by the growth of free trade between and among countries in many parts of the world. Most obvious of these agreements was the expansion of the European Union (EU). In 2007, 27 countries were members of the EU. For Canada, economic globalization has led to a free-trade agreement with, first, the US and later with Mexico and the US. Beyond this, there have been significant attempts to include Canada in free-trade agreements that would involve, in one case, the nations of the Americas, and in another, the Pacific Rim countries.

The dramatic shift to neo-liberalism in the developed world has had an impact on the developing world. Whether this impact has been negative or positive depends on the political leanings of the observer. In reality, it is too early to be sure whether the benefits of free-market economics outweigh the costs. On one hand, proponents of neo-liberalism feel that the elimination of trade barriers and other such restrictions will allow developing countries to speed their transitions toward economic maturity. In theory, the removal of barriers will guarantee developing countries a market, since their inexpensive labour allows them to price their products competitively. On the other hand, opponents of globalization contend that the elimination of barriers is designed to help transnational companies. The elimination of trade barriers allows transnationals to move their production to less developed countries that have cheap, unregulated labour and low environmental standards. For opponents, globalization is no more than an excuse for sweatshops and high profits.

During the early years of the 21st century, there has been a backlash against neo-liberal thought because of the realization that many societal needs cannot be provided for by a free-market economy. For example, the number of homeless people in the cities of Canada and other industrialized countries has grown. Some of the homeless are people who have fallen through the cracks of the new economic system. They do not have the skills to compete successfully in a competitive economy and, at the same time, have lost many of the social supports that they had when more progressive government policies were in place.

In South America, the dissatisfaction with neo-liberalism and the desire to try something else has resulted in the election of several governments that advocate progressive policies. For example, in Brazil, President Lula da Silva has implemented moderate social programs to end hunger among the poor. In the US, the Democratic Party has proposed more healthcare for the poor and less free trade with the rest of the world and within NAFTA.

Whether governments support progressive policies or neo-liberal policies, they sometimes must go against their underlying philosophy. For example, during the 1990s, the federal Liberal government reduced spending on social programs to balance the budget and pay down some of Canada's debt. Neo-liberal governments, like those of many European countries and that of the US, still support huge subsidies to farmers despite advocating free trade (see Figure 11–15). Governments that truly believe in allowing the market to work would not provide farm support, even in such exceptional circumstances. They would allow competition to decide the outcome. The fact that support was made available indicates that governments are prepared to compromise on theoretical beliefs if they believe that circumstances dictate such a response.

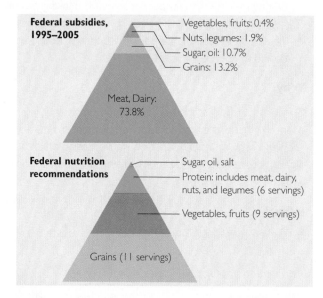

Figure 11–15 Why does a salad cost more than a hamburger in the United States? US farm subsidies primarily support dairy, meat, grain, and sugar farmers, while fruit and vegetable farmers receive very little.

How Will You Vote?

Elections today in democratic countries around the world are often choices between parties that promote neo-liberal or progressive views to varying degrees. Most of you may have just voted in your first election or soon will have the opportunity (see Figure 11–16). Whether it is at the municipal, provincial, or federal level, you may have a choice of voting for individuals or parties that promote progressive or neo-liberal thought or a combination of both.

Figure 11–16 In a democracy, voting is one of the most important civic duties.

Chapter Questions

Knowledge and Understanding

1. Imagine that a developed Western nation is facing a period of economic decline. What might this government tend to do if it believes in

   a) Keynesian economics? b) neo-liberal economics?

2. a) Using Rostow's work as an example, define what is meant by a "model."

   b) What are the advantages and disadvantages of using a model to describe a complex reality?

3. Briefly summarize, in your own words, the impacts that colonialism has had on former colonies. For each impact, suggest why, after 50 or more years of independence, the effects of colonialism are still causing problems in these countries.

4. Suggest how colonialism and concession companies aided the economic takeoff of imperial nations and hindered that of colonies.

5. a) What is neo-colonialism?

   b) What are the similarities and differences between colonialism and neo-colonialism?

   c) How do strong nations exert control over weak nations through economic and trade policies?

Thinking

6. a) Summarize the characteristics of the five stages of Rostow's model of economic growth.

   b) Give evidence, from our economy and lifestyles, to show that Canada is in Rostow's Stage 5 (high mass consumption).

7. All countries have mixed economies. Some countries, however, have economies highly controlled by their governments while others have economies with relatively little government involvement. Through research, identify three countries that have

   a) limited free markets (great deal of government involvement)

   b) a balance between free markets and an involved government

   c) free market (little government involvement)

   (Note: A good place to begin your research is the CIA's World Factbook Web site.)

8. a) Canada has more extensive social programs than some countries, such as the US. Do these social programs put Canada at a competitive disadvantage compared to these countries?

   b) In what ways might Canada's extensive social programs give it a competitive advantage?

9. Many countries that used to have command economies have abandoned them. These include the countries that were formerly part of the Soviet Union (including Russia), the countries of eastern Europe, and China.

   a) Choose one of these countries and research how the change from a command economy was accomplished.

   b) Describe how this process has resulted in some people "winning" and others "losing."

Communication

10. What impact has colonialism had on the level of development of former colonies? One commonly used measure of social development is the UN Human Development Index (HDI). Complete a mapping exercise of HDI values, using either a paper base map or ArcView. (Your teacher will provide you with full instructions.) What relationship is there between those countries that were colonies and those with low HDI values? What pattern do you see?

11. Choose a country in Africa, or elsewhere, that was formerly a colony. Research its history during three eras: pre-colonial, colonial, and post-colonial. Prepare a poster or paper to show this history and to show how this country was affected by the process of colonization, the process of de-colonization (independence), and in some cases how it is affected by the process of neo-colonialism. In your research, consider at least the following: original tribal boundaries, language distribution, boundaries established by the colonial power, boundaries today, type of government, economic development, social development, and cultural patterns.

12. Interview a person born before 1950 to discover how the impact of globalization has changed life in Canada. In a group, compare your findings with those of others using a short oral report to show the social and economic impacts.

Application

13. a) Suggest reasons why relatively small countries such as Great Britain and the Netherlands were able to develop huge empires.

b) Research the reasons why this happened. Were your suggestions on this question accurate?

14. a) Identify one country for each stage of economic development in Rostow's model. Give evidence to support your choices.

b) Is Rostow's model still valid for describing economic development in the 21st century? Why or why not? (Hint: Consider the impact of economic and financial globalization—discussed in Chapter 2.)

c) Work with one or more classmates to suggest how Rostow's model could be modified to better fit the economic characteristics of the 21st century.

15. Imagine you are a government official in an actual former colony that is in Rostow's Stage 1 of economic development. Your mandate is to prepare the country for the "takeoff" stage. What steps would you propose? Consider the following as you develop your strategy:

a) How did countries such as South Korea, Singapore, and Japan make this transition?

b) Where on the spectrum shown in Figure 11–12 would you want the economy to be?

c) What importance would you place on programs like education, health, and environmental protection?

Present your recommendations in a two-page report.

16. In Figure 11–11, it was stated that the new beneficiaries of economic activities in the former colonies are transnational corporations. It could also be argued that the beneficiaries of the presence of transnational corporations are the former colonies. Select a transnational company and examine its presence in a developing country. Is there a mutual benefit from the investment of the transnational, or does one party seem to gain more? Explain. Share your findings within a group in an oral or written report as directed by your teacher. **G**

CHAPTER 12

The Growth of Economic Globalization

Key Terms

Global 500

capitalization

multinational companies

transnational companies

BRIC

free trade

tariffs

World Trade Organization
(WTO)

North American Free Trade
Agreement (NAFTA)

Free Trade Area of the Americas
(FTAA)

Asia–Pacific Economic
Cooperation (APEC)

Doha Round

The globalization of business is
not only connecting the world
ever closer, it is also making
different places in the world
more alike. These two buildings
could be in almost any city.
Where do you think they are?

Key Questions

By the end of this chapter you will be able to answer
the following questions.

- What roles do giant corporations play in the world?

- What is Canada's experience with free trade?

- What is free trade and why should you care?

- In what ways is economic power in the world shifting?

- How will world economic changes affect you?

Can you guess where the photos on the previous page were taken? The answer is at the end of the chapter. Globalization is changing the nature of business in the world. Each year, *Forbes* magazine publishes a list of the **Global 500**, the 500 largest companies in the world based on a combination of sales, profits, assets, and **capitalization.** Capitalization is the market value of all of the stock issued by a company, determined by multiplying the number of shares in existence by the current price per share. What do you know about international big business? Take our quiz to find out. The answers to this quiz are based on *Forbes*' 2006 rankings. Changes to the list tend to happen fairly slowly, so rankings in later years are likely to be similar. For an updated list, go to the *Forbes* Web site, and search for the latest list.

See how many of these questions you can answer without doing any research.

1. What company headed the Global 500 list in 2006? That is, what is the largest company in the world?

2. What are the next top four companies on the list?

3. What country had the most companies on the Global 500 list? How many Global 500 companies did this country have?

4. What are the next top four countries with the greatest number of Global 500 companies?

5. What company in the world had the largest profits?

6. What is the name of the largest Canadian company on the list? Where did this company rank?

7. How many Global 500 companies were Canadian?

8. Name as many of these companies as possible.

9. Estimate the number of Global 500 companies that have their head offices in the Old Core, New Core, Near Core, and Far Periphery.

10. Which of the following companies are on the Global 500: Nike, Wal-Mart Stores, Tim Hortons, L'Oreal, BMW, Royal Bank of Canada, McDonald's, FedEx?

The answers to these questions can be found on page 195.

Transnational Corporations

If you are like most people, you probably knew the answers to only a few of the questions in the quiz above. Most of us give little thought to the huge companies that dominate our economic life, and increasingly, our political life. This lack of concern should be disturbing since these companies have enormous influence in the world. In the past, such large companies were often called **multinational companies** because they operated in several, or even many, countries. They are now more frequently called **transnational companies**, because not only do they operate across the world, but they are also becoming less clearly identified with any particular nation. Transnational corporations are not new. In fact, some experts say that the first transnational "corporation" was a religious/military order called the *Knights Templar*, founded in the early 12th century. This order acquired so much wealth that by the end of the 13th century, it acted as bankers to the courts of Europe. (The Knights Templar feature prominently in Dan Brown's enormously successful novel, *The DaVinci Code*.)

Some important features of the world's largest companies are shown in Figure 12–1.

When you examine this list, you may marvel at the enormous size of these companies. In fact, their economic power rivals that of many nations. A reasonable comparison can be made between the revenues of Global 500 companies and the gross domestic product (GDP) of some countries (see Figure 12–2). For example, each year, the revenues generated by Wal-Mart are comparable to the GDP of Argentina, Ireland, or Greece. General Electric's revenues are similar to the GDP of Pakistan, which has a population of more than 165 million. Similar comparisons can be made between smaller companies on the Global 500 list and other countries. For example, #500 on the list, a Japanese company called Snow Brand Milk, had revenues that were similar to the GDP of oil-rich Brunei, while Office Depot's (number 439 on the list) revenues were greater than the GDP of Bolivia.

	Company	Focus	Country	Revenues (US$ billions)
1	Wal-Mart Stores	Retailing	US	217.8
2	ExxonMobil	Oil and gas	US	187.5
3	General Motors	Motor vehicles	US	177.3
4	BP	Oil and gas	UK	174.2
5	Ford	Motor vehicles	US	162.4
6	Daimler-Chrysler*	Motor vehicles	Germany	136.8
7	Royal Dutch Shell	Oil and gas	UK/Netherlands	135.2
8	General Electric	Multi-industry	US	126.9
9	Toyota	Motor vehicles	Japan	120.7
10	Citigroup	Finance	US	112.0

Figure 12–1 The ten companies in the world with the highest revenues in 2006 had their headquarters in only five countries. Six of the ten were in the United States, and all were from the Old Core.

*In 2007, Daimler sold its Chrysler subsidiary.

Company	Company Revenues (US$ billions)		Country (GDP rank in world)	Country GDP (US$ billions)
Wal-Mart Stores	218	⇔	Greece (28)	224
ExxonMobil	188	⇔	Hong Kong (35)	189
General Motors	177	⇔	Portugal (36)	177
BP	174	⇔	Portugal (36)	177
Ford	162	⇔	UAE (37)	164
Daimler-Chrysler	137	⇔	Israel (39)	140
Royal Dutch Shell	135	⇔	Malaysia (40)	132
General Electric	127	⇔	Pakistan (41)	124
Toyota	121	⇔	Singapore (42)	122
Citigroup	112	⇔	Hungary (45)	112

Figure 12–2 Compare the annual revenues of the companies on the left with the GDP of countries on the right. For example, Wal-Mart's revenues are almost the same as the GDP of Greece. How does the enormous, and growing, economic power of transnational corporations affect their relationships with the countries within which they operate?

Global Distribution of Transnationals

One striking feature of the Global 500 companies is that few have their headquarters outside the Old Core. The Old Core is the home of 469 of these companies, or 94 percent of the total. It is startling to realize that Finland, with a population of about five million, is the home to as many of these companies (three) as China, India, and Russia. The remaining 31 companies are located in the New Core. None of the 500 largest companies is located in Periphery nations, which is likely not a surprise considering our understanding of

the relationship between wealth and globalization. The British colony of Bermuda, with a population of about 70 000, is the home of five Global 500 companies. Other than the nice weather, why might they be located there?

Despite the fact that only 6 percent of the Global 500 are outside the Old Core, there is evidence of an economic shift away from the Old Core—at least as far as the New Core. In 2000, only 19 Global 500 companies were located in six New Core countries (China, India, Mexico, Russia, South Korea, and Taiwan). By 2006, this number had grown to 31 companies in nine New Core countries—with Brazil,

Singapore, and South Africa joining the list. If we were able to look at a "Global 2000" list (the 2000 largest companies), we would likely see many companies in the New Core and perhaps some in the Near Core. Since many of these regions are growing faster than the Old Core, it is almost certain that a future Global 500 list will have many more non–Old Core companies. Central to the spread of economic power in the world are the **BRIC** countries (**B**razil, **R**ussia, **I**ndia, and **C**hina). Each of these nations has a particular combination of natural and human resources that are aiding its rise into the world's economic "big leagues."

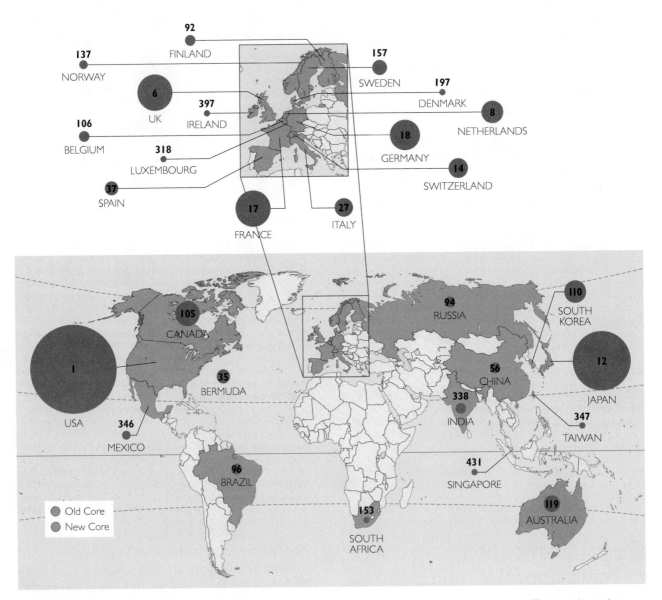

Figure 12–3 The circles on the map indicate the number of Global 500 companies in that country. The numbers show the highest ranked company in that country.

NEW CENTRES OF GLOBAL ECONOMIC POWER

Another important change in recent years is in the nature of large companies in the New Core. In the past, many of these companies were government owned or controlled and designed primarily to meet domestic demands. Now they are often privately owned companies focusing on global business and trade. The most obvious examples of these emerging global powerhouses are the manufacturing companies, especially those in China and South Korea, that now dominate the production of goods ranging from inexpensive clothing to advanced products like computers and cars. Some examples of these powerhouses:

- Hyundai and Kia from South Korea are already major car exporters to the Old Core.
- The Brazilian company, Embraer, is the major competitor for Canada's Bombardier in the market for smaller passenger jets (see Figure 12–4).
- Russian companies are the dominant supplier of natural gas to much of Europe. Control of this vital commodity means that Russia has a great deal of influence over the decisions of several of its neighbours.
- Chinese companies have become heavily involved in resource-development opportunities in oil production, mineral production, and forestry in Asia, Africa, and the Americas. (Controversy often follows this sort of globalization. A Canadian oil company sold its oil assets in Sudan because it did not want to be seen as economically supporting a brutal, repressive regime that has been accused of involvement in the genocide in the Darfur region. Chinese companies have now taken over as the biggest investors in Sudan's oil industry.)

Questions

Talk to your classmates or your parents to help you answer these questions. If you are still stuck, a bit of Internet research should do the trick.

1. Identify a major New Core company that meets the criteria below.

   a) PC manufacturing in China and sold worldwide

   b) PC manufacturing in Taiwan and sold worldwide

   c) sixth-largest steel-making company in the world, with interests in many countries

   d) Chinese company involved in oil development outside China

   e) Chinese company involved in another resource-development field outside China

   f) auto manufacturing company in China that produces vehicles for sale in many countries, including Canada and the US

   g) auto manufacturing company in India that sells vehicles in many countries outside the Old Core

   h) Russian company that controls much of the energy market in eastern and central Europe

2. What advantages do these companies have compared to their Old Core rivals? (Hint: It will not be the same advantage(s) in each case.)

Figure 12–4 It is a serious mistake to think that companies outside the Old Core can produce only low-cost, low-tech products. Brazil's Embraer builds a wide range of passenger and executive jets like this 37-passenger model.

One of the most important characteristics of transnational companies is the international scope of their operations. The organization of Ford provides an excellent example (see Figure 12–5). A major impact of the large number of acquisitions and mergers that has occurred in the auto industry is the loss of clear national identities for brands of automobiles. This is particularly true for a number of famous British car brands:

- Tata Motors, an Indian automotive company, purchased Jaguar and Land Rover brands from Ford Motor Co. in 2008.
- The rights to the Mini were sold to BMW, which has very successfully reintroduced the brand.

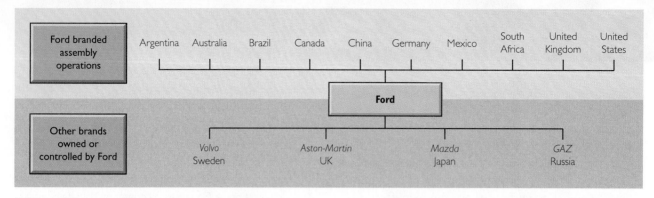

Figure 12–5 The small number of global auto companies operates in a highly globalized world. Ford, for example, builds cars in its own name in many Core nations and sells its own cars in almost every country. In addition, it has a variety of ownerships, part-ownerships, and partnerships with many of the most famous car brands. In 2007, because of its poor financial health, Ford was trying to sell its British brands.

- The rights to the legendary MG sports car were sold to a Chinese company that plans to reintroduce this brand, as BMW did with the Mini.

- Bentley, which used to be part of Rolls-Royce, was sold to Volkswagen.

- The right to use the Rolls-Royce name for auto production was sold to BMW.

The "family connections" of one particular car model illustrate the complexity of the auto industry. Someone thinking about buying a Volvo S40 might assume that Volvo in Sweden made the car. However, Volvo no longer makes cars at all! In 1999, they sold their car-making division to Ford. A Ford division called Volvocars now makes, as you might expect, Volvo cars. The S40 is actually made in Belgium in a factory that is a joint venture between Ford with the Japanese automaker Mitsubishi. But Mitsubishi is partly owned by Chrysler. Two traditional rivals, Ford and Chrysler, in fact produce the S40 cooperatively. To complicate matters further, the same car is sold as a Mitsubishi in some parts of the world and as a Volvo in others.

Another feature of transnational corporations in the 21st century is the enormous scope of their operations. What products do you associate with General Electric? Things like refrigerators and electrical equipment probably come to mind, but GE's manufacturing goes far beyond this. It also makes aircraft engines, locomotives, generating station equipment, plastics, medical-imaging equipment, and even nuclear reactors. But manufacturing is only part of the story. More than half of GE's revenues come from a division called GE Capital, which provides a wide range of financial services to millions of customers. GE also owns NBC Universal, which is a major player in both the television and movie industries. GE also had enormous geographic scope. Its Web site includes links to more than 60 national GE pages ranging from Oman to Vietnam to Peru. A check of the Angolan link, for example, indicates that GE has operated there since 1967 when it first sold locomotives to the country. Today its interests in that country include energy exploration and development, aviation, infrastructure building (such as water treatment plants), healthcare, and industrial products (such as home appliances).

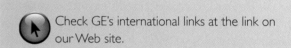

Check GE's international links at the link on our Web site.

Did You Know?

Rolls-Royce remains a Global 500 company specializing in jet engines and defense products. In an interesting historical coincidence, BMW and Rolls-Royce made engines for fighter planes in World War II that often fought against each other.

Some companies are even more international than GE. According to its Web site, Coca-Cola operates in more than 200 countries, while the United Nations has 191 members. This disparity is largely based on one's definition of "country," but it is fair to say that Coca-Cola's operations are about as international as it is possible to be. What is also clear is that Coca-Cola's future growth prospects are greatest outside the Old Core, since Coca-Cola consumption in the Old Core is already so high. This future growth potential can be seen if we look at their per capita annual sales in various parts of the world (see Figure 12–6).

Questions About the Growth of Transnationals

In the contemporary world few issues have proven as controversial as the increase of economic globalization. Criticism of economic globalization has focused on two related trends—the growing power of transnational corporations and the global expansion of freer trade. The protest against transnationals is evident in campaigns against companies that operate sweatshops to produce clothing, shoes, and other goods in developing countries. It can also be seen in attacks made on the franchises of companies like McDonald's and Starbucks during anti-globalization protests in North America, Europe, and elsewhere.

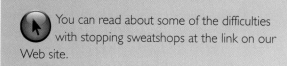

You can read about some of the difficulties with stopping sweatshops at the link on our Web site.

Those who support the growth of huge transnational corporations maintain that this growth is an inevitable and desirable outcome of an efficient, global free market. They point out that this development provides enormous benefits for the peoples of the world.

These benefits include

■ The provision to consumers of an ever-widening range of products and services at affordable prices. This allows an ever-larger proportion of the world's population to enjoy the benefits of everything from consumer goods to entertainment and pharmaceuticals.

■ An overall increase in world economic growth that will make everyone wealthier by providing more jobs and greater economic production. This benefit has been described as "a rising tide that lifts all boats."

■ A stimulus for the economic development of developing nations (see Figure 12–7)

■ A faster and more equitable sharing of the most recent technological breakthroughs

Year	World	North America (US, Canada)	European Union (incl. Germany, Spain, Great Britain, Central Europe)	Latin America (incl. Mexico, Brazil, Latin Centre, Argentina)	East Asia, South Asia, and Pacific Rim (incl. Philippines, Australia, India, Thailand)	North Asia, Eurasia, and Middle East (incl. China, Japan, Russia, Turkey)	Africa (incl. South Africa, East and Central Africa, Nigeria, Egypt)
1986	35	243	64	108	8	7	18
1996	58	356	127	163	17	19	24
2006	79	411	171	235	21	39	37

Figure 12–6 The data shown are the number of 237 mL servings of Coca-Cola products consumed, per capita per year, in the world and in the regional groups used by the company. The countries and company-defined sub-regions listed are the biggest markets within each region. Note that sales of Coca-Cola products are above the world average only in the Old Core and Latin America. Where is the possibility of growth greatest? (A serving here is defined as 237 mL and is two-thirds of a standard Canadian soft drink can.)

Figure 12–7 This optical fibre factory provides employment in the technological sector for women in a developing nation.

GLOBALIZATION

–Those who support the growth of huge transnational corporations maintain that this growth is an inevitable and desirable outcome of an efficient, global free market.

–The growth of transnationals encourages the worst aspects of globalization.

How can the impact of the growth of transnationals be seen in such diametrically different ways?

Critics of the growth of transnationals say

■ The growth of transnationals encourages the worst aspects of globalization. There could be a loss of local cultural identities as the products of US, European, and Japanese companies become commonly used everywhere. In particular, US cultural values could erode local cultural identities, since US companies dominate the market for entertainment and consumer products.

■ Corporations are becoming so large that it is not clear whose laws apply when a company's operations extend far beyond the borders of any one country.

■ Rather than making everyone richer, the growth of transnationals will benefit Old Core nations far more than other nations. Most of the best jobs and the profits go to the former. The latter will obtain low-paying jobs, provide markets, and suffer the possibility of environmental damage. In this way, economic globalization is little more than a form of neo-colonialism. (See Chapter 11 for more information on neo-colonialism.)

■ The operation of transnationals produces economic uncertainty. These companies "shop around" for the best places in which to do business. This means they can play one country against another in their search for the cheapest labour or the weakest environmental standards.

Growth of Free Trade in the World

Key to the growth of economic globalization has been the explosion in the number and extent of **free-trade** agreements. Free trade means trade that occurs without the financial and non-financial constraints that have been created to make trade more costly and/or more difficult. Financial barriers are **tariffs**, which are "taxes" on imports. Tariffs make cheap imports more expensive, and hence make it easier for domestic manufacturers to compete. An example of a non-financial barrier is a set of trade regulations so complex that importing becomes impractical. For example, a dispute broke out within the North American Free Trade Agreement (NAFTA) over the labelling requirements for jelly beans that made it difficult for Canadian jelly beans to be sold in the US and Mexico. (NAFTA is discussed later in this chapter.)

During the 1930s, most Old Core nations erected barriers to trade in an ultimately futile attempt to protect their economies from the economic chaos of the Great Depression. By the late 1940s, growing numbers of economists, politicians, and business leaders believed that these barriers were slowing the growth of the world's economy. The first international meetings to liberalize trade were held in 1947 under the General Agreement on Tariffs and Trade (GATT). GATT was the precursor of the **World Trade Organization (WTO)** that was formed in 1995 to coordinate trade and trade liberalization in the world. By 2007, ten "rounds" of trade meetings had been held that gradually were able to reduce tariffs and other restrictions to trade. A round starts with a major meeting that creates a set of objectives. Additional meetings are held to work out and agree on the detailed rules that are needed to meet these objectives. Rounds are typically named after the place where the first meeting is held or after a person, for example, the Tokyo Round or the Kennedy Round.

The WTO also coordinates the creation of regional free-trade agreements between and among countries. The number of these agreements has grown enormously since the early 1990s as support for freer trade has grown. The expansion of free trade in the world allows much larger free markets to exist; this, according to supporters, promotes greater worldwide economic growth and prosperity. Barriers to investment and the movement of technology disappear, and artificial limits to growth are eliminated. Opponents fear a loss of national sovereignty and the loss of a country's ability to protect its culture, environment, labour standards, and social programs.

Let's use one industry in North America—popular entertainment—to look at the complexity of free-trade agreements. Canada has rules that require that radio stations play a certain percentage of Canadian-produced music. This guarantee of a domestic market has aided the careers of a wide range of performers from Avril Lavigne to Celine Dion. Many people concerned about protecting Canada's culture think that similar protection should be given to Canadian films—for example, that 10 percent of the screens in the local multiplex should be reserved for Canadian films. (Chances are good that you are much more familiar with Canadian music than you are with Canadian films. There is a good reason for this.) Not surprisingly, the American film industry is vehemently opposed to this idea. Can you see why this difference of opinion exists? Fundamentally the two sides are not even on the same page when this issue is being discussed. For Canadian nationalists, it is a question of cultural protection. For American movie studios (and the American government), it is a question of commerce. Similar concerns exist all over the world.

Free Trade in Western Europe

The first major region to move toward free trade was Western Europe. This region had suffered the loss of tens of millions of lives, along with terrible economic destruction, in two world wars within barely 30 years. They wanted to find a way to come together so that a third war could never happen. In a famous speech in 1946, Winston Churchill, the British prime minister, called for the eventual creation of a "United States of Europe." The countries of Western Europe were not ready for such close political linkage, but there was willingness to cooperate economically if that could prevent a new war. Support for this cooperation grew gradually over many years. The first step was the creation of the European Coal and Steel Community (ECSC) in 1951. This agreement integrated the coal

and steel industries of Belgium, France, Germany, Italy, Luxembourg, and the Netherlands. Coal and steel were chosen because they were the key commodities needed for the manufacture of heavy weapons. The partners in the ECSC were pleased with its success. This led, in stages, to further integration of the partners' economies, including free trade. The Treaty of Rome, signed in 1957, liberalized trade in goods, services, capital, and labour within the same group of six nations of the ECSC. The newly created body was called the European Community (EC).

Since then, the EC, which became known as the European Union (EU) in 1992, has expanded greatly both in size and purpose (see Figure 12–8), with 27 member countries in 2007, and three more trying to join. The collapse of communism is a factor in the growth of the EU. The Union's purpose has also expanded beyond that of a free-trade agreement. A common currency, the euro has replaced most national currencies. In addition, the EU has a rapid-response military force that can be used instead of national armies for peacekeeping and peacemaking missions.

The EU has also negotiated bilateral free-trade agreements with many countries.

- Some of these agreements were with the Czech Republic, Poland, and Hungary.

- Others were with European countries (including Switzerland and Norway) that wanted closer trade relations with the EU, but did not want to become members of the EU.

- Others were with countries and peoples that the EU wanted to aid (for example, South Africa and the Palestinian Authority).

Free Trade in North America

Canada's history is full of disagreements over whether we should have free trade with the US. In fact, national elections have been won or lost over this issue. Canada's first prime minister, Sir John A. Macdonald, won an election in 1878 based on his National Policy, which was anti–free trade. In 1911, Prime Minister Wilfrid Laurier ran for re-election on a platform that would have allowed freer trade with the US. He lost. Twenty years later, during the Great Depression, even more *protectionist* policies (policies opposed to free trade) were put in place in a futile attempt to minimize the impact of the Depression by protecting local producers.

As in Western Europe, Canada's move toward free trade began with an agreement within a single part of the economy—auto manufacturing. Before the 1965 Auto Pact came into effect, the "Big Three" car manufacturers

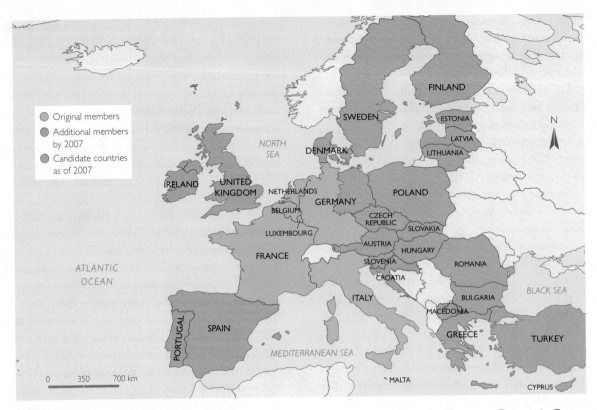

Figure 12–8 In the 50 years between 1957 and 2007, the European Union (formerly the European Economic Community) grew from six nations to 27 with a population of more than 450 million people. The EU allows a high degree of economic integration within this region.

(General Motors, Ford, and Chrysler) made cars in Canada that were sold only in Canada, and cars in the United States that were sold only in the US. Cars like the Mercury Montcalm and Pontiac Laurentian, which were produced only for the Canadian market, were virtually identical to similar models (with different names) built and sold in the US. This was not very efficient, but was done to avoid the high tariffs on car imports. The Auto Pact allowed cars to be shipped across the border without tariffs for the first time.

GLOBALIZATION

Canada's move toward free trade began with an agreement within a single part of the economy.

Why is it not a surprise that free-trade agreements start small and then grow?

In most ways the Auto Pact was a free-trade agreement, but in one important respect it was not. Although auto plants in Canada and the US were now able to make a particular model for both countries that could be shipped freely across the border, the agreement included one additional component that certainly did not reflect a free-trade sentiment. The Canadian government feared that, in a completely uncontrolled free-trade environment, all auto assembly might end up in the US. To prevent this, it insisted on a rule that would require at least one vehicle to be assembled in Canada for each car that was sold in Canada. Because of this clause in the Auto Pact, it might be most accurate to describe the agreement as managed free trade. The Auto Pact ended in 2000 as a result of a challenge made to the WTO by foreign carmakers, who felt that the Big Three had an unfair advantage in selling cars in North America.

At the time of its inception, few would have predicted that the Auto Pact would be a bonanza for Canada. The Big Three found that assembly of automobiles in Canada made good sense. The Canadian dollar began a steady decline in 1976. This meant labour costs were lower in Canada than in the US and quality was high. As a result, auto production in Canada grew significantly, with southern Ontario becoming one of the greatest auto production regions in the world. With the Canadian dollar reaching parity with the US dollar in 2007, a major advantage for Canadian auto plants was lost. All Canadian plants, likely with considerable help from the federal and Ontario governments, will need to find ways to remain competitive in a high-loonie economy.

At the same time, tariffs remained on cars produced in Asia and Europe. The result was that manufacturers like Honda and Toyota established factories in Ontario to build cars for Canada and the US. Several assembly plants, and additional auto-parts plants, were built.

The Auto Pact showed that freer trade could offer advantages to Canada's economy. It inspired a broader free-trade pact with the US. The Free Trade Agreement (FTA) came into effect in 1989, with all tariffs and other trade restrictions removed by 1999.

In 1994, the FTA was extended to include Mexico in the **North American Free Trade Agreement (NAFTA).** This change reflected the growing economic importance of this New Core nation. The extension of free trade southward offers both opportunities and risks to Canada and the US. Mexico has a large and growing market of more than 100 million people who are becoming wealthier. Hence, it is an attractive new market for businesses. On the other hand, wage rates in Mexico are a fraction of those in Canada and the US. Less skilled jobs can, and have been, lost to Mexico. It is interesting to note that Mexico has also lost jobs to countries that have even lower labour costs, for example, China and India.

Canada has also signed bilateral free-trade agreements with Chile, Costa Rica, and Israel in an attempt to stimulate trade and to expand opportunities for Canadian companies in these markets. As of 2007, Canada was involved in negotiations to establish additional free-trade agreements with many other countries. These include Iceland, Norway, Switzerland, South Korea, Singapore, and a host of nations in the Caribbean and South America.

Free Trade Elsewhere

Regional free-trade agreements have also been made in many other parts of the world. In addition to these multilateral regional free-trade agreements, there are dozens of bilateral agreements. Many more are in the negotiation stage. The result is that much of the world is already part of one or more free-trade agreements, and there have been proposals to go even further. Two massive trade blocs have been proposed—and have met with considerable opposition.

- **Free Trade Area of the Americas (FTAA).** At three meetings—the first in Miami in 1994—leaders of all of the nations of the Americas, except Cuba, met to develop a huge free-trade zone that would involve 34 nations. (Cuba is not a member of the Organization of American States, the US-dominated organization that organized the initiative, and was not invited to the meeting.)

- **Asia–Pacific Economic Cooperation (APEC).** A series of meetings has been held to create an even larger free-trade agreement among the 21 countries along the Pacific Rim that are members of APEC (see Figure 12–9). The agreement would dwarf any others by far and would involve countries with 40 percent of the world's population that produce 56 percent of the world's economic output.

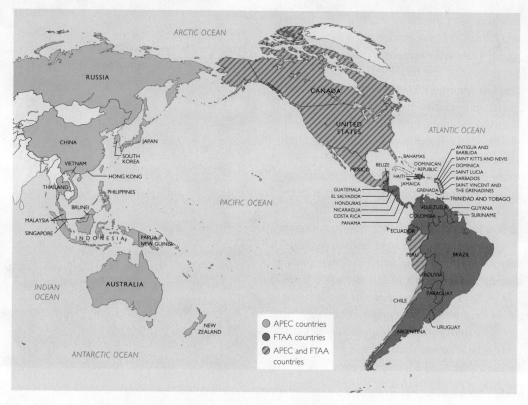

Figure 12–9 These nations, the members of APEC, were to be linked by a free-trade agreement between the years 2010 and 2020.

Creating these giant free-trade areas has proven to be a daunting task. The FTAA was originally to be in place by 2005, while the first stages of APEC (involving developed countries) were to be in place by 2010, with full free trade for all nations by 2020. Both proposals are now stalled, and there is little evidence that either will proceed in the immediate future.

Doha Round and Beyond

The popularity of free trade seems to ebb and flow like the tides. During the 1990s, free trade attracted a great deal of support, but this is no longer the case. In many ways, the WTO meeting in Seattle in 1999 marked the turning point. This meeting was designed to start the Seattle Round—a new round of trade-liberalization initiatives. Past meetings of the WTO had received little attention. They tended to be rather dull, technical affairs full of statistics and legalistic talk. Seattle changed all that. More than 30 000 demonstrators, representing many different groups opposed to free trade, turned up in Seattle (see Figure 12–10). With the demonstrations came the world's media. Around the world, the deliberations of the WTO moved from the business pages to the front page of newspapers. Lost in the attention paid to the battles between demonstrators and the police and National Guard was the fact that delegates at the meeting were unable to agree on the "explicit consensus" needed to launch the new round of trade talks. (A 2007 movie, *Battle in Seattle*, starring Charlize Theron and Woody Harrelson, was based on this incident.)

As a result of the 1999 Seattle debacle, a new round of talks was launched in Doha, Qatar, in 2001. Free-trade opponents do not consider it a coincidence that this meeting was held in a non-democratic country that was not easily accessible to demonstrators.

Figure 12–10 Demonstrators in Seattle tried, with some success, to keep delegates from attending WTO meetings. Scenes like this, from the so-called "Battle in Seattle," were shown around the world—promoting interest in (and often opposition to) the WTO and its efforts to reduce trade barriers.

Figure 12–11 Shortly after this picture was taken in 2001 during an anti-WTO demonstration in Cancun, Mexico, Lee Kyung Hai (left), a South Korean farmer and president of the Korean Federation of Advanced Farmers Association, stabbed himself in the heart. This dramatic action indicates how seriously many people in the world take WTO actions.

The **Doha Round** focused on several issues:

- Freer trade in world agricultural and manufacturing markets. This involved a significant reduction in agricultural subsidies in the EU and the US and the reduction of tariffs on manufactured goods in developing and developed countries.

- Freer world markets for trade in services

- Improved protection of intellectual property to eliminate (or at least seriously reduce) counterfeiting of movies, music, and software

- Changes to make trade rules fairer for countries outside the Old Core

Many more meetings were held in Cancun, Geneva, Paris, Hong Kong, Geneva (again), and Potsdam. The final agreement was to have been signed by 2006. The talks, however, were a complete failure, and the Doha Round was abandoned. This failure may have been foretold by a tragic protest in Cancun in 2001 (see Figure 12–11).

No one knows what is next for the growth of free trade. Two important developments suggest that further progress is unlikely in the near term.

Political Changes in the United States

Further trade liberalization requires the complete support of the US. The US economy is just too large and the US government too powerful to be ignored. Two political developments suggest the US will be less interested in freer trade for the near future.

- From 1975 to 1994 and from 2002 to 2007, six US presidents had what was called "fast track" authority with respect to trade agreements. This authority made it much easier for the US government to sign on to various trade agreements—for example, both the FTA and NAFTA were approved under this authority. The authority is now gone and is unlikely to be brought back any time soon.

- The other development has been an increase in the power of the Democratic Party. In the 2006 midterm elections, Democrats took control of the Congress. Democratic politicians have tended to be less supportive of free trade than Republicans. Even Republican politicians seem less supportive of free trade than in the past.

Changing attitudes to free trade can be summed up by looking at the opinions of the candidates who ran for their party's presidential nomination in the 2008 election. Early in the campaign, there were eight Democrats and nine Republicans running. Of these only three Republicans were completely supportive of expanded free trade, while several other candidates were even in favour of getting out of NAFTA and the WTO.

Growth of Power Outside the Old Core

The Cancun meetings were the first time that countries led by Brazil, China, India, and South Africa, felt confident enough to challenge the economic powerhouses of the US, the EU, and Japan. The three BRIC countries along with South Africa, representing the growing power of the New Core, had led a loose group of around 20 countries throughout the Doha Round deliberations. The economic power of the New Core and even the Periphery can only grow in the years to come. Agreements on trade liberalization will have to better meet the needs of the developing world. It is highly unlikely, however, that such trade liberalization would be accepted by Old Core nations since their economic dominance would decrease.

Chapter Questions

Knowledge and Understanding

1. a) List the benefits and drawbacks of transnational corporations.

   b) In your mind, do the benefits outweigh the drawbacks? Explain the basis for your conclusion.

2. a) Why is a comparison between a company's sales and a nation's GDP a meaningful one?

   b) What does this comparison suggest about the amount of influence that a large company might have when it comes into conflict with smaller nations?

   c) Give two examples of the ways in which a large corporation could influence the decisions of a country's government.

3. Examine the statistics in Figure 12–1 and answer the following questions.

   a) What kinds of businesses are most common among the largest companies in the world? (Remember that the majority of GE's revenues come from financial services with the remainder from manufacturing.) Why is this not a surprise?

   b) What factors make it easier for a large corporation to get even larger than for smaller competitors to emerge in the same field? In what ways is this a desirable situation, and in what ways is it not?

   c) Give two reasons why you may have heard of some of these companies and not others? Is this likely to change in the future?

4. a) How are the trade agreements of NAFTA and the countries of the EU similar?

   b) In what ways are they different?

   c) Could NAFTA develop to be more like the EU? Why or why not?

Thinking

5. a) Use an atlas to compare the distribution of Global 500 headquarters among the world's countries to the distribution of the world's population. What differences do you see between these patterns? Why are these differences a problem?

   b) Give two reasons why countries like the Netherlands, Belgium, Italy, the United Kingdom, and France have so many large companies.

6. a) Who are the BRIC countries? Why are they often grouped in this way?

   b) How might the growth of their economies (and those of other New Core countries) change the Global 500 list that we might look at in 2020?

   c) Is this a good or bad thing? Be sure to explain your choice.

7. Investigate the current status of the FTAA and APEC free-trade negotiations. What progress has been made, since the publication of this book, in implementing these agreements and in meeting the concerns of free-trade critics?

8. Opposition to the work of the World Trade Organization and to economic globalization has come from a great many directions. Explain briefly why someone in each of these groups might be part of this opposition:

   a) a unionized worker from the US

   b) a wheat farmer from France

   c) a cotton farmer from Mali

   d) an environmentalist from Canada

   e) a human-rights activist from China

   f) a university student from the EU

9. "The economic power of the New Core and even the Periphery can only grow in the years to come." How might the growing economic power outside the Old Core affect your life in the future? Consider both positive and negative impacts.

Communication

10. Construct a metaphor that an opponent to economic globalization might use to counteract the pro-globalization comment, "A rising tide lifts all boats." Compare your metaphor to that of a classmate. Within the context of globalization, was each understandable to the other person?

Application

11. Assume that you have a particularly bright and involved sister in grade ten. She sees what you are studying and asks you whether economic globalization is a good or bad thing. You decide that it would make more sense for her to make up her own mind, but that you can create a table to summarize the arguments in favour of and in opposition to economic globalization. Do so. **G**

12. In this chapter, you saw how complex the interconnections are in the auto industry and how the number of brand names is actually much greater than the number of auto companies. Similar situations exist in other industries as well. Research one of these and produce an organizational diagram showing the relationship between ownership and brand names. It might be easiest to look at some area of consumer spending like packaged foods, clothing production and retailing, soft drinks, or brewing. You should be able to research this topic by visiting the Web sites of major corporations.

13. To some people, the operations of transnational corporations in developing countries are almost completely exploitative (for example, sweatshop manufacturing). Others think that they are a necessary step in the economic growth of these countries since they provide vital jobs and foreign income that will allow these countries to advance. With which of these sides would you agree? Explain your view.

14. Has free trade been good for Canada or not? Research the impact of free trade on Canada and try to determine if it has, in your opinion, been a good thing. You might want to consider the impact of free trade on such issues as the growth of the GDP, the number and quality of jobs created, and the environment. The report of your findings should be 300 to 400 words in length and should include a bibliography.

15. a) In this chapter it was suggested that the best opportunities for growth for the Coca-Cola company lie outside the Old Core. Why is this so?

   b) Is this situation likely to be common for other transnational corporations?

   c) Is this a good development, a bad development, or should we not be attaching value judgments like "good" and "bad" to such situations? Be sure to explain your answer.

16. Will a point be reached when free trade exists across the entire world, or will this aspect of economic globalization decline in importance as economic protectionism re-emerges? Write a brief paper (400 to 500 words) to address these questions. Besides giving your own opinions based on your current knowledge of the situation, describe any additional information that you might need to obtain to make the most reasoned position possible.

17. Protests have erupted whenever meetings are held to discuss trade liberalization.

   a) What causes are promoted by the protestors at these events?

   b) Why do so many of these protests become violent?

   c) Does this violence help or hinder the causes of various groups?

   d) How can protestors who do not promote violence get their points of view across so that the negotiators will take their arguments seriously?

Answers to Quiz page 182

1. US financial company Citigroup was #1; 2. #2 General Electric (multi-industry), #3 American International Group (industry), #4 ExxonMobil (oil and gas), #5 Bank of America (banking); 3. US (205 companies); 4. #2 Japan (91 companies), #3 (tie) France and UK (34), Germany (24); 5. Exxon-Mobil (US$15.1 billion); 6. #105 Royal Bank of Canada; 7. 16; 8. #105 Royal Bank of Canada, #142 Bank of Nova Scotia, #168 Toronto-Dominion Bank, #170 CIBC, #208 – Bank of Montreal, #222 Manulife Financial, #233 Sunlife Financial, #243 BCE, #297 Power Corporation, #307 Bombardier, #329 George Weston, #349 Alcan, #353 Imperial Oil, #359 Onex, #373 Nortel Networks, #386 Magna International; 9. Old Core 469, New Core 31 (South Korea [13], Brazil [4], China, Russia, and India [3 each], Mexico [2], Singapore, Taiwan, and South Africa [1 each]); 10. All, except Tim Hortons, are on the Global 500 list.

The photos on page 181 were taken in Gaborone, Botswana; (right) and Santiago, Chile (left).

CHAPTER 13

Economic Disparity in the World

Key Terms

economic disparity

extreme poverty

development assistance

official development assistance
(ODA)

private development assistance
(PDA)

non-governmental organizations
(NGOs)

bilateral aid

multilateral aid

Canadian International
Development Agency (CIDA)

aid fatigue

civil society

Gini index

income redistribution

The expression "economic disparity" is a way of saying that some people and countries are very rich, while others are very poor. The opulence of the entrance hall of the Burj al Arab Hotel in Dubai is a stark contrast to the poverty shown below.

Key Questions

By the end of this chapter you will be able to answer
the following questions.

■ What is the nature of economic disparity in the world?

■ What can be done to reduce economic disparity?
What should be done?

■ How successful has foreign aid been in helping to reduce
economic disparity?

■ What role do remittances play in reducing economic disparity?

■ Why do issues related to remittances get relatively little attention?

The Nature of Economic Disparity

As you learned in Chapter 2, Dubai has tremendous wealth—evident in its fancy hotels (page 196), residences, and megayachts. In contrast, many people in many other countries, like the person picking through garbage on page 196, have few possessions and little likelihood of ever rising above a life of extreme poverty. Their lives are likely to be very short and desperate. The two photos on the previous page illustrate an extreme example of the **economic disparity** that exists in the world. While the idea of economic disparity—the economic differences between the "haves" and "have-nots"— is quite simple, the implications of disparity are highly complex, as are the possible solutions to this problem. Economic disparity can be examined in different ways—between countries and also between people within a country. This chapter explores the implications of the growing gap between rich and poor nations and among the rich and poor people within each nation.

As Figure 13–1 shows, one simple value, US$2161, divides the world's people economically. (This statistic applies to adults only and was based on 2000 data from the World Institute of Economics Research.) If the total value of your assets (including financial assets, real estate, livestock, vehicles, and other property) is more than US$2161, you are in the wealthy half of the world population; if it is less than this amount, you are in the poor half. If you consider the value of the assets of a typical Canadian, this is a remarkably low number. In fact, if your assets are worth only US$61 041, you are in the richest 10 percent of the people of the world. (For comparison's sake, consider that an average house in Toronto was selling for about US$360 000 in 2007. Houses in cities such as Vancouver, Boston, and London were even more costly.)

Most observers agree that economic globalization has created more wealth in the world. Unfortunately, the economic growth has not been shared equitably among all nations and among the people within each country. While the wealthier nations (like Dubai and Canada) have seen their economies grow steadily, the economies of many poor countries have stagnated or even declined in recent decades. At the same time, some people—whether in rich countries or poor—are much better off financially than others. Figure 13–2 shows the distribution of wealth in the world.

If the total value of your assets is at least ...	You are in the world's richest ...
US$2 161	50%
3 517	40%
6 318	30%
14 169	20%
61 041	10%
150 145	5%
514 512	1%

Figure 13–1 These data, for adult individuals, show the value of assets (real estate, investments, and personal property) needed to be included at various global wealth levels. The data are for 2000.

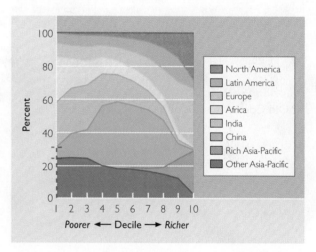

Figure 13–2 Global wealth distribution by region and decile percent, 2000. A decile is 1/10th of the world population based on wealth; for example, the 10th decile would include the wealthiest 10 percent of the world's people. Read this graph by choosing a decile and then look vertically up from the decile value to see the distribution of people with that wealth limit. The example shows that about 23 percent of the poorest decile are in "Other Asia-Pacific" with about 7 percent in China.

AN UNEQUAL WORLD

1. What is "purchasing power parity GDP per capita?" Why is this a more useful statistic than absolute GDP per capita? (Review page 42 in Chapter 3 to help you answer these questions.)

2. a) Figure 13–3 includes per-capita GDP (PPP) of a sample of countries in four parts of the world.

   i) Calculate an index value for each of the 16 countries. To do this, divide the lowest GDP per capita in 2004 for any of the countries into each of the 16 values. Express each index value to one decimal point. For example, divide Canada's GDP by Zambia's (the lowest) and you will get an index value of 33.2.

   ii) What does this value represent?

   b) Create a graph that shows the per-capita GDP of the two countries with the highest and lowest index values within each category of countries. Note that you will

end up with eight bars on your graph. On the left side of the graph use the index values you calculated previously. Be sure to label your graph appropriately. What significant differences do you notice among the four worlds?

3. a) In much of the world, the highest GDP (per capita and in total) was achieved in the most recent year. In other parts of the world, this was not the case. What obvious pattern do you see in this?

   b) What does this suggest about the role played by globalization in world economic growth?

4. a) Rank the groups of countries on the basis of the rate of their economic growth. Calculate this

   i) on a percentage basis
   ii) on a dollar basis

   b) What patterns do you see? What significance does this have for the future?

		GDP Per Capita (PPP basis) US$, 2004	Highest Annual GDP Per Capita (PPP basis) US$	Year Highest GDP Reached	Annual GDP Growth Rate (non-PPP basis) 1975–2004	Annual GDP Growth Rate (non-PPP basis) 1990–2004
Old Core	Canada	31 263	31 263	2004	1.6	2.1
	Germany	28 303	28 303	2004	2.1	1.5
	Japan	29 251	29 251	2004	2.3	0.8
	US	39 676	39 676	2004	2.0	1.9
New Core	Chile	10 878	10 878	2004	3.9	3.7
	China	5 896	5 896	2004	8.4	8.9
	Malaysia	10 276	10 276	2004	4.1	3.5
	Poland	12 974	12 974	2004	N/A	4.0
Near Core	Georgia	2 844	6 514	1985	4.2	1.0
	Iran	7 525	8 679	1976	0.1	2.3
	Nicaragua	3 634	7 429	1977	2.3	0.1
	Philippines	4 614	4 689	1982	N/A	0.9
Far Periphery	Angola	2 180	2 764	1992	0.7	1.2
	Bangladesh	1 870	1 870	2004	1.7	2.5
	Haiti	1 892	3 423	1980	2.3	2.2
	Zambia	943	1 577	1976	2.0	1.1

Figure 13–3 Per-capita GDP of a sample of countries in the Old Core, New Core, Near Core, and Far Periphery

Disparity Among Nations

As you have seen in the previous activity, enormous economic disparity exists in the world (see Figure 13–4.) and the situation is not improving—at least for the poor. For the world's poor, the situation has been described as "a race to the bottom." The United Nations has reported that per-capita incomes in 100 countries, with a combined population of 1.6 billion, have dropped from the highest levels previously reached. This decline has not been just a recent phenomenon. Sadly, almost 20 countries reached their maximum per-capita income in 1960 or before, and 50 more reached theirs in the 1960s and 1970s. While 200 million people saw their incomes fall between 1965 and 1983, the situation was even worse between 1980 and 1993, when more than a billion people experienced a decline in income.

By 2006, the world found itself in the grim situation in which its 20 richest countries had per-capita PPP GDPs of more than US$30 000, while the 60 poorest countries had per-capita PPP GDPs of less than US$3000 per year. Another way of looking at the problem is that the assets of the three wealthiest people in the world total about the same as the total GDP of the poorest 47 nations.

At the same time that many countries have become poorer, there have been a smaller number of significant economic winners, some of whom have enjoyed remarkable success. While the traditional "fat cat" countries of the Old Core have maintained their economic growth, they have been joined by many hundreds of millions of people who live in New Core countries. The most notable of these New Core countries are China and India, whose economies have been growing at enormously fast rates. In each of these countries, hundreds of millions of people have benefitted from rising standards of living, although even more people remain dreadfully poor. Clearly, globalization has contributed to the growth of these and other nations. China, for example, has become, by far, the most important manufacturing nation in the world. Much of India's growth can be tied to its ability to supply low-cost information technology services to Old Core nations.

Supporters of globalization have used a metaphor to explain how it should work: they say that "a rising tide lifts all boats." Critics of globalization would change the metaphor to "a rising tide drowns those who do not own boats." Some observers say what seems to have happened is not that poorer countries are being harmed by globalization, but rather, they are being ignored.

Extreme Poverty in the World

Hundreds of millions of people live on less than US$1 per day (using absolute, non-PPP dollars). The UN calls this situation **extreme poverty**. Compare this amount to how much you spend to go to a movie or buy a new pair of jeans. In India, 47 percent of the population lives on less than US$1 per day, while another 40 percent lives on between US$1 and US$2 per day. This means that more than 900 million people have to survive for a day on a fraction of what you might spend for popcorn at a movie theatre. The situation is much worse in Zambia, where 85 percent have less than US$1 per day and another 13 percent have between US$1 and US$2 per day. Figure 13–5 shows the distribution of poverty in the world.

The UN established a number of Millennium Development Goals in 2000. One of them was to dramatically reduce the amount of poverty in the world. As Figure 13–6 shows, considerable progress has been made in this regard but much remains to be done, and many people feel that the 2015 goal for poverty reduction will not be reached without a considerable increase in contributions from wealthier nations and citizens in New Core and Near Core countries.

Figure 13–4 Economic disparity can be seen in all aspects of life—in this case, in transportation. Travel in Japan on the bullet train could not be more different than travel by bullock cart in rural India.

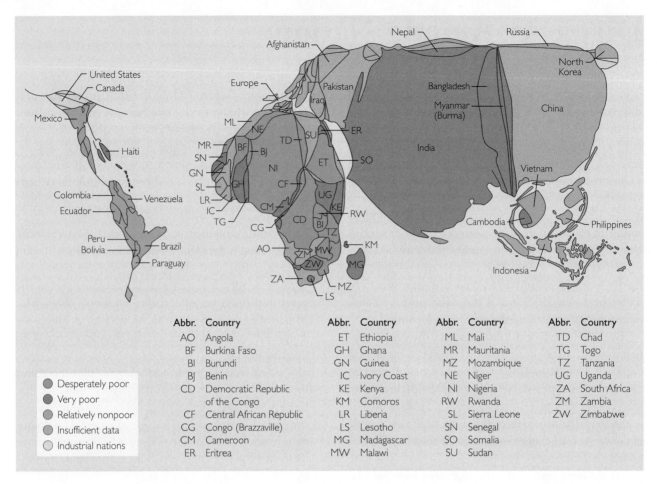

Figure 13–5 The distribution of the world's poor. The marked area of the country on this map represents the number of poor people in the country. The colour shows the relative degree of poverty. Notice that data for the degree of poverty are lacking for such important countries as China, Pakistan, and Indonesia. Why?

Legend for map:
- ● Desperately poor
- ● Very poor
- ● Relatively nonpoor
- ● Insufficient data
- ○ Industrial nations

Abbr.	Country	Abbr.	Country	Abbr.	Country	Abbr.	Country
AO	Angola	ET	Ethiopia	ML	Mali	TD	Chad
BF	Burkina Faso	GH	Ghana	MR	Mauritania	TG	Togo
BI	Burundi	GN	Guinea	MZ	Mozambique	TZ	Tanzania
BJ	Benin	IC	Ivory Coast	NE	Niger	UG	Uganda
CD	Democratic Republic of the Congo	KE	Kenya	NI	Nigeria	ZA	South Africa
CF	Central African Republic	KM	Comoros	RW	Rwanda	ZM	Zambia
CG	Congo (Brazzaville)	LR	Liberia	SL	Sierra Leone	ZW	Zimbabwe
CM	Cameroon	LS	Lesotho	SN	Senegal		
ER	Eritrea	MG	Madagascar	SO	Somalia		
		MW	Malawi	SU	Sudan		

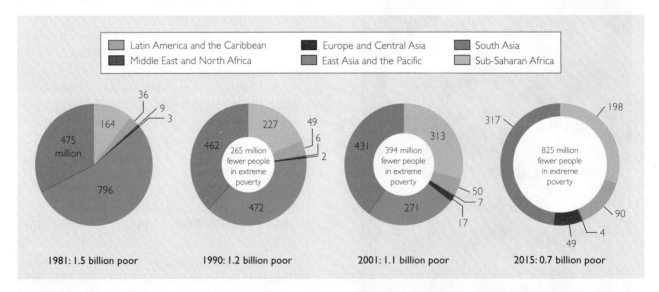

Legend for pie charts:
- Latin America and the Caribbean
- Middle East and North Africa
- Europe and Central Asia
- East Asia and the Pacific
- South Asia
- Sub-Saharan Africa

1981: 1.5 billion poor — 475 million; 164; 36; 9; 3; 796

1990: 1.2 billion poor — 265 million fewer people in extreme poverty; 462; 227; 49; 6; 2; 472

2001: 1.1 billion poor — 394 million fewer people in extreme poverty; 431; 313; 50; 7; 17; 271

2015: 0.7 billion poor — 825 million fewer people in extreme poverty; 317; 198; 90; 4; 49

Figure 13–6 The Millennium Project goal is to reduce the number of people living in extreme poverty to 0.7 billion by 2015. In this graphic, the white area in the middle of each circle represents progress in the reduction of poverty in each year, along with the goal for 2015.

Causes of Economic Disparity

The causes of the world's economic disparity are complex. The reasons for economic disparity will be discussed here and in other chapters of this book. As you look at the reasons that follow, remember that economic disparity between countries is often a product of poor or unfair political and economic decisions in the past rather than a result of fundamental differences in the richness of the resource base of different countries. Better decisions will have to be made in the years to come if the disparity is to be reduced.

Impact of Colonialism

Most poor countries were, at one time or another, colonies. Colonization produced distortions in the economic structures of these countries that still have a huge impact, even though they may have been independent for a half-century or more. (See Chapter 11.)

Lack of Investment

In contrast to the countries of the Core, most Periphery nations have not been able to fund an economic take-off as described by Rostow. Without large amounts of either *domestic* (coming from within a country) or foreign investment, economic growth occurs slowly at best. (See Chapter 11 for more about Rostow's theory.)

Population Growth

In general, Periphery countries have experienced (and are still experiencing) substantially higher rates of population growth than the developed world. This means that economic growth in these countries has provided at best a miserable level of existence for more and more people, rather than a higher standard of living for a more stable population. (See Chapter 6.)

Disease

In Core countries, disease may actually aid economic growth since the healthcare industry is an important part of the economy. For example, in Canada, healthcare makes up about 10 percent of our GDP. In poor countries where people and governments do not have much money to spend on healthcare, disease has a major negative economic impact. While diseases like malaria and tuberculosis have had an impact on economic growth for centuries, the most profound effect is the impact of HIV/AIDS in sub-Saharan Africa. You can learn more about the effect of disease on economic growth by completing the case study on this page.

Foreign Debt

In 1977, the 60 poorest countries owed US$550 billion for various loans that they had received. In the next 30 years, they made US$540 billion in loan payments and still owed US$523 billion to foreign governments and private lenders. Another way of looking at this sad reality is that developing countries paid US$13 in debt repayment (almost totally for interest) for every dollar they received in aid. The result is that they had little money left to invest in vital

---

CASE STUDY — Minding the Gap II

A Web site called Gapminder (see the link on our Web site) allows you to create a variety of visually effective, animated graphs of a range of development data. If you did not use this site in Chapter 5, you can learn how to use Gapminder on page 78 and experiment with the program. In this case study you will be looking at how the HIV/AIDS pandemic (as shown by the dramatic decline in life expectancy in sub-Saharan Africa) has affected economic growth.

Questions

1. **a)** Select "Income per capita" for the y-axis, with a logarithmic scale, and "life expectancy" on the x-axis, with a linear scale.

   b) Move the date slider to the earliest date, 1975.

   c) The countries with the highest HIV/AIDS infection rates in the world are Botswana, Lesotho, and Swaziland. Choose them. Run the animation.

2. **a)** What relationship do you see between economic growth rates and decrease in life expectancy? In what year did this trend become apparent in each country?

   b) How have high HIV/AIDS infection rates contributed to lower economic growth rates? In your answer, consider which groups in society would be most likely to become infected with HIV/AIDS.

economic development, education, and healthcare. (The reasons for, and problems associated with international debt are examined in Chapter 14.)

War

The poorest countries, most of which are in Africa, have often had to deal with the devastation of wars and civil unrest arising from tribal conflicts and the ambitions of warlords (see Figure 13–7). Some civil conflicts, like those in Colombia, Mozambique, and the Democratic Republic of the Congo, have been going on for decades. An argument can be made that, in the years after World War II, the world could be divided into a "zone of war" (which included most of Africa), where conflicts continually stifled efforts to improve the economy, and a "zone of peace," where economic growth occurred in an atmosphere free of the constant threat of conflict. Frequently, in a "zone of war," a rebel group will overthrow the government only to have to focus its energies (and money) on protecting itself from the next insurgency. Far too little of these governments' time and money is spent on promoting economic growth. (World conflict is examined in Chapter 22.)

Leadership Issues

Many of the poorest countries in the world have had leaders who had little interest or skill in improving the economic lot of their citizens. Far too often they have used their positions to steal millions—and in some cases, billions—of dollars (see Figure 13–8).

When leaders emerge who put the interests of their country ahead of those of the international business community, they often face fierce opposition. For example, the United States has imposed strict economic sanctions on Cuba since Fidel Castro's government *nationalized* (took over without payment) the assets of US companies in the early 1960s, after the US refused to buy Cuba's sugar. It is also generally believed that the Central Intelligence Agency (CIA), the US's main international information-gathering and espionage body, was responsible for the 1973 overthrow of the democratically elected government of Salvador Allende in Chile because it feared that his socialist government might adopt policies similar to those of Castro's Cuba.

In a remarkable event, Alberto Fujimori, who had dual Peruvian/Japanese citizenship because his parents were born in Japan, ran for election in 2007 to the Japanese parliament (he campaigned from Chile where he was under house arrest). If elected, under Japanese law he would have been immune to being sent back to Peru to face charges for his crimes, which included sanctioning death squads. Fujimori was not elected.

Trade Inequities

The Group of Eight (G8) nations (with the exception of Russia) has traditionally used tariff and non-tariff barriers to restrict imports from developing countries.

President	Country	Years	Amount Stolen (US$ billions)
Mohammed Suharto	Indonesia	1967–98	15–35
Ferdinand Marcos	Philippines	1972–86	5–10
Mobutu Sésé Seko	Congo DR	1972–86	5
Sani Abacha	Nigeria	1993–98	2–5
Slobodan Milosevic	Serbia/ Yugoslavia	1989–2000	1
Jean-Claude Duvalier	Haiti	1971–86	0.3–0.8
Alberto Fujimori	Peru	1990–2000	0.6

Figure 13–8 A global "hall of shame"—these men used their positions as national presidents to steal at least US$500 million for themselves, their families, and close friends. Their thefts reduced the economic growth of these countries.

Figure 13–7 This Ethiopian soldier sits in the ruins of Zalambessa, Ethiopia, in May 2000. This strategic military town, taken by the Eritrean army in 1998, had just been recaptured.

This has occurred in spite of the fact that these nations have traditionally spoken out in favour of free trade.

For example, the tariffs placed by these countries on cloth and clothing produced in Africa and the Middle East are four times as high as the tariffs on similar products from other G8 countries. At the same time, the G8 nations, and in particular the EU, the US, and Japan, subsidize their agricultural products so that they are often as cheap, or cheaper, than commodities from developing countries. Trade policies in the Old Core that are fair to all would help poorer countries to reach their economic potential without relying on direct aid from richer countries.

Lack of Local Control

Citizens of developing countries complain that they lack the power to control their own affairs. They point out that far too many critical decisions are made outside their countries by international groups like the UN, the World Bank, and the International Monetary Fund, and by transnational corporations and the powerful governments of Old Core nations.

Did You Know?

The G8 members include Canada, the US, the United Kingdom, France, Germany, Japan, Italy, and Russia. These nations—except for Russia, which did not join until the mid-1990s—are the main holders of the debt of poor countries.

Addressing the Problem

Economic disparity is a very complex problem and the solutions to it are, as you might expect, equally complex. The following are some suggestions that might help to reduce economic disparity in the world:

- Political colonialism disappeared in most colonies only to be replaced by a kind of economic colonialism; the demands of huge transnational and foreign-owned corporations frequently came to replace those of imperial powers. Many developing countries rely on the export of one or two unprocessed raw materials, such as lumber, mineral ores, or agricultural products such as cocoa or coffee beans for much of their income. Other developing countries rely on income generated by products that have been manufactured by cheap labour in factories within their borders. These products are generally produced for foreign-owned companies and exported to richer countries. The developing countries are entirely dependent upon the operation of these companies for vital income. In other words, they have no control over their own economies. Also, the developing countries need the income generated by these companies more than the companies need the profits generated by the developing countries. Developing nations must find a way to control their economies for their own benefit. This would help diminish economic disparity between Old Core and New Core/Periphery countries.

- Demographic transition is occurring slowly in a number of poor countries in Africa and South Asia.

This means that the benefits of any economic growth in these countries must be spread over a population that is growing very rapidly. If a way can be found to reduce the population growth rate, these countries can use more of their resources to improve the quality of life for the resulting smaller number of people.

- When an epidemic such as HIV/AIDS kills millions, including many of the most productive members of society, an entirely new set of economic problems is created. Production of food declines, and the number of business people, healthcare workers, teachers, and other vital workers is reduced. Effective, affordable treatments and controls for HIV/AIDS and other infectious diseases would boost economic growth rates, which in turn would diminish economic disparity. (You can learn more about the impact of HIV/AIDS in Chapter 26.)

- It is generally agreed, in both the developed and developing worlds, that the amount of debt owed by the poorest countries is unsustainable. Cancelling, or at least reducing, this debt and the huge amounts of interest payable would go far in alleviating the economic disparity between rich and poor countries.

 You can learn more about corruption around the world at the link on our Web site.

- The governments of the developing world are demanding a greater voice in the vital decisions that affect them. For example, most of the governments of Africa agreed in 2001 to work toward the creation of an African Union that would be modelled after the European Union. The creation of such a large and powerful economic and political bloc would make it easier for African governments to stand up to foreign interests during negotiations over international debts and globalization rules. Economic disparity would be diminished when countries have the power to make decisions in their favour. It took many years for the size and influence of the EU to grow, and there were many obstacles to overcome along the way. The growth of the African Union is likely to follow a similar course.

- Developing countries need leaders who are prepared to work for the national good rather than for their own interests. Honest, democratic governments and low rates of corruption are slowly becoming more common in the Periphery, but much remains to be done in this respect. Good government within countries would reduce the economic disparity among citizens.

Development Assistance

Development assistance, which is more commonly called foreign aid, is the best-known process by which money moves from richer countries to poorer ones. It consists of two parts: **official development assistance** (**ODA**), which is delivered by governments, and **private development assistance** (**PDA**), which is delivered by **non-governmental organizations** (or **NGOs**).

ODA can take many forms. It can be bilateral or multilateral, for example. **Bilateral aid** goes from one country directly to another, while **multilateral aid** is given to an international agency, like the World Health Organization, which may use it to pay for a program that operates in a number of countries. Bilateral aid can be given in the form of money, materials, or through the provision of expertise. A final difference is that ODA may be provided directly by a government agency (for example, the **Canadian International Development Agency** [**CIDA**] in Canada, and USAID in the US) or through an NGO.

The Role of NGOs Worldwide

As you learned above, a significant amount of aid is provided by non-governmental organizations, which are non-governmental, non-profit organizations that operate internationally in fields such as development

programs and human rights. There are many hundreds of NGOs in the world.

Some are world famous, such as Oxfam, while others are very small and known only to those who work with them or who benefit from their work. CIDA works with NGOs and often helps to fund them. NGO funding comes from three principal sources:

- One is fundraising from private citizens. (By the way, it is not uncommon for World Issues classes to fundraise in support of groups like the Red Cross, World Vision, or Oxfam.)

- A second is from rich individuals who establish *foundations* (a special kind of NGO) to handle the distribution of their very large donations. The Bill and Melinda Gates Foundation would be the best known current example, but the model for its work would be that done by groups like the Ford Foundation and the Rockefeller Foundation.

- A third (and growing) source of funding is from government ODA budgets. Governments will often provide financial support to NGO projects because they feel that NGOs use this money in a more responsive, less bureaucratic fashion than might a large government or international agency. (Governments will also sometimes agree to match the contributions of private citizens for special appeals like those after major disasters in poor countries.)

Figure 13–9 The Canadian Foodgrains Bank is a partnership of 15 church groups dedicated to the elimination of hunger in the world. In this case, wheat was sent to Afghanistan to help feed thousands of internally displaced people after war broke out in 2001.

 You can learn more about the Foodgrains Bank on our Web site.

Reasons Why Donor Countries Provide Development Assistance

- **Religious and Humanitarian Motives.** Wealthy parts of the world (for example, North America, Europe, and some middle Eastern countries) have a strong tradition of providing aid to those in need. For example, governments and citizens in wealthy Islamic countries like Saudi Arabia and the United Arab Emirates provide a great deal of humanitarian aid to poorer Muslim countries.

- **Economic Motives.** Giving aid may benefit the economy of the donor country. In many cases, aid is given *in kind* (that is, as material such as food or industrial equipment) or is linked directly to purchases from the donor. For example, Canada may give aid in the form of wheat from Saskatchewan or provide the funding to purchase transportation equipment from Ontario.

- **Political Motives.** Aid may be given to foster strong relationships between the donor and the recipient (or not given, to punish a country that a donor might disapprove of for whatever reason). When describing the president of one Latin American country that received US aid during the Cold War, President Lyndon Johnson allowed that, given the harsh and corrupt rule of the man, he could be described as a "bastard." But, Johnson added, "He is our bastard."

- **Historical Motives.** Assistance is often linked to former colonial relationships. This has even influenced the way in which Canada gives aid. We have a stronger record of giving aid to former British and French colonies than to other developing countries. In giving such aid, Canada talks about having "special relationships" with members of the Commonwealth and La Francophonie. The prime requirement for belonging to either of these organizations is that a country was a former colony in either the British or the French empire.

ODA from the Marshall Plan to Today

The Marshall Plan created a model for development assistance for the next half-century. In fact, the chancellor of Austria called for a "Marshall Plan for the South" in 1959. This proposal was followed, in 1960, by a call from the World Council of Churches for the world's

---

CASE STUDY — The Marshall Plan: A Standard for ODA

Foreign aid has been used for over a half-century to address the problem of global economic disparity. One example in particular stands out. In 1947, when Europe lay in ruins after World War II, General George C. Marshall, the US Secretary of State at the time, instituted a generous reconstruction plan for Western Europe. The United States gave the non-communist nations of Europe US$13 billion to aid their recovery from the war. Similar aid was given to Japan. The cost of the Marshall Plan was very high, but postwar aid to Western Europe and Japan ultimately resulted in the economic, political, and social success of these now globalized nations.

The Marshall Plan was successful, because of the huge amounts of money and material goods that were made available to countries that had been devastated by war. It was also successful because, unlike many developing countries today, the war-ravaged countries of Europe still had an economic and political infrastructure in place, even though it needed much repair. These countries also had political know-how and a centuries-old tradition of economic leadership that they relied upon to help them re-build.

Although the provisions of the Marshall Plan were generous, the US was not acting entirely in an *altruistic* (lacking in self-interest) way. By making the products that Europe needed for re-building, US industries were spurred on to convert from wartime to peacetime production. Peacetime production helped prevent a serious economic downturn in the US economy. Furthermore, postwar Europe became a good customer for US products. Beyond these benefits, the Marshall Plan ensured that as much of Europe as possible would remain non-communist. In fact, international assistance became a major weapon in the Cold War between the Soviet Union and the West that dominated world relations for the next four decades.

Questions

1. The Marshall Plan, and similar aid to defeated Japan, is generally considered to have been a remarkable success. Why?

2. In spite of its success, an aid effort on the scale of the Marshall Plan has never been repeated. Why not?

3. The Marshall Plan had clear benefits for the donor (the US) as well as for the recipients. Could future efforts to reduce economic disparity be organized in a way to benefit rich countries as well as poor? How?

richer countries to give 1 percent of their GNP—from ODA and NGOs—for aid. Eventually, a UN Commission led by former Canadian Prime Minister Lester Pearson decided that the target for development assistance should be set at 0.7 percent. Although this admirable goal remains today, countries rarely reach it. (The reason for calling the world's developing nations the "South" was described in Chapter 2.)

Overall, foreign aid was relatively successful from the early 1950s until the early 1980s. Evidence of this success can be seen in the growth in income, increased life expectancy, and the decline in fertility rates and infant mortality that occurred virtually everywhere in the developing world. Most impressive of all was the impact of the Green Revolution, which dramatically increased food production and reduced the potential for mass starvation. (The Green Revolution was discussed in Chapter 10.)

The 1980s became known as development's "Lost Decade." Donor countries' confidence in the benefits of foreign aid started to drop significantly because they saw slow economic and social growth in many recipient countries, in spite of many years of constant aid. As a result, the amount of aid being given, as a percentage of GDP, stagnated in many countries and declined in others. This indifferent commitment to development continues today (see Figure 13–10).

Another reason why aid was not as successful as it might have been was because of the sheer difficulty of the challenges being faced. It was not as simple as in Europe and Japan after World War II. In the developing world, the problems were much more complex and the solutions less clear. A modern economic system had to be built from scratch, not just rebuilt. Of primary importance was the need to deal with the economic, political, and social problems that colonialism had caused. This was a daunting task, since it was impossible to know how these countries might have developed if colonialism had never existed.

A Flawed Model of Development Assistance

Fundamentally, most development assistance in the last half-century has used a flawed model for growth, that is, a top-down, centralized approach that is insensitive to local needs and differences. A simple example will illustrate the problem.

The government of a foreign aid donor looks at a poor country and determines that chronic food shortages exist. They know that their own country's farmers produce a surplus of food, so a perfect match seems to exist.

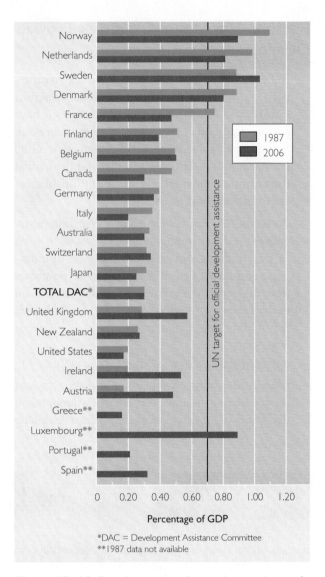

Figure 13–10 Development assistance by members of the Development Assistance Committee of the Organisation for Economic Co-operation and Development (OECD)

The donor nation can help its farmers by buying food products from them and giving them to the poor country. There are, however, several problems with this assumption:

- The first problem is that the sudden availability of so much "free" food aid in the recipient country distorts local markets for agricultural products. Demand for locally produced food declines, so prices drop. Depressed prices hurt the very farm families who may be those most in need.

- A second problem with food aid is that it rarely reaches those who need it most—often the rural poor. In most cases, the food aid stays in the cities, going to people there who could survive without it.

A third problem may be that what is sent is not what people need or can use. For example, powdered milk may be sent to countries where the people are lactose intolerant—eating dairy products makes them ill.

Canada's Uneven History of ODA

For many years, Canada was regarded, in foreign aid terms, as a North American version of a Scandinavian country. This was clearly a compliment, as the Scandinavian countries were the most generous foreign aid donors. Canadians took pride in Lester Pearson's role in establishing the 0.7 percent of GDP aid target, and that Canada was seen by the world as one of the more generous aid donors. While Canada never actually reached the 0.7 percent target, for many years in the 1980s, considerable progress was made toward it. More recently though, Canada's foreign aid has dropped steeply, and aid efforts have lost focus.

One incident illustrates the confused approach that Canada takes toward foreign aid. In 1995, an earthen dam collapsed in a remote region of Guyana. The dam had been built to hold waste from the Omai gold mine that was owned by Cambior, a Canadian mining company. When the dam broke, it released vast quantities of cyanide-laden water into the Essequibo River, which was both a vital source of drinking water for many people and the most important source of fish in the country. Canadian official development assistance played two quite contradictory roles in this incident. Funds from CIDA had been used to train the workers at the Omai mine. At the same time, other Canadian aid had been used to fund the activist indigenous groups that had opposed the Omai mine at every step and had predicted that the dam would collapse.

What's Next for Development Assistance?

There is general agreement on the need for development assistance that meets well-established needs and provides as much "bang for the buck" as possible. Unfortunately, there is a growing feeling in the world that foreign aid does not seem to accomplish very much. After a half-century of development assistance, much of Africa seems worse off than it was before the aid began. There are many concerns. These include that

- much aid money is wasted
- it only ends up supporting a vast, bureaucratic "aid industry"
- it is used politically in both donor and recipient countries (that is, to gain popular favour)

- it is too often diverted to the rich in recipient countries

As a result, there is a general fear that **aid fatigue** has set in—that people in donor countries do not feel as committed to the provision of aid as in earlier decades. To prove this point, observers point to the fact that only muted protests were heard in countries like Canada when aid expenditures were severely cut by the Liberal government in the 1990s.

> **SUSTAINABILITY**
> After a half-century of development assistance, much of Africa seems worse off than it was before the aid began.
>
> *Does this necessarily mean that the aid has proven ineffective?*

Donor and recipient countries alike have agreed that something must be done to remedy this situation. A major step in making the foreign aid system work better was the agreement in 2005 on the Paris Declaration. More than 100 countries signed on as did dozens of major international organizations and NGOs. The Declaration is, for the most part, a highly technical document that strives to increase accountability for aid both for donors and recipients. It includes 12 specific indicators that can be used to see how effectively aid is being given and used. Many would argue that the Paris Declaration should be seen as no more than a good first step in the process to reform how development assistance is managed. They say that the Declaration does not go far enough to improve a badly flawed system.

In both the developed and developing worlds, a battle is being waged between business interests and what has been called the **civil society**. The latter is a largely unorganized group that includes many NGOs and independent citizens concerned about labour rights, the environment, human rights, and social development. The most public face of the civil society has been seen in protests at a variety of anti-free-trade demonstrations in North America and Europe. Many business supporters view the idea of giving aid as a distortion of the free market system that has been proven not to work. They feel that the best hope for poorly developed countries lies in the economic growth that will occur if the free market system is allowed to operate. In contrast, most members of the civil society feel that more and better aid must be given.

It is not just business interests who are saying that development aid should be reduced, or even eliminated. Often, it is activists in recipient nations who are suggesting this. (The only exception to this stance would be aid provided in the event of emergencies such as earthquakes or wars.) They have several reasons for making this remarkable statement. They point out that too much aid today has strings attached to it that force the receiving country to cut government services, sell off government assets, boost production of cash crops, and allow foreign competitors into the country.

These activists also point out that most aid does not reach the poorest of the poor—in 1998 and 1999, only 23 percent of the US$61 billion of aid in the world went to the poorest nations. Too much aid is tied to meeting the needs of the donor rather than the recipient. For example, activists point out that aid given in the form of products from the donor country or to provide debt forgiveness does not directly aid the poor country (see Figure 13–11). (In many cases, everyone realizes that these debts will never be repaid. Debt forgiveness recognizes this and helps private lenders recover their money.) In both cases, the aid money ends up going back to the donor country. The final argument against aid is that it leads to a sense of dependency in developing countries.

	Total ODA (US$ billions)	ODA not Including Debt Forgiveness (US$ billions)	Debt Forgiveness Part of ODA (%)
2000	54	52	3.7
2001	52	49	5.8
2002	58	53	8.6
2003	69	61	11.6
2004	79	72	8.9
2005	107	82	23.4

Figure 13–11 While debt forgiveness is helpful in the long run for poorer nations, and has grown substantially in recent years, it does not replace the need for spending on development assistance programs.

You can read the indicators of the Paris Declaration and then read a critique of it at the links on our Web site.

Role of Remittances

The vital role of remittances—money sent to home countries by migrants working in wealthier countries—does not receive the attention that it deserves. The situation in Canada illustrates the role of remittances well. In 2005, the Canadian government provided about $3.6 billion in foreign aid, while Canadians donated about $544 million to NGOs that work in international development. In contrast to these sums, Canadian residents send approximately $15 billion to family and friends outside this country—we must say "approximately" because no one knows with any accuracy how large the remittances really are. Internationally, it is thought that remittances may total US$167 billion per year. This is an amount considerably larger than the amount of official and private development assistance. Remittances play a unique part in addressing world economic disparities, since the money that moves from richer to poorer countries is injected directly into local economies that are much in need of economic stimulation.

GLOBALIZATION

Remittances play a unique part in addressing world economic disparities.

What are at least three ways in which remittances are a "unique" means of reducing economic disparity?

Certainly this is a subject that needs to be studied in much more detail so that remittance "aid" can be delivered more efficiently. For example, when an average Canadian wants to send money to a family member living outside Canada, he or she uses a money-transfer agency that may charge a fee as high as 17 percent of the amount being sent. Ways could be found that would dramatically cut this amount. More regulation of remittances could also ensure that money is not being sent to support criminal or terrorist organizations.

You can read more about remittances from Canada at the link on our Web site.

Income Disparity Within Countries

Measuring Disparity Within Nations

As a result of drastically different rates of economic growth, the gap between the world's rich and poor has grown steadily wider. Income disparities can be measured using a statistical tool called the **Gini index**. Gini values can range from zero (which means that income is distributed evenly among everyone) to one (which means that all income is owned by one person). Gini values can also be shown graphically (see Figure 13–12). (Depending on the source, Gini index values are sometimes given as decimals [for example, 0.34] and sometimes as whole numbers [for example, 34.0]). Gini index values range widely from one country to another. The UN uses a Gini value of 0.40 as a warning level that a country's economic disparities are becoming excessive. Old Core countries typically have values less than 0.40, while values higher than 0.60 exist in a few countries outside the Old Core (see Figure 13–13). The people in the most desperate circumstances are those who are poor in an already poor country. They do not even get a fair share of a small pie. Generally the poorest of the poor are those who live in rural areas, since economic growth is almost always focused in urban areas and especially in large cities.

Income Redistribution Within a Country

It is beyond the scope of this book to delve in any depth into the question of what role income redistribution should play in the economy of any particular country.

		Gini Index (Year of data)	
Old Core	Canada	0.33	(1998)
	Germany	0.28	(2000)
	Japan	0.38	(2002)
	US	0.45	(2004)
New Core	Chile	0.54	(2003)
	China	0.44	(2002)
	Malaysia	0.46	(2002)
	Poland	0.34	(2002)
Near Core	Georgia	0.38	(2003)
	Iran	0.43	(1998)
	Nicaragua	0.55	(2002)
	Philippines	0.46	(2002)
Far Periphery	Bangladesh	0.32	(2000)
	Cameroon	0.45	(2001)
	Papua New Guinea	0.51	(1996)
	Zambia	0.53	(1998)

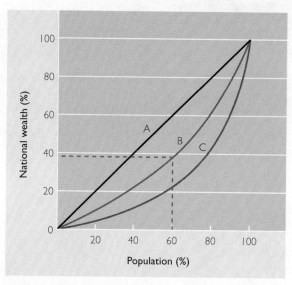

Figure 13–12 The diagonal line A represents a country with a perfectly equal distribution of income—each 20% of the population has 20% of the nation's wealth. Line B represents a country with a relatively low Gini index. This would be typical of an Old Core country. In this case, the poorest 60% of the people have about 38% of the country's wealth. Line C represents a typical income distribution outside the Old Core. In these countries, wealth is even more concentrated in the hands of the rich. What percentage of this country's wealth is held by the poorest 60% of the people?

Figure 13–13 Old Core countries generally have a more equal distribution of wealth than most countries elsewhere. Note that Gini index data was not available for Angola and Haiti, so Cameroon and Papua New Guinea were substituted as representatives of the Far Periphery. Also, calculation of Gini index values is complex, so it is not done very often—hence the wide range of dates of this data.

It is helpful though to at least examine, in a general way, the nature of this issue, which has very important economic, social, and political implications.

Fundamentally the question is what role (if any) governments should play in overcoming income disparities and, following from this question, what is the purpose of taxation? For some people, taxation exists only to provide the money that governments need to pay for such things as roadways, garbage pickup, and national defence. Other people believe that taxation has a second important role—that of **income redistribution**. This means taxes can, and should, be used to transfer money from the rich to the poor. This is seen in many aspects of life—such as the facts that richer people pay a higher income tax rate than poorer people and that governments provide more pension money to poorer seniors than to richer ones. In reality, it is not that simple. For example, government spending on things like higher education could be seen as contributing to income redistribution since it helps poorer students to get a high quality education that they otherwise could not afford.

Different countries have taken different approaches to this problem. Traditionally, countries like Sweden have believed in a "womb to tomb" approach to providing support for its citizens, while countries like the US have believed in a somewhat more hands-off approach, with less government support. Canada falls somewhere in between the US and European nations. A good way to look at whether income redistribution is happening in a country is to look at historical values of the Gini index (see Figure 13–14). What patterns, if any, do you see?

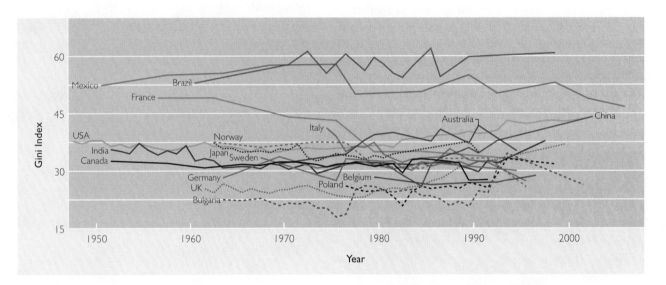

Figure 13–14 This graph shows changes in Gini index values for selected countries since World War II. Declining Gini index values indicate that more effective means are being found to redistribute income.

Chapter Questions

Knowledge and Understanding

1. **a)** Summarize the causes of the large economic disparities that exist among countries in the world.

   b) Suggest how each of these causes can be addressed in the future.

2. Give evidence to support the statement that since World War II, "The rich get richer and the poor get poorer."

3. Give two different reasons why it is more helpful for foreign aid to be given as cash than as material goods.

4. Examine the editorial cartoon in Figure 13–15. What is the significance of the images chosen by the cartoonist? List the main ideas from this chapter that the cartoon expresses.

5. Give at least three reasons why US aid to Western Europe and Japan at the end of World War II was so much more generous than any aid that was given to the rest of the world.

Thinking

6. We tend to take the concept of continuous growth for granted. Why is this so? Were you surprised to learn that most of the world's countries are poorer now than they were at some point in the past? Why or why not?

7. **a)** Explain in your own words what the Gini index is designed to show.

   b) Explain why Gini index values for individual countries are lower (generally between 0.25 and 0.60) than the Gini index for the entire world (higher than 0.66).

Figure 13–15 The horn of plenty—a "cornucopia"

   c) Would the Gini index for your community (city, town, or rural area) be higher or lower than that of all of Canada? Why?

8. **a)** Examine the data shown in Figure 13–10. Group the countries according to their pattern of foreign aid assistance over the 19-year period shown.

   b) What do these groupings say about attitudes toward aid during this time? (Hint: The early 1990s was a time of economic recession in the OECD, while the late 1990s was a time of great economic growth.)

9. Do you feel that you have any personal responsibility to help those who are less fortunate than you are? Explain.

Communication

10. Complete the foreign aid mapping exercise that your teacher will give you. You will do this activity either on a paper base map or using ArcView GIS software.

Application

11. Should economic globalization have a purpose? There are three possible answers to this question:
    - *"No. Globalization is a value-free concept. It is no more than the free market operating in an unfettered way."*
    - *"Yes. Globalization should operate in such a way as to diminish poverty in the world."*
    - *"Yes. Globalization should be a tool that will both diminish poverty and reduce the gap between rich and poor."*

    Choose one of these statements and explain why you agree with it. Your teacher will tell you specifically what is required, but a variety of approaches could be used to answer this question. These include a short, formal essay, a photographic essay, or a Web site that provides links to sites that support your thesis.

12. Battlefield casualty hospitals use a triage system to decide which patients should get immediate assistance when the number of wounded exceeds the capacity of the hospital. Casualties are put into one of three groups:
    i) those likely to survive with or without medical aid
    ii) those likely to die even if they get medical aid
    iii) those likely to die without medical aid, but likely to survive with it

Only those in group (iii) would receive immediate aid. It has been suggested that a similar system should be put in place to decide on recipients for foreign aid, since the amount of aid available is far less than what is needed.

a) How might a triage system work?

b) Identify two countries that would likely be put into each group.

c) Do you agree that such a system should be used? Explain your answer.

13. A question that is often asked is: "Why should Canada give away huge amounts of money for foreign aid when there are so many serious problems at home?" What factors should a Canadian consider before trying to answer this question?

14. Assume that you have just been elected to the House of Commons and that you have been named the minister responsible for the efficient use of the money that Canada and Canadians send overseas (ODA, PDA, and remittances). State at least six specific reforms that you would introduce to achieve this goal. For each reform, indicate what the problem is today and indicate how your reform will improve the situation. **G**

CHAPTER 14
The International Debt Crisis

Key Terms

hard currency

debt service charges

World Bank

Human Development Index (HDI)

debt/export ratio

highly indebted poor countries (HIPC)

odious debt

sovereign default

International Monetary Fund (IMF)

debt relief

Highly Indebted Poor Countries (HIPC) initiative

Poverty Reduction Strategy Paper (PRSP)

Jubilee 2000 Campaign

A two-bed dispensary in a debt-ridden African country. The World Bank and International Monetary Fund (IMF Director General Dominique Strauss-Kahn is below) lend money to indebted countries.

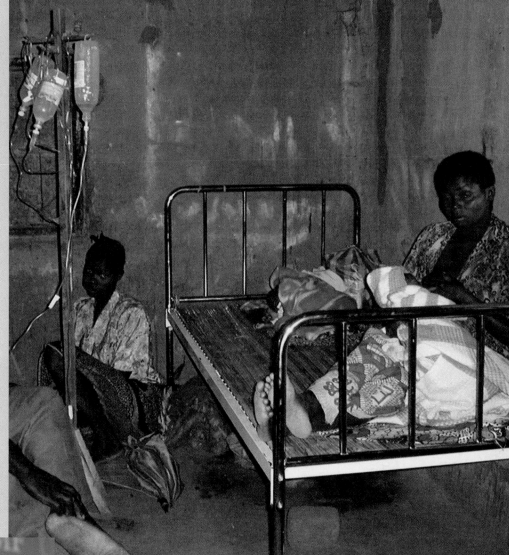

Key Questions

By the end of this chapter you will be able to answer the following questions.

■ How are the economies of Periphery nations adversely affected by decisions made in the Old Core?

■ How are the quality of life and job prospects of poor people linked to the global economy?

■ How did many poor countries come to have so much external debt?

■ Should these countries be excused of all or much of their debt? If so, how should this happen?

Figure 14–1 What would you do if you had a mountain of debt?

What would you do if you found yourself in the following situation in a few years?

- You took out student loans each year to help pay for your post-secondary studies, so that at graduation you were $20 000 in debt.
- After working for someone else for a couple of years, you decided to start your own business making custom motorcycles (see Figure 14–1). The bank liked your business plan and loaned you $50 000 to start your company. You did not like the idea of being $65 000 in debt (you had started to pay off your student loan by then), but you were sure that your business would be profitable and that you could pay off your loans while building a better future for yourself.

- After two years of disappointing sales, you came to realize that your business was just too small to be successful. You needed a showroom and half a dozen sample bikes to show what your small company (three employees) could do. The only way to rescue your business was to expand. The bank agreed and decided to lend you another $120 000. This loan would put your total debt at almost $170 000.
- To obtain the loan, you had to offer all your business and personal assets as *collateral* (security for a loan, such as property or a vehicle). If you are not able to pay back your loan, you could lose your business, your truck, and your furniture.
- Unfortunately, your expansion occurred at the worst possible time—just as a serious downturn in Canada's economy was accompanied by much higher interest rates for loans. You now find yourself owing the bank more than $180 000. Even though you have paid almost $70 000 in interest since you left school, you have paid less than $10 000 off the principal of the loan. The interest alone is more than $1 500 per month. The economy is very bad, so your sales are slow, and you just can't make your loan payments! What should you do?

Questions

1. Consider how you got yourself into this mess:

   a) For what reasons did you borrow money?

   b) Did you make reckless financial decisions?

2. To what extent is the situation your fault and to what extent is it a result of factors beyond your control? What factors might these be?

3. What options do you have at this point? Try to give at least two.

4. Can nations find themselves in a similar situation to the one faced by the fictional "You" in this scenario? How?

The Burden of International Debt

Ms. Persaud gave her World Issues class an introductory assignment on international debt. Let's "listen in" and see how two of her students did.

Jenn: Sorry I'm late. My appointment with the guidance counsellor took longer than I thought. Pretty good, though—I feel better about my university choices.

Ben: Hey, no problem. I just downloaded some 2007 external debt stats for countries in our four groups into a spreadsheet. Got some extra countries from the Far Periphery since that's supposed to be where the problem is.

	Total External Debt (US$ billions)
1 Japan (Old Core)	1547.0
2 Canada (Old Core)	684.7
3 China (New Core)	305.6
4 Brazil (New Core)	176.5
5 Peru (Near Core)	27.9
6 Jamaica (Near Core)	7.4
7 Nepal (Far Periphery)	3.1
8 Mali (Far Periphery)	2.8
9 Kyrgyzstan (Far Periphery)	2.5
10 Eritrea (Far Periphery)	0.3

Jenn: Wow, look at the way the groups hang together! The rich countries owe the most and the poor countries don't owe very much at all.

Ben: Yeah, look at Japan. They owe 1547 billion bucks! That's like a trillion and a half—hard to imagine a stack of loonies that high!

Jenn: Ms. Persaud did say the debt problem was in the poor countries. That doesn't seem right here—looks like Japan and Canada have the debt problem. Places like Eritrea look like they need to get some credit cards and go shopping!

Ben: You know, when I found this stuff on the Internet I noticed that of the 18 countries with the highest debt, 17 were in the Old Core. I don't think "the Teach" is wrong about where the problem is, though. She's taught this course like a million times. We better do some more checking.

Jenn: These countries have really different populations. What if we check out per-capita debt—that's easy to do, right?

	Total External Debt Per Capita (US$)
1 Canada (Old Core)	20 506
2 Japan (Old Core)	12 140
3 Jamaica (Near Core)	2 656
4 Peru (Near Core)	974
5 Brazil (New Core)	929
6 Kyrgyzstan (Far Periphery)	470
7 Mali (Far Periphery)	233
8 China (New Core)	231
9 Nepal (Far Periphery)	106
10 Eritrea (Far Periphery)	63

Ben: Not a big change here, Jenn, although the New Core and Near Core sort of switched places.

Jenn: Maybe that says something about why New Core countries are growing so quickly?

Ben: Since we're looking at per-capita debt, does this mean that I owe 20 000 bucks to someone?

Jenn: No way, dude. This is money that the Canadian government has borrowed for various things. We are not talking about private debt here.

Figure 14–2 Students discuss international debt

Ben: Still looks like Eritrea and Nepal need to go shopping. What if we compare the amount of debt to the size of the economy instead?

Jenn: Okay, let's divide the total debt by the country's GDP and see what we get.

		Total External Debt/GDP
1	Kyrgyzstan (Far Periphery)	1.13
2	Jamaica (Near Core)	0.92
3	Canada (Old Core)	0.70
4	Mali (Far Periphery)	0.58
5	Nepal (Far Periphery)	0.46
6	Peru (Near Core)	0.41
7	Eritrea (Far Periphery)	0.34
8	Japan (Old Core)	0.34
9	Brazil (New Core)	0.29
10	China (New Core)	0.19

Ben: Look at that, the Far Periphery countries are moving up the table big time.

Jenn: You know, we may be on to something here. It isn't just the size of debt—it's the size of the debt related to the size of the economy that matters.

Ben: Certainly starting to look like Kyrgyzstan has a problem.

Jenn: Something just occurred to me. When countries have to make payments on their debts, a big bank in New York or Tokyo isn't going to want to take payments in Kyrgyzstan dollars or whatever. They want a **hard currency** like the US dollar or the euro. Countries can get hard currencies only by exporting. Let's compare debt to exports and see what we get.

		Total External Debt/Value of Goods Exported
1	Eritrea (Far Periphery)	17.5
2	Mali (Far Periphery)	8.7
3	Nepal (Far Periphery)	3.7
4	Kyrgyzstan (Far Periphery)	3.5
5	Jamaica (Near Core)	3.5
6	Japan (Old Core)	2.6
7	Canada (Old Core)	1.7
8	Brazil (New Core)	1.3
9	Peru (Near Core)	1.2
10	China (New Core)	0.3

Ben: Cool, Jenn! Something else—these stats only look at exports of goods. Old Core countries also export a lot of services, so Japan and Canada would be doing even better on this table if we included those.

Jenn: Look at poor Eritrea! They had the smallest debt of all these countries, but they export so little that they can't pay off even a small debt.

Ben: Yeah, let's write this up for class. The important thing isn't how large a country's external debt is—it's what shape the country's economy is in to pay their debt.

The statistical analysis done by Jenn and Ben shows that it is not the total amount of debt that is most important. If it were, Old Core countries would have the debt problem. Typically they take on vast amounts of debt. However, this is rarely a problem for three reasons:

- In a globalized financial world, countries like Canada and Japan are both borrowers and lenders. They could have less external debt if they borrowed from a lender within the country, but it is often cheaper to borrow from a lender in another country.

- Loans are taken out for particular purposes that promote the growth of a country's economy.

- Old Core countries have economies that are active enough that they can afford the interest and principal costs of their loans so total debt loads do not grow over time.

The debt situation of many countries in the Periphery is very different from that of Core countries. In fact, many of these Periphery countries find themselves in a situation not unlike the one faced by the fictional "You" described earlier in the Working It Out on page 214. There are some significant differences, however. For one thing, rather than owing tens of thousands of dollars, Periphery countries may owe billions. For another, there is no clear way for a country to declare *bankruptcy* (a legal process by which a person or company may have debts dismissed).

The debts of many Periphery countries far exceed their ability to pay. This situation exists because of the poor economic growth that they have experienced for many years—at least partly because the loans they took in the past were often not used to grow the country's economy. The future promises only greater debt because many countries are not even managing to pay the interest on the debts they already have. As well, as you will see later in this chapter, many of these countries have been forced by their creditors to take out even more loans. By 2006, developing countries owed the staggering sum of US$2.9 trillion (see Figure 14–3), with this

amount increasing each year. **Debt service charges**, or interest, in 2005 were US$513 billion per year. Countries in all parts of the developing world (see Figure 14–4) owe this debt.

Three types of lenders hold this debt. The source of loans varies somewhat from one country to another. In 2006

- 71 percent of developing country debt was owed to private lenders like commercial banks

- 13 percent of the debt was in the form of *bilateral loans* (loans from another government)

- 16 percent of debt was held by international agencies like the **World Bank**, a specialized agency that furthers the economic development of member nations, chiefly through guaranteed loans

Banks and other private lenders consider some regions, like Latin America and the Caribbean, to be "safer" places in which to make loans compared to many African nations. They consider these regions better risks for the same reason that some private borrowers are considered safer than others—the lender feels that the loan has a better chance of being repaid. In the case of these regions, it is because their economies are stronger and more stable than most African economies.

There are two main reasons why banks feel that loans to regions like sub-Saharan Africa are too risky. First, because it is the poorest region of the world, there are questions about the ability of the region's nations to pay off substantial loans. Second, the region has a

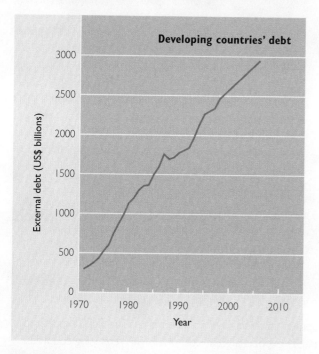

Figure 14–3 Growth of external debt for all developing countries, 1970–2005

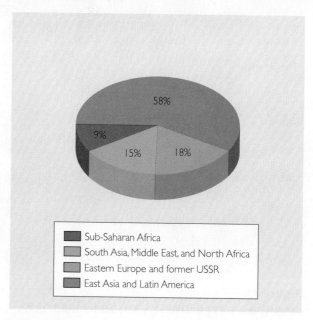

Figure 14–4 Percentage of developing countries' debt, by region, 2006

reputation for political instability. Frequent civil wars and violent overthrows of government do not inspire confidence among bankers. As a result of this lack of confidence, the poorest areas of the world get a relatively smaller proportion of their loans from private lenders and must rely more heavily on bilateral loans and on money from international agencies like the World Bank.

Effects of Debt

Being deeply in debt has an enormous impact on a poor country. Nowhere is this more true than in the poorest continent of the world, Africa. A sample of the debt situation in this area is given in Figure 14–5. A careful analysis of these data is needed if we are to understand the importance that debt plays in African countries. Let's see what this table tells us.

- Column 1—Allows you to confirm that Africa is the poorest region in the world and has the lowest

level of social development. The United Nations' **Human Development Index (HDI)** is a measure of the quality of life in a country, calculated from life expectancy at birth, the adult literacy rate, and per-capita GDP.

- Columns 2 and 3—As Ben and Jenn discovered, it is important to consider both the total external debt and the per-capita external debt. Also remember the relationship between the size of the debt and the poverty of these countries. To most Canadians, a debt of a few hundred dollars per capita does not seem like very much, but if you remember that the per-capita income in many of these countries may be 1/50th of Canada's per-capita income, you will have a better understanding of the significance of these debts.

- Column 4—Jenn and Ben also discovered the vital importance of the **debt/export ratio**, which is the relationship between the amount of debt and the size of a country's exports that provide hard

	HDI Rank (of 177), 2006	Total Debt, 2004 (US$ millions)	Debt Per Capita, 2004 (US$)	Debt/ Export Ratio, 2004	Spending on Debt Service, 2004 (% GDP)	Spending on Education, 2005 (% GDP)
Angola	161	9 521	614	0.7	10.4	2.6*
Burundi	169	1 385	190	28.9	1.3	5.1
Cameroon	144	9 496	594	3.6	4.1	1.8
Ethiopia	170	6 574	94	11.0	1.0	5.0
Ghana	136	7 035	324	2.7	2.7	5.4
Kenya	152	6 826	204	2.6	2.3	6.7
Malawi	166	3 418	271	7.3	3.2	5.8
Mauritania	153	2 297	766	5.6	3.8	2.3
Niger	177	1 950	144	5.0	1.6	2.3
Nigeria	159	30 315	279	0.8	3.3	0.9**
Senegal	156	3 938	345	2.7	4.4	5.4
Sierra Leone	176	1 723	325	9.9	2.5	3.8
Sudan	141	19 332	545	5.1	1.4	6.0**
Uganda	145	4 822	174	8.0	1.5	5.2
Zambia	165	7 279	633	4.0	7.9	2.0

Figure 14–5 The relationship between debt and social development in selected African countries. The debt/export ratios for Angola and Nigeria are very low because each of these countries exports a great deal of oil. The remaining countries were not lucky enough to win the "great geological lottery."

*2001 data; **1999 data

currencies for debt repayment. Some African countries, with debt/export ratios of greater than 7:1, find that they cannot pay even the interest on their debts, even if they use all of the country's export earnings for this purpose.

- Column 5—The next statistic to consider is how much the country spends to service its debt, that is, to at least pay the interest on their loans. This is expressed as a percentage of the country's gross domestic product (GDP). While there is no clearly defined limit beyond which a country should not go, the simple fact is that the more a country spends on debt payments, the less it will have for other needs. Some countries pay an enormous amount of their limited wealth to keep up with the interest on their debts. Other countries cannot even cover these debt service charges. In such cases, the level of their debt increases by the amount of the unpaid interest.

- Column 6—This is the amount of money the country is able to spend on education. (In most countries, a comparable amount would be spent on healthcare.) You can compare education spending to the amount spent to service debt. Experience has shown that money spent on education and healthcare is vital to the economic and social development of a country (see Figure 14–6). Unfortunately, many African countries find themselves spending more money on servicing their debt than they do on either education or healthcare.

Figure 14–6 The burden of debt servicing means that many poor countries do not have enough money to spend on education. In this photo you can see half of an African school building and two of the four classes held in this building. The school is built of stone plastered with a mixture of mud and cow dung. There is no heat, even though it can snow in this mountainous area, and most students sit on the mud floor.

How the Debt Crisis Happened

The debt crisis did not occur as a result of any single event. Rather, it can be linked to a "perfect storm" of interconnected events. None of these events, in and of itself, caused the debt crisis, but each contributed to the creation of an economic environment within which the crisis became inevitable.

- **Loans, not grants**. In 1957, the United States announced that future US foreign aid would be in the form of loans rather than grants. The logic behind this decision was that the loans would be used for investments in developing countries that would generate sufficient wealth to more than pay for themselves. Other countries followed the US's lead and changed from a grant model for aid to a loan model. From the perspective of the lenders, this approach might have made sense, but for poor nations it meant that they had to accept loans if they wanted to get

money that they desperately needed. While many of these loans were made at below-market-level interest rates, they still had to be paid back.

- **Skyrocketing oil prices**. In the early 1970s, there was a great deal of uncertainty in world financial markets. The Organization of Petroleum Exporting Countries (OPEC) felt that the lower value of the US dollar at this time was costing them a great amount of money since oil prices were (and still are) expressed in US dollars. In response, in late 1973, they increased the price of oil by 70 percent over a relatively short period of time. Additional large oil price increases occurred in 1979. Though these "oil shocks," as they were called, were a big problem for wealthy countries such as Canada, for nations outside the Old Core or those with no resources of their own, they often proved economically devastating.

- **A glut of "petrodollars."** Because of the massive increase in the price of oil, OPEC nations had vast sums of money to invest in the 1970s. They deposited this money in banks in North America, Europe, and Japan. These banks had to find customers to borrow the cash so that they could pay interest on the deposits and make a profit themselves. In fact, according to what are called fractional reserve requirements in a bank, $1 billion in deposits allowed as much as $30 billion in loans. The world's developing countries became more than willing customers for loans that had low, but floating, interest rates. Floating rates go up and down with market conditions. Hence they offer no guarantee of stable costs to borrowers. In reality, a major reason why these countries had to borrow money was to pay for the oil they needed— oil that had become dramatically more expensive. When a country uses loans to pay for day-to-day needs like oil, little capital is left over for economic development. These oil purchases, of course, enriched the oil exporters even more and meant that more petrodollars were available for loans. This situation continues today in an era of very high oil prices.

- **High inflation.** Things might still have worked out for the developing countries except for one other complication. During the 1970s and early 1980s, the world experienced high inflation rates that drove up interest rates. Loans that might have been affordable when the cost of borrowing was 5 percent became totally unaffordable with rates between 10 and 15 percent.

- **Falling commodity prices.** As we have seen, countries can pay for their debts only with hard currencies like the US dollar that are earned by exporting. Most **highly indebted poor countries (HIPC)** rely on the export of agricultural, forestry, and mining commodities to earn foreign currency. To add to the growing economic mess, for a number of reasons, the price of many of these commodities declined during the 1970s and early 1980s. Hence, these countries had to pay higher prices for their imports (especially oil) while earning less from their exports.

- **Declining exchange rates.** To make matters worse, throughout this whole period, the value of the currencies of most African and other very poor nations has declined significantly compared to major currencies like the US dollar and the euro (see Figure 14–7). Much of the decline in currency values was because of falling commodity prices. If a currency lost half its value compared to US dollars and other hard currencies (and many lost much more than that), the debt load doubled in terms of local currency.

While these conditions were largely beyond the control of the developing countries, their governments also contributed to the crisis. The availability of cheap credit encouraged many of them to go on spending sprees. In many cases, the loans were used to invest in useful development projects and to pay for education and healthcare improvements. Too often though, governments spent money on consumer goods, military hardware, and hydroelectric dams that might not have been the most pressing need at that stage of these countries' economic growth. Leaders, like Mobutu Sésé Seko spent the country's money indulging himself (see Figure 14–8). Corrupt leaders (see Figure 13–8 in Chapter 13 for the global "hall of shame") stole billions of dollars of the loans. The debt they created is called **odious debt**.

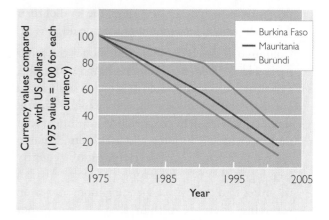

Figure 14–7 Many African currencies have lost much of their purchasing power in recent decades. This decline would be even more dramatic when compared to other major currencies like the euro and yen that gained in value compared to the US dollar.

Figure 14–8 In 1974, when his country might have been the poorest in the world, Mobutu Sésé Seko (left), the dictator of Zaire (now the DR of the Congo) put up a US$10 million purse to lure a heavyweight championship bout to his country between Muhammed Ali (right) and George Foreman.

Dealing With the Debt Crisis

Threat of Defaults

Countries cannot claim bankruptcy, although some financial authorities think that a process should be established that would allow them to do so. Instead they can create a situation called **sovereign default**. This is just a fancy way of saying that they refuse to pay for all, or, more likely, some of their loans. This has not occurred very often, and the results have been decidedly mixed for both the lenders and the borrowers. In 1881, The Ottoman (Turkish) Empire tried to do this. The European countries that had loaned the Ottomans money seized a number of their customs houses and took what they were owed. In 1902, a Venezuelan attempt at sovereign default ended when German, British, and Italian gunboats showed up along the coast of Venezuela to force repayment. More recently though, there have been two very large sovereign defaults—Russia in 1998 and Argentina in 2001. (These defaults applied to only some of the country's debt in each case.) In the latter case the default was on bonds worth the tidy sum of US$81 billion. Argentina eventually agreed to pay 35 cents on each dollar of this debt, so lenders lost more than US$50 billion. After this default Argentina still owed US$120 billion.

If a country does default, it opens itself to lawsuits as lenders try to recover their losses. For example, a lender might sue in a court outside the defaulting country to seize assets of the country. Also, a defaulting country may find it much harder to borrow next time. At worst, loans will not be available; at best, they may carry much higher interest rates to reflect the increased risk of loaning to a country that has a record of default. This might be a particular problem for a very small country that does not have any vitally needed products to sell or resources to develop.

Debt Restructuring

There is an old expression: "If you owe the bank a thousand dollars and cannot pay, you have a problem. If you owe the bank a million dollars (or in the case of a country, a billion dollars) and cannot pay, the bank has a problem." That is more or less the situation the world finds itself in today. By 1982, the borrowing and spending spree had ended. Many nations outside the Old Core had run up huge debts and were considering default. But banks in North America, Europe, and Japan had loaned so much money to these countries that their very existence would be threatened if defaults became common. If a significant number of these banks were to go bankrupt, the financial stability of the entire world would be in serious jeopardy. The question was what to do about this problem.

GLOBALIZATION

"If you owe the bank a thousand dollars and cannot pay, you have a problem. If you owe the bank a million dollars (or in the case of a country, a billion dollars) and cannot pay, the bank has a problem."

Why does a huge debt become a problem for the bank?

The governments of the Old Core countries had to choose between forcing already heavily indebted countries to accept additional financial aid so they could keep paying at least something on their loans, or running the risk of devastating their own economies. The choice was an easy one. Typically, the support took the form of additional loans or the rescheduling of existing loan payments so that they could be paid off more slowly. In either case, the result was higher debt charges to be paid and a greater total debt load.

Much of this aid came from the World Bank and the **International Monetary Fund** (**IMF**), a multilateral organization that works to stabilize the world's economy and to supervise the international debt payment system. This aid had many strings attached for the recipient countries.

- They had to reduce the value of their currencies when compared to major hard currencies, since this would discourage imports and stimulate exports. This would provide an influx of hard currencies that could be used to make debt payments. The problem is that the debt load became much greater in terms of local currencies.

- They were forced to find other ways to increase their export earnings. This often meant accelerating the rate of rainforest destruction, the overuse of sensitive agricultural resources, or the expansion of destructive mining practices.

- They were also required to restrict their social and education spending so that they would have more money available for loan payments. These cutbacks had an obvious impact on the rate at which countries could develop.

- They were not allowed to use foreign currencies to import critical necessities, like food and medicines.

From the perspective of the World Bank and the IMF, these economic reforms were seen as a form of international "tough love" that would put the economies of these nations on track toward sustainable growth and economic health.

The result of all of these restrictions was that most of the residents of the poorest debtor nations of Africa and Latin America experienced a significant decline in their standards of living in the 1980s. For example, in Mexico the average income, adjusted for inflation, dropped by more than 40 percent between 1982 and 1988, while the cost of a selection of basic foodstuffs for a family of five increased from 46 percent of the minimum wage to 161 percent between 1983 and 1992. In most developing countries, only the richest citizens avoided this squeeze between falling incomes and rising costs.

Debt Relief for Developing Countries

By the last half of the 1990s, it had become apparent to just about everyone, debtor and lender alike, that the international debt situation was unsustainable. It did not matter how much debt restructuring there was; the immense debt of many developing countries would not, and indeed could not, ever be paid. The only possible solution was some form of **debt relief**—that is, the debt would have to be written off the books. What the amount and nature of this relief should be has proven highly controversial. Some people believe the relief should be only enough to ensure that a debtor nation is able to pay off its remaining obligations. For others, nothing less than the complete elimination of the debt of the poorest countries will do.

Critics of debt relief suggest that it sends entirely the wrong message—both to debtors and to creditors.

- **Message to Debtor Countries** If you are a country that is given debt relief, there is no real consequence if you do not meet your responsibilities. Next time you overborrow, don't worry—eventually your debt will be erased for you.

- **Message to Creditors** Don't make future loans to Africa and other very poor parts of the world because of the perception (not unfairly) of high risk.

Highly Indebted Poor Countries Initiative

The **Highly Indebted Poor Countries (HIPC) initiative** has actually resulted in some debt relief, with more to come. This is a program created by the World Bank and the IMF and was the first serious international attempt to reduce the debt faced by the poorest countries of the world (see Figure 14–9). The governments of the world agreed to the basic idea of the HIPC program in 1996. This initiative was strengthened three years later. It applies to only the 41 poorest nations in the world, which had a debt of US$175 billion in 2004.

The HIPC program is complex, and participation in it imposes many demands on the debtor country. The HIPC initiative has three main stages: a *pre-decision point* followed by a *decision point,* and finally a *completion point.*

- When a country is determined to be eligible for the initiative (for example, if its debt is unsustainable and programs like debt restructuring are not sufficient to solve the problem), it is at the *pre-decision point.*

- The country must then prepare, in consultation with the country's *civil society organizations* (nongovernmental, non-profit organizations, and voluntary associations such as charities, faith groups, and trade unions), and with the aid of the World Bank and the IMF, an acceptable **Poverty Reduction Strategy Paper (PRSP)**. The PRSP details what plans the country has for economic, structural, and social reforms that will both promote economic growth and reduce poverty. It also highlights the economic aid that the country would need to achieve its goals. (Critics have suggested that the emphasis of these plans is on economic growth at the expense of poverty reduction.) If the country has an acceptable PRSP and if it has met its responsibilities under previous debt restructuring schemes, it moves on to the *decision point.*

- Next the country must put the plans of its PRSP into place. If the World Bank and IMF agree that it is working satisfactorily, the country will move to the *completion point.* It is at this stage of the process that debt relief actually happens. Governments of Old Core countries pay off the debt that the country owes. This is considered to be foreign aid by the donors, even though no money goes to the indebted country. Instead, the money goes either to banks in rich countries or just moves from one account to another within the government of a rich country.

 You can learn more about the HIPC initiative at the link on our Web site.

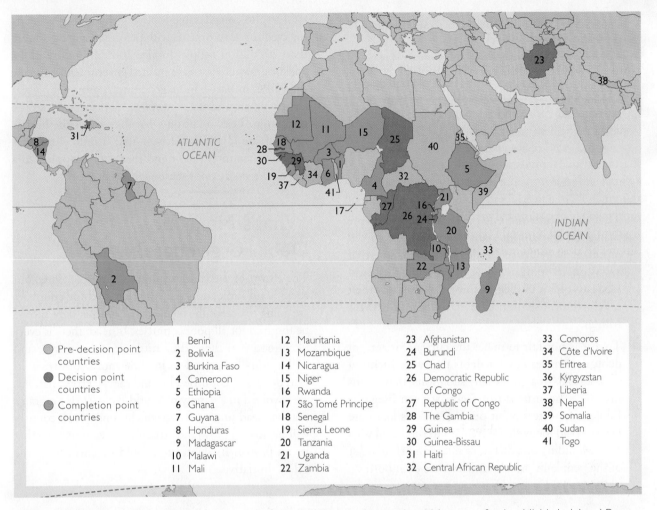

Figure 14–9 The 41 developing countries classified in 2007 by the International Monetary fund as Highly Indebted Poor Countries

○ Pre-decision point countries	1	Benin	12	Mauritania	23 Afghanistan
	2	Bolivia	13	Mozambique	24 Burundi
	3	Burkina Faso	14	Nicaragua	25 Chad
● Decision point countries	4	Cameroon	15	Niger	26 Democratic Republic of Congo
	5	Ethiopia	16	Rwanda	27 Republic of Congo
	6	Ghana	17	São Tomé Principe	28 The Gambia
● Completion point countries	7	Guyana	18	Senegal	29 Guinea
	8	Honduras	19	Sierra Leone	30 Guinea-Bissau
	9	Madagascar	20	Tanzania	31 Haiti
	10	Malawi	21	Uganda	32 Central African Republic
	11	Mali	22	Zambia	

33	Comoros
34	Côte d'Ivoire
35	Eritrea
36	Kyrgyzstan
37	Liberia
38	Nepal
39	Somalia
40	Sudan
41	Togo

Jubilee 2000 Debt Campaign

To many, the HIPC initiative is based on a fatally flawed premise—that the main purpose of debt relief is to re-establish a country's ability to pay its debts. Instead, these critics feel that debt relief should occur so that poor countries can use their limited wealth to fund their economic and social growth.

In this chapter, you have been reading about the impact of the World Bank and the IMF on developing countries. Using the example on page 14, create a profile of one or both of these institutions.

In the News

An international campaign called the **Jubilee 2000 Campaign** was begun in 1990 with the goal of marking the new millennium by having all US$230 billion owed (at that time) by the 50 poorest countries forgiven. The world's major faith communities spearheaded it. The Jubilee campaign was centred on three principles:

■ That the debt of developing countries is ruinous. Ethically, those of us who live in rich countries must not accept a situation that condemns a majority of the world's citizens to poverty. Supporters of the Jubilee campaign want to see a program of debt elimination that focuses on the needs of debtors and not those of the creditors.

GLOBALIZATION

Ethically, those of us who live in rich countries must not accept a situation that condemns a majority of the world's citizens to poverty.

What is the basis for making this statement? Do you agree? Why or why not?

Despite considerable lobbying, including presenting creditor governments with petitions signed by more than 20 million people, Jubilee 2000 did not reach its goal but may at least have pushed governments to make the HIPC initiative more generous. A group of NGOs associated around the concept of Jubilee continues the compaign. They focus on what they see as the limitations of the HIPC initiative—that it only eliminates some of a country's debt and that it only applies to a few of the many poor nations in need.

- That the debtor nations have already paid more than a fair amount for loans that were often forced on them. As evidence, Jubilee supporters note that between 1980 and 1992, debtor nations paid US$1.6 trillion to their creditors, and yet saw their indebtedness rise from US$567 billion to US$1.4 trillion.

- That it is not fair to make the current citizens of debtor countries pay for debts that were incurred decades ago. In a great many situations, these loans may have been used unwisely, or even illegally. Jubilee supporters point out that odious loans are being repaid today that were used to fund civil wars or the building of a dictator's mansion before most of the people in these countries were even born.

What's Next for Debt Forgiveness?

The efforts of the various Jubilee groups continue, but there is no indication that the rich creditor countries are going to accept the blanket concept that debt should be forgiven for all poor countries. Instead, there is every likelihood that the HIPC initiative will continue and will gradually expand to include more countries. In fact, dozens of countries, beyond the 41 HIPC nations, are involved in a variety of World Bank/IMF programs that will lead to one of two conclusions—each country will be able to grow and structure its economy so that it can pay off its debt, or it could be enrolled in the HIPC initiative.

Chapter Questions

Knowledge and Understanding

1. Identify similarities and differences between the hypothetical situation of the person in the chapter opening ("A Difficult Dilemma"), and the situation in many developing nations today.

2. **a)** Briefly describe the reasons why the international debt became so large.

   b) Compare the role played by developed and developing countries in the growth of this debt. To what extent can "blame" be attached to the actions of each side?

   c) Consider the various factors that have contributed to the international debt crisis. What information suggests that at the time these events were occurring, the developed nations gave little thought to the impact they might have on developing nations?

3. **a)** Create an organizer to compare the HIPC and Jubilee approaches to debt relief.

   b) Do you think that the HIPC approach is fair to debtor nations? Why or why not?

Thinking

4. **a)** Canada owes billions of dollars. Should we be worried about the debt of distant countries when we are, ourselves, deeply in debt?

   b) Much of Canada's debt is owed to Canadians, for example, as Canada Savings Bonds. How is this situation different from the debt situation in developing countries? How does this difference affect the problem of our debt?

5. **a)** Multilateral aid from the World Bank/IMF typically has many strings attached. Discuss the reasons for these conditions and the impact they have.

   b) One of these conditions is that a debtor country must devalue its currency. Why is this a desirable development from the perspective of debt repayment? Why is it an undesirable development from the perspective of ordinary citizens in the debtor country?

6. "Do you think it is appropriate that when debt relief is part of the official development assistance of an Old Core country, the money goes to lenders in the rich country rather than to the poor country?"

   Answer the above question twice—once in support of the statement and once in opposition. In each case, provide support for your answer.

Communication

7. "While the ethical reasons for the Jubilee Debt Campaign are admirable, this approach is totally impractical in the modern world."

   Do you agree with this statement or not? Explain in a well-organized paragraph of four to six sentences.

8. Your teacher will provide you with an expanded version of the data in Figure 14–3 and will tell you whether to do the following exercise on a paper base map or using ArcView GIS.

   a) Examine the data carefully to decide how you would classify countries' debts as "severe," "serious," or "moderate."

   b) Apply your criteria to the countries of Saharan and sub-Saharan Africa.

   c) Locate and shade each country on a base map of Africa according to its category.

   d) How did your categorization of the most indebted nations compare to the HIPC list?

9. Work with two other students to complete this question. Each person will write a formal letter expressing his or her views on debt relief. One person will write to the prime minister of Canada, another to the president of the World Bank, and the third to the editor of your local newspaper. Your letter should be about 200 words in length. Before writing, your group should agree on the main points that you wish to make in your letters. Note that the letters will be organized differently depending on who the recipient is; for example, readers of the newspaper's letters page will not have the same level of knowledge of this issue as the president of the World Bank. If you feel strongly about this issue and are pleased with how your letter turned out, you may want to actually send your letter.

Application

10. a) External debt means different things in different parts of the world. Consider the meaning in each of the following parts of the world: Old Core, New Core, Near Core, and Far Periphery. Indicate the relationship between debt and development in each part of the world.

b) Investigate the concerns that exist today over the level of debt in the US. How might this debt affect Canada?

11. a) Define the term "odious debt."

b) Describe at least three ways in which odious debt can occur.

c) For each of your answers to b), decide whether the nature of the debt justifies its forgiveness. Explain your conclusions.

d) Do lenders have a special responsibility to ensure that their loans do not lead to additional odious debt for a nation? Explain your views.

12. Choose one country listed in Figure 14–3 and research to find out how its debt was incurred, as well as details of its economic status and its recent political history, and how likely it is to be able to repay its debt.

13. Using the Internet, research the current status of debt relief in the world. Find out Canada's present attitude toward debt forgiveness.

UNIT 4 THE EARTH IN BALANCE

The polar bear has become the "poster child" for a world facing major sustainability issues. Climate change is eliminating the ice conditions that these magnificent animals need to survive. The next few decades are critical if we are to save them and perhaps ourselves.

CHAPTER 15

Land Issues

Key Terms

land degradation

erosion

terrain deformation

chemical deterioration

salinization

physical deterioration

desertification

solid waste management

3Rs

source reduction

extended producer
    responsibility (EPR)

protected area

Unlike the collapse of these backyards into a rain-swollen river, most soil erosion happens gradually and is not obvious to the casual viewer. Terracing of fields (below) is a soil-protection method that allows farming in hilly areas, with minimal soil loss.

Key Questions

By the end of this chapter you will be able to answer the following questions.

■ Why do some world issues get a great deal of attention while other equally important issues do not?

■ How does agricultural land become degraded?

■ How can we reduce the impact of the solid waste we create?

■ On what basis do we decide what land to protect in various types of parks?

THE NATURE OF ISSUES

There are issues...and there are issues. Some environmental issues get a great deal of attention—think of climate change and the seal hunt in Atlantic Canada. Other issues like **land degradation**, which is any deterioration of the productive capacity of soil for either present or future use, get relatively little worldwide attention. Why is this so? The answer lies in the very nature of such issues. Some of them are vitally *important* to the global population, while others are relatively *unimportant*. (Note that "important" and "unimportant" are used here in a relative sense.) At the same time, some issues are inherently *interesting* to the average person, while others are *uninteresting*. When you combine these characteristics, you get four broad categories of issues (see Figure 15–1).

What category do other world issues fall into? Complete the following questions to find out. Browse through this book to identify issues and then try to classify them.

1. Identify at least two environmentally focused issues not mentioned in this activity that fall into each of the following categories. (You can ignore U & U issues!)

   a) Important and Interesting

   b) Unimportant but Interesting

   c) Important but Uninteresting

2. Identify at least two globalization-focused issues that fall into each of the following categories.

   a) Important and Interesting

   b) Unimportant but Interesting

   c) Important but Uninteresting

3. a) What factors contribute to an issue being considered important?

   b) What factors contribute to an issue being considered interesting?

1. Important and Interesting Issues

By their nature, issues in this group, like climate change, which many believe could cause an increase in the severity of storms, *should* and *do* get a great deal of attention.

2. Unimportant but Interesting Issues

Because they are highly interesting, issues like the seal hunt get a great deal of attention. Unimportant but Interesting issues tend to detract attention from ones that are much more important.

3. Unimportant and Uninteresting Issues

How often you clean your room is of little importance and interest to the rest of the world. "U & U" issues usually get the amount of attention they deserve—none.

4. Important but Uninteresting Issues

Our last group, the Important but Uninteresting issues, like land degradation, which falls clearly into this category, seriously affects the well-being of billions of people every year. Yet, they get little attention.

Figure 15–1 Four broad categories of issues

It can be argued that land degradation affects more people (and other living things) more seriously than any other environmental problem. Our ignorance of this issue is not altogether a surprise, since the problems of land degradation are not always visible. Also, land degradation is largely a rural problem, and most of us live in cities.

The problems of land degradation are not new. More than 2000 years ago, the famous Greek philosopher Plato wrote that

> Attica [Athens] *was no longer cultivated by true herdsmen, who made husbandry* [raising domestic animals] *their business, and were lovers of honour, and of a noble nature. As a result Attica had become deforested, the soils depleted, and there are*

> *remaining only the bones of the wasted body—all the richer and softer parts of the soil having fallen away.*

Land degradation is closely linked to poverty in the sense that, as the degree of degradation increases, crop and animal yields decline and people have both less to eat and less to sell to support themselves. Even as agricultural advances occur, the benefits may be lost as the total agricultural capability of a region is reduced by land degradation. In 1948, Lord John Boyd Orr, first Director-General of the UN Food and Agriculture Organization (FAO), said

> *If the soil on which agriculture and all human life depend is wasted away, then the battle to free mankind from want cannot be won.*

Types of Land Degradation

The United Nations has estimated that about 15 percent of the world's productive farmland has been significantly affected by some form of land degradation. The UN recognizes four categories of degradation: erosion, chemical deterioration, physical deterioration, and desertification. The impact of the first three of these is summarized in Figure 15–2.

Erosion

Erosion is the removal of the nutrient-rich layer of topsoil by either wind or water. Water erosion can occur in any climate zone, although it tends to be worse in areas with higher rainfall and hence with more runoff. Wind erosion occurs most commonly in arid and semi-arid climates. Most erosional processes are subtle and not easily noticed. For example, we are used to seeing rivers that look "muddy." In fact, what we are seeing is the removal of valuable, eroded topsoil. Erosion has many effects, including some that may not be obvious at first glance (see Figure 15–3).

In a mature forest that is not affected by human activities, the amount of topsoil loss is between 0.004 and 0.05 tonne per hectare per year. This relatively minor loss (between 4 and 40 kilograms) can easily be made up by the natural soil-forming processes at work in the forest. As you will see, the amount of erosion in an area can be much higher, depending on the particular natural and human characteristics of that area.

Type of Land Degradation	Affected Arable Pasture Land Worldwide (million ha)	As a % of Total Farmland in Canada
Erosion		
Loss of topsoil	504	403.2
Terrain deformation	96	76.8
Chemical deterioration		
Loss of nutrients	40	32.0
Salinization	28	22.4
Pollution	8	6.4
Acidification	2	1.6
Physical deterioration		
Compaction	25	20.0
Overblowing	4	3.2
Waterlogging	4	3.2
Subsistence	1	0.8

Figure 15–2 Compare the amount of land affected by each of these forms of degradation to the total amount of farmland in Canada. While the "supply" of farmland is being reduced by degradation, what is happening to the demand for food?

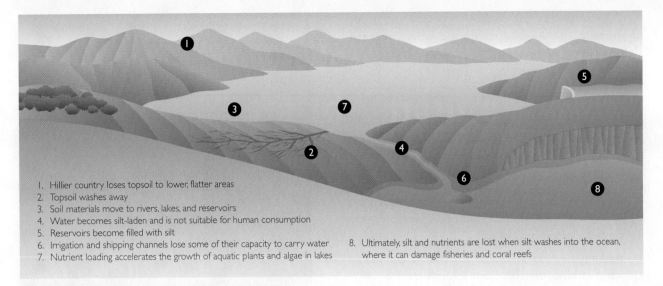

1. Hillier country loses topsoil to lower, flatter areas
2. Topsoil washes away
3. Soil materials move to rivers, lakes, and reservoirs
4. Water becomes silt-laden and is not suitable for human consumption
5. Reservoirs become filled with silt
6. Irrigation and shipping channels lose some of their capacity to carry water
7. Nutrient loading accelerates the growth of aquatic plants and algae in lakes
8. Ultimately, silt and nutrients are lost when silt washes into the ocean, where it can damage fisheries and coral reefs

Figure 15–3 Erosion involves much more than the removal of soil from land areas to the ocean. Consider how each of the aspects of erosion shown has a negative impact.

The overall average soil erosion for *cultivated* (prepared for use by ploughing and similar processes) land in North America and Europe is about 17 tonnes per hectare per year—or about 300 to 4000 times as much as in an untouched forest. This dramatic increase in topsoil loss is the direct result of the change from forest to farmland. Another way of thinking about the amount of soil lost is that it is about a typical dump-truck load from each hectare of farmland each year. This enormous amount of soil loss cannot be replaced by soil-forming processes. The situation is even worse in Asia, Africa, and South America, where the average topsoil loss is between 30 and 40 tonnes per hectare per year, or about two dump-truck loads each year.

Soil erosion becomes even worse when hilly land is used for farming. For example, in a hilly farming area of the Philippines, soil loss was measured at 400 tonnes per hectare per year—or more than 20 dump trucks full of soil from an area measuring 100 metres by 100 metres in only one year! Steep slopes obviously accelerate water more than gentle ones. One study of cassava cultivation (cassava, or manioc, is an important food crop in many tropical areas) showed dramatic differences in erosion depending on the slope of the ground (see Figure 15–4). This is not surprising if you think back a few years to the science class where you learned about kinetic energy—that is, $E = \frac{1}{2} mv^2$. If you double the mass of the water on a slope, you double the amount of kinetic energy available to erode the soil—but if you double the speed at which the water is moving (that is, if the slope is steeper), the energy produced is four times as great.

Figure 15–4 As this example shows, soil erosion dramatically goes up as slopes increase. The diagram (left) shows a 1 percent slope, which would typically lose 3 tonnes per hectare per year (t/ha/yr). As the slope increases to 5 percent (centre), soil loss increases to 87 t/ha/yr. At 15 percent (right), soil loss is 221 t/ha/yr. Why do farmers choose to farm land with steep slopes if they know that soil erosion will be so high?

When more severe erosion occurs, we may see changes in the landscape. This is called **terrain deformation**.

In the case of water erosion

- large or small gullies may be cut into farmers' fields (see Figure 15–5)
- mass movements (landslides) may occur (see page 228)

With wind erosion

- we may see dunes or deflation hollows, which are depressions created when the wind removes topsoil from a previously level area
- the land may also be "overblown," that is, covered by wind-eroded materials from somewhere else

Chemical Deterioration

Chemical deterioration, the deterioration of soil as a result of leaching, salinization, acidification, or pollution, can take four forms. The first and most important of these is loss of soil nutrients. Vital nutrients (especially nitrogen, phosphorus, and potassium) can be lost in two main ways. In an area with an excess of precipitation (over the amount of *evapotranspiration*), nutrients can be washed away, or leached. (Evapotranspiration is loss of moisture from the soil as a result of evaporation and transpiration from plants.) Significant leaching occurs in most of Canada, but the problem is less serious here than in tropical areas that receive large amounts of precipitation. In these areas, the severely leached soils have an orange-red colour that indicates the dominance of oxides of aluminum and especially iron in the soil (see Figure 15–6). These compounds are not soluble and cause soil exposed to the sun to become very hard.

Figure 15–5 Gullying, a form of terrain deformation, can destroy the agricultural capability of an area.

Figure 15–6 This farmland in Vinales, Cuba, shows the severely leached soils typical of a tropical area.

This problem frequently occurs in tropical rainforest regions, like large areas of South America, Africa, and southern Asia, where vegetation has been cleared to allow for farming. Leaching is made worse if a dense layer of vegetation does not protect the soil. For a few years after the land is cleared, yields are high because some organic materials remain in the soil, but the leaching soon destroys the fertility of the soil. The second way that soil nutrients are lost is through the growth of crops, particularly if the same crop, with the same nutrient needs, is grown each year.

A second type of chemical degradation is **salinization**—an increase in the concentration of soluble salts in the soil to the point where the soil becomes toxic for plant growth (see Figure 15–1, page 229). Although salinization can occur naturally if the water table is close to the surface in an arid area, it can be greatly accelerated by excessive irrigation. The water used for irrigation carries dissolved salts that will be left in the soil when the water evaporates from the soil's surface. If these salts are not flushed from the soil into drainage ditches, the salt concentration will eventually reach a dangerous level. Significant areas of formerly highly productive irrigated farmland have to be removed from production when salt levels get too high. About one-eighth of all irrigated land in the world has been degraded by severe salinization, with as much as another third being somewhat affected. Salinization is a particular problem in drier parts of the United States, China, the Middle East, and Australia.

Two other forms of chemical deterioration are less common. Land can become acidified by the use of excessive fertilizers or because of poor drainage. Finally, land can be polluted by emissions from nearby industries, or by the dumping of liquid or solid waste. For example, in many parts of southern Canada, treated sewage waste (sludge) is spread on farmers' fields. If this is done properly, it avoids the need to dump this waste in landfills and also provides nutrients to the soil. If too much sludge is dumped in one area, however, it can damage the land and seep into the water table.

Physical Deterioration

The productivity of land can be reduced by **physical deterioration**, that is, degradation of land caused by compaction, waterlogging, or subsidence. This happens in three ways. Soil can be *compacted* (densely packed) by the use of heavy machines or by the trampling of herds of animals. Waterlogging—for example, after floods recede from an area—can also damage land. The third form of physical damage is subsidence, or sinking, of land, which can be caused when a significant amount of water is removed from the water table.

Desertification

Desertification is a special type of land degradation. It differs from those mentioned previously in that it refers to the results of degradation rather than the causes.

Desertification occurs when human activities reduce the productivity of an arid or semi-arid area to the point that it resembles a desert. These desert-like conditions destroy the agricultural capability of the land (see Figure 15-7). As much as 40 percent of the world has climates dry enough that they face the possibility of desertification. This situation puts over one billion people at risk.

Figure 15–7 The gradual spread of desert-like conditions into formerly productive farmland is a major threat in arid and semi-arid areas around the world.

Causes of Land Degradation

While land degradation can be caused by natural factors, overwhelmingly it occurs as a result of human activity. These human causes fall into five main categories:

- **Deforestation.** When land is cleared for agricultural use, particularly in tropical rainforests, soil is exposed to serious erosion and leaching.

- **Overgrazing.** Too many grazing cattle, sheep, or goats can destroy vegetation beyond its ability to recover. As a result, soil is exposed to erosion and leaching.

- **Unsustainable agriculture.** If carried out too intensively to allow soils to renew themselves, agriculture reduces nutrient levels and, in dry areas, can result in salinization. Such farming is considered to be "agricultural mining" and is not sustainable in the long run. The most obvious factor is monoculture, the

practice of growing the same crop year after year. This happened in the Canadian Prairies during the 1930s. Even if chemical fertilizers provide nutrients, the soil may still degrade because it loses the vital structure provided by organic matter.

- **Overuse of natural vegetation.** In most developing parts of the world, people rely on trees and shrubs for fuel and for building materials. If the population density of an area becomes too high, overuse of vegetation can have an impact similar to that of overgrazing and deforestation.

- **Urban/industrial pollution.** In heavily industrialized urban regions, pollution can foul the soil of adjacent farms and make the land unusable for farming.

The relative importance of these causes of soil degradation is shown in Figure 15–8.

	Deforestation	Overgrazing	Unsustainable Agriculture	Overuse of Vegetation	Urban/Industrial Pollution
Africa	14	49	24	13	*
North/Central America	11	24	57	7	*
South America	41	28	26	5	—
Asia	40	26	27	6	*
Australasia	12	80	8	*	*
Europe	38	23	29	*	9
World	29	35	28	7	1

Figure 15–8 Causes of land degradation, by percent. The table shows the distribution of the various causes of land degradation by region and worldwide in 1995. It is important to note that newer data are not available. Why might that be?

* Indicates amount less than 0.5% (Because of rounding, rows may not total 100%.)

Overview of the Impact of Land Degradation

There is a strong *correlation* (relationship between items that is too strong to be due to chance alone) between land degradation on one hand, and poverty and conflict on the other. During the 1980s and 1990s, famines in Ethiopia and Sudan that killed tens of thousands of people were routinely blamed on drought and civil wars. Rarely did observers acknowledge the contribution of land degradation to these tragedies. Unfortunately, comprehensive research on land degradation is not readily available. Is this because scientists find other issues more interesting to study, or that research funding is more readily available for studies in more "trendy" areas?

Land Lost from Production

Estimates suggest that somewhere between 50 000 and 70 000 square kilometres of land are lost from production worldwide each year because of erosion, with another 20 000 to 30 000 square kilometres being lost because of salinization and waterlogging. In total this means that land degradation takes between 70 000 and 100 000 square kilometres of land out of production per year. The growth of cities means that an additional 20 000 and 40 000 square kilometres are lost from production each year. To put these amounts in context, the area of New Brunswick is about 73 000 square kilometres.

Loss of Productivity

As well as land going out of production because of degradation, there is a decline in the productivity of the land that remains in production. For example, salinization and waterlogging can reduce the yields from irrigated fields by between 30 and 80 percent. In total, estimates of food production that will be lost because of land degradation between 1985 and 2010 are 19 to 29 percent. Another estimate suggested that this degradation would result in a loss of about 14 million tonnes of grain annually—or about half the amount needed to feed the world's population growth during this time.

Global Patterns of Degradation

Not all parts of the world are equally affected by land degradation. On a global basis, about 26 percent of agricultural land is degraded to some extent, but the range of degradation is from 13 percent in the Americas to 41 percent in Africa (see Figure 15–9).

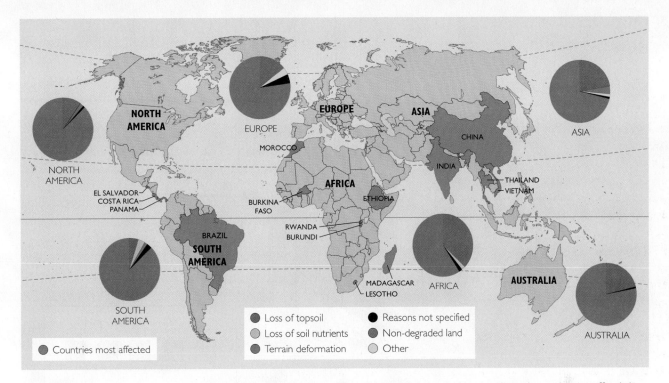

Figure 15–9 Unfortunately, those parts of the world most affected by land degradation are those least able to afford the lost agricultural productivity. Which parts of the world are these?

Solid Waste Management

What is your postal code? Check Figure 15–10 to see how many old dump sites there are in your part of Ontario. Does this number surprise you? Now let's zoom in a little. Figure 15–11 shows the number of dumps in each of the postal-code areas of Toronto. The total number of dumps here is particularly surprising if you remember that more than 2.5 million people live in the "M" postal code area and that almost all of the land there has been developed for some urban use. If you live in Toronto, how many dumps are in your neighbourhood? How would you know exactly where they are?

Should you be worried about what is in these dumps? Some say there is little to worry about because most of the garbage will have decomposed over the years, but this is not the case. Anthropologists have done excavations at the now closed "Fresh Kills" landfill in New York City, the largest landfill site in the world, and discovered that decades-old newspapers are still readable, and food wastes are easily identifiable.

First Letter of Postal Code	Number of Old Dump Sites
K	1186
L	877
M	860
N	1446
P	1232
Total	5601

Figure 15–10 Distribution of closed dump sites in Ontario. Old dump sites are widespread across Ontario. Why would there have been a larger number of dumps in the more distant past than today, especially considering that the population is much higher now?

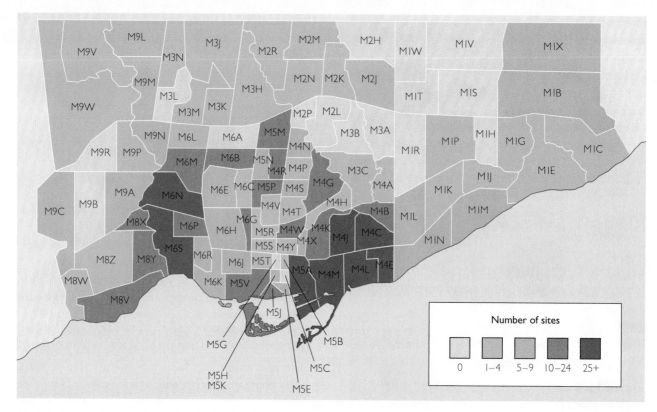

Figure 15–11 Closed dump sites in the "M" postal code area of Toronto. If you live in Toronto, how many dump sites are near your home? Do you know where any of them are?

Our society's (and perhaps your own) reaction to these old dumps illustrates a lot about our attitude toward garbage disposal or, as it is more properly called, **solid waste management**. For most of us it's "out of sight, out of mind," but for a variety of reasons the reality is not that simple. The disposal of solid waste can and does cause serious environmental damage—for example, sanitary landfills (or what we sometimes call "garbage dumps") can pollute groundwater and, even when operating properly, produce methane gas, which is a powerful greenhouse gas. As well, all methods of solid waste disposal are costly and add significantly to our taxes.

Types of Solid Waste Disposal

Different forms of waste disposal are used in different parts of the world. In North America, we have focused on throwing away our solid waste. In rural areas, this has most often meant small, open dumps located in inconspicuous places. Larger towns and cities use carefully engineered sanitary landfills, which are designed to accept large amounts of waste while ensuring as little environmental damage as possible (see Figure 15–12).

In Europe and Japan, where land is scarce, incinerators are commonly used. As with dumps, the environmental impact of incineration varies greatly. Older incinerators often burn waste inefficiently and produce large amounts of pollution, including extremely hazardous materials like *dioxins* (a group of hydrocarbons, many of which cause cancer). State-of-the-art incinerators burn at much higher temperatures and produce significantly lower levels of air pollution. The heat generated by the burning garbage is often used to generate electricity.

Waste management in Near Core and Far Periphery countries cannot be compared to that in richer countries. There are four main reasons for this—some of which reduce the problem of waste disposal while others increase it.

■ Poor people consume less than richer people, and hence generate less waste.

■ The things that poor people buy typically have less packaging that must be thrown away.

■ For obvious economic reasons, governments in poorer countries do not provide effective methods to handle solid waste. At best, garbage is dumped in huge, unplanned, totally unsanitary dumps. At worst, it is left in the street.

■ For residents of the Near Core and Far Periphery, waste materials are much more likely to be seen as economic resources than in the Old Core. People earn a poor living by carefully picking over trash for anything of value such as food, building supplies, and clothing (see Figure 15–13).

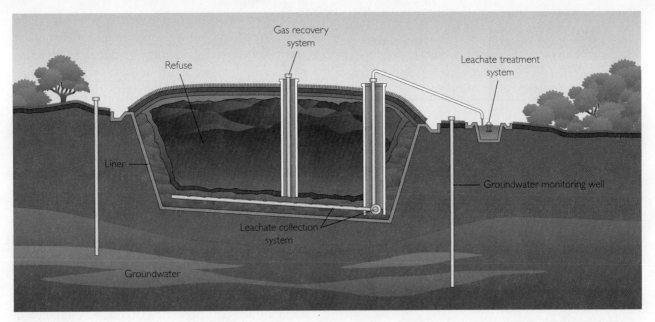

Figure 15–12 A modern sanitary landfill is designed to have as little environmental impact as possible. Before the "dump" is used, it is lined with waterproof materials to prevent *leachate* (water containing potentially dangerous dissolved materials) reaching the surrounding groundwater. The landfill is monitored to ensure that leakage has not occurred. Leachate is collected and treated in an adjacent plant to remove dissolved materials. Methane and other gases are collected and often burned to generate electricity.

Figure 15–13 About 2000 people live and work at this garbage dump in Phnom Penh, Cambodia. The dump is called "Old Smoky" because the dump and the methane it produces are constantly (but slowly) burning. Adults picking through the trash for valuable items can earn US$1 to US$1.25 per day. Children will earn about half that amount. And yes, those black specks are flies!

SUSTAINABILITY

For residents of the Periphery, waste materials are much more likely to be seen as economic resources than in the Old Core.

How can residents of wealthy countries like Canada apply this concept to the waste they create?

Better Ways of Managing Our Waste

What are our options if we want to do a better job of managing our waste? The often-mentioned **3Rs**, *Reduce, Reuse*, and *Recycle*, are a good starting point. It is important to remember that the 3Rs are always listed in the same order—and for a good reason (see Figure 15–14). *Reduce* is the best solution, with *Reuse* being next best, followed by *Recycle*.

Next in line after the 3Rs, in terms of desirable ways of dealing with waste, is the practice of energy recovery from waste; this can take two forms—incineration, where the heat from burning garbage is used to generate electricity, and methane collection from rotting garbage in a landfill. The methane can be burned for heating or electrical generation. At the bottom of the heap in terms of ways of dealing with waste is to dump it without even collecting the resulting methane.

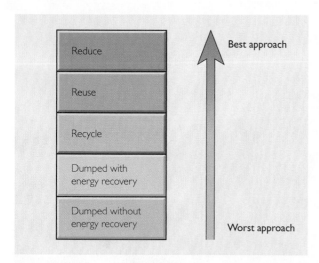

Figure 15–14 Solid waste management can be done in a number of ways that have varying impacts on the environment. In this diagram, solutions near the bottom of the list are less desirable than those higher up.

Reduce

The idea of not producing waste in the first place is the best approach to waste management. This principle is called **source reduction**. A century ago, relatively few commodities were sold pre-packaged. Shoppers would go to the market with a cloth or wicker shopping bag and a number of reusable containers to pick up groceries. Growth in the use of packaging occurred for several reasons—to provide convenience for consumers, to protect the product, and to make material handling and product identification easier for manufacturers and retailers. Shoppers today have some opportunities to buy grocery products with less packaging. For example, bulk food stores and farmers' markets use much less packaging than supermarkets. A number of supermarket chains sell reusable cloth bags that shoppers can use instead of plastic bags.

Source reduction occurs only when the public demands it. This demand could have two impacts: companies might see that it is in their commercial best interests to meet the demands of consumers who want less packaging; and political parties might realize that they can gain votes if they propose more stringent packaging laws (not to mention the reduced impact on the environment). North Americans have been slow to demand source reduction. This is not the case in many European countries. For example, Germany has enacted strict packaging laws to reduce the amount of garbage that is created.

Reuse

When further reductions in waste creation are not possible, the next best approach is to reuse. As a society, we are not as good at reusing as we used to be. Thirty years ago, most people bought their milk in reusable plastic and glass containers. Similarly, soft drinks were most often purchased in glass bottles that could be used dozens of times before being recycled. In both industries, the companies that bottled and sold these beverages sought to replace reusable containers with one-time-use plastic, cardboard, and aluminum containers. Using disposable containers was cheaper and more convenient than having to maintain a container return system. In exchange for being allowed to abandon returnable containers, the soft-drink industry became a major sponsor of the first blue-box recycling systems.

One highly successful example of a returnable container system exists in Ontario—the reuse of beer bottles. Brewers Retail Incorporated (better known as "The Beer Store") has been reusing bottles since 1927, when a three-cent-per-bottle deposit was imposed to encourage people to return their bottles. The return rate is more than 97 percent, and each bottle is used, on average, 15 to 20 times before it is recycled. Such a well-developed bottle return system has put Ontario in the unfamiliar position of being a world leader in an environmental field (see Figure 15–15). In 2007, Ontario decided to use the effective container collection infrastructure of The Beer Store to collect wine, beer, and liquor containers sold by LCBO (Liquor Control Board of Ontario) stores. At this time, these containers are recycled rather than reused, but this could change in the future.

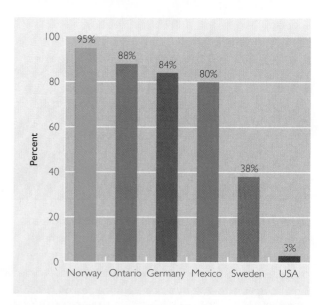

Figure 15–15 Percentage of beer sold in refillable bottles, 2000. Ontario's beer industry has been a rare bright-light example of how the reuse of containers can eliminate waste from landfills.

Reuse applies not only to containers. You have probably walked along a road on garbage pickup day and noticed useful things being thrown out: sofas, tables, toys, sporting goods, and other items. Perhaps you have even knocked on a door to ask if you could take something that was left for pickup. This residential version of "dumpster diving" does not happen as often as it should, and a great deal of still-usable material ends up in the local landfill. In many parts of Canada, there has been a growth in the number of second-hand and consignment stores; people see an opportunity to sell rather than throw away what they no longer need, and others realize that they can save money by buying previously used goods. Even Web sites like eBay and craigslist help reduce the amount of waste going to landfills by providing links between those who want to get rid of something and those who might be able to use it.

Recycle

The importance of recycling has grown dramatically in large North American cities in recent years as landfills become increasingly more costly to operate and politically less acceptable. Recycling began with blue-box programs that focused on only a few materials like aluminum and steel containers, but the amount of recyclable material has grown significantly. For example, many communities now recycle various types of papers, garden waste, and household organics like kitchen waste. Originally, householders had to separate various types of recyclables but recent technological improvements mean that this is now less necessary. Manual and high-tech methods are used to separate the different types of materials that are collected in the same box. (The amount of user separation required varies in every community.)

GLOBALIZATION

Reducing solid waste is not a matter of choosing one or another of the 3Rs, or of looking at the problem of waste disposal in isolation from other environmental issues.

Why does it make sense to look at waste reduction in an integrated, comprehensive way?

Reconsideration

Reducing solid waste is not a matter of choosing one or another of the 3Rs, or of looking at the problem of waste disposal in isolation from other environmental issues. A comprehensive, integrated approach makes most sense. As individuals and as a society, we must reconsider the environmental loads we create. Two examples of such reconsideration follow.

Reconsider I

In recent years, the city of Toronto has had to reconsider how it handles its waste. For decades a series of dumps on the outskirts of the always-growing city were used for trash disposal. (Check back to the map on page 236 for details.) The last of these was the Keele Landfill in Maple that closed in 2002. After this, a landfill in Michigan was used. In 2006, however, an agreement was reached between the Ontario and Michigan governments, to close the border to trash from Toronto and other parts of southern Ontario. Toronto then bought an existing commercial landfill near St. Thomas, Ontario, but still faced the same sorts of problems common to all large cities—landfill was costly and there was no assurance that new landfill space would always be available. Toronto set out on an ambitious plan to divert 70 percent of its solid waste from landfills by 2010. By 2006, the city had diverted 42 percent and was working on ways to increase this amount (see Figure 15–16). Chief among these methods was the desire to expand the highly successful waste-reduction schemes that were working for single-family homes—blue-box recycling of many metals, plastics, and paper, and green-bin organic composting—into more multi-family dwellings, and commercial properties.

Reconsider II

Significant reduction in the amount of waste going to landfills is admirable but it is *reactive* (in response to something that is happening) rather than *proactive* (in anticipation of future events). For example, cities like Toronto have to deal with whatever waste is generated by their residents and businesses. It would be better to deal with waste reduction (and hence protect the environment) earlier in the life cycle of a product. A good way that this can be done is by implementing the idea of **extended producer responsibility (EPR)**. This complex idea can be illustrated with a simple example. Many laser cartridges come with a prepaid shipping bag in which a used cartridge can be returned by mail to the manufacturer. Most of the cartridge is then reused and other parts are recycled by the manufacturer. This is not a totally unselfish example, since the manufacturer's costs of producing cartridges are reduced, but the environmental result is less waste going to landfills, fewer resources used to produce new cartridges, and less greenhouse-gas production.

Obviously, this is a very restricted example of EPR. The manufacturer does not take back the printer itself when it wears out. Nor does it take any responsibility for

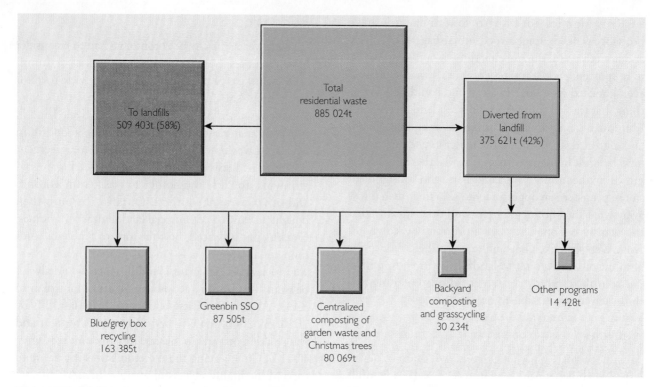

Figure 15–16 Toronto has an ambitious goal to divert 70 percent of its solid waste from landfills by 2010. This diagram summarizes how the city was doing by 2006. SSO stands for "Source Separated Organics." Greencycling is a program to encourage homeowners to leave grass cuttings on their lawns rather than rake them up for disposal. Why is it harder to divert waste from high-rise apartments than from single-family homes?

the packaging that comes with a new printer. With a fully implemented EPR program, both of these things would happen.

EPR is coming, but very slowly. On one hand, European carmakers like BMW and Volvo are trying to make their vehicles completely recyclable by using types of plastic that are in demand by recyclers and by labelling pieces to aid in recycling. This is not EPR, but it would make EPR easier to implement in the future. On the other hand, the enormous shift of manufacturing to

China is making EPR harder to implement. The great distance between producer and consumer makes it more of a challenge. The only way that EPR will become common is if governments require it. This is most likely to happen in the European Union rather than in the US, China, or Japan because of the size of the European market and a greater commitment to sustainability there than elsewhere. Because of the small size of the Canadian market, we are likely to piggyback on US initiatives.

World Protected Areas

Most countries have come to accept the idea that they should preserve substantial parts of their land and marine areas in as natural a condition as possible. This is usually done by creating what the World Conservation Union (WCU) calls "protected areas." A **protected area** can be defined as "…*an area of land and/or sea especially dedicated to the protection and maintenance of biological diversity, and of natural and associated cultural resources, and managed through legal or other effective means.*" There are a number of important aspects included in this definition that will help you to understand more about land protection.

1. **"…an area of land and/or sea…"**

▪ The international goal, established in 1993, was to protect 10 percent of the earth's land. In less than a decade this goal was exceeded—at the World Parks Congress in 2003, it was announced that 12 percent was, in fact, protected.

▪ The amount of protected land is actually higher than 12 percent, since well-protected but privately owned land is not included. Examples of these areas are huge private land preserves in eastern Europe and Central America, along with large privately owned game preserves in southern Africa.

Figure 15–17 Australia's Great Barrier Reef has been protected, unlike most of the world's threatened unique marine environments.

 You can learn more about these categories at the link on our Web site.

■ The total area of land protected by 2003 was about 17 million square kilometres—which is about the area of the US and China combined.

■ We are doing a much worse job of protecting oceans. Only 0.5 percent of the oceans (1.7 million square kilometres) has been protected, and most of this is in one place—Australia's Great Barrier Reef (see Figure 15–17).

2. "...dedicated to the protection and maintenance of biological diversity, and of natural and associated cultural resources..."

■ The WCU has identified six different categories of protected areas depending on what aspect of protection and management is most important. These are

• **Category I—Strict Nature Reserve/Wilderness Area.** Focus is on protecting the ecosystem or preserving the area for scientific research.

• **Category II—National Park.** Focus is on both ecosystem protection and recreational activities in an area with nationally or internationally recognized natural significance.

• **Category III—National Monument.** Focus is on conservation of a particular natural or cultural feature (or features) like waterfalls, caves, or archaeological sites.

• **Category IV—Habitat/Species Management Area.** Focus is on management activities to improve the health of habitats like wetlands, natural grasslands, and coral reefs.

• **Category V—Protected Landscape/Seascape.** Focus is on management to protect natural environments and associated traditional cultural and economic activities. Most often, the land involved will not be owned by a government.

• **Category VI—Managed Resource Protected Area.** Focus is on management for sustainable use of ecosystem (for example, forestry or fishery) by local people.

3. "...managed through legal or other effective means."

■ The problems associated with the management of lands to be protected will vary depending on the particular circumstance. Examples of some of the considerations are

• A wealthy country like Canada is better able to protect land than a poorer country. If poor countries are to put land aside, the international community may have to provide funding.

• Some areas to be protected cross national boundaries, so international cooperation is needed.

• Some areas to be protected will be very large while others will be very small. Each provides its own special challenges.

• Some areas to be protected will be in areas with large populations; others will be in remote areas with few people.

• Some areas to be protected will be inhabited by indigenous people who must become partners in the planning and management of the area.

Canada's Protected Areas

Canada's first national park, Banff, was created in 1885. It was only the third national park in the world—evidence of Canada's long history of protecting land resources. Fourteen major national parks, with a total area of almost 70 000 square kilometres, were created in Canada before the Great Depression started in 1929. These parks, most of which are in western Canada, remain the core of the national park system today and are what most people think of when they think about Canadian national parks. Since they can be easily, and relatively cheaply, visited by Canadians and foreign visitors, they have important economic impacts for the regions in which they are located.

The competing demands of the Depression and World War II for government spending, along with governmental disinterest after the war, almost stopped the creation of national parks. The resulting sad fact is that, between 1930 and 1966, only four small parks in

Atlantic Canada (totalling 1775 square kilometres) were established.

Two events revitalized the process of national park creation. One was Canada's Centennial celebration in 1967, when people became more aware of the glories of Canada's geography and of the need to protect special places. The other was the election, in 1968, of Pierre Trudeau as prime minister. Trudeau had travelled widely, by canoe and airplane, in the more remote parts of Canada and had a personal appreciation of the wonders that existed and that needed to be protected. By the time Trudeau left office, the concept of an expanding national park system was well established in the federal government. Between 1967 and 2007, 26 national parks, national park reserves, and national marine conservation areas had been established. These parks had a combined area of about 200 000 square kilometres and were mainly located in remote areas of the Yukon, Northwest Territories, and Nunavut. In 2008, Parks Canada was working on the creation of eight new national parks.

Canada's national parks range in size from fewer than 9 square kilometres to more than 44 000 square kilometres. In total, they include almost 3 percent of all of the land area in the country, or an area of about 277 000 square kilometres. Using these figures, Canada's protected land would appear to be much below the international 10 percent goal. In reality the situation is not quite so bad since federal parks are only one part of Canada's protected lands. We have many other protected areas run by provincial and local governments. For example, Ontario has 270 provincial parks of varying sizes that make up about 9 percent of the province's territory.

Some parks have existed for more than a century, while others are only a few years old. Some, like Banff in the West, and Gros Morne in eastern Canada, are world famous and attract thousands, even millions of visitors each year. Others, like Ivvavik National Park and Vuntut National Park, in the Yukon, have names that are unfamiliar to most Canadians and are visited by only a handful of people each year.

In addition to national parks, Parks Canada has the responsibility for two national marine conservation areas (with one more being developed). Only 1250 square kilometres of Canada's water areas are protected. This is only 0.14 percent of the total. Parks Canada also administers 157 national historic sites. These tend to be fairly small in area.

The long-term vision is that there should be at least one national park in each of Canada's 39 natural regions. In 2007, this meant that there were still 12 regions that needed a national park (some regions have more than one). While work is progressing on the creation of these additional parks, progress is slow because agreement must be reached among many interested parties including provincial and territorial governments, Aboriginal groups, and forestry and mining companies.

Canada's national parks are created based on three principles:

- to protect representative natural areas that are of Canada-wide significance

- to provide for public understanding, appreciation, and enjoyment of the natural environment

- to maintain the parks in an unimpaired state for future generations

While these principles are relatively simple, their application is often not. A major problem for Parks Canada is trying to reconcile these principles when they come into conflict with one another. Typically what happens is that the need to "provide public understanding, appreciation, and enjoyment" conflicts with the need to maintain the park in an "unimpaired state." While these conflicts exist in most of the parks in southern Canada, they are perhaps most critical in the parks that receive the most visitors.

To see a map of Canada that shows the progress toward completing the national park system, check the link on our Web site.

Chapter Questions

Knowledge and Understanding

1. **a)** Name six significant environmental problems of any type.

   b) Suggest one approach to solving each of these problems.

   c) Indicate how each of these solutions might change our lifestyle.

   d) Would these changes be negative or positive for our lifestyle? Explain. How is this sort of value judgment made?

2. Summarize the most important characteristics of each of the four types of land degradation.

3. **a)** What happens to the rate of erosion on hillier land? Why?

   b) Why is it not surprising that more hilly land is being used for farming today than in the past?

4. The WCU has identified six categories of land that should be protected. In your own words, explain their differences and, where possible, give examples of them in Canada or elsewhere.

Thinking

5. It is possible to talk about the proximate and ultimate causes of something. For example, you may feel that your favourite team lost in the playoffs because of a bad play in the final game. This would be the proximate cause of the loss. In reality, the team may have lost because, in the pre-season, they were poorly coached in the skills needed to make that play. This would be the ultimate cause of the loss. Using this logic, explain, with specific examples, how the ideas of proximate and ultimate causes can be applied to land degradation

6. **a)** Consider the packaging on the various products that you buy. What advantages does it have for the producer? For the consumer? What advantages are there for the company selling the product?

   b) Think about the products that you and your family buy. Give at least three examples of products in each of these two categories: an appropriate amount of packaging; an excessive amount of packaging. In the latter case, describe how the packaging could be improved to make it more ecologically sound.

   c) How might changes in consumer behaviour result in different product packaging?

   d) How might the operations of businesses have to change to allow reduced packaging?

7. **a)** How would you feel if it was announced that a waste disposal site (a landfill or incinerator) was to be built near where you live? What would you do about this?

   b) Explain the meaning of the following statement: "The *NIMBY* (Not In My Back Yard) syndrome is alive and well when it comes to waste disposal." Give specific examples to support your explanation.

   c) Give at least three examples of projects, in addition to waste facilities, that tend to result in *NIMBY* reactions.

8. Often when a waste-disposal facility is to be built, there is a conflict between the needs of the many (to get rid of their waste) and the costs to be paid by the few (those who live near the facility who will suffer economic damage and a possible reduction in their quality of life). How should conflicts be handled? **S** **G**

9. At times, there can be conflicts between the various purposes for which national parks exist, for example, between habitat protection and tourism. Choose two of the parks below, one from the Old Core and one from another part of the world, to study.
   - Banff, Canada
   - Point Pelee, Canada
   - Grand Canyon, US
   - Yosemite, US
   - Everglades, US
   - Kruger, South Africa
   - Amboseli, Kenya
   - Mahatma Gandhi Marine National Park, India
   - Huascarán National Park, Peru
   - A park of your choice

   a) What is the fundamental reason for the conflict in each park?

   b) Do the conflicts differ? If so, how?

   c) Are the differences related to the part of the world in which the park is found?

   d) What reforms, if any, have been put in place to deal with the conflict?

   e) Can a popular national park fulfill all of the demands put on it? In addition to your written answer to this question, be prepared to defend your conclusion in a class discussion.

Communication

10. a) Choose a national park to research. The park could be in Canada or in another country. Determine the principal characteristics of your park including its size, location, and history.

b) Investigate the characteristics of the ecosystems that are being protected by your park.

c) Determine what threats the park may face.

d) Present your findings in a poster, or in another form as directed by your teacher. Be sure to include appropriate illustrations as well as text.

11. a) Create a display to show the difference between ecologically sound packaging and wasteful packaging. Consider such factors as the amount of material used, the environmental impact of making the packaging, whether it can be recycled, and, if possible, how much it costs.

b) Choose an example of particularly wasteful packaging. Write a letter to the company responsible expressing your concerns about their packaging and suggesting an alternative approach that would be desirable both environmentally and from the perspective of the company. Ask for a reply.

Application

12. a) Research the natural and human factors that intensify the severity of water and wind erosion.

b) Determine how erosion can be minimized in at least three different types of natural environments.

13. Compare the packaging methods of the beer industry in Ontario to the province's dairy, soft-drink, wine, and liquor industries.

a) Why has the beer industry been so successful with its container reuse and recycling program compared to the others?

b) What is being done now to improve the situation in the non-beer beverage industries? How well is this reform working? You may want to check on the Internet or talk to someone who works in the industry to find out.

c) What further reforms could be made to improve the situation even more? **S**

14. Do a waste audit of your home or school.

a) First, determine how much waste is created both in total and on a per-capita basis.

b) If you are doing a family audit, how does the amount of your family's waste compare to that of your classmates' families?

c) How is the waste from your home or school handled?

d) What efforts have been made (by your family or the school) in recent years to improve its waste-handling practices?

e) What other improvements could be made? **S**

CHAPTER 16

Forest Issues

Key Terms

biodiversity

deep ecology

deforestation

Forest Stewardship Council
(FSC)

chain of custody (CoC)

reduced-impact logging (RIL)

old-growth forest

Ecosystem-Based Management
(EBM)

SLAPPs (Strategic Lawsuits
Against Public Participation)

monoculture

political consumerism

Steve Sillett (right) climbs a
3000-year-old redwood. Can
the demands on our forests be
met in a sustainable way?

Key Questions

By the end of this chapter you will be able to answer
the following questions.

■ What is the current state of the world's forests?

■ How can the forests be used more effectively?

■ Can all of the demands being put on our forests be met
in a sustainable fashion?

■ Why are forests important to you?

The State of the World's Forests

In 1987, 19-year-old Steve Sillett found himself 60 metres above the ground, without a safety harness, roaming around the previously unexplored *canopy* (the tops of trees forming a "ceiling") of a redwood forest in northern California. On impulse, and to the horror of his brother watching below, Sillett had scrambled up a 25-metre-high neighbouring tree, and had then flung himself into the spreading branches of a gigantic 3000-year-old redwood he later called "Nameless." Climbing more than 30 metres farther up into Nameless's top branches, Sillett discovered a unique environment—one that was different from anything else on Earth. Sillett became a botanist and later helped create a new science to study the canopy environment. Now, canopy scientists estimate that about two-thirds of all species on Earth live in forest canopies.

Sillett's foray into this new frontier was only possible because parts of the rainforest in Northern California have been protected since the early 1900s. Today, the world has just under four billion hectares of forest and woodland. These forests and woodlands, composed of frontier and non-frontier forest, cover about 30 percent of Earth's land surface, excluding Antarctica (see Figure 16–1). Between 1990 and 2005, the world lost 3 percent of its forest area to human activities and natural events (see Figure 16–2).

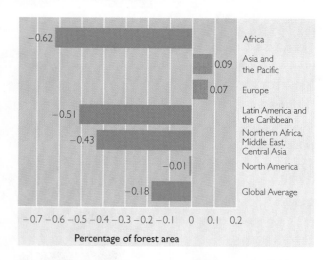

Figure 16–2 Annual net change in forest area, 2000 to 2005. Why might changes vary from region to region?

There are basically three types of forest covering the globe: boreal forest in cold climates (about one-third of Canada is covered by boreal forest); temperate forest in the mid-latitudes (for example, forests in southeastern Canada and western Europe); and tropical forest between the tropics of Cancer and Capricorn (for example, forests in South America, Africa, and Southeast Asia).

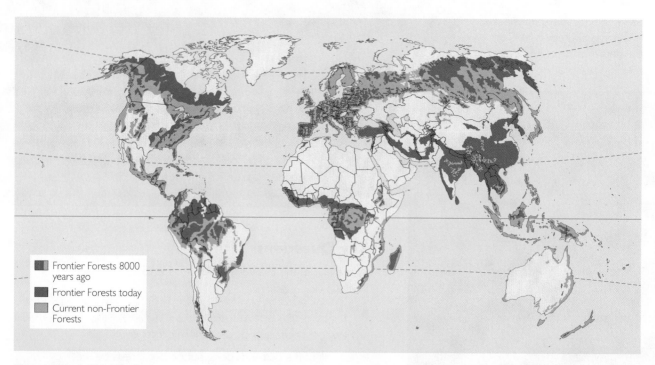

Frontier Forests 8000 years ago

Frontier Forests today

Current non-Frontier Forests

Figure 16–1 Frontier forests are the world's only remaining intact natural forest ecosystems—undisturbed and large enough to maintain their full biodiversity. Non-frontier forests are tree farms, degraded (logged) forests, and patches of forest with limited biodiversity.

Take These Trees and...

SUSTAINABILITY

...forests are frequently sources of conflict ... some people want to cut them down while others want to leave them standing.

How can we reduce conflicts over forests?

Unfortunately, all forests are frequently sources of conflict because, to put it very simply, some people want to cut them down while others want to leave them standing. Let's examine the points of view of these two groups, and perhaps by the end of the chapter, you will know if you are a "tree-hugger," a "tree-mugger," or if you stand somewhere in between.

Figure 16–3 Logging provides primary material for two large manufacturing industries in Canada: sawmills, planning mills, and shingle mills industry; and the pulp and paper industry.

...Cut Them Down

Trees are a tremendously valuable commodity. They provide lumber, paper, fuel, nursery stock (new young trees for planting), and raw material to make chemicals (see Figure 16–3). Forests also provide major economic benefits in the form of jobs in the lumber and transportation industries, building trades, and in many retail businesses. In 2005, forest products contributed $37.6 billion to Canada's GDP and provided more than 860 000 direct and indirect jobs. Furthermore, Canada is the world's number-one exporter of forest products. No wonder the survival of so many Canadian communities depends on products and jobs that come from trees. Excessive restrictions on cutting trees down would

- increase the cost of wood products for consumers

- cause unemployment in many parts of the country

- lower the value of the country's exports

- increase imports, since we would need to get our forest products from somewhere else

- cause a downturn in the country's economy

...Leave Them Standing

Why should we try to preserve as much forest as possible?

- Trees contribute to the planet's **biodiversity**—the variety of *species* (different groups of living organisms) on Earth. They provide habitats for about two-thirds of the world's species. For example, the four million square kilometres of the Amazon rainforest is home to millions of species.

- About 60 million indigenous people live in forests around the world and depend on them for their subsistence. Forests are their habitat and the source of their food, shelter, medicines, and clothing.

- Carbon is stored in trees. As a tree grows, it removes carbon dioxide, a greenhouse gas, from the atmosphere. The carbon remains in the tree until the wood is burned or decays, and the carbon is returned to the atmosphere. Expanding forests by 20 million hectares is a major part of the Asia-Pacific Economic Cooperation's (APEC) approach to climate change. (See Chapter 20 for more information about APEC and the storage of carbon by trees as part of the carbon cycle.)

- Trees contribute oxygen through photosynthesis and recycle moisture into the atmosphere through transpiration. They also create a microclimate by releasing moisture that makes the immediate area cooler and more moist. There is so much moisture in the canopy of a redwood forest that it creates an "airborne aquifer," or water supply, that supports species that never touch the ground.

- Tree roots absorb rainwater and prevent it from becoming runoff. This prevents flooding. Roots also hold the soil in place and prevent erosion.

- Trees provide economic benefits through jobs related to forest tourism and recreational activities, such as cross-country skiing, hiking, and snowmobiling.

- Trees have *aesthetic* (relating to beauty or the appreciation of beauty) and spiritual value to many people (see Figure 16–4).

Figure 16–4 John Terpstra is a poet and carpenter who lives in Hamilton, Ontario. He was inspired to write this poem when observing a magnificent tree. His poem embodies many of the reasons why trees should be preserved.

Place

A tree, when it first begins to shoot from the ground, immediately senses the potential lying within that one location and is persuaded to stay.

By never moving from its original location a tree is in the unique position of learning all there is to know about that one particular spot: the composition of earth, the characteristic of each wind, the inquisition of water, both above ground and under, the traffic of animals, humans, and more—most of which is modified, or determined, by its presence.

Every tree therefore is a specialist, the one expert in its own self-defined field, and cannot be made redundant.

John Terpstra, 2002

Take These Trees and Defend Them...

Protecting the forests is a role that some groups perform peacefully and others try to do through any means necessary. Let's examine both of these methods.

...Using Legal Methods

There are many non-governmental organizations (NGOs) that defend forests. These groups use non-violent means. For example, the Rainforest Action Network encourages consumers to boycott products from companies that do not adopt sustainable logging practices. Global Forest Watch has set up a worldwide forest-monitoring network that collects data on such things as endangered forest animals and land-clearing for agriculture, and distributes the information at no cost on the Internet. The Nature Conservancy of Canada purchases timber rights from forest owners so that no commercial interest may cut down the trees. Many other NGOs like these have different—but still legal—ways of raising public awareness about the importance of sustainable forests. These groups also lobby governments to create parkland, sanctuaries, or wildlife preserves to further protect the forests.

...at Any Cost

Some NGOs believe that any action is suitable as long as the end result is the conservation of forests. For example, supporters of a group called Earth First! believe

in an approach called **deep ecology**. They use confrontational, direct action to protect the environment and, as a rule, are not willing to accept compromise solutions. Earth First! has the motto "No compromise in defence of Mother Earth."

Figure 16–5 According to officials, this new-home construction site was set on fire by members of the Earth Liberation Front (ELF), in California, 2003.

While some people have described groups like Earth First! as eco-terrorists, there is a fringe group of environmentalists, such as the Earth Liberation Front (ELF), who better deserve this title (see Figure 16–5). They have resorted to tactics that are called "monkey-wrenching." These tactics range from relatively benign, if illegal, activities like removing survey stakes to slow down the building of logging roads, to much more serious acts such as burning down buildings and tree-spiking.

consists of driving long nails into a tree at the height at which a logger would cut the tree with a chainsaw. At best, the logging company would have to spend considerable time and money determining which trees had been spiked, since nail heads rust over and become hard to see. The trees would then have to be cut down with great care to avoid the nails. At worst, a logger could be killed or severly injured if a chainsaw hit a nail and the chain tore apart.

Effective Use of Forest Resources

Earth is losing about 20 000 hectares of forest per day (see Figure 16–6). The word **deforestation** appears frequently in the media because of large-scale cutting of forests in many countries including those in the Amazon and Congo basins. Why are people cutting forests around the world to such a large extent?

■ Trees are harvested in commercial logging operations to meet domestic needs and foreign demand.

■ In developing countries, farmers clear forests to make room for subsistence agriculture.

■ Developing countries harvest forests as exports to earn foreign currency to repay debts.

■ Some countries, such as Brazil, encourage their rapidly growing populations to settle in newly cleared forest lands to reduce the population pressures elsewhere.

SUSTAINABILITY
Earth is losing about 20 000 hectares of forest per day.

What actions can you take to reduce this loss?

We do not usually consider how deforestation is related to our lifestyle. On one hand, we are concerned about the impact of deforestation on wildlife, river systems, and the land. On the other, we take it for granted that forest products, which seem so plentiful in Canada, will always be available and at a price we can afford. We must overcome the divide that exists between our role as people concerned about the environment and our role as consumers. In the case of forest products, a good way to do this is to ensure that the products we buy have been produced in the most environmentally responsible way possible.

In 1993, 130 representatives from around the world met in Toronto to create the **Forest Stewardship Council (FSC)**. Its purpose is to fight deforestation by supporting "environmentally appropriate, socially beneficial,

and economically viable management of the world's forests." The FSC receives funding from foundations, governments, environmental NGOs, and membership fees. Its central focus is to protect forests by the implementation of a forest certification system. This system identifies products that have come from forests that are managed according to an agreed-upon set of standards. At the present time, about 90 million hectares in over 70 countries are certified under this system. Products produced according to these standards are entitled to carry the FSC logo (see Figure 16–7). Consumers who support sustainable forests can look for wood products with the FSC mark. There are other forest certification programs in various parts of the world, but the FSC guidelines are the ones most widely used.

Figure 16–6 Deforestation in Haiti (left) marks its border with the Dominican Republic.

Figure 16–7 The Forest Stewardship Council (FSC) fights the type of deforestation shown in Figure 16–6. Look for the FSC symbol on products that you buy. © 1996 FSC A.C.

Many companies in Canada and around the world now use FSC-certified papers and FSC products: the City of Toronto, Google, Home Depot, IKEA, McDonald's, Staples/Office Depot, RONA, Sony, The Toronto Star, Toyota, and Wal-Mart are some of them. You can learn more about the FSC and FSC-certified products and companies at the link on our Web site.

Although the forest certification system appears relatively straightforward, it has two major problems:

■ **Tracing the chain of custody (CoC).** A clear link must be established between trees growing in certified forests and the wood products that appear in the marketplace. Logs must be tracked through all processing and transportation stages until the final product reaches the consumer. Only by certifying sawmills, lumberyards, manufacturers, carpenters, building contractors, retailers, pulp and paper producers, and printers can the FSC trace the chain of custody and thereby verify the end product. This is a complex procedure to say the least.

■ **Ensuring a market for certified wood products.** Logging companies are often reluctant to go through the certification process if they are not sure whether a market exists for "green" products. Consumers, however, will not look for ecologically produced wood products if they never see such items in the marketplace. Certification standards, like those promised by the FSC logo, are a start in the process, but ultimately, market forces will determine the success or failure of this initiative.

For several years, Home Depot found itself the target of protests and boycotts by various NGOs that wanted the world's largest lumber retailer to "go green" and become a leader in the sale of certified lumber and lumber products. By the mid-1990s, executives at Home Depot had decided that it was in the corporation's interest to be associated with the Forest Stewardship Council, and to work toward selling only FSC-certified products in its stores. Home Depot's decision has both a practical and a symbolic importance. Practically, it provides a huge new market for "green" wood and encourages suppliers to become FSC certified. Sources of certified lumber have to be identified (and, in many cases, developed). Manufacturers who want to sell products such as doors and kitchen cabinets to Home Depot have to "go green" as well. Symbolically, it gives the message that being environmentally responsible can be good for business, even for one of the world's largest retailers. Now, Home Depot's competitors are faced with the choice of selling certified products or being viewed as environmentally insensitive.

Reduced-Impact Logging

The first stage in using forests wisely is to ensure that logging activities cause as little ecological damage as possible. Forest conservationists, including the FSC, are promoting the advantages of **reduced-impact logging (RIL)**. RIL systems are being developed all over the world, but especially in areas like the Amazon basin, central Africa, and parts of Southeast Asia, where tropical hardwoods grow. The purpose of RIL systems is to ensure the long-term economic and ecological sustainability of forestry in an area. RIL generally includes the following features:

■ An accurate study of the forest is done well before logging begins. The study identifies the trees to be cut, called "crop trees" (based on such characteristics as tree species and age), and maps their location. This inventory allows the logging company and government regulators to determine how much timber can be removed from a particular forest tract.

■ The study can be used to plan the cutting to protect streams, minimize forest-fire risks, promote forest regeneration, and maintain biological diversity.

■ Roads and skid trails for dragging logs to central locations for transport must be limited in number and size. They should be built to minimize soil erosion.

- Trees must be cut without damaging surrounding trees.

- Wood should not be wasted. For example, trees should be cut as close to the ground as possible, using sawing methods that maximize the production of usable lumber.

- Slash (the branches, bark, and unusable wood left over after logging) must be managed carefully to prevent fires.

Experts have done studies that compare the impacts of RIL with those of conventional logging (CL) in tropical hardwood forests (see Figure 16–8). With CL, little effort is made in planning how to log or where to build roads and skid trails. Logging crews go into the forest and decide, on the spot, which trees to cut. Many other trees are damaged or destroyed in this process. Since logging is mainly thought of as an *extractive* (concerned with the removal of natural resources) activity in these cases, not much attention is paid to ensuring that the forest will recover quickly.

Foresters have found that RIL has several benefits. RIL methods waste only about 8 percent of the volume of harvested trees, while CL methods waste 24 percent. The more careful logging practices of RIL cause significantly less damage to the remaining forest. RIL kills fewer than half the trees killed by CL and damages forest soils substantially less through the careful use of heavy logging machinery.

At first glance, it might appear that RIL would be more expensive than CL because of the cost of planning and the time taken for extra care. In fact, the cost of RIL is about 12 percent less per hectare, because less wood is wasted.

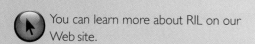
You can learn more about RIL on our Web site.

Figure 16–8 In conventional logging (top), harvesting is not planned but uses a "hit and miss" approach. Reduced impact logging (bottom) greatly decreases damage to unharvested trees and surrounding land.

Balancing Competing Interests

This chapter opened with the statement that forests are a source of conflict between those who want to cut them down and those who want to leave them standing. Of course, this is a very simplistic view of an extremely complex issue. It's fair to say that neither one side nor the other is wrong, and both have valid and strong arguments to support their points of view. Consequently,

we have to balance competing interests—that is, we have to preserve forests while we benefit from all they provide.

In Canada, 80 percent of *commercial forests* (forests that are accessible and contain trees large enough for commercial harvesting) are owned by the provinces, 11 percent by the federal government (mainly in the form of parks and military reserves), and 9 percent by private individuals and companies. Because of the large percentage owned by provincial governments, it usually falls to them to decide how the resource will be used. As a result, provincial governments find themselves being pressured by competing interests. They must deal with lumber and mining companies, pulp and paper companies, First Nations groups, environmentalists, NGOs, labour unions, the tourism industry, developers, and recreational organizations. The governments' dilemma is to make decisions that affect these groups, and ordinary citizens, in a fair and objective way. (See the following Case Study.)

Provincial governments tackle the problem by allocating rights to harvest or manage public forest land (called Crown land) to private companies. In effect, they act as regulators and enforcers rather than managers of public forest lands. For example, they grant *timber tenures* (permits that clarify the rights and obligations of companies toward the forests). The tenures specify such things as reforestation and road-building obligations and the size of timber cuts and require that companies submit their plans for operations. In this way, governments try to balance the health of the forests and animals living in them with the demands of the marketplace. Sometimes they are successful in finding the right balance, sometimes they are not.

CASE STUDY   The Great Bear Rainforest

The Gitga'at people of British Columbia say that the Raven came to the land and changed one out of every ten black bears into a white "spirit bear" (see Figure 16–9). The Raven created the white spirit bears to act as a reminder to future generations that the land and its inhabitants must be protected. This forested land of the Gitga'at, now known as the Great Bear Rainforest, is on Canada's west coast. It has deep fjords, soaring mountains, rich salmon streams, and old-growth forests with 1000-year-old cedars.

About 60 percent of the world's coastal temperate rainforests have been logged or cleared for development. One-quarter of what remains is found in British Columbia. The Great Bear Rainforest is a 64 000-square-kilometre protected area on the north and central coast of BC. It is one of the largest unspoiled temperate rainforests in the world. This area (see Figure 16–10) was once the centre of a ten-year environmental battle called the "War of the Woods."

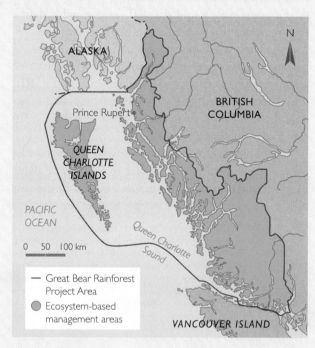

Figure 16–10 Why do you think it took ten years to create this protected area? What are the factors that may contribute to the deforestation of the coastal temperate rainforests?

Did You Know?

There are real white "spirit bears" called kermode bears. These are actually black bears that have a recessive gene that gives them their white coats.

Figure 16–9 A spirit bear in the Great Bear Rainforest

In the late 1990s, several environmental groups (Greenpeace, ForestEthics, the Rainforest Action Network, and the Sierra Club of Canada) began an active campaign to publicize the clear-cut logging that was taking its toll on the coastal forests of BC. By 2004, after a global media campaign, government lobbying, and sit-ins in the forests by First Nations people and environmentalists, many paper companies and retailers, including IKEA, Home Depot, and IBM, stopped purchasing and selling wood and paper products made from ancient forests. This boycott forced logging companies to negotiate with environmentalists. Environmentalists put additional pressure on the BC government to complete negotiations with First Nations groups and to finalize an agreement protecting the region. In 2006, the provincial government announced that the Great Bear Rainforest Agreement had been signed. The Agreement includes the following:

• Almost two million hectares are protected from logging (an area more than three times the size of Prince Edward Island). It includes existing parks, newly negotiated parks, and no-logging zones.
• The protected areas include salmon-spawning streams and key habitats of the spirit bear.
• First Nations groups are involved in the management of their territory that falls within the boundaries of the newly protected area.
• **Ecosystem-Based Management (EBM)** will be implemented by 2009. EBM, known as a "light-touch" forestry approach, aims to achieve a sustainable ecosystem. A light-touch forestry approach involves
  • harvesting trees of only a certain size in small, spread-out areas, and avoiding sensitive terrain such as steep slopes, thereby preventing soil erosion
  • building fewer roads
  • protecting wetlands and salmon-spawning streams
  • logging in winter when soil is less vulnerable
  • leaving behind material on the ground to maintain the ecosystem
  • no clear-cutting

EBM for the Great Bear Rainforest also includes a number of principles:

• to develop goals based on First Nations' traditional and local knowledge, their spiritual attachment to the land, and their respect for the land and its wildlife
• to develop goals based on current scientific knowledge of natural ecological patterns and processes
• to continue to develop a network of protected areas to preserve ecological and cultural heritage values
• to provide better protection for lakes, streams, biodiversity, old-growth forest areas, and bear habitats
• to include First Nations groups, community representatives, and other interested parties such as forestry companies and NGOs in future decision making

In 2007, the federal government pledged $30 million to match the $30 million pledged by the BC provincial government. This government funding will be combined with $60 million from conservation groups to support conservation-management projects and ecological businesses.

Some environmentalists still doubt that the ideals of the Agreement will be achieved because the proposed parks are not yet fully realized, and the pace of development is slow. EBM also requires logging companies to change their practices, which means new ways of thinking, new technologies, and the placement of long-term ecological goals ahead of short-term economic gains. Despite these reservations, however, environmentalists realize that the Great Bear Rainforest Agreement is a major step in preserving a precious resource.

Questions

1. In what ways are forests important other than as a source for wood products?

2. What tactics did NGOs and First Nations groups use to pressure logging companies and the government to sign an agreement protecting the Great Bear Rainforest?

3. What lessons can be learned from this dispute and its resolution?

4. Do you think this process could be successful—or impossible—in other countries, especially in developing or newly industrialized countries? Explain.

Getting SLAPPed

In democracies, acting in a lawful manner to protect the environment may seem to be a simple and straightforward business. Some people who have taken the "defend them legally" approach have often found this not to be the case.

The Daishowa company is a Japanese multinational that purchased the logging rights to a 29 000-square-kilometre tract of land in northern Alberta from the provincial government in 1988. A local Aboriginal group, the Lubicon, declared that they were the rightful owners of the land and disputed Daishowa's right to cut timber there. In an effort to support the Lubicon claims, interested parties formed an NGO called "Friends of the Lubicon." This group organized a boycott of Daishowa's products. As a result, Daishowa lost some of its major customers, such as The Body Shop and Pizza Pizza. They stopped buying Daishowa's products to avoid being picketed by the Friends of the Lubicon (and possibly to demonstrate their concerns about the environment).

In response to the boycott and the loss of its customers, Daishowa brought a lawsuit against the Friends of the Lubicon. Such lawsuits are called **SLAPPs (Strategic Lawsuits Against Public Participation)**. Under the law, the usual purpose of a lawsuit is to right a wrong that has been done to a person or an organization. In the case of a SLAPP, the principal purpose of the suit is to stop the protest by forcing the NGO or individual to focus time and money on a legal defence rather than on continuing to support its cause.

The Daishowa lawsuit against the Friends of the Lubicon was not settled until 1998. The court's decision established the right of NGOs and private citizens to protest the activities of companies by any legal means. The judge ruled that the boycott was not only legal, but also "a model of how such activities should be conducted in a democratic society." Shortly after the decision, the company agreed not to log any of the 10 000-square-kilometre area claimed by the Lubicon, until a land-claims settlement was reached between the Lubicon and the Alberta government.

The Platinex Suit

The Ojibwa First Nation community of Kitchenuhmaykoosib Inninuwug First Nation (KIFN) has 1200 residents, is located 600 kilometres north of Thunder Bay, and can only be reached by air. In 1998, the Ontario government gave the Ontario-based mineral company Platinex permission to drill for platinum deposits on KIFN land. In 2005, the KIFN called for a *moratorium* (a halt to a specific activity) on mining and forestry until its land claims could be settled. In 2006, however, the company slapped KIFN with a $10-billion damage suit for blockading access roads and stopping exploration. That same year, KIFN counter-sued the company. An Ontario Superior Court Justice granted the KIFN a court order called an injunction, which stopped exploration. In October 2007, however, the injunction was lifted and the company began drilling again. During the same month, the KIFN withdrew from the court process because it could no longer afford the legal bills defending itself from the $10-billion Platinex lawsuit.

The protests, however, did not stop. Several members of the community occupied the drilling site despite the court order to allow drilling to resume. The protestors were cited for contempt of court for this action. In March 2008, six protest leaders were given six-month jail sentences.

Governments in Canada have not yet passed laws against SLAPPs to protect NGOs and First Nations groups. In 2001, BC passed anti-SLAPP legislation, but after a provincial election later in the year, the legislation was repealed. In 2006, the Quebec government set up an expert panel to study the feasibility of anti-SLAPP legislation for that province. As of early 2008, no decision had been made.

In the US, about half the states have enacted anti-SLAPP legislation that would protect individual environmentalists or NGOs from lawsuits designed to distract those people or organizations from their original purpose. In 2005, California passed a "SLAPPback law," under which victims could recover their costs against SLAPP filers if a SLAPP suit were dismissed.

Forests Versus Biofuel Plantations

Making biofuels, which are fuels derived from *biomass* (plant matter), has led to an escalation of deforestation. (To learn more about biofuels, see Chapter 19.) The growing market for these new fuels has started a worldwide surge in the clearing and burning of forests to make way for fields of corn, soy, and canola in temperate countries and oil-palm plantations in tropical countries. The US southeast is covered with pine plantations that provide 15 percent of the world's paper supply. However, the demand for alternative fuels is creating pressure to use the pine trees to produce cellulosic ethanol.

Throughout the tropical regions of the globe, rainforests are being replaced by oil-palm plantations. Palm oil is an edible oil that is probably the most widely produced vegetable oil in the world; it is an engine lubricant, a base for cosmetics, and a major ingredient in food products. As a source of biofuel, it is unsurpassed. The oil palm is very productive—a single hectare of oil palm may yield 6000 litres of oil. Indonesia wants to develop 5.25 million hectares of biofuel plantations by 2010. Malaysia, the largest producer of palm oil, has already mandated that all diesel sold in the country must contain 5 percent palm oil. In the near future, it plans to phase out diesel altogether and use biofuels in its place. Environmentalists are concerned about the use of palm oil as a biofuel, because this **monoculture** (growing only one crop) leads to the loss of biodiversity, the loss of animal habitat, the extensive use of petroleum-based pesticides, herbicides, and fertilizers, and the clearing of vast areas of forest, often through burning.

SUSTAINABILITY

The growing market for [biofuels] has started a worldwide surge in the clearing and burning of forests...

How can we protect the world's forests as the demand for biofuels increases?

Promoting Sustainability

This chapter has shown how complex and interrelated environmental issues are. Everything is interconnected, so that virtually every decision about the environment, and in this case about forests, has many implications, both expected and unexpected. We want to protect forests, but we all use lumber and paper products and do not want to see the workers in wood-product industries lose their jobs. Many people are happy to see companies like Home Depot "go green," but some wonder if this choice is more about gaining a marketing advantage than protecting the environment.

One of our hardest tasks is to reconcile these apparent contradictions. A good way to do this is to focus on the concept of sustainability. If an action promotes sustainability, then it is a "good" decision because it preserves the resource or species for the benefit of future generations. If it does not, it is a "bad" decision. The challenge then shifts to deciding whether the result of a particular decision promotes sustainability.

As a consumer, you have the ability to express your attitudes and values, persuade others to your point of view, and even change their behaviour. How? By adopting the concept of **political consumerism**. Making decisions about what to buy is considered a political act. It assumes that the consumer has knowledge about the impact the production and marketing of a given product has on society, the environment, human rights, and labour standards for local and foreign producers. These impacts are then evaluated by consumers to determine if they meet or conflict with their personal values. In other words, you can decide to buy some products while refusing to buy others. For example, if you are concerned about diminishing forest resources, you can decide to purchase only recycled paper products. As sales of this product increase, paper companies will be encouraged to manufacture more recycled products to meet this demand. As a consumer, you have the power to make a difference.

Chapter Questions

Knowledge and Understanding

1. **a)** Describe the role that inexpensive forest products play in our lives.

   b) Describe three ways the average consumer can ensure that we will continue to have inexpensive, readily available forest products and still protect forests.

2. Explain the different points of view held by the various groups in this chapter regarding the use of forests.

3. **a)** What are the environmental consequences of deforestation?

   b) Why is there so much deforestation in countries of the Near Core and Far Periphery?

4. What roles do provincial governments play in forest use and preservation?

5. **a)** What is a SLAPP?

   b) Describe the pros and cons of a SLAPP.

6. **a)** What problems for the world's forests are associated with the increasing use of biofuels?

   b) Why are tropical countries developing so many oil-palm plantations?

Thinking

7. **a)** Why is Reduced Impact Logging (RIL) better than conventional logging (CL)?

   b) If RIL is better than CL, why is RIL not done more often?

8. Are extreme forms of protest, like monkey-wrenching, acceptable? In other words, do the ends justify the means? Explain your answer.

9. **a)** What is the purpose of the Forest Stewardship Council?

   b) What two problems must be overcome in the certification process?

   c) Will FSC certification make a difference to what forest products you buy and where you buy them? Explain.

Communication

10. Give two reasons why NGOs are most likely to target companies, such as Home Depot and McDonald's, when they wish to challenge the activities in a particular industry sector.

11. One of the founders of Greenpeace, Canadian Patrick Moore, has become disillusioned by the fact that many NGOs are unwilling to seek compromises on their goals. Do you agree with his observations? Why or why not?

 Read the essay written by Patrick Moore on this topic at the link on our Web site.

12. In his long-running series *The Nature of Things*, internationally acclaimed environmental scientist David Suzuki has been informing Canadians for decades about forest degradation. Do you think his TV programs have made a difference to forestry practices in Canada? Explain why or why not.

Application

13. Investigate the operations of any NGO that is involved in forest protection. Determine the following characteristics of the organization:

    a) its purpose

    b) its history

    c) its membership and funding sources

    d) the location of its activities and headquarters

    e) the tactics it uses

    f) how successful it is in achieving its aims

14. It is often difficult for a private citizen to determine the facts in an environmental or other dispute. This difficulty is understandable, since all parties in the dispute do their best to present their side of the case and to discredit their opponents. Describe a method that a person can use to analyze a forest dispute intelligently.

15. The Tropical Rainforest Dilemma

Introduction. Tropical rainforests are shrinking because of extensive logging, clearing for agricultural purposes, and urban expansion. One estimate states that of the approximately 1.6 billion hectares of original tropical rainforest, only half remains. In this Webquest, you will examine the competing points of view regarding the use of tropical rainforests in a developing country.

Task. Your teacher will divide the class into groups to discuss the competing points of view. Each group will consist of the following individuals:

- a government minister who wants to develop the rainforest resources (for example, wood, minerals) to improve the economy

- a poor farmer who wants to clear the land to enable his or her family to grow enough food to make a living and survive

- an environmentalist from an NGO who wants to protect the rainforest from development

- a forest company manager who wants to log the forest to meet the demand for wood products from the growing industries in a nearby city, and make money for the company

- a professor from a local university who wants to find a compromise that all interest groups can agree to in order to protect the forest, while at the same time using the forest resources for the benefit of the local population

- a forest worker with three children

Process. Jigsaw activity

1. In your "home" group, determine who will play each of the six roles.

2. Students from different groups who have similar roles work together in "research" groups.

3. Using resources found on the Internet, develop your arguments based on your character's point of view.

4. Prepare your arguments to defend your point of view.

5. Rejoin your "home" group. One member of the group should be appointed as a facilitator to organize and manage the discussion. Each character presents his or her point of view and supporting arguments to the other members of the "home" group.

6. Discuss the issues and identify
    i) any points of view you can agree on
    ii) what the real points of disagreement are

Note: When disputes in the "real world" cannot be resolved, what courses of action can be taken to find solutions?

7. Develop a presentation in your "home" group that describes your deliberations and the outcome you have reached.

8. Make your presentation to the class.

Evaluation. Your teacher will decide if this activity will be evaluated and what form it may take.

Conclusion. When the "home" groups have completed their presentations, the class as a whole should reach a consensus about how the rainforests should be used.

CHAPTER 17
Earth's Water Resources

Key Terms

groundwater

biodegradable

International Joint Commission

source control

natural recovery

environmental dredging

thick-layer capping

eutrophication

aquifer

fossil water

drip irrigation

United Nations Convention on the Law of the Sea (UNCLOS)

Exclusive Economic Zones (EEZs)

Las Vegas is an "artificial" city in that it exists and grows using water brought in from some distance away and used lavishly. Our American neighbours look with interest at Canada's freshwater reserves. This picture shows part of Georgian Bay.

Key Questions

By the end of this chapter you will be able to answer the following questions.

■ Does the earth have enough fresh water to meet the needs of its growing population?

■ What are the major causes of freshwater pollution?

■ What is groundwater and why should you care?

■ Why is the importance of wetlands often overlooked?

■ What are the benefits and negative impacts of large-scale dams and irrigation projects?

■ Is enough being done to protect the earth's oceans?

Where in the World . . . ?

Sign into Google Earth and follow the instructions. Choose the location 36°06'30"N 115°18'51"W—with an eye altitude of eight kilometres. Note that in the time between the publication of this book and when you are doing this exercise, the city shown will have grown and you may have to look a bit farther west. The area shown is part of the western suburbs of Las Vegas—the fastest-growing major city in the United States, and likely in the entire Old Core. The rapid growth of Las Vegas is particularly striking because it is occurring in the middle of a desert. (Las Vegas averages 114 millimetres of rain per year. In comparison, Toronto gets about 800 millimetres and Vancouver about 1200 millimetres.) Strangely enough, for such a dry environment, people and businesses tend to use water lavishly (see page 258). Why might this occur?

Questions

1. What is the natural vegetation of this area?

2. What land uses do you see here? How can you tell that this land use is expanding?

3. What apparent contradiction do you see when you consider the type of natural vegetation and land use in this area?

4. Research where Las Vegas gets its water from. Is additional water available from this source?

5. What water-supply problems does Las Vegas face in the future? What proposals have been made to deal with these problems?

Preserving Our Water Resources

Nearly three-quarters of the earth's surface is covered with water in the form of oceans, rivers, lakes, permanent snow cover, and glaciers. In addition, there is a great deal of **groundwater**—water within the earth that supplies wells and springs—and water in the atmosphere (see Figure 17–1). It makes sense to look at the world's water in two broad categories: freshwater resources on the land, and salt water in the oceans.

Figure 17–1 The earth has an enormous amount of water—more than 1376 million cubic kilometres. Unfortunately the vast majority of this water cannot be used for vital needs like agriculture and drinking water because it is either salty or inaccessible.

	Percentage of total	Volume of water
Water in atmosphere	0.00072%	0.01 km³
Lakes, rivers, and bogs	0.007%	1.10 km³
Groundwater and permafrost	0.8%	10.85 km³
Glaciers and permanent snow cover	1.8%	24.87 km³
Oceans	97.4%	1340.74 km³

(not to scale)

Fresh Water

It has been estimated that, under ideal circumstances, the amount of fresh water on Earth could support 20 billion people, more than three times the current population of the world. But the reality is quite different. Consider these three factors.

■ Most fresh water exists in forms that are not directly accessible, for example, in polar glaciers and permafrost, and as water vapour in the atmosphere (see Figure 17–2).

- Large usable freshwater reserves are often not located where the demand for water is greatest. In Canada, for example, 60 percent of rivers drain north, away from where 90 percent of Canadians live.

- In wealthy Old Core nations, water pollution *can be* a significant problem. In the rest of the populated world, water pollution *is* a problem almost everywhere. The sad reality is that hundreds of millions of people are forced to rely on unsafe water sources. As a result, millions die of water-borne diseases each year.

There have been proposals to obtain water from icebergs in Antarctica. You can learn more about this and about fog harvesting in Chile at the links on our Web site.

Freshwater Resource	% of all water	% of Fresh Water	Use of Resource	Threats to the Resource
Glaciers and permanent snow cover	1.8	69.41	• About 99 percent of this is in the ice sheets of Antarctica and Greenland and has no practical use. • The other 1 percent is in glaciers that are an important source of water. Meltwater from mountain glaciers adds to river flow and hence water supplies in western North America, western Europe, China, India, and South America.	• Climate change is dramatically reducing the size of mountain glaciers worldwide. This trend has major water-supply implications.
Groundwater and permafrost[1]	0.8	30.28	• Groundwater (using wells) is one of the two important sources of fresh water in the world. • Water tied up in permafrost is not available for human use.	• Groundwater is being overused in many parts of the world to the extent that the water table is being reduced. • Permafrost is threatened by climate change. Melting permafrost would temporarily increase stream flow and the size and number of bogs.
Lakes, rivers, and wetlands	0.007	0.28	• Lakes and rivers are the second major freshwater source in the world. • Wetlands have great ecological significance and hold water for dry spells.	• Overuse is becoming a problem in many areas. • Climate change is likely to reduce amounts of surface water. • Many surface waters and wetlands are polluted.
Water in atmosphere	0.00072	0.03	• This is a vital part of the hydrologic (water) cycle but of little direct value as a water source. Some rainfall (and even fog) is collected for use.	• Climate change may increase evaporation and hence the amount of water in the atmosphere.

Figure 17–2 A summary of the earth's freshwater resources

[1] Permafrost is a permanently frozen layer of the earth's surface in very cold parts of the world. About 20 to 25 percent of the earth's land has permafrost. (See a photograph of permafrost in Figure 20–13, Page 327.)

Pollution of Surface Waters

Human activity is the main source of pollution of fresh water. Urbanization, industry, mining, forestry, agriculture, and shipping are among the many activities that affect water quality. You may not have thought about it very much (or perhaps you have), but your daily activities, and activities by others that support your lifestyle, contribute to water pollution every day.

Sewage Waste

Human and animal wastes contain bacteria that spread disease. When these wastes enter the water supply, people may contract serious illnesses such as cholera, diarrhea, typhoid, polio, and intestinal parasites. About 1.5 billion people worldwide do not have access to safe drinking water, and about another three billion do not have adequate sanitation (see Figure 17–3), that is, the ability to dispose of their sewage safely. Considering these statistics, it is not surprising that about 80 percent of the infectious diseases in Far Periphery, Near Core, and New Core countries result from impure water. Although sewage technology that prevents the transmission of disease is available, many communities in Old Core nations and most in the rest of the world do not have adequate sewage treatment (see Figure 17–4).

By the early 2000s, more than 97 percent of sewage from Canadian towns and cities had at least primary treatment. The situation is quite different in many rural areas, though, where a great deal of sewage gets no treat-ment. Even if cities have treatment plants, not all the water returned to the environment is treated. In some older parts of Toronto, for example, storm sewers and sanitation sewers are not separate. After a heavy rain, the sewer system can carry so much water that the treatment plants cannot handle the load, and large quantities of untreated water is discharged into Lake Ontario.

Figure 17–3 For hundreds of millions of people, this is what sewage disposal looks like. In total, about three billion people in the world lack adequate sewage disposal.

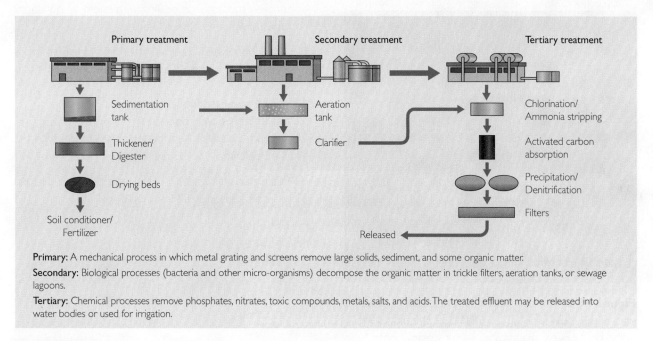

Primary: A mechanical process in which metal grating and screens remove large solids, sediment, and some organic matter.

Secondary: Biological processes (bacteria and other micro-organisms) decompose the organic matter in trickle filters, aeration tanks, or sewage lagoons.

Tertiary: Chemical processes remove phosphates, nitrates, toxic compounds, metals, salts, and acids. The treated effluent may be released into water bodies or used for irrigation.

Figure 17–4 The three stages of sewage treatment. Sewage treatment in Canada is slowly improving, but much remains to be done, particularly in less-populated areas.

Chemical Waste

The chemical by-products of manufacturing often reach our water bodies and, as a result, pose a threat to our health. Some industrial pollutants are **biodegradable**, that is, they break down as a result of natural processes in the environment. Nevertheless, when they are flushed into rivers or lakes, care must be taken that an overload does not occur and upset the natural environment. Other by-products, such as heavy metals like mercury, lead, copper, and arsenic, are very dangerous even in small quantities and will never biodegrade. Since these by-products can eventually contaminate surface and underground sources of water, extra care must be taken by industry to control or eliminate them through proper waste treatment.

About nine million Canadians and 33 million Americans depend on the Great Lakes–St. Lawrence River basin for their drinking water. You would think that such an important source of water would be protected from pollution. Sadly, this has not always been the case. In the 1960s, large amounts of phosphates from laundry detergents, and phosphorus and nitrogen from industry and agriculture, entered Lake Erie and fertilized the growth of aquatic plants. When the plants died and decayed, so much oxygen was used in the process that the fish populations dropped significantly.

CASE STUDY   Lessons from Love Canal

In the 1970s, over 360 industrial chemical compounds were found in the waters of the Great Lakes. Over 100 of them are toxic to humans and wildlife. The best (or worst, depending on how you look at it) example was in the Love Canal area in Niagara Falls, New York (see Figure 17–5). For many years, this area upstream from Niagara Falls was used by chemical companies in the area as a dump for an enormous range of dangerous compounds. Figure 17–6 (on page 263) provides a history of Love Canal. Look at this figure before you do the questions.

Figure 17–5 This deceptively park-like scene is actually part of the most famous (and infamous) chemical dump in the US—Love Canal, an area just upstream from Niagara Falls.

Questions

You will need to do some research to answer these questions.

1. **a)** Identify at least two points in the history of Love Canal when the problems that followed could have been prevented.
    b) Why did prevention not happen at any of these points?

2. The Love Canal incident led to the creation of the "Superfund" in the US. In what ways has the Superfund proven successful in dealing with chemical pollution? In what ways has it been a failure?

3. Many observers would say that the Sydney Tar Ponds in Nova Scotia are Canada's closest equivalent to Love Canal.
    a) What caused the Tar Ponds?
    b) What has been done to fix this problem?
    c) Has Canada done a better or worse job with the Tar Ponds than the US did with Love Canal? Why?

4. Is there an area where chemical waste has been dumped near where you live? How would you know?

When	What Happened?	Comments
1893	Love Canal is built.	The canal is built to add waterfront footage to the growing industrial area of Niagara Falls, NY.
1910	The canal is abandoned as a shipping route.	
1920s	The use of the canal for chemical-waste dumping begins.	
1942–1953	Hooker Chemical dumps more than 20 000 tonnes of waste in Love Canal.	Hooker Chemicals is now part of Occidental Petroleum.
1953	Love Canal is sold to Niagara Falls New York Board of Education for $1.	The chemical company does not want responsibility for site.
Starting in 1953	Hundreds of houses are built on the site.	Residents are not told about the former use of the land.
Mid-1950s–1970s	Health concerns emerge.	Children playing in puddles experience chemical burns on their skin. Leukemia, cancer, and miscarriages occur at very high rates.
1974–1978	A study finds birth defects in 56 percent of Love Canal births.	
1978 (Aug. 1)	Massive amounts of rain erode soil and expose rusty barrels leaking chemicals.	
1978 (Aug. 7)	Love Canal site is declared a disaster area by the federal government. The evacuation of 239 families occurs.	In the United States, this is the first time ever that a disaster declaration is issued for a human-made cause. The Environmental Protection Agency (EPA) identifies 82 different compounds at the site, including 11 that cause cancer.
1989	Occidental Petroleum pays for damages.	US$45 million is spent on site remediation; US$129 million is paid to former residents.
1999	Much of the Love Canal area is declared safe for people to live in.	Some residents move into this area, now called Black Creek Village.

Figure 17–6 A Love Canal chronology. As you might expect, houses in Black Creek Village are relatively inexpensive.

In 1972, Canada and the US signed the first Great Lakes Water Quality Agreement, and steps were taken to reduce phosphate discharge into the Great Lakes. Then, in 1985, the **International Joint Commission (IJC)**, the body set up by Canada and the US in 1909 to deal with issues concerning the Great Lakes, identified "areas of concern" in the Great Lakes characterized by poor water quality, largely as a result of the deposition of chemical waste (see Figure 17–7).

The IJC's approaches to solving the chemical-waste problems in the Great Lakes are logical but expensive. For example, as of 2006, US$382 million had been

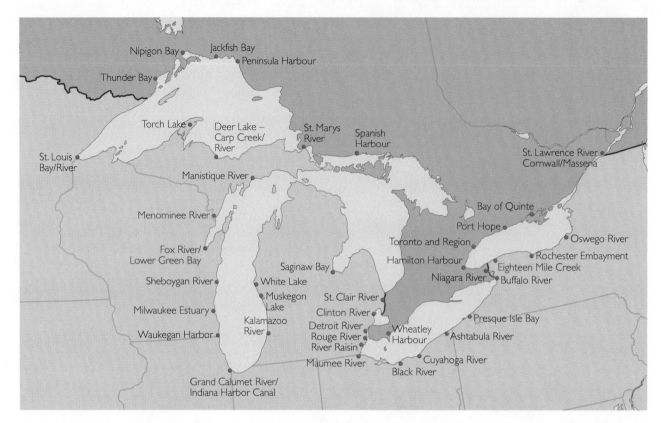

Figure 17–7 These Great Lakes "areas of concern" were designated by the International Joint Commission because of chemical pollution. Collingwood Harbour and Severn Sound at the southern tip of Georgian Bay used to be areas of concern, but conditions there have improved sufficiently for them to be removed from the list. Spanish Harbour on Lake Huron and Presque Isle Bay on Lake Erie are close to being removed from the list.

spent on cleaning up the old chemical dumps on the American side of the Niagara River (including Love Canal). Estimates are that US$249 million more will have to be spent in this relatively small area. Progress is slow, but steady, and the approaches currently used in the Great Lakes basin could stand as models for other places with similar problems. A study by the World Bank in 2003 found that Old Core countries made some improvement in the water quality of their rivers. River-water quality in many New Core countries generally showed little change, while river-water quality in other New Core countries and in the Periphery continued to deteriorate. Why is this difference not at all surprising?

Although each particular situation will have unique characteristics, some general approaches to remediation can be considered.

■ **Source control.** The obvious first step is to stop the addition of more contaminants.

■ **Natural recovery.** Frequently the best approach (after source control is in place) is to give nature a chance to solve the problem. The two most important ways that this happens occur when natural sedimentation covers dangerous materials on lake and river bottoms and when biological processes break down dangerous compounds.

■ **Environmental dredging.** When natural recovery is not enough, large dredging machines can remove dangerous materials. This is the most widely used intervention, and costs between $100 and $200 per cubic metre. Materials that are removed are placed in specially designed landfills.

■ **Thick-layer capping.** This is a relatively new approach in which the contaminated materials are sealed off from the water by placing 20 to 100 centimetres of clean materials, like clay or sand, on top of them. The cost is $50 to $60 per cubic metre.

Agricultural Wastes

Although modern agricultural techniques greatly increase food production, they can damage surface water and groundwater. For example, irrigation washes away soil sediments that then clog waterways, destroy fish habitats, and fill in wetlands; manufactured chemical fertilizers become pollutants when they are washed by precipitation into lakes and rivers, or into the groundwater; and nitrogen and phosphorus from fertilizers cause **eutrophication**, the growth and decomposition of excess vegetation that depletes oxygen in the water. Fish and other marine organisms cannot survive in excessively eutrophic water bodies. Fortunately, ecosystems can recover if source control occurs, that is, if the source of the eutrophication is removed.

Pesticides (insecticides, herbicides, and fungicides) often affect organisms other than their intended target. Designed to kill insect pests, weeds, and plant diseases, they can also adversely affect surface water. Excessive use of pesticides that frequently end up in lakes, ponds, and rivers has been linked to high rates of cancer and birth defects. *Persistent* (long-lasting) pesticides that are no longer legal in Old Core countries are commonly used in nations outside the Old Core because they are cheap and available.

Water pollution can also occur from the raising of animals for human consumption. In May 2000, a torrential downpour carried water contaminated with cattle manure containing a deadly strain of *E. coli* bacteria into one of the wells of the Ontario community of Walkerton. The well, located downhill from a cattle farm, used water from an **aquifer**—an underground layer of water-filled rock or loose materials (for example, gravel)—covered by only 2.4 metres of sand and gravel. This was not enough material to filter out the bacteria that can kill by causing a person's kidneys to shut down. Since problems with cattle waste in the well water had been identified as early as 1978, the Ministry of the Environment had told local officials to chlorinate the water and monitor for bacteria. The process of water treatment and monitoring was not done properly. Seven people died and another 2300 became ill after drinking the town's water.

Groundwater

Three things can occur to precipitation. Some of it will evaporate into the atmosphere. Much of it will run off over the surface of the land into rivers and lakes and eventually to the ocean. The remainder becomes groundwater. This is water that filters downward through the soil under the force of gravity, collecting in rock fissures and cavities and in loose sediments underground. In general there are two types of groundwater reservoirs.

■ **Open aquifer**. Water percolates into the aquifer from above, through *permeable* (having small spaces through which water can move) soil, rock, and sediments.

■ **Closed aquifer**. Water cannot percolate into the aquifer from directly above because the aquifer is surrounded, on top and bottom, by impermeable rock or sediments, such as shale or clay. Instead, water enters the aquifer from a source at a higher elevation and often a considerable distance away. Much of the water in a closed aquifer may be fossil water—from rain that fell thousands or even millions of years ago.

The Ogallala Aquifer

The Ogallala (also called the High Plains) Aquifer is an important source of water in the US. This largely closed aquifer underlies a major agricultural area that is part of eight states, stretching almost 1300 kilometres from north to south and 650 kilometres from east to west (see Figure 17–8). It is estimated that there is enough water in the Ogallala Aquifer to fill Lake Huron.

The aquifer consists mainly of sand, gravel, silt, and clay that eroded from the Rocky Mountains over 20 million years ago. Over time, these sediments soaked up water like a sponge to form an enormous underground reservoir of **fossil water** that is now many thousands of years old. About 1000 years ago, the Ogallala was cut off from its recharging area in the Rocky Mountains. The fossil water in the aquifer cannot be replenished except by small amounts of water from

Figure 17–8 Because the rate of water withdrawal for irrigation is much higher than the rate of recharge, the level of the Ogallala Aquifer has dropped by as much as 15 metres in some areas of Kansas and Texas.

precipitation, lakes, and streams that percolate into those few areas of the aquifer that are open.

The area of the Ogallala Aquifer is one of the world's major agricultural regions, producing great quantities of wheat, alfalfa, soybeans, cotton, corn, cattle, poultry, and hogs. Whether this will continue is open to question, unfortunately. In 1950, water from the Ogallala Aquifer irrigated about 1.4 million hectares; today, it irrigates about 6.5 million hectares (see Figure 17–9). In some areas, water withdrawal is occurring at up to ten times the rate of natural recharge. Consequently, in almost one-third of the region, the water level in the aquifer has declined by at least three metres. In some regions, the decline has been as much as 15 metres. Despite conservation measures, such as the introduction of less wasteful methods of irrigation and the planting of crops that require less water, the level of the Ogallala Aquifer continues to drop.

The area over the aquifer is facing other problems as well. The removal of large amounts of water is causing the land above the aquifer to *subside* (sink) in some places. (Land subsidence caused by removal of groundwater is a worldwide problem; for example, Beijing is subsiding about ten centimetres per year, and parts of Mexico City as much as 30 centimetres per year.)

Fossil Water Use in Saudi Arabia

Saudi Arabia also relies heavily on fossil water. This is not a surprise if one realizes that the average annual precipitation for the country is only 59 millimetres—or slightly more than half of that of Las Vegas, a city that we already know is in a desert. One-third of

Figure 17–9 Irrigation dramatically increases agricultural productivity, but if overused, it can destroy ancient water resources.

Saudi Arabia's water comes from a combination of renewable water from aquifers, *desalinated* water (seawater from which salt has been removed), and reused wastewater. The remaining two-thirds comes from fossil water in underground aquifers. Another way of looking at these statistics is that Saudi Arabia uses more than 700 percent of its renewable water resources each year. The kingdom's non-renewable water resource is being used up very quickly. In the 1980s, in an effort to help the country become self-sufficient in wheat production, the Saudi Arabian government provided subsidies and interest-free loans to its farmers, and guaranteed to pay them more than four times the world price for wheat. Farmers, motivated by this assistance, produced more than twice the wheat needed to meet domestic demand. By 1991, Saudi Arabia had become the world's sixth-largest exporter of wheat, but at what cost? In essence, the country was subsidizing the export of its scarcest resource—water. By 1993, the government had stopped buying wheat owing to changing market conditions and a tight budget, but today farmers are irrigating other crops with fossil water. When Saudi Arabia's fossil aquifers can no longer be tapped—and this outcome is inevitable unless current rates of use are curtailed—the expanded agricultural sector that depends on fossil water will undoubtedly collapse.

Wetlands

Wetlands can be found in every major climatic zone on Earth. Known by different names—swamps, marshes, bogs, fens, tidal marshes, and mangrove swamps—wetlands form a transition zone between permanently dry land and lakes, streams, rivers, and oceans (see Figure 17–10). Wetlands were once considered useless land, and many have been filled in or drained for residential, industrial, and especially, agricultural purposes. In tropical areas, mangroves have been cleared to allow the construction of tropical beach resorts. If you have had a holiday at one of these beach resorts, you may have noticed that mangroves are found in areas adjacent to the resort.

Many factors, however, have led to the protection of wetlands, especially in Old Core countries.

■ They are temporary water-storage sites that recharge aquifers, moderate stream flow, and lessen floods.

Did You Know?

A global review found that 24 percent of the world's wetlands are in Canada.

How do you know you have fallen into a ...

- **swamp?**
  The ecosystem is dominated by trees. The soil is saturated for part of the year and may have standing water at other parts of the year.

- **marsh?**
  The ecosystem is dominated by soft-stemmed vegetation. It is frequently or continually inundated with water.

- **bog?**
  The ecosystem is dominated by spongy peat deposits and has highly acidic water. It is fed by surface water.

- **fen?**
  The ecosystem is similar to a bog but with less acidic water. It is fed by groundwater.

- **tidal marsh?**
  It is found in middle and high latitudes along oceans. The ecosystem is dominated by tall grasses. It can have salt, brackish, or fresh water.

- **mangrove marsh?**
  It is found in tropical and subtropical latitudes along oceans. The ecosystem is dominated by the mangal plant.

Figure 17–10 The important roles played by wetlands are often not well understood. The result is that swamps have often been drained for agriculture while mangrove marshes are cleared and filled for the development of beach resorts.

- Their vegetation holds soil in place and anchors shorelines.

- They provide habitats and breeding grounds for fish, invertebrates, birds, and mammals.

- Many are migratory stopovers for birds.

- The natural recycling of their water filters out chemicals and circulates nutrients to plants and animals. In fact, artificial wetlands are being used to treat sewage (see Figure 17–11).

- They provide people with aesthetic environments, food, and fuel. For example, peat cut from bogs in northern Europe is dried for burning in fireplaces and stoves.

The Ramsar Convention, signed in Ramsar, Iran, in 1971, was the first significant international attempt to protect the world's wetlands. Since the Convention does not have any legal power to force countries to stop the loss of their wetlands, it uses persuasion and moral arguments to accomplish this end. By 2007, the Ramsar List of protected wetlands comprised 1675 sites of international importance around the world.

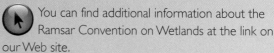

You can find additional information about the Ramsar Convention on Wetlands at the link on our Web site.

Figure 17–11 This artificially constructed wetland in Phoenix, Arizona, is used to provide secondary sewage treatment. It has been such a great success that the city is now going to construct a much larger (545 hectares) facility to handle a much larger amount of sewage.

Upon signing the Convention, each country must designate at least one wetland for the "List of Wetlands of International Importance." Canada signed the Convention in 1981, and currently has 37 sites on the list with a combined area of over 13 million hectares. Eight of these sites, including Point Pelee, Polar Bear Provincial Park, and Minesing Swamp, are found in Ontario. Unfortunately, many of the world's most important wetlands are not listed, and these productive environments are among Earth's most threatened ecosystems. This is particularly true in Periphery countries, where rapidly growing populations are putting pressure on governments to drain wetlands for agriculture.

Managed Water

There are over 800 000 small dams and more than 45 000 large ones (dams higher than a five-storey building) in the world today. Of these, 100 are "superdams"—measuring 150 metres or more high (see Figure 17–12). Large-scale dam projects present a variety of issues related to preserving the earth's freshwater supplies.

Figure 17–12 The Katse Dam in Lesotho is the largest dam in Africa (185 metres high) and is a typical superdam. It was completed in 1996. The purpose of this dam is to provide water to a dry area in neighbouring South Africa, and hydro-electricity for Lesotho, and for sale to South Africa. Eventually five dams are to be built in Lesotho for this purpose.

Benefits of Large Dam Projects

- Dams store water in artificial lakes for electricity production, irrigation, and industrial, urban, and other uses. For example, more than 20 dams on the Colorado River provide water and power to over 25 million people throughout the US Southwest. Without these dams, much of this land would still be desert.

- Dams regulate the flow of water downstream to reduce flooding and to hold water for use in drier times of the year. For example, the construction of the Hoover Dam along the Colorado River in the early 1930s reduced flooding and saved water from the spring runoff for use later in the year (see Figure 17–13).

- Dams provide nearly 20 percent of the world's electricity. The power they produce is relatively inexpensive, and does not create greenhouse gases, acid rain, and nuclear waste. Dams help make countries more self-sufficient in energy and hence reduce the cost of oil imports.

- Dams create artificial lakes that provide habitats for fish, migrating birds, amphibians, and shoreline animals.

- Reservoirs often provide a location for boating, swimming, fishing, and other recreational activities.

- Management of water levels may allow a barge-shipping transportation system that is cheaper and more fuel-efficient than trains or trucks. For example, barge shipping on the Columbia River system in the US carries the equivalent of 120 000 railroad cars of goods annually.

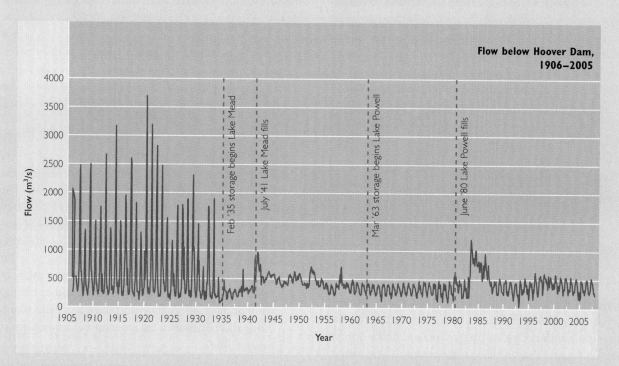

Figure 17–13 This graph of river flow on the Colorado River at the Hoover Dam shows the dramatic ability of a superdam to regulate a river. Massive amounts of water that were lost through runoff in the spring and early summer are now held back to prevent flooding downstream and for later use. Lake Mead is the reservoir created by the Hoover Dam. Lake Powell is the reservoir created by the newer Glen Canyon Dam upstream. The large flow in 1983 resulted from an enormous spring runoff and from the need to pass as much water downstream from the Glen Canyon Dam as possible. Stream flow was so high that year that the Glen Canyon Dam was in danger of being breached. If this had happened there would have been a massive flood downstream that might have destroyed the Hoover Dam as well. Downstream from the Hoover Dam, so much water is taken from the river for irrigation in the US and Mexico that, at times, virtually no river flow reaches the river's mouth.

Negative Impacts of Large Dam Projects

- Dams are often built in areas with dry climates. In such areas, large quantities of water are lost through evaporation. (About one-third of the Colorado River's water evaporates from reservoirs built along its length. Because of the amount of evaporation, it is estimated that the salinity of the Colorado River is double what it was before the construction of dams along its course.)

- There are frequently geological problems associated with dam building. Sometimes the rock structure beneath the dam site is unsuitable for storing water. For example, part of Lake Nasser behind the Aswan High Dam in Egypt lies on porous sandstone that soaks up much of the water in the reservoir. In earthquake-prone regions there is always the fear that the weight of water in the reservoir could trigger an earthquake, or that a quake might cause damage to the dam.

- People's way of life, culture, and often their spiritual focus are lost when their ancestral homes and lands are flooded and they are forced to move to higher ground. Many suffer from a resettlement syndrome characterized by *passivity* (lack of energy or will), depression, and less self-reliance. This is occurring in China now, where 1.3 million people have been and are being displaced by the Three Gorges Dam.

- People, who are forced to move from productive farmland that will be flooded to poorer quality land elsewhere, experience a decline in their standard of living.

- The damming of a river inevitably changes the ecology of the river and surrounding areas. For example, animals and fish that are adapted to living in an environment with flowing, highly oxygenated water cannot survive in the still, low-oxygenated reservoir that builds up behind a dam.

- Economic benefits of large dams may not be as great as originally thought. In developing countries, there is often not enough industry to use the power generated by such projects. Also, funds may be lacking to pay for the infrastructure needed to distribute electricity to the population. Furthermore, the payback of building loans plus interest is difficult for countries with a limited tax base.

- Sediments are no longer carried downstream and deposited in wetlands, on the floodplain where they fertilize the land, and in the river delta. For example, the Aswan High Dam on the Nile River has eliminated annual floodwaters that used to deposit sediments in the Nile Delta and onto the floodplain. Sediments end up being deposited in the dam's reservoir, reducing its storage capacity.

- Dams and associated irrigation projects in tropical areas lead to an increase in water-borne diseases. Throughout Asia and Africa, mosquitoes (which carry malaria, yellow fever, and elephantiasis), and snails, which carry bilharzia (schistosomiasis), find ideal breeding conditions in the still waters of reservoirs and irrigation ditches.

Irrigation Schemes

Large-scale irrigation schemes are frequently associated with large dams. They can provide water for the irrigation of thousands of hectares of land. In fact, some studies suggest that as much as 40 percent of the world's food supply is produced on irrigated land. Despite the high productivity of irrigated farmland, there are significant concerns to consider.

- In hot, dry climates, much of the water stored in reservoirs evaporates, thus increasing the salinity of the water.

- When the water evaporates from irrigated farmlands, it adds unnaturally large amounts of salt to the soil. The salt poisons the earth to the point that important organisms in the soil die, and crops will not grow.

- High levels of salinity affect about 20 percent of the world's irrigated agricultural land, and about one million hectares of farmland have to be abandoned annually because excessive salinity makes farming impossible.

Some irrigation schemes have created major ecological disasters. The most serious concerns the Aral Sea, a saltwater lake that straddles the boundary between Kazakhstan and Uzbekistan in Central Asia. Beginning in the early 1960s, the Soviet Union (Kazakhstan and Uzbekistan were then part of the Soviet Union) diverted water from two large rivers that formerly fed the Aral Sea, at that time the fourth-largest inland body of water in the world. This was done in an effort to make the Soviet Union self-sufficient in cotton production. A 1300-kilometre canal and a vast network of irrigation ditches were used to help expand existing cotton fields.

With the loss of 90 percent of its inflow, the Aral Sea shrank to one-third its former volume, and in 1988, it split into two smaller lakes (see Figure 17–14). The remaining water has a salinity equal to that of seawater, as well as increased concentrations of toxic agricultural chemicals and human waste. The fishery that supported 60 000 jobs has disappeared, and abandoned fishing villages are found kilometres from the sea (see Figure 17–15). Every year, millions of tonnes of dust laced with salt and toxic chemicals are picked up and deposited on surrounding farmland by the wind. The result is lower crop yields. The climate in the region has changed; it is now drier and hotter, and this has reduced the region's wetland areas, together with their vegetation and waterfowl. The World Bank has provided billions of dollars in loans to try to stop the region's decline, and time will tell how successful these efforts will be. As of 2008, the size of the northern part of the Aral Sea has stabilized, while the southern section continues to shrink.

You may well ask why dams and their irrigation schemes are not dismantled if the damage they create is so great. Unfortunately, in many ways, dismantling an existing dam is impractical. It costs about as much to tear down a dam as it does to build one. Furthermore, people desperately need the agricultural products from irrigated cropland along with the electricity produced by large dams.

SUSTAINABILITY

It costs about as much to tear down a dam as it does to build one.

Why does this make it virtually certain that a dam will not be removed?

Alternatives to Large Dams

Alternatives to large dams do exist. They include

- building small dams that manage water on a local rather than regional scale

- planting many trees to hold rainwater back until the rainwater has a chance to sink into the ground where it can be accessed via wells

- choosing to grow crops that require less water

- using **drip irrigation** (see Figure 17–16), which reduces the need for water and fertilizer by letting

Figure 17–15 A canal was built to allow vessels to continue to have access to the shrinking Aral Sea. Unfortunately the shrinkage happened faster than the canal could be built.

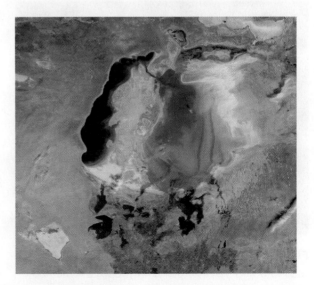

Figure 17–14 The Aral Sea in 1976 (left) and 2007 (right). Notice the salt deposits (white) in the 2007 photo.

water drip gradually to the roots of plants, either through the soil surface, or directly onto the roots through a network of small pipes—this technique, though more expensive than traditional irrigation methods, can lower water consumption by up to 70 percent

- using rooftop or mountain-slope water collection

- reducing waste, since only 40 percent of water diverted for agriculture actually contributes to food production. An example of improving efficiency is to reduce leaks in irrigation pipelines.

Because large-scale dams and irrigation projects are the source of such controversy, the World Bank and the World Conservation Union set up a World Commission on Dams (WCD) in 1998. Its mandate was to review the effectiveness of large dams, to assess alternatives, and to develop criteria for future decisions related to the design, construction, operation, and decommissioning of dams.

In the final report of the WCD, the chair of the Commission, Professor Kader Asmal, wrote

…Nowhere in the Report will you read "large dams are bad." Or "good." Large dams simply are. The Report shows how, where, when, and why certain aspects of those dams have performed for better or for worse, and how we can improve decisions to develop resources for all…. The Report does not call for a moratorium. Dams should be judged on a case-by-case basis, and pass or fail according to the criteria and guidelines societies set for them.

Figure 17–16 In drip irrigation, small plastic pipes are used to deliver water to plants. Why does this method of irrigation waste much less water than conventional methods?

Water Transfers

In many parts of the world, fresh water is in short supply; in other parts, it is abundant. One method of dealing with this inequity is to transfer water from one place to another. The subject of large-scale transfers of water from Canada to the US is a contentious issue for Canadians. Consider the two sides:

- **In favour of transfers**. Supporters of transfers (often from parts of the US that are short of water) argue that Canada has an enormous amount of surplus fresh water—an amount far beyond what the country needs now or is likely to need in the future. Further, they reason that since Canada is happy to export non-renewable oil, gas, and other minerals, why should we not export renewable water? Also they argue that a properly managed water-export industry would provide jobs and money that could benefit Canada, and help parts of the US that are dry now and likely to be drier still as a result of global warming. A strong economy in these regions could only help Canada since so much of our export trade is with the US.

- **In opposition to transfers**. Those who oppose transfers (including environmentalists and Canadian nationalists) also make strong arguments. They state that although fresh water is plentiful in Canada, it is located in the north, far away from where it is needed for human activities. As for the water in the Great Lakes, 99 percent is non-renewable fossil water from the glaciers that melted more than 10 000 years ago; only 1 percent is renewed annually by rainfall and river inflow. From this perspective, the case is made that there is much less water available for transfer to the US than would first appear. In addition, they argue that higher global temperatures will increase evaporation and change precipitation patterns—we may, in fact, need all the water we have. They also suggest that the US does not use the water it already has very wisely (Las Vegas being a prime example), and that this behaviour should change before we consider selling them our water.

In 1994, opponents of the then-unsigned North American Free Trade Agreement (NAFTA) expressed their conviction that Canada's fresh water might be shipped to the US under the terms of the agreement. The Canadian government, in its effort to counter this belief and encourage the adoption of NAFTA, negotiated a secondary agreement asserting that NAFTA did not give any one country a right to the water resources of another. (Water companies are currently allowed to export water provided the containers are no larger than 20 litres.)

Preserving Our Oceans

The world's oceans are vast, covering 72 percent of Earth's surface. Much exploration and trade has taken place on the oceans, and they have always been an important source of food. However, we dump our garbage and chemicals into them and catch many kinds of fish beyond sustainable levels. We do these things even though we know very little about how oceans sustain themselves and how pollutants may be affecting marine organisms. We do know, however, that the damage we do to our oceans is having a serious impact on all life on Earth.

A Mari Usque Ad Mare

Canada's motto, "From sea to sea," indicates the significance of oceans to our country. Canada's 244 000-kilometre coastline is the longest in the world, and its continental shelf is the second largest at approximately 3.7 square kilometres. In 1977, after years of enduring the indiscriminate fishing practices of other nations, Canada declared a 200-nautical-mile (370-kilometre) exclusive fisheries zone extending from its coastlines. In so doing, Canada took upon itself the protection of over five million square kilometres of its coastal waters.

In 2007, Canada and other northern nations faced a new oceanic challenge. (Nations with jurisdiction in the Arctic Ocean basin are Canada, Russia, the US [Alaska], Norway, and Denmark [Greenland].) Russia declared that its jurisdiction extended from its coastline to the North Pole—far beyond the 200-nautical-mile limit. The land Russia claimed was roughly equal to the size of western Europe and was thought to contain potentially rich reserves of oil and natural gas, gold, diamonds, and other minerals. The other northern nations were quickly forced to reconsider how they thought about the northern oceans, where the permanent ice cover is diminishing as a result of global warming.

International Initiatives

In 1994, after 22 years of negotiations among 150 nations, the **United Nations Convention on the Law of the Sea** (**UNCLOS**) put into force a legal agreement for promoting peaceful uses of the world's oceans, the equitable use of ocean resources, and the protection of marine environments. The Convention declared that 45 percent of the seabed, along with its resources, was a common resource for all humanity, and as such, should be managed as a global resource. The remainder of the oceans would fall into 200-nautical-mile **Exclusive Economic Zones** (**EEZs**), within which maritime countries, like Canada, would have control.

The Problems of the Oceans ... and the Solutions

You will now have the opportunity to study a major issue that affects the world's oceans, or an organization that works to solve oceanic problems.

Some possible research topics are given (see list at right), although you may choose an alternative after checking it with your teacher. Your teacher will advise you on the type of product you will create after doing your reseach and will let you know whether you are working alone or in a group.

1. If you are studying an issue

   a) What is the history of the issue?

   b) What are the "sides" of the issue?

   c) Where is it an important issue?

   d) What progress has been made to resolve this issue?

   e) What are the "next steps" to take?

2. If you are researching an institution or NGO

   a) What is the nature of the organization?

   b) Who are the members of the organization (where do they live, and what do they do for a living)?

   c) What is the organization's mandate?

   d) What are its recent activities?

   e) What successes and failures has the organization had? **S**

- International Seabed Authority
- International Tribunal for the Law of the Sea
- Overfishing
- Scripps Institution of Oceanography
- Cousteau Society
- Commission on the Limits of the Continental Shelf
- Offshore oil drilling
- Fishery by-catch
- Protection of marine areas
- Ocean sovereignty issues
- Mercury contamination
- Whaling
- Drift-net fishing
- MARPOL 73/78 (the International Convention for the Prevention of Pollution from Ships)
- Invasive species
- Cruise ships
- Threats to coral reefs
- Destructive fishing methods
- Runoff pollution
- Ocean Sciences Centre
- International Whaling Commission
- Woods Hole Oceanographic Institute
- Ocean-based tourist attractions like aquariums and opportunities to swim with dolphins, sharks, etc.
- Bedford Institute of Oceanography

Chapter Questions

Knowledge and Understanding

1. Briefly describe the various types of pollution that affect fresh water.

2. What is an aquifer, and what is the difference between an open aquifer and a closed aquifer?

3. a) Why are wetlands so important?

   b) For what purposes are wetlands drained?

   c) What is being done to protect the world's wetlands?

4. You may find it helpful to collaborate with classmates to answer this question.

   a) Identify a wetland near where you live. Estimate its size—note that 100 metres by 100 metres is a hectare and that there are 100 hectares in one square kilometre.

   b) Which type of wetland is it?

   c) Is it protected? If so, how and by whom?

5. a) Identify two reasons for and two reasons against allowing water transfers from Canada to the US.

   b) Discuss with a small group of classmates what you think should be done about such transfers. What might happen in the future that would change your attitude in this respect?

6. a) What problems are we creating for the world's oceans?

   b) What initiatives have been taken to deal with some of these problems?

Thinking

7. The word "conservation" can be defined as "the wise use of resources." Based on this definition, why might it make sense to suggest that the application of the principle of conservation to water resources is absolutely critical to the future of the human race?

8. a) What is fossil water and what importance does it have to our understanding that water is a renewable resource?

   b) In using water, particularly fossil water, society must make a choice: consume the groundwater and water from large lakes today, or conserve it for future generations when the climate may be less favourable because of global warming. What are your recommendations? Explain your reasons.

9. In the 1950s and 1960s, there was an almost universal acceptance of the idea that giant dams were a "good thing" for the development of both rich and poor countries. By the 1980s and 1990s, attitudes had changed dramatically and many people thought large dams were very bad things indeed. Keeping this attitude change in mind, reread the statement by Professor Kader Asmal on page 272 in this chapter. What notes of wisdom do you see here?

Communication

10. The International Joint Commission has identified areas of concern in the Great Lakes. Working in pairs, select two sites, one in Canada and one in the US. Create a poster and a written presentation to show the substances creating the problem, their sources, the dangers associated with these substances, and the actions taken (or not taken) to improve the situation.

11. a) Examine the pros and cons of a large-scale dam/irrigation project in a developed country and in a developing country. You can consult our Web site for information. Create a poster or other visual aid to demonstrate to the class how appropriate the project was for each country.

    b) Decide, on balance, whether each project was a "good thing" or "bad thing" for the countries involved.

    c) Combine your findings with those of your classmates. Does it appear that large-scale dams/irrigation projects are more successful in developed countries or developing countries? Why might this be true?

12. As a class, debate the following statement: *Resolved—That water, like other commodities, should be exported in bulk to the US and other countries as long as its export does not affect Canadian needs.*

Application

13. a) Examine the causes and consequences of the *E. coli* outbreak in Walkerton, Ontario, in 2000.

b) A judicial commission studied what happened in Walkerton and issued a report in 2002. What major recommendations were included in this report?

c) To what extent have these recommendations been followed?

14. Major environmental changes can be caused by large-scale irrigation schemes. Examine the Aral Sea scheme, the Colorado River water diversions, or some other project, and write a report, with visual aids, to demonstrate its positive and negative aspects.

15. In February 2002, the government of Quebec and the Cree people of Quebec signed a $3.5-billion agreement to allow Hydro Quebec to build large dams and power plants on the Eastmain and Rupert rivers, and to permit mining, logging, and further industrial development on Cree territory. Write a report in which you examine and explain

a) the three decades of conflict between the Cree people and the government of Quebec that existed before this agreement was reached

b) what the 2002 agreement gives to both sides

c) what opponents say about this agreement

d) whether the deal appears fair to both sides

CHAPTER 18

Earth's Fragile Atmosphere

Key Terms

ultraviolet (UV) radiation

persistent organic pollutants (POPs)

grasshopper effect

bioaccumulation

acidic deposition

critical load

temperature inversion

photochemical smog

chlorofluorocarbons (CFCs)

Montreal Protocol

hydrochlorofluorocarbons (HCFCs)

Smog and acid rain can affect daily life in a variety of ways. On a smog day in Toronto, outdoor exercise can become risky. The Taj Mahal, an internationally acclaimed structure, is at risk of permanent damage due to air pollutants from a nearby oil refinery.

Key Questions

By the end of this chapter you will be able to answer the following questions.

■ How does air pollution affect your health?

■ What poisonous chemicals are in smog, what is their impact, and what is being done about them?

■ How does acidic deposition occur, what is its impact, and what is being done about it?

■ Why is ozone depletion a danger to you?

The Atmosphere

When the curved edge of the earth is seen from space, our atmosphere appears as a thin blue layer. This thin atmospheric layer sustains all life on our planet and protects it from **ultraviolet** (**UV**) **radiation** (invisible radiation with a shorter wavelength than visible sunlight, that can cause a sunburn).

Earth's atmosphere, which is a mixture of particles, gases, and *aerosols* (suspensions of droplets in gas), is approximately 1000 kilometres thick. The lowest five kilometres, less than the height of Mount Everest, contain 50 percent of all atmospheric gases (see Figure 18–1). The "greenhouse" gases—water vapour, carbon dioxide, methane, nitrous oxide, and ozone—represent only a small percentage of the atmosphere, but they play an important role in regulating Earth's temperatures. Like the glass walls and the roof of a greenhouse, they trap the heat rising from the earth, thereby maintaining temperatures suitable for life over most of the planet's surface.

The layer of atmosphere that most concerns us is the troposphere, which varies in thickness from 9 to 16 kilometres. It is here that weather occurs and most air pollution is found. Differences in temperature and pressure keep the atmosphere in constant vertical and horizontal motion. This motion carries with it pollutants from natural processes such as forest fires and volcanoes, and the wastes that are discharged into the atmosphere from burning fossil fuels and from industrial processes.

Human activities have had a profound effect on the atmosphere, especially since the time of the Industrial Revolution, when smoke and gases from burning coal began to be released in huge quantities. In modern times, airborne chemical contaminants from industrial processes have caused poisons to accumulate in the air we breathe, formed smog and acid rain, and opened a hole in the ozone layer.

We know that air pollution affects people's health, especially that of young children, the elderly, and those with respiratory and heart conditions. Environment Canada attributes almost 6000 premature deaths each year to air pollution in Canada's eight major cities. The Ontario Medical Association estimates that the economic costs of hospital admissions, emergency room visits, absenteeism from work, and premature death due to air pollution were almost $8 billion in 2005. This figure is expected to rise to $13 billion by 2026.

Did You Know?

The David Suzuki Foundation estimates that between 6000 and 16 000 deaths occur annually from air pollution across Canada.

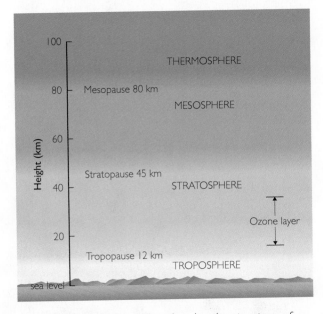

Figure 18–1 Cross-section showing the structure of Earth's atmosphere. The heights shown are approximations, as precise heights vary with latitude and time of year.

Poisons in the Atmosphere

Some of the most dangerous of the human-made pollutants released into the atmosphere are **persistent organic pollutants** (**POPs**). These are chemicals used in pesticides and industrial chemicals, such as PCBs (polychlorinated biphenyls, used in coolants, sealants, adhesives, etc.), and are found in by-products of industrial processes, such as dioxins. For example, dioxins and furans are by-products of the pulp and paper industry.

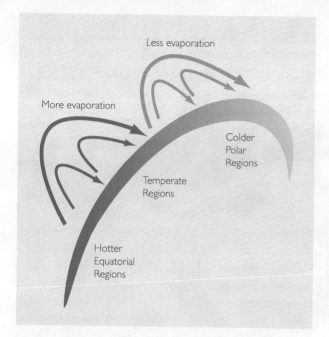

Figure 18–2 POPs evaporate and travel from their point of origin based on air-circulation patterns. Because less evaporation occurs in colder regions, POPs tend to concentrate in climates such as that of Canada's North.

POPs often turn up far from their place of origin because they evaporate, travel through the atmosphere on air currents, and then condense in a new location. This is known as the **grasshopper effect** (see Figure 18–2).

The Impact of POPs

POPs are highly toxic and can cause cancer, reproductive problems, birth defects, damage to the immune and central nervous systems, and, ultimately, death. They are also *insoluble* (that is, they will not dissolve) in water, are very stable, and can last for years in the environment before breaking down.

Through a process known as **bioaccumulation**, POPs build up in the fatty tissues of fish, predatory birds, and mammals, including humans, because these living organisms are high on the food chain (see Figure 18–3).

Canada and other temperate and polar countries are particularly susceptible to pollution from POPs because of slower evaporation due to low temperatures. When POPs are deposited in these regions, they become trapped in the environment and eventually enter the food chain. In Canada the highest rates of POPs are found in the Arctic. Polar bears in the Arctic and around Hudson Bay have some of the highest levels of POPs ever detected in wildlife. Their highly contaminated cubs are weaker and may suffer more health problems.

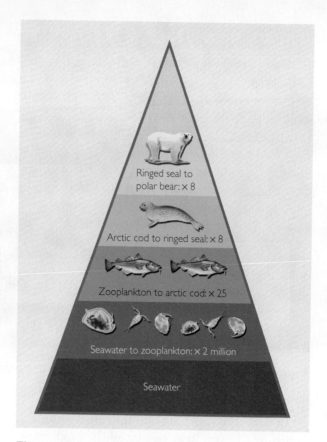

Figure 18–3 Bioaccumulation causes POPs to become increasingly concentrated as they move through the food chain.

What Can Be Done?

The 1999 Canadian Environmental Protection Act (EPA) established regulations regarding the manufacture, storage, processing, and export of POPs. In 2007, the regulations were updated to make them more *stringent* (strict). Ultimately, the goal is to eliminate the release of POPs into the environment. However, the United States and many countries in Latin America, eastern Europe, and Southeast Asia still produce and use these chemicals because they are cheaper and easier to use than the alternatives.

Efforts have been made in other countries to eliminate POPs, although it will be years before results are seen. Eight northern countries—Canada, Denmark (Greenland), Finland, Iceland, Norway, Russia, Sweden, and the US (Alaska)—have developed the Arctic Monitoring and Assessment Program to establish a database of Arctic contaminants and to provide scientific advice on remedial and preventive actions regarding contaminants in the Arctic.

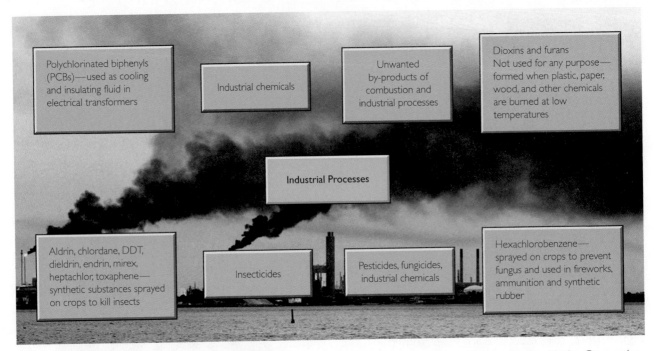

Figure 18–4 The dirty dozen: the 12 original persistent organic pollutants (POPs) controlled by the Stockholm Convention.

In May 2004, the Stockholm Convention was signed by 147 countries to control the production, import, export, disposal, and use of 12 POPs (see Figure 18–4). As of 2007, ten additional chemicals had been proposed and were being evaluated. A decision on whether to include these chemicals in the Convention is expected to take place in 2009.

SUSTAINABILITY

Canada will not be able to meet all the targets outlined in the Stockholm Convention.

Do you think Canada should change the Environmental Protection Act so it can meet the Stockholm targets?

One important aspect of the Stockholm Convention is that financial and technical assistance is available to help developing countries minimize and, eventually, eliminate POPs from their environments.

Canada will not be able to meet all the targets outlined in the Stockholm Convention because under the 1999 Canadian EPA, companies can continue to use some old equipment (for example, electrical transformers) that contains PCBs. During the use, maintenance, storage, and transportation of this equipment, there are usually some releases of PCBs into the environment. It is estimated that if the Act is not changed, up to 3300 kilograms of carcinogenic PCBs will be released into the environment between 2005 and 2035.

The Dilemma of Acid Rain

Imagine buying French fries at your favourite chip wagon and then holding them up in the air to get your vinegar from the sky. Sounds far-fetched, but in Pitlochry, Scotland, one rainfall had precipitation with a pH level of 2.4—the same acidity level as vinegar.

Acid rain is only one form of **acidic deposition**. Acidic pollutants may be deposited close to their source as dry deposition (acidic gas or dust), or be carried by the prevailing winds for thousands of kilometres to return to Earth as acid rain, snow, fog, or hail (see Figure 18–5).

Areas underlain by bedrock that is normally acidic, such as the Canadian Shield and the Appalachians, are very susceptible to the effects of acidic deposition and may receive levels that exceed their **critical load**. Critical load refers to the amount of pollution that an ecosystem can tolerate before that pollution harms the environment. Approximately 95 000 of the 700 000 lakes in southeastern Canada are already acidified and unable to support much life.

In many parts of the world, such as North America, Europe, India, and China, large amounts of sulphur

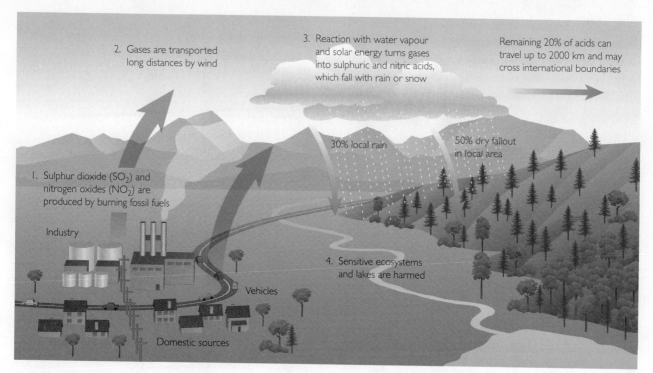

Figure 18–5 How acid rain is produced

Labels within the figure:

2. Gases are transported long distances by wind

3. Reaction with water vapour and solar energy turns gases into sulphuric and nitric acids, which fall with rain or snow

Remaining 20% of acids can travel up to 2000 km and may cross international boundaries

30% local rain

50% dry fallout in local area

1. Sulphur dioxide (SO_2) and nitrogen oxides (NO_2) are produced by burning fossil fuels

Industry

Vehicles

4. Sensitive ecosystems and lakes are harmed

Domestic sources

dioxide are being released into the atmosphere from the burning of fossil fuels for energy, and especially from the smelting of sulphur-bearing metal ores. Nitrogen oxides are released during the combustion of fuels. Agriculture is also a source of atmospheric pollutants when ammonia from fertilizers and manure is released.

Many factories, smelters, and power plants have "superstacks" up to 300 metres high. This reduces the impact of acidic deposition in the local area by releasing pollutants high into the atmosphere. Air currents, however, then carry the pollutants to other regions, often thousands of kilometres away. This creates an international political dimension to the problem. For example, a study in Sweden in 2003 indicated that only about 8 to 9 percent of the country's sulphur and nitric oxide depositions came from domestic sources.

SUSTAINABILITY

...Ontario [ranks] third...on the list of top polluting jurisdictions in continental North America.

What can or should residents of the province do to change this?

Environment Canada estimates that more than half of the acidic deposition in eastern Canada originates from emissions in the US, particularly from Ohio, Indiana, Illinois, and West Virginia. The US

Environmental Protection Agency, on the other hand, argues that the US receives most of the pollution produced at the Nanticoke generating station on Lake Erie, about 60 kilometres south of Hamilton (see Figure 18–6). Nanticoke is Ontario's largest coal-fired generating plant and the province's largest polluter.

The US Commission on Environmental Cooperation reported in 2002 that Ontario is third, after Texas and Ohio, on the list of top polluting jurisdictions in continental North America. Figure 18–7 shows the annual emissions of polluting gases, in Canada and the US, that cause acidic deposition.

Coal-fueled generating stations produce about 20 percent of Ontario's electrical generating capacity. In 2003, the provincial Liberal government promised to close all coal-fueled stations by 2007. It was not able to do so as there was not enough generating capacity from other sources to meet the demand for electricity. The Lakeview Generating Station, near Toronto, did close in 2005 and was demolished. The new closure date for the four remaining coal-fueled generating plants in Ontario (Thunder Bay, Atikokan, Lambton, and Nanticoke), however, is 2014.

The Atlantic provinces receive acidic precipitation from smelters in Manitoba, Ontario, and Quebec, while southwestern British Columbia is affected by pollution from the US and from local sources such as

Figure 18–6 The Nanticoke generating station, the largest coal-fired plant in North America, generates enough electricity to power nearly 1.5 million homes each year, but it is Canada's largest polluter.

	United States	Canada
Sulphur dioxide		
1980	23.4	4.6
2002	14.4	2.5
2004	13.3	2.3
2010 (Projected)	10.0	2.2
Nitrogen oxides		
1980	22.8	1.8
2002	19.3	2.5
2004	17.3	2.5
2010 (Projected)	13.6	2.3

Figure 18–7 Annual emission (millions of metric tonnes) of gases that produce acidic deposition, in Canada and the US

smelters and pulp and paper mills. The long-range, transboundary flow of pollutants has led to regional and international disputes, with parties on both sides laying blame on others while at the same time refusing to accept responsibility for their own pollution.

Impact of Acidic Deposition

Acidic deposition has negative impacts on life in aquatic and terrestrial environments, the health of people, and the longevity of human-made structures (see Figure 18–8).

What Can Be Done?

The most obvious way to combat acidic deposition would be to eliminate pollutants at their source by developing alternative sources of power or by installing anti-pollution equipment in factories. This is easy to say, but difficult to do because of the political, economic, scientific, and social forces that come into play.

For example, the nitrogen oxide emissions from motor vehicles could be reduced by the use of catalytic converters and the regular testing of vehicle emissions,

a method now used in Ontario but not in many other parts of the world. Government funding for efficient and economical public transit would seem an appropriate measure, but this long-term commitment is not on the agenda for many governments. Politicians are subject to pressure from automobile manufacturers, oil companies, groups that want lower taxes, and people who want the convenience of driving a car.

The 1994 UN Convention on Long-Range Transboundary Air Pollution was signed by 35 countries, including Canada. With 2010 as the target year, Canada agreed to reduce its sulphur dioxide emissions by 42 percent, the US by 40 percent, Britain by 80 percent, Germany by 87 percent, and Russia by 40 percent (below 1980 levels). Under this agreement, countries have different reduction targets based on the ability of each environment to tolerate pollution.

In 2005, the Canadian Acid Deposition Science Assessment confirmed that the impact of acidic deposition was more serious than had been anticipated. Despite the considerable decline in acid rain–causing emissions, over 550 000 lakes that were tested in eastern Canada continue to receive acidic deposition in excess of critical loads. Highly acidified lakes are not returning to their pre-acidification condition and may require action, such as the addition of lime, to neutralize the acidity.

Aquatic life	Terrestrial life	Human health	Material damage
• Plankton and vertebrates die when pH drops below 5 • Fish may be born deformed • Food supply for water-fowl is depleted • Aluminum leached from soil into water causes fish gills to be coated so fish suffocate • Mercury and lead leached from soil make water more toxic	• Microorganisms in soil are damaged • Minerals needed for plant growth may be leached from soil • Trees are damaged as protective waxy coating is removed from leaves; decreases resistance to disease, reduces germination. Major diebacks of deciduous and coniferous forests have occurred in eastern North America and western Europe • Reproductive rates for wildlife are reduced as habitat is degraded	• Respiratory problems increase for asthmatics, children, and the elderly as sulphate particles are inhaled • Water is contaminated by dissolved minerals, especially copper and lead in water pipes	• Corrosion is increased in automobile finishes, bronze, cement, rubber, paint, cotton, linen, and nylon • Limestone, marble, and sandstone buildings and monuments are damaged (see image below) 

Figure 18–8 Acidic deposition has many wide-ranging effects on both living and non-living things.

A London Smog or an LA Smog?

There are two types of smog created by human activity: the London type and the Los Angeles (LA) type. A London-type smog is the result of burning a fuel that releases particulates and sulphur dioxide into the atmosphere; an LA-type smog is the result of a chemical reaction between sunlight and the components released by the burning of certain petroleum products.

How London-type Smog Forms

"Although broad daylight, a shadow moved darkly through the cold, dense fog in the narrow alley … ." A line from a Sherlock Holmes mystery? More likely, a line from a report in a London newspaper in 1880.

Air at ground level is normally warmer than air above it. As this warm air rises, it not only cools, it carries away pollutants. Under certain conditions, however, a cold layer of air may become trapped at ground level by a warm layer above it. This **temperature inversion** often produces fog at ground level and stops the air from rising. In this "dead air," pollutants become trapped and create a dirty air mass close to the ground. Throughout the 19th century and well into the 20th century, the fog on many winter nights in London, England, was particularly dense and deadly. Most Londoners at the time were burning inexpensive, highly polluting coal to heat their homes. On cold winter nights, the pollution from burning coal became extremely high. Water droplets condensed around soot and particles of tar, then combined with the sulphur dioxide in coal smoke to form sulphuric acid. Londoners were living in, and breathing, tiny droplets of acid. In 1905, this lethal combination of smoke and fog was termed "smog."

Impact of a London-type Smog

Between December 5 and 10, 1952, Londoners experienced the worst air pollution disaster on record (see Figure 18–9). A temperature inversion, fog, and high concentrations of soot and sulphur dioxide created a deadly environment. People with respiratory diseases, children, and the elderly were particularly vulnerable. Over 4000 people choked to death on their own mucus or died from heart attacks as they struggled to breathe.

A study completed in 2000 by researchers in the US estimated that 12 000 people died in London between December 1952 and February 1953 because of the intense smog (see Figure 18–10). Smog levels today in New Delhi, Beijing, and many other cities in the New Core are comparable to London's killer 1952–53 smog.

In response to the London disaster of 1952–53, the British government passed the Clean Air Act in 1956. The act set up smokeless zones, and gave grants to homeowners to convert their coal fires to heaters that used gas, electricity, or a higher-quality coal that produced fewer pollutants. According to a recent study, London's air is the cleanest it has been for over 400 years. Exhaust from motor vehicles is now the main source of London's pollution. During the occasional temperature inversion in winter, nitrogen oxides build up and cause a dangerous health hazard.

In Southeast Asia, a similar London-type smog is created by the burning of forests. Logging, mining, and oil-palm plantation companies, as well as farmers, for example, clear land by burning the trees because this method is cheap and fast. Fires in Kalimantan (Borneo), are particularly polluting because they produce a great deal of smoke and ash particles, and release gases that produce sulphuric acid. They are difficult to put out because they are on peatland, which is composed of decaying vegetation that burns easily. Almost every year, huge fires across Indonesia create a poisonous smog that blankets the region—including Singapore, Malaysia, Thailand, China, and the Korean peninsula—for several weeks (see Figure 18–11). Local hospitals are overwhelmed with people suffering from asthma and other respiratory diseases. This haze, known as the "Asian Brown Cloud," varies in intensity and size from year to year depending on the weather. In 2006, Indonesia finally agreed to sign the 2002 Association of Southeast Asian Nations (ASEAN) Transboundary Haze Pollution Agreement.

The Arctic also has a haze composed of particles from factories and cars in cities in temperate regions. These particles are carried by winds and mix with thin clouds. This haze, in addition to being a health hazard, is also responsible for making the Arctic warmer. During polluted days, the clouds become more effective blankets, trap more heat, and aggravate climate warming in the Arctic.

Figure 18–9 London's Piccadilly Circus on December 6, 1952

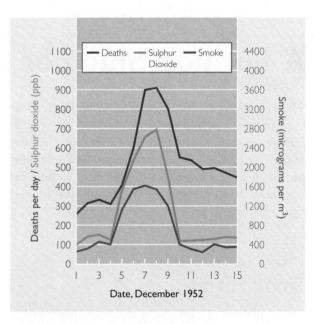

Figure 18–10 The relationship between deaths and sulphur dioxide and smoke in the air in the London smog of 1952–53. Note that the left-hand scale is used for both deaths per day and the amount of sulphur dioxide in the air.

Figure 18–11 (Left) In addition to the hazards on the road, the poisons in the air are hazardous to this scooter rider in Indonesia. (Right) The burning of forests to create farmland turns the atmosphere into a poisonous mixture of smoke and chemicals throughout the Asia-Pacific region.

How LA-type Smog Forms

For most of the world's cities, it is summer smog—formed from a combination of sunshine, high humidity, and pollutants from petroleum products burned by industry and motor vehicles—that causes concern. First identified in the early 1940s in Los Angeles, this "LA smog" is produced from a photochemical reaction between sunlight and hydrocarbons and nitrogen oxides. This **photochemical smog** contains nitrogen oxide, nitrogen dioxide, ground-level ozone, and other compounds. The nitrogen oxides dissolve in the water of the atmosphere to form nitric acid, a component of acid precipitation. The ground-level ozone damages trees, reduces crop yields, and corrodes materials such as metal and rubber.

Impact of an LA-type Smog

Even though LA's pollution levels have dropped, in 2007, the American Lung Association still ranked Los Angeles as the most polluted city in the US. A variety of smog-related health effects are associated with photochemical smog. These include

- irritation of eyes, nose, and throat, and inflammation of lung tissue
- permanent lung damage from exposure to ozone over a long period of time
- increased risk of cancer from exposure to particles in the smog
- increased susceptibility to infections among children
- asthma attacks due to high concentrations of nitrogen dioxide

SUSTAINABILITY

...air pollution (smog) in Toronto contributes to approximately 1700 premature deaths and 6000 hospital admissions each year.

When a smog alert occurs in Ontario, what is the air like? What do you do during such an alert?

This LA-type smog affects southern Ontario, particularly in the summer. A 2004 report indicated that air pollution (smog) in Toronto contributes to approximately 1700 premature deaths and 6000 hospital admissions each year. Smog alerts occur in Toronto each year, but their frequency varies because of weather conditions (see Figure 18–12).

What Can Be Done?

Smog can be controlled to a large extent by

- **Reducing the sources of pollutants.** Since 1975, North American motor vehicles, a major source of the gases that produce smog, have been equipped with catalytic converters to reduce these emissions. Catalytic converters use precious metals like platinum, palladium, and rhodium to create a chemical reaction in which exhaust gases are made less toxic.

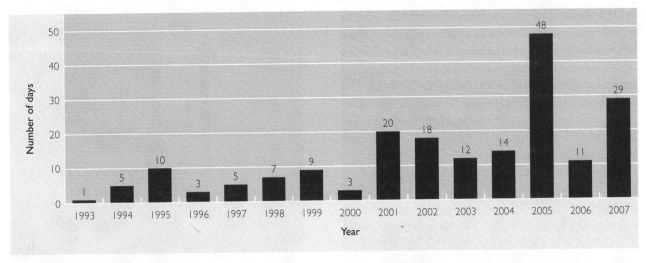

Figure 18–12 Photochemical smog can be created at any time of year, but conditions are best for its formation in the summer. Smog-alert days also occur throughout southern Ontario when polluted air sits over the region.

- **Burning a cleaner gasoline.** In California, a cleaner-burning gasoline has been legislated.

- **Limiting the number of cars during major smog outbreaks.** For example, in Rome and Athens, cars with even-numbered licence plates drive on one day, and those with odd-numbered plates on another.

- **Using more rapid transit and non-gasoline burning cars.**

- **Cleaning the emissions from major polluters.** Power stations and other industries that burn fossil fuels can reduce nitrogen oxides by "scrubbing" emissions from the smoke before it is released into the atmosphere. Unfortunately, the high cost of this procedure is a deterrent to many smaller industries.

- **Switching to devices that produce less pollution.** For instance, gasoline-powered lawnmowers in the US produce as much pollution as four million cars! A switch to electric lawnmowers would reduce a significant amount of pollution—assuming, of course, that the power plants that produce the electricity are equipped with anti-pollution devices. A switch to hand mowers would be even better.

In 2008, Milan implemented a "pollution charge" for cars entering the city. For more information, go to the link on our Web site.

The Ozone Layer

Could humans go the way of the dinosaurs through the use of fire extinguishers and aerosol spray cans, or as a result of junking objects like old cars and broken refrigerators? The answer is—perhaps. These common items often contain substances that can destroy the protective ozone layer found 15 to 35 kilometres above the surface of the earth.

How Ozone Forms

Ozone is a substance that can both hurt and protect us. When formed at ground level from the photochemical reaction of motor-vehicle exhaust and sunlight, it can harm our health. When formed in the stratosphere, however (see Figure 18–1), it protects us by absorbing harmful ultraviolet radiation.

The levels of ozone in the atmosphere alter naturally with the changing seasons and sun cycles. Scientists suspect that even volcanic eruptions affect the concentration of this very unstable gas. Nonetheless, the processes of nature have always regulated the balance of ozone in the stratosphere. But now, human activities are upsetting this balance, and more ozone is being destroyed than created. Ozone depletion refers not only to the "holes" that scientists have observed over the North and South Poles, but also to declining levels of ozone over the entire globe.

One of the main culprits in the destruction of the ozone layer high above the earth is the group of *synthetic* (human-made) chemicals known as **chlorofluorocarbons (CFCs)**. Ozone is also destroyed by other synthetic compounds that are used in dry cleaning, fire extinguishers, and pesticides. These compounds were created for use as fire retardants, propellants in spray cans, and coolants in refrigerators and air conditioners. At ground level, these substances are harmless because they are protected from UV radiation by the ozone layer. However, as they rise into the stratosphere and become exposed to UV radiation, they break apart, releasing their chlorine atoms. A single chlorine atom can destroy thousands of molecules of ozone; bromine, an element similar to chlorine, may be even more harmful. Since CFCs can remain in the atmosphere for hundreds of years, damage to the ozone layer may be very long-lasting.

In 1985, British scientists confirmed that CFCs had created a "hole" in the ozone layer over the Antarctic. The ozone "hole" is actually a seasonal thinning of the ozone layer in the stratosphere over Earth's polar regions. This thinning appears during winter and early spring every year. In 2006, the largest ozone hole ever recorded covered almost 30 million square kilometres over Antarctica and the tip of South America.

In 1986, a scientist with Environment Canada discovered that the ozone layer over the Arctic was also thinning (see Figure 18–13). Arctic ozone depletion varies with meteorological conditions from year to year. Cold temperatures and stable conditions in the stratosphere increase the loss of ozone. The winter of 2004 to 2005 was exceptionally cold and resulted in the largest loss of ozone ever recorded in the Arctic. In the following winter, however, winds in the stratosphere were strong and no ozone hole formed.

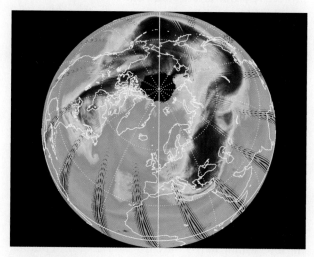

Figure 18–13 This NASA image shows thinning areas of the ozone layer, shown in yellow and green. Areas in red have higher levels of ozone. (There is no data available for the small black area.)

Impact of Ozone Depletion

The sun produces three types of UV radiation, but UV-B has the most impact on humans (see Figure 18–14). Studies indicate that for every 1 percent decrease in the ozone in the stratosphere, the amount of UV radiation that reaches Earth doubles.

The danger to human health as a result of increased levels of UV radiation can be seen in higher levels of skin cancer in Canadians. As of 2005, the number of

	Blocked by Ozone	Effects
UV-A		
longest wavelength	partly	skin wrinkles, premature aging
UV-B		
medium wavelength	partly	sunburns, cancer, eye cataracts (can lead to blindness), weakens immune system, activates some viruses
UV-C		
shortest wavelength	in upper atmosphere	lethal to all life

Figure 18–14 In addition to its effects on humans, UV-B radiation reduces crop yields (e.g., canola, oats, and peppers), damages phytoplankton (the basis of the food chain) in marine and freshwater environments, and damages hatching fish, frog eggs, and new vegetation.

skin cancer cases in Canada had increased by two-thirds since 1990. This increase was probably caused by exposure to the sun during the 1960s, 1970s, and 1980s before ozone thinning became a serious issue. With ozone thinning now an established fact, what will rates of skin cancer be in the future? (See Figure 18–15.) What will be the effects on wildlife and plants?

What Can Be Done?

In 1987, the **Montreal Protocol** on Substances That Deplete the Ozone Layer was signed by 25 countries. By the early 2000s, 191 countries had signed the protocol to cut the production and use of ozone-depleting substances (ODS). This treaty has been called "one of the most successful multilateral treaties ever" because all of the industrialized countries met their deadlines for CFC phase-out, and developing countries continue to make good progress in their transition from CFCs to less-damaging substances. The protocol established an international fund, to which developed countries contribute, to help developing countries switch from using ODS. Canada has contributed over US$5 million annually, partly in the form of technical assistance to Brazil, China, Cuba, and India.

In September 2007, the signatories met in Montreal to mark the 20th anniversary of the Protocol and to deal with the chemicals that replaced CFCs, **hydrochlorofluorocarbons** (**HCFCs**)—compounds containing hydrogen, chlorine, fluorine, and carbon that are used for refrigeration, aerosol propellants, foam manufacturing, and air conditioning. HCFCs are less damaging than CFCs, but now that new chemicals are available that do not damage the ozone layer or act as greenhouse gases, the use of HCFCs can be phased out. Under the Montreal Protocol, the use of HCFCs is scheduled to end in developed countries by 2030 and in developing

Figure 18–15 Skin cancer can develop many years after extensive exposure to UV radiation.

countries by 2040. The 2007 Montreal meeting discussed the phase-out of HCFCs ten years earlier than the Protocol calls for. Dupont, the company that developed CFCs and HCFCs, has even developed 19 alternative chemicals that do not deplete ozone. A study by NASA in 2006 predicted that if the phase-out of ozone-depleting substances was accelerated, the Arctic ozone hole could be repaired and the Antarctic hole could begin to shrink by 2018; by 2070 a full return of the protective ozone layer could result.

The Montreal Protocol is extraordinary because nations have had to place the achievement of a common planetary goal ahead of their own economic self-interest. It demonstrates that nations can work together to meet a common goal.

The Future of Life on Earth

Can we hope to resolve the problems of acidic deposition, smog, and ozone depletion? Yes—but only with international cooperation, constant vigilance on the part of governmental and non-governmental agencies, and only if the political will of citizens around the world is marshalled to bring about the changes that are needed. Citizens must understand the environmental outcomes of unchecked emissions from all sources and make conscious choices as consumers and users of products in their daily lives. We, as well as industry, must be willing to pay the costs associated with putting non-polluting practices into place. Developed countries, which have created most of the problem, should also be prepared to help developing nations adopt technologies that will prevent similar environmental damage. If these steps are not taken, the future of life on Earth is at risk.

Chapter Questions

Knowledge and Understanding

1. **a)** What are POPs? Give examples.

   b) Why are POPs dangerous?

   c) Explain why Canada and the other temperate and polar countries are particularly susceptible to POP pollution.

   d) What efforts have been made to eliminate POPs from the environment?

2. **a)** What parts of Canada are most affected by acidic deposition? Explain why.

   b) Draw a flow chart to show the effects of acidic deposition on aquatic life in a freshwater lake.

3. **a)** Differentiate between London-type smog and LA-type smog.

   b) What methods are used to reduce each kind of smog formation?

   c) How successful are these methods?

4. **a)** How can ozone both protect us and harm us?

   b) Demonstrate the impact of depletion of the ozone layer on humans and the environment.

   c) What can you do to protect yourself from UV radiation?

Thinking

5. Developing countries do not have to phase out the production and use of CFCs and HCFCs for a number of years after developed countries do. Is this reasonable, since all people on Earth will be affected by ozone depletion? Examine both sides of this issue.

6. Chapter 2 discussed the Gaia hypothesis, according to which, the conditions that make the planet habitable were created by the evolution of life. Since human activities are affecting nature in such radical ways, what might the planet be like in the future?

Communication

7. Conduct research to find out

   a) the current status of air pollution levels in Ontario

   b) what is being done in Ontario to combat air pollution by
   i) the federal government
   ii) the provincial government
   iii) local government
   iv) local businesses
   v) your school

   c) Evaluate the efforts of each organization. Which one(s) seems to be the most proactive? Why do you think this is the case?

   d) Write a short newspaper article about your findings.

8. **a)** In a small group, conduct a survey of at least 50 students and teachers to find out what people would be prepared to do to help fight air pollution and climate change. You can develop your own questions for the survey, but here are some to get you started.
   i) Do you feel that you can personally do something to make an impact?
   ii) Are you prepared to pay more for gasoline (10¢ a litre, 50¢ a litre, or more)?
   iii) What personal actions are you prepared to take? Consider such things as
   • recycling
   • using a more fuel-efficient vehicle
   • paying charges for driving in cities
   • using less electricity
   • buying locally grown food
   • using public transit
   • taking vacations close to home
   iv) What actions should businesses and politicians take?
   v) What are you prepared to do to encourage businesses and politicians to put into practice "green" policies?

   b) Based on the information you obtained from your survey about what people would be prepared to do, develop a "green plan" that your community can implement to fight air pollution and climate change.

   c) Present your results in a format of your choice (for example, written report, brochure or flyer, Web site, PowerPoint presentation, etc.). **S**

9. The international organization "TakingITGlobal" (TIG) uses the Internet to connect young people around the world. It gives young people the opportunity to access information and share knowledge and ideas with one another about major world issues.

a) Visit the TIG Web site to access their discussion board.

b) Go to the section on environment and urbanization.

c) Find out what people in other parts of the world are doing to improve the quality of their air.

d) Write a summary of your findings.

Application

10. a) What, if anything, are you doing in your personal life to limit the amount of air pollution and greenhouse gas emissions that you produce?

b) What else could you do? Would it be difficult to do those things? Explain.

c) Write a personal action plan that you can use to reduce your impact on the quality of the air.

11. a) Investigate the relationship between disease and increased UV radiation due to ozone depletion.

b) Why do children suffer the most from UV radiation?

c) What can be done to prevent damage from UV radiation?

 Access the TIG discussion board at the link on our Web site.

12. The burning of coal is a major source of pollution in many cities today, particularly in the countries of the Near Core and Far Periphery. Examine one of these cities and describe

- the conditions that exist
- the problems associated with these conditions
- the measures, if any, taken to alleviate the problems
- the impact of these measures
- whether the changes are permanent

13. What lifestyle changes, in transportation choices, recreational activities, or activities around the home, would you and your family have to make to reduce your contributions to

a) acidic deposition

b) smog

c) ozone depletion

14. Often society has to make choices between the economic benefits of products (e.g., CFCs, electricity, automobiles), and environmental damage (e.g., ozone depletion, acidic deposition, smog). Work with a small group to brainstorm criteria that could be used to make these choices.

15. Some Canadian provinces have cut government spending by reducing the size of their environment ministries. Fines for polluting have been increased as a deterrent, but the number of inspectors has decreased. Will a shift to an emphasis on voluntary compliance have effects on atmospheric and water quality in Canada? Explain your views.

CHAPTER 19
Energy Choices

Key Terms

reserves

R/P ratio

peak oil

oil sands

smart meters

alternative energy

solar energy

biofuels

biodiesel

bioethanol

geothermal energy

earth energy

wind power

green power

hydricity

To meet our lifestyles needs, how many more power plants (such as the nuclear plant below) will be needed?

Key Questions

By the end of this chapter you will be able to answer the following questions.

■ How do the "big five" energy sources compare in production, consumption, and use?

■ Which countries are the biggest energy producers and consumers?

■ Is all the fuss about alternative energy sources justified?

■ What is hydricity and why should you care about it?

■ Are you part of the energy problem or part of the energy solution?

Are You Part of the Problem or Part of the Solution?

During the 1960s and 1970s, people who were engaged in social and environmental activism adopted the following slogan: "If you are not part of the solution, you are part of the problem." We can apply this slogan when examining energy issues today. The way most North Americans use energy certainly makes us part of the problem.

Many important global issues of the 21st century are tied to our use of energy.

- There is a link between energy use and global warming. (You can learn more about global warming in Chapter 20.)

- In Canada, there is often a link between energy production and issues relating to land ownership by Aboriginal peoples.

- The burning of fossil fuels (coal, petroleum products, natural gas) for transportation and electrical generation causes air pollution that damages people's health. (Air pollution is examined in Chapter 18.)

- Supertankers that transport oil pollute the oceans through their day-to-day operations. Oil spills that result from supertanker accidents cause major environmental damage. (Water pollution is discussed in Chapter 17.)

- Environmental damage results from production processes, for example, burning off unwanted gas, oil sands processing, pipeline construction, and refining.

- Wars are fought over energy (Figure 19–1). Two Gulf Wars against Iraq (1991, 2003) were fought in large part to protect the oil supply of the world's Old Core countries.

GLOBALIZATION
Wars are fought over energy.

What other natural resources have been fought over?

Figure 19–1 Toward the end of the first Gulf War in 1991, when Iraq's defeat was inevitable, Iraqi President Saddam Hussein ordered his retreating forces to destroy Kuwait's oil wells. Over a period of seven months, more than one billion barrels of oil went up in flames from 800 burning oil wells.

On a per-capita basis, Canadians are one of the world leaders in using (some would say wasting) energy. In 2002, Canada was ranked as the third worst country in per-capita energy consumption of the 30 OECD (Organization for Economic Cooperation and Development) countries. OECD countries are the world's 30 most developed countries.

SUSTAINABILITY

...Canada was ranked as the third worst country in per-capita energy consumption of the 30 OECD countries.

Can Canadians justify using more energy per capita than people in most other industrialized countries?

It is understandable that Canadians would use a considerable amount of energy. As an Old Core country, Canada needs energy to support its advanced economy. Furthermore, since we have the second largest land area in the world, we use a lot of energy to move goods and people over great distances. Also, we have a demanding climate. We need to heat our homes and other buildings in winter and cool them in summer. But can we justify using more energy per capita than most other industrialized countries? A number of energy initiatives give us hope for the future. We are expanding our use of non-polluting, renewable energy sources such as wind power. Researchers are developing new ways of using energy that are less polluting than those we use now. Most significantly, there has been a substantial increase in the number of people who have decided that they want to be part of the solution and not part of the problem.

A Guided Tour of World Energy

WORKING IT OUT

Your guided tour of the world's energy use will give you the opportunity to work individually or in a cooperative group to learn about

- the pattern of energy production and consumption in various parts of the world

- how energy production, consumption, and trade are related

- the amount of non-renewable energy reserves—the quantity of a resource—that can be removed using current technology (see Figure 19–2)

- a region's (or country's) R/P ratio—that is, the number of years before the non-renewable energy resource runs out

Your guided tour takes you to a number of "destinations," including the "big five" primary energy sources: oil, natural gas, coal, nuclear energy, and hydro-electric power. A symbol like this one [World Energy Tour ▷] will show you the different stops on our tour. Other types of energy, such as wind power, are less significant, or are used noncommercially in a manner that is difficult to document—for example, dried cow dung burned for fuel in India. At each stop on your tour, you may be faced with questions that deal with the future. In this case, your answers may be based on informed speculation.

Figure 19–2 Most of Canada's coal reserves are located in isolated locations in Alberta and British Columbia.

Overall Production and Consumption

Our first stop illustrates energy production globally and in Old Core, New Core, Near Core, and Far Periphery Countries (see Figure 19–3). It also shows patterns of energy use in different countries and regions (see Figure 19–4). In this chapter, you will notice that most energy statistics are given using the basic unit "millions of tonnes of oil equivalent" (Mtoe). This is done so that direct comparisons of energy content can be made between energy sources that are normally expressed using different units, for example, barrels of oil compared to cubic metres of natural gas.

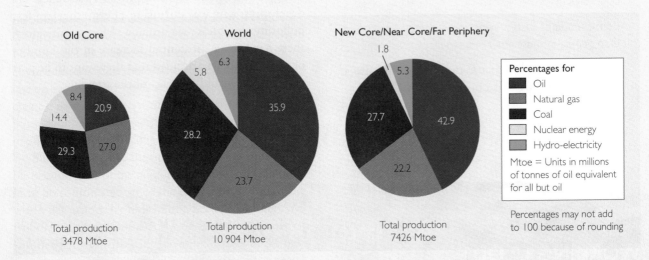

Old Core

8.4
14.4
29.3
20.9
27.0

Total production
3478 Mtoe

World

6.3
5.8
35.9
28.2
23.7

Total production
10 904 Mtoe

New Core/Near Core/Far Periphery

1.8
5.3
27.7
42.9
22.2

Total production
7426 Mtoe

Percentages for
- Oil
- Natural gas
- Coal
- Nuclear energy
- Hydro-electricity

Mtoe = Units in millions of tonnes of oil equivalent for all but oil

Percentages may not add to 100 because of rounding

Figure 19–3 World regional production of energy, 2006 (units in millions of tonnes of oil equivalent [Mtoe])

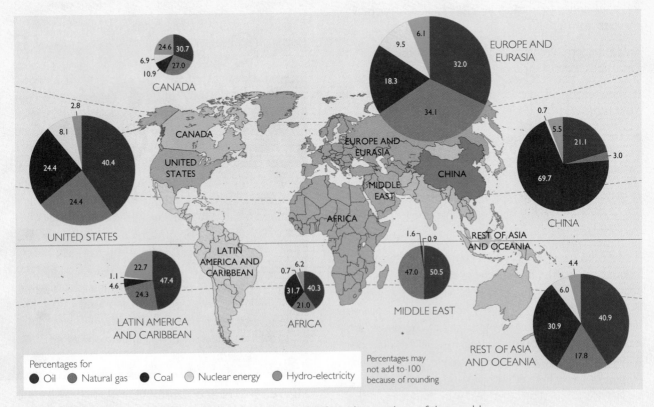

CANADA
24.6 30.7
6.9
10.9 27.0

UNITED STATES
2.8
8.1
24.4 40.4
24.4

LATIN AMERICA AND CARIBBEAN
22.7
1.1
4.6 47.4
24.3

AFRICA
6.2
0.7
31.7 40.3
21.0

EUROPE AND EURASIA
6.1
9.5
32.0
18.3
34.1

CHINA
0.7
5.5
21.1
3.0
69.7

MIDDLE EAST
1.6 0.9
47.0 50.5

REST OF ASIA AND OCEANIA
4.4
6.0
30.9 40.9
17.8

Percentages for
- Oil
- Natural gas
- Coal
- Nuclear energy
- Hydro-electricity

Percentages may not add to 100 because of rounding

Figure 19–4 The proportional pie graphs show energy use in various regions of the world.

Questions

1. Examine Figure 19–3. Suggest at least two reasons why the New Core, Near Core, and Far Periphery produce more energy than the Old Core.

2. Approximately one-sixth of the world's population lives in Old Core countries. How does their energy consumption compare to that of less developed Near Core and Far Periphery countries when you consider the relative populations of each? Why does this situation exist?

3. **a)** What factors might explain the very high rate of coal consumption in many of the countries of the New Core, Near Core, and Far Periphery?

   b) What are the global environmental implications of this pattern?

   c) Why are environmental problems likely to get worse in the years to come?

4. **a)** Examine Figure 19–4. Suggest two reasons for the high consumption of nuclear power in North America, Europe/Eurasia, and in Asia-Pacific countries.

   b) Give one reason why the consumption of nuclear power in these areas may increase in the future.

   c) Give one reason why it might decline.

5. Why do the Middle East and Africa produce relatively little hydro-electricity? Give at least two reasons why.

World Energy Tour ② Crude Oil

Currently, oil is vital as a transportation fuel, an energy source for industry, and for domestic and commercial heating. It is also important in the manufacture of plastics, chemicals, and synthetic materials (see Figure 19–5).

Major oil-producing nations fall into two categories. Countries in the first category, such as the United States, produce large amounts and consume large amounts. They may even use more oil than they produce. Countries in the second category produce more oil than they consume. Countries in this category, which includes Canada, Saudi Arabia, and Mexico, sell crude oil to nations that cannot meet their own oil needs. Figure 19–6 summarizes the patterns of oil production, consumption, and trade in the world.

The Organization of Petroleum Exporting Countries (OPEC) tries to set the price of oil in the world by controlling the level of production and exports. (OPEC members are Algeria, Angola, Indonesia, Iran, Iraq, Kuwait, Libya, Nigeria, Qatar, Saudi Arabia, United Arab Emirates, and Venezuela.) OPEC's ability to control oil prices is limited because together non-OPEC oil exporters, such as Russia, Norway, Mexico, Kazakhstan, the United Kingdom, and Canada, produce more oil than OPEC.

Figure 19–5 What caption would you put with this image?

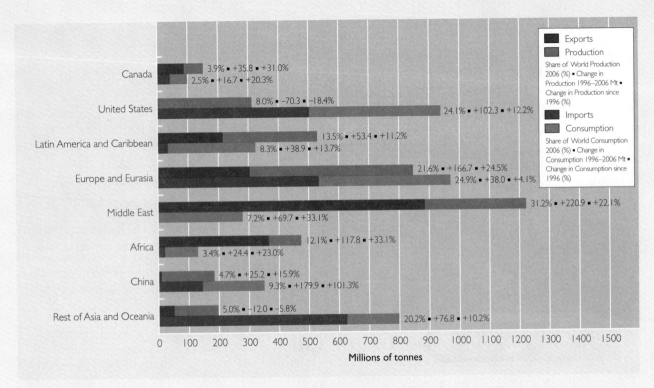

Figure 19-6 World oil production/exports and consumption/imports, 1996–2006

Because Hong Kong was not part of China until 1997, its oil consumption is listed as part of the "Rest of Asia and Oceania" for 1996. In 2006, however, Hong Kong was part of China and its consumption is included in China's total.

Questions

1. a) Which country's oil production seems to be in decline?

   b) Why might this be happening?

   c) What significance does this have for the future?

2. a) Which three regions/countries have experienced the greatest change in production
      i) between 1996 and 2006?
      ii) as a percentage since 1996?

   b) What two regions/countries do not appear in both the list you made for part i) and the list you made for part ii)? Explain why.

3. a) Which three regions/countries have experienced the greatest change in consumption
      i) between 1996 and 2006?
      ii) as a percentage since 1996?

   b) Which country appears in both the list you made for part i) and the list you made for part ii)? Explain why.

4. a) List four regions/countries that are the largest
      i) exporters of oil
      ii) importers of oil

   b) Why is this pattern of exporters and importers not a surprise?

   c) Is there any region/country that is both a major exporter and a major importer? Explain why this situation exists.

5. Assume that the population of the world in 2007 was 6.6 billion, while the population of Canada was 33 million, and that of the US was 299 million. What conclusion can you make about the share of world consumption of oil (as a percentage) by these two North American countries compared to their percentage share of the world's population? Can this situation be justified? Why or why not?

	OPEC	Non-OPEC
2006 Production (Mt)	1632.7	2281.4
Share of World Production 2006	41.7%	58.3%
Change in Production 1996–2006 (Mt)	+252.7	+284.9

Figure 19–7

Note: The non-OPEC category includes the oil production in the former Soviet Union (from 353.3 Mt in 1996 to 599.8 Mt in 2006, an increase of 246.5 Mt). As a result, the increase of 284.9 Mt in non-OPEC production from 1996 to 2006 is mostly due to this increased production in the former Soviet Union.

Old Core	
Share of World Production 2006	23.3%
Change in Production since 1996	-9.5%
Share of World Consumption 2006	58.1%
Change in Consumption since 1996	6.8%

Figure 19–8

6. Examine Figure 19–7.

   a) What is the share of world oil production for OPEC, and for non-OPEC countries?

   b) Which group has experienced the highest growth in production between 1996 and 2006?

   c) Why is this trend important?

7. Examine Figure 19–8.

   a) Compare the share of world production and share of world consumption. What is the significance of these two percentages?

   b) What reasons may account for the percentage change in production since 1996?

   c) How have Old Core nations managed to expand their economies significantly between 1996 and 2006 while increasing their oil consumption, on a percentage basis, relatively slowly?

8. What are the environmental implications of the rapid growth of wealth and industrialization outside the Old Core?

Natural gas has a number of striking differences compared to oil, even though both commodities usually come from the same geological deposits. It is easy to see the oil products, such as gasoline and diesel and lubricating oil, that are used in airplanes and cars. The use of natural gas, however, is not as obvious. Not only is it transported in pipelines that are almost always out of sight, but it also tends to be used "behind the scenes," for example, to heat buildings, generate electricity, or to dry substances in industrial processes. In spite of its invisibility, its costly distribution systems are vital components of many countries' infrastructures.

In general, natural gas production follows the same pattern as oil production (see Figure 19–9). The differences have to do with its transportation. Natural gas cannot be moved to market as cheaply as oil, unless a pipeline can be built. This requires that two conditions be met. There must be a land link (or at worst, shallow water link) between exporter and importer, and the amount of gas to be shipped must be large enough to justify the construction of a costly pipeline. Pipelines have allowed the export of vast quantities of natural gas from Russia to eastern and western Europe, and from Canada to the US. Where pipelines between gas fields and markets are impractical, natural gas is liquefied by cooling it to −163°C and is shipped in specially outfitted ocean tankers. Tankers move liquefied natural gas from a number of countries in the Middle East to western Europe and Japan (see Figure 19–10).

In many oil- and gas-producing countries, however, a supply of natural gas cannot be economically moved to market. In some cases, a technique is used in which the gas is injected back into the ground to increase the pressure on the deposit so that more oil can be recovered. Often, though, the gas is merely flared (burned off) to get rid of it. This is obviously a waste of a valuable resource and a significant contributor to the world's carbon emissions.

Did You Know?

In 2007, Canada began fighting two proposals to ship liquefied natural gas through Canadian territorial waters to terminals in the state of Maine, next to New Brunswick. This area is the only place on the eastern coast of the US deep enough for these massive ships.

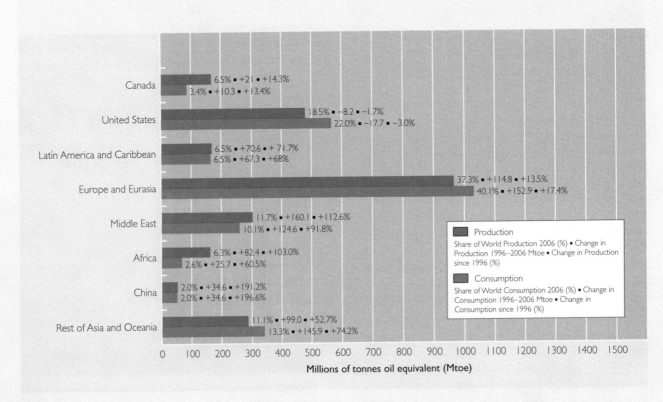

Figure 19–9 World natural gas production and consumption, 1996–2006

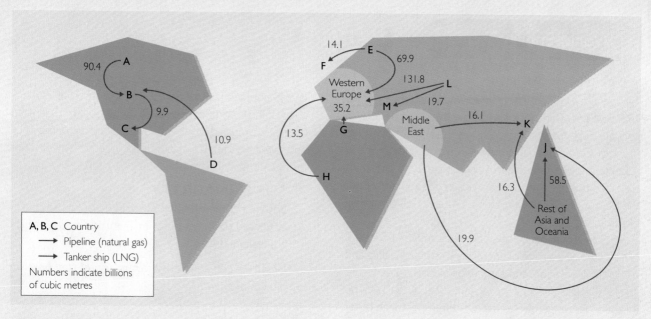

Figure 19–10 Major trade movements of natural gas

Questions

1. **a)** Construct a table listing the top five oil producers and the top five natural gas producers.

   b) Compare the oil producers to the natural gas producers. What similarities do you see between the two lists? Explain the similarities.

   c) Construct a table listing the top five oil consumers and the top five natural gas consumers.

   d) Compare the oil consumers to the natural gas consumers. What similarities do you see? Explain the similarities.

2. Which region/country experienced the greatest percentage change in production and consumption of natural gas since 1996? Why do you think this change occurred?

3. The countries shown in Figure 19–10 are involved in net movements of natural gas of at least nine billion cubic metres. See if you can identify the gas importing and exporting countries that are labelled with a letter.

4. Speculate on why the shipment of liquefied natural gas is not more common. Research this question on the Internet. Was your speculation correct?

Two generations ago, most Canadians heated their homes with coal. Few Canadians today have ever seen a piece of coal, although Canada still produces a substantial amount. Most of Canada's coal is mined in isolated locations in Alberta and BC (see Figure 19–2, page 293) and then exported to Japan. In eastern Canada, coal is imported from the US, but only for use in coal-burning electrical generating plants and in steel plants.

In many countries outside of Canada and the US, coal is widely used as a source of energy for domestic heating and electrical generation, and as fuel for industry (see Figure 19–11). Experts predict a growth in the use of coal because it is often less expensive to mine and transport than other energy sources, and there are still huge reserves in many areas of the world. Between 2005 and 2030, world demand for coal is expected to increase by 2101 million tonnes of oil equivalent (Mtoe). China and India together will account for four-fifths of this increase.

SUSTAINABILITY

Between 2005 and 2030, world demand for coal is expected to increase by 2101 million tonnes of oil equivalent (Mtoe).

What impacts will the increasing use of coal have on the environment?

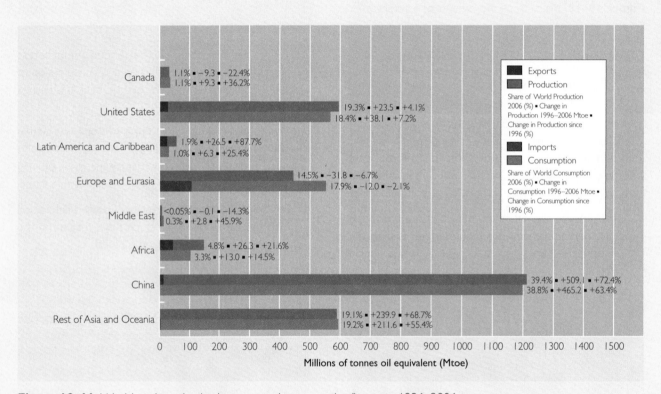

Figure 19–11 World coal production/exports and consumption/imports, 1996–2006

Questions

1. **a)** Which areas of the world are the most significant producers and consumers of coal?

   b) Compare the producers of coal to those of oil and natural gas. What are the similarities and differences?

   c) Compare the consumers of coal to those of oil and natural gas. What are the similarities and differences?

   d) What general conclusions can you draw from the comparisons you made in parts a) and b)?

2. Three regions experienced declines in coal production between 1996 and 2006. Identify these regions and suggest why these declines occurred.

3. Examine the growth in coal production in China and the rest of Asia and Oceania. What environmental significance does this trend have?

Nuclear Power

Our next stop on the tour is a look at nuclear energy. Fifty years ago, nuclear power seemed to hold great promise for the future—a seemingly limitless source of clean, cheap energy. However, this promise has not been fulfilled. Very few nuclear power plants were built in the decade after 1995; Canada's most recent nuclear plant opened in 1993. The cost of building nuclear power plants turned out to be substantially higher than predicted. Also, it was learned that the intense level of radioactivity inside the reactors affected the structural integrity of the plants' elaborate plumbing systems. As a result, the life expectancy of the plants, before they needed very costly refits, was much shorter than anticipated. This drove up the cost of the electricity produced.

There are also serious environmental concerns related to nuclear energy, as no long-term method of disposal of nuclear-waste products has been found. This is a critical shortcoming, since nuclear waste remains hazardous for thousands of years. It is now being stored in temporary facilities all over the world, but a more permanent solution must be put in place.

The ultimate threat from nuclear power is the release of large amounts of radiation into the atmosphere. Two significant radiation releases have occurred, and they have caused concern among many people that nuclear energy is not safe.

In spite of the problems with nuclear power, it remains an important source of electricity in many Old Core countries; in fact, it is making a comeback (see Figure 19–12). In 2007, there were 439 nuclear reactors in 31 countries supplying 15 percent of the world's electricity. France, for example, obtains three-quarters of its electricity from nuclear power plants. Some people believe that nuclear energy is now an essential source of power because climate change makes the burning of fossil fuels less attractive. Furthermore, the price of building, maintaining, and repairing nuclear plants has decreased, and their operation is much more reliable than in the past.

Many Old Core countries are now considering greater use of nuclear energy because they fear that supplies of oil and gas will be unreliable in the future. Much of the world's oil and gas supplies are found in countries with governments that have strongly different political views from governments of many Western countries. Some supplies are found in countries with unstable governments. On the other hand, uranium, the fuel that generates nuclear power, is mined in great quantities in Old Core countries such as Canada and Australia. Although nuclear power plants cost several billion dollars to build, 31 reactors were being built around the world in 2007, and many more were in the planning stages.

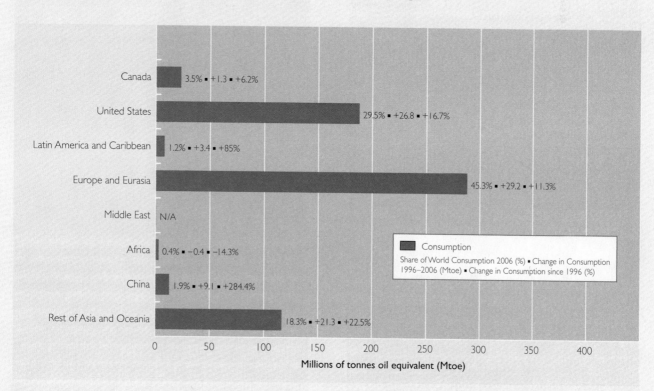

Figure 19–12 World nuclear power consumption, 1996–2006

Nuclear power is becoming increasingly important in India and China. India expects to increase the amount of energy from its nuclear sources from 2.6 percent in 2006 to 26 percent in 2030. China, however, only expects to increase the amount of energy from its nuclear sources from 2.3 percent in 2006 to 4 percent by 2030. To meet its target of 4 percent of its energy requirements, however, China will have to build two reactors per year. Both US-based Westinghouse Electric and France-based Areva SA are competing to build as many as 26 reactors for China by 2020. In 2007, Westinghouse obtained contracts to build four nuclear reactors and Areva obtained contracts to build two in China.

The nuclear power industry gained a surprising ally in 2004. James Lovelock, the developer of the Gaia hypothesis, announced his support for nuclear energy. (The Gaia hypothesis is discussed in Chapter 2.) In his view, nuclear energy is an important alternative to fossil fuels and will help reduce greenhouse gas emissions.

Questions

1. **a)** Which region/country has the world's greatest consumption of nuclear energy? Why do you think this region/country relies so heavily on nuclear energy?

   b) Which region/country has had the greatest change in consumption as a percentage since 1996? Why do you think this change occurred?

2. Old Core countries consume 84.5 percent of the world's nuclear energy. Explain why such a high percentage is used in the Old Core.

3. Determine which Canadian province relies on nuclear power for a significant portion of its electricity. Why is nuclear power not as important elsewhere in Canada?

4. Two nuclear accidents created serious concern among many people about the safety of nuclear power. Research the causes and impact of these two accidents and the current status of the plants.

   a) 1979, Three Mile Island accident

   b) 1986, Chernobyl accident

5. Does it make sense to promote nuclear power in the fight against climate change? Explain.

Hydro-electric power is a wonderful resource if it can be developed without causing undue social disruption and environmental damage. Its production has few negative features compared to the four other big energy technologies. It produces little pollution and does not require fuel. Some hydro-electric plants, like those at Niagara Falls, Ontario, have been in operation for many decades with few problems. Unfortunately, there are very few locations that have the right combination of elevation change and abundant water essential for producing hydro-electricity. (The pros and cons of building large power dams are discussed in Chapter 17.) Figure 19–13 shows world consumption of hydroelectricity over a ten-year period.

Questions

1. Which parts of the world have significant amounts of hydro-electric power? Why is this not surprising?

2. From your knowledge of world climate and physical features, which regions of the world have a significant potential for large-scale hydro-electric development? Why have these sites not been developed previously?

3. Why is the question of reserves not important with respect to hydro-electric power?

4. Suggest why certain regions/countries show a reduction in their consumption of hydro-electricity.

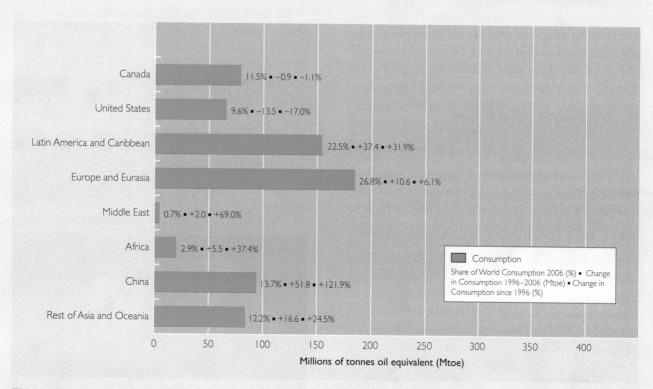

Figure 19–13 World consumption of hydro-electric power over a ten-year period. Note that only consumption data are available.

Outlook for Conventional Sources of Energy

Oil, natural gas, coal, and uranium are non-renewable. Experts try to determine how many years it will be until we run out of these resources. In contrast, the production of hydro-electric power relies on the use of water, a renewable resource. There is concern, however, that climate change will reduce stream flow, particularly as glaciers disappear. Hydro-electric plants that rely on glacial meltwater to fill reservoirs will produce less electrical power.

Two related terms are used to describe the quantity of a non-renewable resource.

■ The first is "reserves," a term that refers to the quantity of a resource, in tonnes, cubic metres, or any other unit that can be extracted using current technology.

■ The second is called the "R/P ratio." The **R/P ratio** for a non-renewable resource is calculated by dividing the size of the recoverable reserves (R) by the amount that is produced and used (P) during the current year. The R/P ratio is measured in years. A simple way of describing it is to say that it is the number of years until the resource runs out.

■ Several factors can dramatically alter the R/P ratio, either upward or downward. For example, if the rate of usage of the resource increases (the P gets bigger), the R/P ratio will become lower.

■ On the other hand, if the reserves increase (the R gets bigger), the R/P ratio will become higher. Reserves increase for two main reasons: new deposits of the resource are found, or improved technologies allow companies to recover deposits that were previously not recoverable.

Figure 19–14 shows world reserves of oil, natural gas, and coal as of 2006.

	Oil (conventional, billion tonnes)	Oil R/P Ratio	Natural Gas (trillion m^3)	Natural Gas R/P Ratio	Coal (million tonnes)	Coal R/P Ratio
Canada	2.4	15	1.67	9	6 578	105
US	3.7	12	5.93	11	246 643	234
Latin America and Caribbean	16.5	31	7.27	23	21 104	229.9
Europe & Former Soviet Union	19.7	23	64.13	60	287 095	237
Middle East	101.2	80	73.47	>100.0	50 775	194
Africa	15.5	32	14.18	79		
China	2.2	12	2.45	42	114 500	48
Rest of Asia Pacific	3.3	16	12.37	39	182 389	161
World Total	164.5	41	181.46	63	909 064	147
OECD	10.4	11	15.90	15	373 220	177
OPEC	123.6	73	n/a	n/a	n/a	n/a

Figure 19–14 World reserves of oil, natural gas, and coal by region, 2006

Questions

1. Describe the relationship that exists between a region's or country's reserves and
   a) the rate of use
   b) the amount of exploration
   c) the recovery technology used

2. a) What does the term "limited" mean to you?
   b) Which countries and regions have limited reserves of oil? Justify your answer with specific statistics.

3. Why might Canada's oil reserve situation not be as desperate as it might appear?

4. How does the size of their oil reserves affect OPEC nations' influence in the marketplace?

5. Compare the R/P ratios for natural gas to those for oil for different countries and regions. What pattern do you see?

6. Which areas of the world have the greatest natural gas reserves? How easy is it for each of these areas to serve major world demands?

7. Compare the R/P ratios for coal to those for oil and natural gas. What does this comparison suggest about the future importance of coal?

8. What environmental concerns are associated with the use of coal?

9. Why does the US have a particular interest in developing new ways to use coal?

Is There an Energy Crisis?

In 1956, US geologist M. King Hubbert theorized that the rate of oil production followed the shape of a bell curve (see Figure 19–15). According to his theory of **peak oil**, once we have consumed half of the world's conventional oil reserves, oil production will start to decline. Peak oil doesn't mean running out of oil—it means running out of cheap conventional crude oil. The remaining oil is likely to be in smaller fields, offshore, far from markets, of lesser quality, or from nonconventional sources such as oil sands. Oil obtained from these sources has reduced rates of extraction.

Hubbert predicted that world crude oil production would peak between 1995 and 2000. Then, in 2005, the Association for the Study of Peak Oil and Gas predicted that peak oil from both conventional and nonconventional sources would be reached in 2011. More optimistic outlooks predict that peak oil won't be reached until the 2020s or 2030s. This belief is based on factors such as new technology and knowledge to increase recovery from existing fields and the discovery of new producing areas. The use of alternative fuels and hybrid vehicles are seen as ways that peak oil will be pushed further into the future. People who support Hubbert's views refer to non-supporters as cornucopians (see Chapter 2).

Does the world face an energy crisis in the near future? The disagreement about peak oil demonstrates the lack of definitive knowledge about our current energy supplies and our future use of energy. Serious problems do exist with regard to discovering or developing new energy sources; consuming current supplies efficiently; replacing one energy source with another, more readily available source; and determining the environmental impact of energy use.

Is there an energy crisis? What do you think?

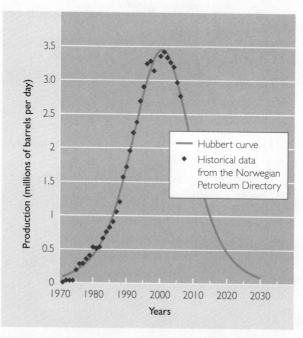

Figure 19–15 Peak oil, according to Hubbert's theory, is the point at which the maximum global oil production rate is reached. Oil consumption will match, then outstrip, the discovery of new reserves, and we will begin to deplete known reserves.

The Alberta Oil Sands: Mining Oil

The tar sands of Alberta pose one of the largest ecological challenges in North America's history.

—Sierra Club Web site (February 3, 2008)

There's a myth out there that oil sands production comes at too high an environmental cost.

—Alberta Premier Ed Stelmach,
Washington, DC (January 16, 2008)

Oil sands (also known as tar sands) are found in about 70 countries around the world. The largest deposits are found in Alberta, followed by those in Venezuela.

Alberta's oil sands are located in three areas that cover 140 200 square kilometres, an area twice the size of New Brunswick. The largest of the deposits are the Athabasca oil sands (see Figure 19–16). The oil sands consist of bitumen, a soluble organic matter that is solid at room temperature, in a mixture of sand and clay. Bitumen makes up about 10 percent of the actual oil sands with the remaining 80 percent consisting of sand, clay, mineral matter, and water. There are an estimated 1.7 trillion barrels of oil in the oil sands, of which 315 billion barrels are recoverable using today's technology. About 20 percent of the oil sands can be recovered by surface mining where the soil, muskeg, and rock is less than 75 metres thick. The remaining 80 percent that is buried below 75 metres requires more expensive techniques to extract the bitumen.

Questions

Research your answers to the following questions to help you understand what is taking place in the oil sands and the environmental, economic, and social impacts of this activity.

1. **a)** Describe the processes used to extract the oil from the oil sands that are less than 75 metres below the surface.

   b) Describe the processes used to extract oil from the oil sands that are more than 75 metres below the surface.

2. In the processes used to extract the oil from the oil sands, explain the significance of
   a) labour
   b) cost
   c) water
   d) energy

3. Discuss the impact of the oil sands development on
   a) the environment: land, forest, water and wetlands, and atmosphere and greenhouse gases
   b) local communities and First Nations, including health, housing, infrastructure, and social problems
   c) energy companies
   d) companies that use oil sands waste products
   e) trade with the US
   f) the economy of Alberta and the rest of Canada

Did You Know?

If the oil sands reserves were included with conventional oil reserves, Venezuela would rank first, Saudi Arabia second, and Canada third in the world.

Figure 19–16 Oil sands deposits in Alberta

Is There a Better Way to Produce and Use Energy?

Many people contend that the way we produce and use energy causes environmental and economic problems that threaten the sustainability of our energy resources. The most important idea to emerge from this point of view is that we must change the ways that we produce and use energy.

Today, most people in Old Core countries think of energy only as a commodity—something to be used, purchased, or sold. Our willingness to use energy wastefully is related to its relatively inexpensive cost and to the way that we are influenced by lifestyle advertising. You can see our willingness to use energy wastefully, for example, in the growth of energy-intensive recreational activities such as the use of personal watercraft or snowmobiles. However, people can learn to change their behaviour. In fact, environmentalists tell us that if we make different choices, we can significantly reduce the impacts of energy production and use on Earth.

GLOBALIZATION

Most people in Old Core countries think of energy only as a commodity—something to be used, purchased, or sold.

Is energy more than just a commodity? Explain.

When we talk about using energy in a better way, we mean just that! We can use it in a better way by shifting our consumption of electrical power from times of peak demand to times of low demand. For example, instead of washing your clothes in the afternoon on a weekday, wait until late evening or the weekend. Not only will you save money, but you will help reduce the huge demand for electricity that occurs on weekday afternoons (see Figure 19–17). As a result, we won't need to build more power plants or import more power to meet the great demand at peak times.

In 2004, the Ontario government announced that it will equip over four million homes and small businesses with **smart meters** by 2010. Smart meters track how much electricity you use and when you use it. This information tells the power company what rate to charge you, based on your energy consumption at any particular time of day.

Day	Weekends and Holidays	Summer Weekdays (May 1–Oct 31)				Winter Weekdays (Nov 1–April 30)				
Time	All day	7 a.m. to 11 a.m.	11 a.m. to 5 p.m.	5 p.m. to 10 p.m.	10 p.m. to 7 a.m.	7 a.m. to 11 a.m.	11 a.m. to 5 p.m.	5 p.m. to 8 p.m.	8 p.m. to 10 p.m.	10 p.m. to 7 a.m.
Time of Use	Off-peak	Mid-peak	On-peak	Mid-peak	Off-peak	On-peak	Mid-peak	On-peak	Mid-peak	Off-peak
Price (cents/kWh)	3.0	7.0	8.7	7.0	3.0	8.7	7.0	8.7	7.0	3.0

Figure 19–17 Electrical rates as of 2007 for Ontario customers with smart meters

Alternative Sources of Energy

Scientists are researching and developing several **alternative energy** sources in the hope of finding better ways to supply our energy needs. These include wind and solar power for heating and electricity production, tidal power, geothermal energy, and biomass conversion. To describe all these as new energy sources would be incorrect. For example, centuries ago, the Dutch used wind power in the form of windmills to pump water from the land that they were trying to reclaim from the sea.

Our energy future may include a startling change. For more than a century, oil products have been central to our energy use, economy, and way of life. However, oil has the lowest R/P ratios, and in the decades to come, use of oil may shift to a more flexible combination of energy sources. Solar power, biofuels, geothermal power, wind power, and the possibility of a hydrogen-electricity-based economy may be part of such a combination.

Here Comes the Sun: Solar Energy

Scientists have developed both simple and complex technologies to harness **solar energy** that can then be used in different ways, as shown in Figure 19–18.

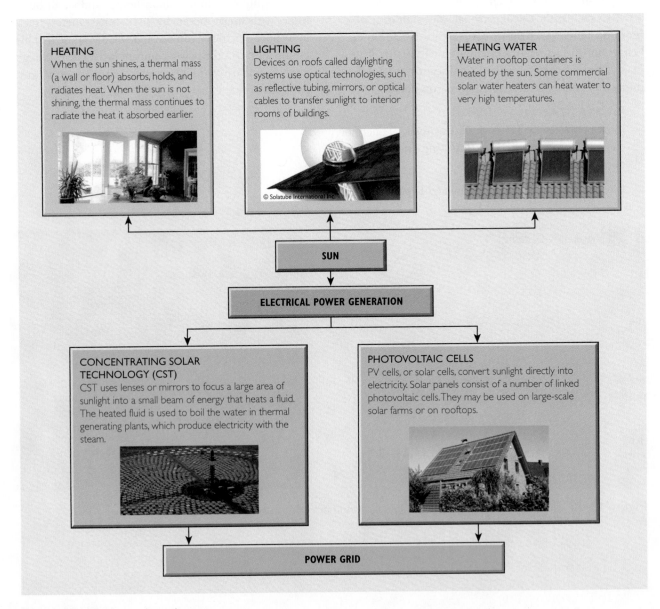

HEATING
When the sun shines, a thermal mass (a wall or floor) absorbs, holds, and radiates heat. When the sun is not shining, the thermal mass continues to radiate the heat it absorbed earlier.

LIGHTING
Devices on roofs called daylighting systems use optical technologies, such as reflective tubing, mirrors, or optical cables to transfer sunlight to interior rooms of buildings.

© Solatube International Inc.

HEATING WATER
Water in rooftop containers is heated by the sun. Some commercial solar water heaters can heat water to very high temperatures.

SUN

ELECTRICAL POWER GENERATION

CONCENTRATING SOLAR TECHNOLOGY (CST)
CST uses lenses or mirrors to focus a large area of sunlight into a small beam of energy that heats a fluid. The heated fluid is used to boil the water in thermal generating plants, which produce electricity with the steam.

PHOTOVOLTAIC CELLS
PV cells, or solar cells, convert sunlight directly into electricity. Solar panels consist of a number of linked photovoltaic cells. They may be used on large-scale solar farms or on rooftops.

POWER GRID

Figure 19–18 Harnessing solar energy

Solar power can be produced ideally in locations where sunlight is abundant throughout the year. This limits the number of sites where plants can be built. The great advantage to solar power plants is that they do not produce greenhouse gases or other pollutants during the production of electricity.

At the present time, the cost of electricity produced from solar energy is greater than the cost of electricity produced from fossil fuels. Consequently, governments must subsidize the production of solar power to make it economical enough for consumers to buy it.

In 2007, the Ontario government approved the construction of North America's largest photovoltaic solar power plant, also called a solar farm, near Sarnia. It will cover 365 hectares—the equivalent of 419 Canadian football fields. On sunny days, it will produce enough electricity to power between 10 000 and 15 000 homes.

For more information on the use of solar power and other green building practices, go to the link on our Web site.

Biofuels

Vegetable oil can be processed to make one of several **biofuels**, which are broadly defined as solid, liquid, or gas fuels derived from biomass—plant or animal material used to make fuel. The two biofuels most associated with transportation are biodiesel and ethanol.

Biodiesel is a combination of a non-petroleum-based fuel, made from vegetable oils or animal fats, and diesel oil. It is the most common type of biofuel in Europe. In the US, more than 3.8 billion litres of biodiesel were produced in 2006. Since biodiesel can be used in conventional diesel engines, and since most commercial trucks, city buses, and an increasing number of cars and light trucks are powered by diesel engines, the potential for the growth of the biodiesel market in North America is huge.

Bioethanol, usually referred to as ethanol, is the most common biofuel in the world. Ethanol can be mixed with gasoline for use in all engines. It is produced by the fermentation of sugars in corn, sugar cane, wheat, and sugar beets. E-85 is a mixture of 85 percent ethanol and 15 percent gasoline. It can be used in flex-fuel vehicles that have modified engines designed to operate on any mixture of gasoline and ethanol of up to 85 percent ethanol.

Critics of E-85 point out that fuel economy will be 20 to 30 percent less because it contains less heat energy per unit volume than gasoline. In addition, some researchers say ethanol made from corn produces only 34 percent more energy than is consumed in growing the corn, converting it into ethanol, and shipping it for use in gasoline. Other researchers say ethanol production consumes more energy than it yields. In the US, government subsidies for corn ethanol amounted to approximately $6 billion in 2006. Without the subsidies, making ethanol from corn would not be economical.

The production of ethanol fuels is rising. In 2006, about 19 billion litres of ethanol were made in 112 US plants—consuming one-fifth of the country's corn crop. If all the planned ethanol plants come online in the future, about 50 percent of the US corn crop would be consumed. Also in 2006, the Canadian and provincial governments announced a plan to increase the amount of ethanol in all Canadian gasoline to 5 percent by 2010. In 2006, the largest ethanol plant in Canada was opened near Sarnia, Ontario. It can produce 200 million litres of ethanol per year using 20 million bushels of surplus corn.

In the 2007 US budget, $150 million was allocated to research ethanol production from wood chips, switchgrass, and agricultural waste. Using these materials requires a different technology than that used to make ethanol from corn or sugar cane. Commercial production of this "cellulosic" ethanol is likely several years in the future but would be a significant advance, since it would not take up farmland needed for food production.

Biofuels have several positive aspects:

- When biofuels burn, they generally give off fewer pollutants than conventional fuels.
- They are biodegradable and relatively harmless to the environment when spilled and are made from renewable resources.
- Many developing countries have extensive biomass resources for producing biofuels.
- Most countries can grow their own biomass resources and produce their own biofuels. If they are able to produce a sufficient domestic supply of biofuels, they will no longer have to face interruptions to their supply of conventional fuel imports from countries involved in conflict or political upheaval.

Did You Know?

Brazil has become self-sufficient in fuel as a result of its biofuel development.

- Although these fuels release carbon dioxide when burned, the growing plants absorb large amounts of CO_2 from the atmosphere.

- Domestically produced biofuels reduce oil import costs.

Biofuels also have several negative aspects:

- Biodiversity is lost as more land is devoted to the production of biofuels. For example, tropical countries might destroy their rainforests in order to build oil-palm plantations.

- Oil can be more efficiently pumped and processed than biofuels can be grown and processed because the infrastructure is already in place.

- Ethanol is less efficient than conventional gasoline. It contains 34 percent less energy per unit volume than gasoline.

- Some researchers have reported that the production of ethanol from corn and similar crops consumes more energy than it yields.

- Huge subsidies have been given to ethanol producers, particularly in the US. Subsidies distort the true cost of production.

- High food prices have reduced the amount of food the US government has purchased for its food aid programs around the world. Since US food aid represents 50 percent of global food aid, many people in developing countries will suffer.

- The increasing production of corn and similar crops for ethanol use is driving up the price of many food crops. For example, the rising price of feed corn is increasing the price of chicken, pork, beef, and milk. Feed corn accounts for about 40 percent of the cost of producing chicken and 50 percent of the cost of producing pork.

Geothermal Energy and Earth Energy

Geothermal energy comes from steam or boiling-hot water found in the earth's crust. Geothermal energy can heat buildings and water, or power turbines to produce electricity (see Figure 19–19). Although it is widely used in Iceland, the Philippines, Italy, Indonesia, Mexico, New Zealand, Japan, and China, geothermal energy produced less than 1 percent of the world's energy in 2007. A test site in the Meager Mountain/Pebble Creek area in southwestern BC may be developed in the future.

Figure 19–19 A geothermal source with a temperature of more than 100°C is needed to drive a generating turbine in a geothermal plant.

Advantages

- Extraction of energy is safe and produces no human-made pollution or environmental damage.
- Use of geothermal energy produces no greenhouse gases.
- Water can be put back into the earth's crust after it has been used.
- Electricity storage is unnecessary since geothermal energy provides electricity continuously.

Disadvantages

- Geothermal plants must be located where geological formations create hot areas that are easily accessible.
- Sometimes a geothermal site may lose its heat or its hot water/steam.
- Hazardous gases and minerals that are difficult to dispose of may come up with the water/steam.
- The initial cost of building a geothermal plant can be high.

Though geothermal energy comes from hot water found in the earth's crust, energy can also be extracted from the earth itself. The use of **earth energy** to heat buildings (or to cool them) is based on the fact that Earth's mean ground temperature is quite constant, no matter how greatly the air temperature varies. For example, even though the air temperature in southern Ontario can range from $-30°C$ in the winter to $35°C$ in the summer, the average mean temperature of the ground a couple of metres below the surface is a fairly constant $10°C$.

The system that extracts the energy from the ground and uses it to heat your house (see Figure 19–20) works like this:

1. A ground loop (made of a network of polyethylene pipes containing a fluid), buried near the house, picks up heat from the ground and runs it to the heat pump.

2. The heat pump concentrates the low-grade heat, raising its temperature.

3. The heat is distributed through the house via a forced-air or in-floor heating system. Heat is also fed to the hot-water tank. In the summer, the system is reversed. The heat in your house is extracted and pumped into the ground.

Earth energy is more efficient than a furnace; rather than burning fossil fuels to generate heat, the heat pump redistributes existing heat. There are more than 30 000 earth energy installations in Canada, but it is more widely used in northern Europe.

Wind Power

In northern Europe and for more than 1000 years in China, Tibet, India, and the Middle East, people have harnessed the power of the wind to pump water through the use of windmills. During the 19th and first half of the 20th century, farmers in North America commonly used windmills to power water pumps. The use of **wind power** declined in the latter half of the 19th century as electricity became available and oil-based fuels were developed to provide power. However, some farmers today still use windmills (see Figure 19–21).

Wind power was usually used where other sources of power were not available, for example, on farms without electricity. Although its use declined over the last half of the 20th century, researchers continued to take an interest in it. As a result, wind energy has recently become a more mainstream source of electricity. Wind-power generation more than quadrupled between 2000 and 2006, at which time the amount of electricity generated by wind was about 74 gigawatts per year, or about 1 percent of worldwide electricity use. In Denmark, wind power produces about 20 percent of the country's electrical energy.

Most large windmills are located on "wind farms" where they are massed together in areas with strong, constant winds. Although called wind farms, they are actually large-scale electrical generating plants (see Figure 19–22).

Wind power has advantages and disadvantages (see Figure 19–23).

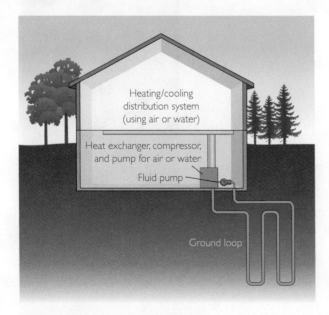

Figure 19–20 How an earth energy system works

Figure 19–21 Power has been generated from wind-mills in rural areas since the 19th century.

Figure 19–22 Wind-power energy produced in Canada in 2007 totalled 1856 megawatts, enough to power 560 000 homes. The map shows the wind energy generated in each province/territory in kilowatts and megawatts.

810 kW
103.95 MW
390 kW
523.97 MW
422.25 MW
72.36 MW
171.18 MW
501.31 MW
59.26 MW

For more information on wind power and how it is generated, used, and stored, go to the link on our Web site.

Is Green Power for You?

If you've decided to choose a better way to consume energy, but you don't want to give up your lifestyle entirely, you do have the option of purchasing **green power**, which is electricity generated from emission-free sources (wind farms, low-impact hydro plants).

Most provinces have some green power programs provided by either public utilities or private companies. For example, ENMAX, a public utility in Calgary, first offered green power to Canadians in 1998. Residents of Alberta and Ontario can now purchase green power from a private company called Bullfrog Power. To meet the increasing demand for green power, Bullfrog and a company called Sky Generation built a wind farm on the shores of Lake Huron near Grand Bend, Ontario, in 2007. It produces more than 26 million kilowatt hours of clean, renewable energy annually.

Green power is often more expensive to generate than conventional power. The costs of building new facilities are high, and high costs are passed on to consumers. Nevertheless, despite the fact that you pay a little more, you do have the satisfaction of knowing that you are supporting carbon-free power.

Advantages

■ Wind power is non-polluting.
■ Wind power does not produce greenhouse gases because it does not use fossil fuels.
■ Windmills can be easily installed and dismantled.
■ Land where windmills are located can be used for other purposes, for example, farming.
■ Wind power is economical and practical in developing countries and in places that have limited energy needs.
■ Countries could keep money in the country because they wouldn't need as much imported oil.
■ Wind power will become competitive with fossil fuel and nuclear energy as the technology improves.

Disadvantages

■ Windmills can be located only in areas that have moderately strong, reliable winds.
■ Windmills can be noisy.
■ Some people consider windmills to be unsightly.
■ Windmills can be damaged by excessively strong winds.
■ Windmills can interfere with electromagnetic communications, for example, radio broadcasts.

Figure 19–23 Modern windmills vary in design and size.

Hydricity

The ways that we produce, transport, and use energy has caused enormous damage to the environment. The resulting problems have given rise to many of the most important environmental issues of today, including global warming, smog, and acid rain. We are also faced with questions about the reliability and cost of the future supply of oil. Experts are suggesting other ways to supply energy. One way, in particular, does not involve the discovery of a new energy source. Rather, it focuses on a new way to use the energy we already have. It is **hydricity** (hydrogen electricity).

Fundamental to hydricity is that it is relatively easy to convert hydrogen to electricity and back again. The simplest way to produce hydrogen is by electrolysis of water, using electricity that has been produced in an electrical generation plant. The plant, in effect, converts fossil fuel energy, hydropower, nuclear energy, and perhaps in the future solar energy, into hydrogen.

$$2H_2O + energy \longrightarrow 2H_2 + O_2$$

Benefits of the Hydricity System

An energy system that focuses on hydrogen and electricity offers a number of important benefits.

- **Economic benefits**. Hydricity would save people money, because they would not be tied to one type of energy. For example, Canadians who heat their homes with natural gas are faced with large price increases and have to pay because their furnaces burn only natural gas. If a hydricity system were in place, however, the most economical fuel at any given time could be used to provide hydrogen or electricity to heat their homes.

- **Self-sufficiency**. A hydricity-based economy would allow the US, Japan, and countries in western Europe to reduce their dependence on imported oil and increase their security by insulating themselves from the political uncertainties of the world oil market. Vehicles could be powered, indirectly, by fuels like coal or natural gas, or by energy from wind and solar power.

- **Environmental benefits**. Compared to the current system, a hydricity system causes less environmental damage. When hydrogen is burned, the only by-product is water. The chemicals responsible for smog production and acid rain (mainly sulphur and nitrogen compounds), plus the carbon compounds responsible for global warming, are not produced.

Problems of Implementing a Hydricity System

A hydricity system is not without its problems.

- **Fuel**. Energy is needed to release hydrogen from water. The use of conventional fuels to accomplish this task burns non-renewable resources and releases greenhouse gases and pollutants into the atmosphere.

- **Infrastructure**. The infrastructure of our current energy system (pipelines, oil refineries, gas stations) has taken decades to build and has cost trillions of dollars. Replacing it will take a similar length of time and will cost a comparable amount. In the interim, vehicles could use fuel cells that chemically convert a compound containing hydrogen into electricity, without any burning. These fuel cells could be constructed to use a variety of fuels, such as reformulated gasoline, methanol, ethanol, hydrogen, and compressed natural gas (CNG).

Earlier in *Global Connections*, you learned about the cornucopian view of Earth's future. Some observers believe that the development of a hydrogen–electricity-based economy would be nothing more than the next step to a cornucopian future. Others strenuously reject this idea. They feel that the only way we can achieve a sustainable energy future is by fundamentally changing the way in which we think about and use energy.

Chapter Questions

Knowledge and Understanding

1. Construct a one-page summary chart for each of the "big five" energy sources—oil, natural gas, coal, nuclear power, and hydro-electricity—to compare the advantages and disadvantages. Include a column for the typical geographical location for each resource and whether the resource is renewable or non-renewable.

2. Consider the pros and cons of solar, geothermal, and wind power. Would any of these alternative energy sources be effective in your region or community? Explain.

3. Explain how earth energy and geothermal energy systems function.

Thinking

4. Do you think Canada should build more nuclear reactors to limit greenhouse gas emissions? Explain.

5. The theory of "peak oil" has both supporters and opponents.

    a) Research both sides of this theory.

    b) What is your opinion of this theory?

6. a) Do you think the Ontario government policy of installing smart meters in homes and businesses throughout Ontario is a good idea? Explain.

    b) Will smart meters affect your electrical consumption patterns? Explain.

7. Biofuels might reduce our dependence on fossil fuels, but if we grow crops for fuel rather than food, what impacts, both positive and negative, will there be in

    a) Old Core countries

    b) New Core/Periphery countries

    Consider such things as the diversity of crops grown, food prices, fuel prices, environmental impacts, food aid, and whether the overall impact is positive or negative.

8. The change to a hydricity-based energy system could be a very complex one. What particular elements of the current energy system might be obstacles to the change? What elements of the current system could be easily integrated into this energy revolution?

Communication

9. In Canada and many other OECD countries, many large hydro-electric mega-projects have been built over the last century. In these countries, very few undeveloped large hydro-electric sites remain. Research and prepare a poster to show one of the following situations:

    a) The history of an existing major hydro-electric development in Canada or another country. Consider the reasons why the site was chosen, the nature of the construction, the amount of electricity produced, and how the electricity is used. Describe any environmental concerns related to the project.

    b) The potential of, and plans for, the development of any undeveloped large-scale hydro-electric site in any country. Be sure to include a discussion of environmental concerns related to the development of this site.

    c) The potential for the development of very small hydro-electric power sites that, in the past, may have been ignored because they were not economically feasible.

10. Conduct a round-table discussion focused on the five conventional energies. One person will represent oil, another natural gas, and so on. Together, rank the potential for each of these energy sources to satisfy future global requirements. **S**

11. Develop a ten-point survey to determine levels of student awareness of various alternative energy sources. Conduct the survey, using a sample of at least 25 students from different grades. Analyze the data to identify patterns and relationships, then prepare a report of your findings.

12. Oil shale deposits, like oil sands, are another source of unconventional oil. Research and prepare a presentation (written, oral, visual, etc.) on

    a) the location of oil shale deposits

    b) the process of extracting the oil

    c) the pros and cons of this source of oil

Application

13. The subject of nuclear power draws strong reactions from both supporters and opponents. Investigate the arguments on both sides of this issue. After you do your research, decide whether you think that additional nuclear plants should be constructed in a) Canada, and b) other countries. Give reasons for your views.

14. Is there an energy crisis? Comment on this question from the following perspectives:

a) We are running out of energy.

b) We are running out of some types of energy only.

c) We are likely to discover additional sources of conventional energy.

d) The energy crisis is really a cultural construction—we have plenty of energy as long as we are prepared to change our attitudes and behaviour.

15. Examine the concept of green power by answering the following questions:

a) What is meant by green power?

b) What are the pros and cons of green power?

c) What is the current state of green power in Canada? What is its potential for growth?

d) What green power initiatives are taking place around the world?

e) Do you think you will use green power? Explain. **S**

16. Examine Environment Canada's Environmental Choice Program and the use of the EcoLogo symbol by answering the following questions:

a) When did the program start and what is its purpose?

b) What must companies do to get certified?

c) How do you think the EcoLogo benefits companies' sales and marketing?

d) What is your role as a consumer?

CHAPTER 20

Climate Change— *the* 21st Century Issue

Key Terms

climate change

tipping point

greenhouse effect

greenhouse gases (GhG)

carbon cycle

carbon source

carbon sink

fixed carbon

positive feedback loops

Kyoto Protocol

energy intensity

cap and trade system

carbon tax

geo-engineering

In 2005, Hurricane Katrina made people consider how lack of sustainability could threaten well-being. Burning of fossil fuels has contributed to global warming.

Key Questions

By the end of this chapter you will be able to answer the following questions.

■ Is climate change really as big a "deal" as it seems to be in the media?

■ Why is the concept of tipping points useful in explaining how public opinions on issues change?

■ What are the environmental, social, and economic implications of climate change for Canada and for the rest of the world?

■ Why must climate change solutions occur at the global level?

■ What relationships are there between individual decisions and global problems (and their solutions)?

The Tipping Point Has Been Reached

At the turn of the millennium, it was fair to say that **climate change** was just one item on a long list of major issues that the world was facing. Suddenly though, in the middle of the first decade of the 2000s, attitudes changed—and they changed dramatically. Climate change is now seen as the issue that has the greatest likelihood of causing major damage to human and animal life on Earth. A theory borrowed from sociology may provide us with an explanation for this attitude shift. The idea of a **tipping point** was popularized in a book that appeared in 2000 called *The Tipping Point: How Little Things Can Make a Big Difference* by Malcolm Gladwell. Gladwell's idea was that dramatic changes in behaviour take place when a "social epidemic" occurs.

Because a tipping point had been reached, the general public became genuinely concerned about the implications of climate change—polls indicated that they wanted something done and they wanted it now. Politicians were caught unprepared. All parties realized that they had to be seen to be serious about combatting climate change—before it cost them the next election. Note that the key phrase here is "seen to be serious," since we are talking primarily about perceptions and attitudes.

One of the most remarkable changes in attitudes toward climate change has come from the business community. Business leaders increasingly see that the effects of climate change will profoundly reduce economic growth in the decades to come. Sir Nicholas Stern, a former World Bank economist, stated in a 2006 report for the British government that climate change must be dealt with "...to preserve current living standards and safeguard economies." He concluded, "If we act now, we can avoid the very worst."

Some understanding about how tipping points happen will help you to understand the dramatic turnaround in attitudes toward climate change.

- Gladwell stated that the "law of the few" suggests that a small number of people, who are knowledgeable and *charismatic* (possessing powerful magnetic charm or appeal), play a critical role in the spread of an idea or a trend. In Canada, David Suzuki would be the best example of this type of individual. In the United States, Al Gore would fill this role.

- Gladwell also talked about the "stickiness" of ideas or products contributing to a tipping point. The implications of climate change, both in terms of short-term and long-term effects, are "sticky"—they are inherently interesting to most people.

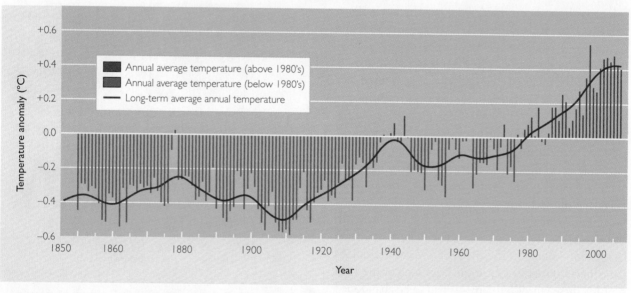

Figure 20–1 The graph shows three things: the annual average global temperature compared to 1980 values (brown lines are years above average; blue lines are years below average), and the trend in average annual temperatures (the green line). People have noticed that temperatures in recent years have been much warmer than those of years gone by.

- Gladwell also discussed the "power of context" in explaining why tipping points happen. This means that if people can see how an idea fits into the reality of their life, they find it easier to accept the idea. With respect to climate change, people had a sense that something was changing in the weather they were experiencing. Temperatures were noticeably higher than ever (see Figure 20–1 on the previous page) and severe storms seemed more frequent. Best known of these was Hurricane Katrina (see page 316).

- Gladwell's theory also relied on pioneering work by Everett Rogers on how ideas spread through a population (see Figure 20–2). Using Rogers' model, Gladwell believes that concern about climate change has passed the early majority stage and has moved well into the late majority stage of acceptance—at least in Old Core countries.

The key question, though, is what next? How will concern for climate change be reflected in political action or changes in behaviour? In this chapter, you will have the opportunity to start to answer these vital questions.

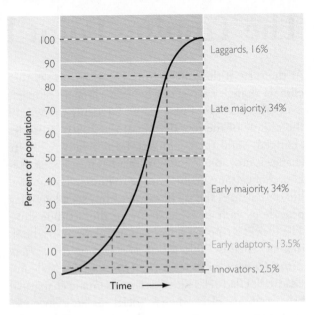

Figure 20–2 This graph indicates the rate at which acceptance of a new idea occurs—at first quite slowly with the Innovators and Early adaptors, and then much more quickly with the Early and Late majority of the population. A tipping point is said to occur when the latter stage is reached. Because of its complexity and implications, acceptance of climate change started very slowly. When the tipping point was reached, it became *the* critical environmental issue of our time.

Climate Change Is Not New

Scientists have determined that over the last million years, global temperatures have ranged from about one Celsius degree warmer than they were in 1950 to about four Celsius degrees cooler (see Figure 20–3). If we narrow our time focus (see Figure 20–4), we can see that temperatures have changed continuously even in the last 1000 years.

While the changes might appear to be quite small (±0.5 Celsius degrees), historical climatologists maintain that even such small changes can be important. They suggest that the warmer period that began 1000 years ago allowed the Vikings to settle in southern Greenland and the northern tip of Newfoundland. Archaeological evidence shows that these settlements lasted only as long as the Medieval Warm Period. As the climate started to cool at the beginning of the 14th century, these Nordic settlements had to be abandoned as food production became a problem.

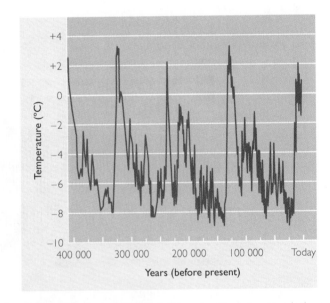

Figure 20–3 Average global temperatures have varied widely over the last 400 000 years. If you have studied physical geography, you should know about the four glacial periods that are shown on this graph as long periods of time with abnormally cold temperatures.

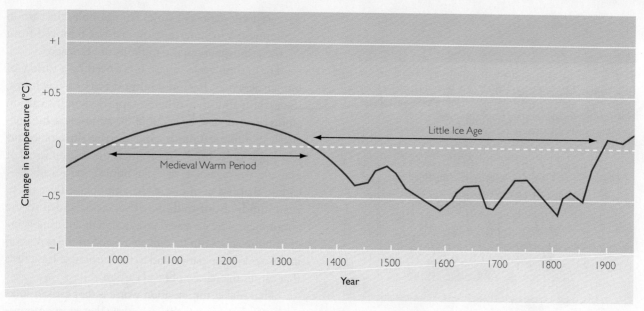

Figure 20–4 Average temperatures in the last 1000 years have also varied widely. Note that the vertical scales of this graph and of Figure 20–3 are different.

The Greenhouse Effect

Often, people talk about the **greenhouse effect** and global warming as if they are the same thing, but this is incorrect. The greenhouse effect has existed for as long as the earth has had an atmosphere. Without it, there could be no life on Earth. In fact, scientists have calculated that without the greenhouse effect, the average temperature on Earth (which is now about 14°C) would be 33 Celsius degrees cooler (that is, −19°C)—more like the temperature on Mars!

The earth's atmosphere functions like an agricultural greenhouse. Instead of glass to hold heat in, there are **greenhouse gases** (**GhG**). Most of Earth's atmosphere is composed of nitrogen (78 percent of the total), oxygen (21 percent), and argon (0.9 percent). None of these gases is a greenhouse gas. Rather, it is some of the gases that make up the remaining 0.1 percent that are the greenhouse gases. The most important greenhouse gases are water vapour (H_2O), carbon dioxide (CO_2), and methane (CH_4).

The effects of higher concentrations of atmospheric water vapour on global warming are not entirely clear. (Increased levels of water vapour may cause temperatures to rise because water molecules absorb heat, but they may also lower temperatures by increasing cloud cover, which would reflect more solar radiation back into space.) The amount of water vapour in the atmosphere does change relatively quickly from place to place and from time to time. We see evidence of this in humidity changes that occur from one day to the next or in the different weather patterns in the Sahara desert as compared to the Brazilian rainforest. There is no evidence that human activities are significantly changing the concentration of water vapour in the atmosphere.

Anthropogenic Greenhouse Gases

The impact of varying concentrations of carbon dioxide and methane is much clearer. Studies of ancient air bubbles trapped in glacial ice have identified a strong relationship between levels of greenhouse gases in the air bubbles and the temperature changes that caused the ice ages (see Figure 20–5). It is generally agreed that human activities are increasing the magnitude of the greenhouse effect by producing more of the gases that cause it.

If we are to understand climate change, we must consider the role played by these *anthropogenic greenhouse gases*. This term refers to the greenhouse gases created by people. There are four principal anthropogenic greenhouse gases: carbon dioxide, methane, nitrous oxide, and halocarbons. The first three exist naturally; halocarbons are produced only by human activities.

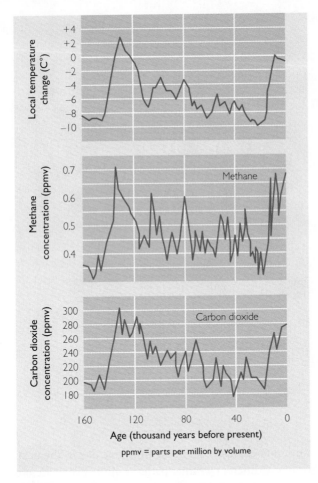

Figure 20–5 There is a strong correlation between global air temperature and concentrations of carbon dioxide and methane, going back 160 000 years.

Carbon Cycle

To understand climate change, it is critical to understand the **carbon cycle**—that is, how carbon moves through the environment (see Figure 20–6). Given sufficient time, a particular carbon atom could circulate through all the various parts of the cycle.

To understand why more carbon is finding its way into the atmosphere, it is key to understand the role played by carbon sources, carbon sinks, and fixed carbon.

■ A **carbon source** is anything that provides additional carbon to the atmosphere, for example, when the vegetation in a swamp decomposes and gives off methane.

■ A **carbon sink** exists when carbon is removed from the atmosphere for a relatively short time, for example, when you plant a tree that takes up carbon as it grows. In general, carbon will stay in a sink for a period ranging from a few minutes to a few centuries.

■ **Fixed carbon**, on the other hand, is any carbon that has been removed from the atmosphere for a

very long period of time. For example, the carbon contained in limestone or coal was removed from the atmosphere many millions of years ago.

The carbon cycle can be influenced by a variety of human activities. If a forest burns down or a cow burps, the carbon sink that is being tapped contains carbon atoms that will have been out of the atmosphere for a relatively short time. A much more worrying situation occurs when previously fixed carbon enters the atmosphere. For example, when gasoline or coal is burned, "new" carbon—carbon that has been out of the atmosphere for tens, or even hundreds, of millions of years—is added to the atmosphere. The increased production of anthropogenic greenhouse gases can be directly related to the explosion in the world's population and to the burning of fossil fuels that causes the release of fixed carbon.

What makes the situation worse is that carbon sinks are being destroyed at the same time that great amounts of fixed carbon are being released into the atmosphere. Scientists estimate that without effective measures to limit carbon dioxide production, the amount of carbon dioxide in the atmosphere in 2080 will be twice what it was before the Industrial Revolution.

Carbon Dioxide. Carbon dioxide is the most significant anthropogenic greenhouse gas, but not because of the effectiveness of each CO_2 molecule in absorbing heat. (To allow comparison to other gases, scientists assign a CO_2 molecule a *global warming potential [GWP]* of 1.) Other gases are able to hold more heat on a per-molecule basis. Rather, it is significant because of the vast quantities of the gas produced by human activities. To date, most of the attention paid to fighting climate change is focused on ways to reduce the amount of carbon dioxide that humans produce.

Methane. Methane (with a GWP of 62) is a powerful greenhouse gas produced whenever organic materials break down in the absence of oxygen—if oxygen is present, decomposition produces carbon dioxide instead. Between 60 percent and 80 percent of global methane production now comes from human activities. There are three main sources of anthropogenic methane:

■ from decomposing garbage in various kinds of dumps

■ as a waste product during the extraction and processing of fossil fuels

■ from the digestive tracts of domestic animals like cows and pigs, and from the decomposition of their solid waste. Researchers say that most of this methane comes from cows burping rather than from the other end of the cows' digestive tract. We leave it to your imagination to picture how this research was done.

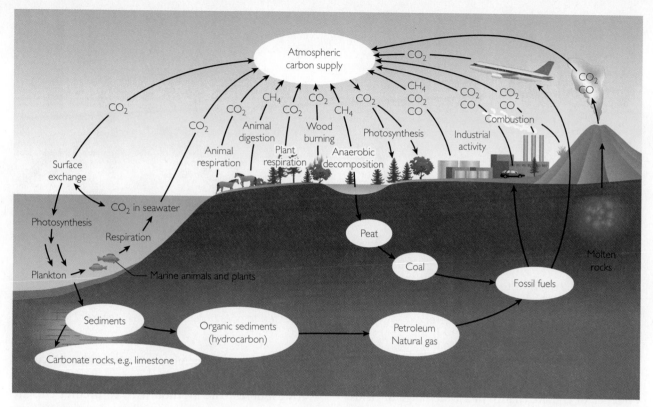

Figure 20–6 The carbon cycle includes carbon in many forms: carbon dioxide, methane, carbon monoxide, limestone, hydrocarbons, and even diamonds. In this diagram, try to identify carbon sources, carbon sinks, where fixed carbon is created, and where fixed carbon is released into the atmosphere.

Halocarbons. Halocarbons do not exist naturally. They are a family of highly stable compounds that were created for various industrial uses. (The GWP ranges for common halocarbons are very high, from 1700 to 10 600.) However, their prevalence in the atmosphere is much less than carbon dioxide and methane so they are less significant greenhouse gases.

Nitrous Oxide

Not all greenhouse gases are carbon-based. Nitrous oxide (N_2O) is the best example of these. It comes from both natural and anthropogenic sources. Its main human sources include the burning of fossil fuels in vehicles, the use of nitrogen-based fertilizers, and the production of industrial chemicals like nitric acid. Nitrous oxide concentrations have risen with the growth of population and the industrial economy. Although nitrous oxide is a more powerful greenhouse gas than carbon dioxide or methane (the GWP of nitrous oxide is 296), its overall impact on global warming is much less because it is present in much lower concentrations.

Impact of Global Warming

Climate change is having a remarkably broad range of impacts on the earth's ecosystems and on the people who depend on them (see Figure 20–7). Climate change is monitored by a United Nations–sponsored group of 2500 climate scientists called the Intergovernmental Panel on Climate Change (IPCC).

This agency, formed in 1988, issued major "Assessment Reports" in 1990, 1995, 2001, and 2007. In these reports, based on the *collation* (critical comparison to verify the truth of something) of enormous amounts of research, scientists predicted that global warming will have a wide, complex, and at times, surprising range of

Figure 20–7 As this cartoon by a Swiss artist suggests, climate change is having a dramatic and varied impact on the earth. What point is being made here?

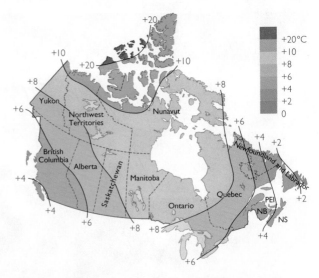

Figure 20–8 Some areas of Canada will experience much more warming than other areas. This map shows expected temperature increases by the year 2100.

impacts. The IPCC's 2007 report referenced research that produced almost 30 000 data sets that might show evidence of climate change in a wide range of fields. Of this total, 94 percent supported the contention that climate change is happening. As a result, predictions about the impact of climate change are presented with more confidence. For example, the IPCC now says that it is *"unequivocal"* (leaving no doubt) that the earth is warming and they have a "very high confidence" that this trend is happening because of human activities. In the section below we will use the terms "will" or "will happen," acknowledging that there is great support for (but not 100 percent certainty of the truth of) these predictions.

Higher Average Temperatures

In its 2007 report, the IPCC predicted that average global temperatures will increase by between 1.1 Celsius degrees and 6.4 Celsius degrees by the year 2100. (The IPCC estimated that the temperature increase in the past century was 0.74 Celsius degrees. In its 2001 report, the IPCC estimated that the temperature increase over the 20th century was 0.6 Celsius degrees.) This

relatively broad range of values reflects the difficulties associated with accurate computerized modelling of the atmosphere—the method used to predict climate change. For a better understanding of the significance of changes of these magnitudes, please refer to the wide variations of average global temperatures over the years shown in Figures 20–4 and 20–5.

Temperature increases will not occur evenly in all parts of the world. In general, the farther a location is from the equator, the greater the amount of increase. The average temperatures of polar areas are expected to increase by as much as 10 Celsius degrees by 2100. Within Canada, temperatures are expected to increase at dramatically different rates (see Figure 20–8).

Changes in Precipitation Patterns

Changes in precipitation patterns as a result of climate change have been studied less than changes in temperature patterns. On average, scientists think that there will be slightly more precipitation, but with great variation from region to region. Places that now have relatively high amounts of rainfall will get more; places that are relatively dry will have less. In particular, three changes are foreseen, none of which is desirable.

■ Heavy precipitation events will become more common and a higher proportion of our precipitation will come during these intense rainstorms and snowfalls.

- The area of the world affected by droughts is likely to get larger. The frequency of droughts is likely to be higher.

- Areas of the world that are affected by tropical cyclonic storms (hurricanes and typhoons) are likely to experience more storms, and more severe storms than at present.

To see, very graphically, the impact that sea level increases of differing amounts would have on a number of American cities, check the link on our Web site.

Sea Level Increases

Two factors will increase sea levels.

- Water expands slightly as it gets warmer. As the average temperature of the oceans increases due to global warming, thermal expansion of ocean water will contribute to higher sea levels.

- Higher temperatures will melt ice caps in Antarctica and Greenland and mountain glaciers elsewhere. The meltwater generated will also contribute to higher sea levels.

Areas at risk include many of the world's great cities, along with many islands and highly populated rural lowlands. Between 1961 and 2003, sea levels increased by an average of 1.8 millimetres per year for a total rise of about 77 millimetres. While this is not a large total, the rate of rise is increasing. Between 1993 and 2003, the rise was measured at 3.3 millimetres per year. If all of Earth's glaciers and ice sheets were to melt, global sea levels could increase by as much as 9 metres. Although no one is suggesting that this amount of melting is imminent, the earth's ice sheets and glaciers are getting smaller. It is not hard to imagine sea level increases in the 1- to 3-metre range in the next century. Increases of this magnitude will have dramatic impacts (see Figure 20–9).

Ecosystem Change

Ecosystems are very *resilient* (capable of withstanding shock without permanent damage), but scientists believe that there are limits beyond which they cannot recover. Part of the reason for this is that ecosystems will face many challenges, all at the same time—direct ones like higher temperatures, changed rainfall patterns, droughts, more grass and forest fires, more insect infestations; and indirect ones like land-use pressures and over-exploitation of resources.

If temperature increases are more than 1.5 Celsius degrees to 2.5 Celsius degrees, there are serious implications for the structure and functioning of ecosystems. Here are just two.

- The geographical range of many species will change, and 20 to 30 percent of species will be at greater

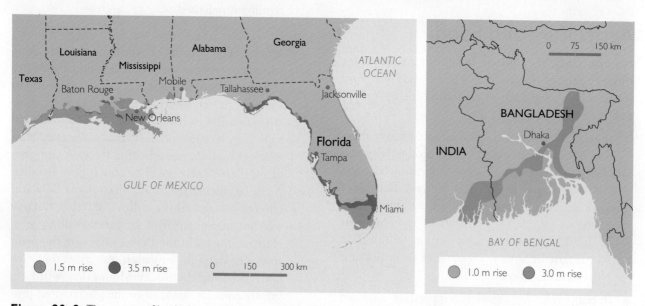

Figure 20–9 The coasts of both the southeastern US and Bangladesh are threatened by rising sea levels. Higher sea levels can flood low-lying areas and increase the risk posed by storm surges caused by hurricanes and other major storms.

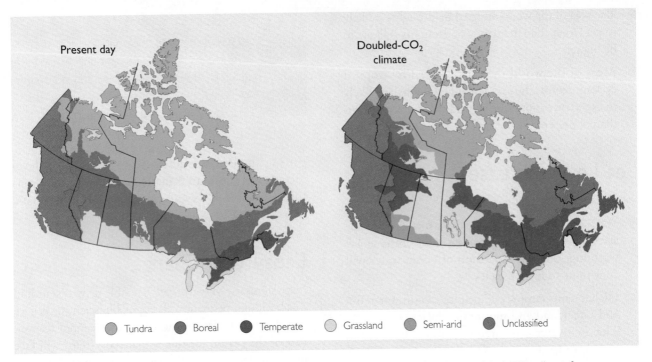

Figure 20–10 What changes do you see in the forest and grassland boundaries with a doubled CO$_2$ climate?

Tundra Boreal Temperate Grassland Semi-arid Unclassified

risk of extinction. Grizzly bears are expanding their range northward, and there is evidence that they are mating with polar bears. Interbreeding could be another threat to the existence of polar bears.

- The extent of the boreal forest in North America will change (see Figure 20–10). In general, the temperate forest and grassland regions will move northward into the boreal forest, while the boreal forest will expand into the tundra region.

Agriculture and Food

Unfortunately, the outlook for farming is worse for those regions of the world that are already *marginal* (close to the lower limit of capability) for agriculture today.

- In tropical and semi-tropical areas, especially those that tend to be dry today, crop productivity will likely fall, even with modest temperature changes (1 Celsius degree to 2 Celsius degrees). The risk of food shortages in these areas will be significantly greater as a result. (A recent report suggested that by 2080, the value of farm outputs will decline 50 percent in Sudan, 29 percent in India, and 16 percent in Australia.)

- In temperate areas, modest temperature increases will actually raise productivity—assuming that enough water is available for farming. Overall, food production will rise with temperature increases of up to 3 Celsius degrees. It will fall, however, with temperature increases greater than this. (The same report suggests that Canada's agricultural output will increase in value by 13 percent, with 28 percent increases in Egypt and Scandinavia.)

- Increases in the frequency of floods and droughts will have a negative effect on food availability. This will be most significant in areas where subsistence farming is practised.

- In Canada, many areas will have longer growing seasons. The growing season might become long enough to grow wheat near Yellowknife, while rice cultivation might become common in southern Ontario. At first glance, it might appear that these changes will greatly improve Canada's agricultural capability, but this will likely not be the case. Most of the current Prairie agricultural region and parts of southern Ontario will be too dry for farming. Areas of northern Canada that might be warm enough for agriculture will not develop suitable soils for many centuries. Irrigation will not be a realistic option in the Prairies because the main source of water for irrigation, the rivers that flow eastward from the Rocky Mountains, will have greatly reduced flows, since the glaciers that provide much of their water will be much smaller or entirely melted.

- Significant changes in fish distributions and production catches are likely to occur as waters warm up. Scientists say this is already happening on the west coast of North America: the range of various salmon species is moving northward. The commercial salmon fisheries in Oregon, Washington, and British Columbia could disappear.

Health

Global warming will cause an increase in diseases and animal pests. For example, as temperatures rise, residents of tropical highland areas will be exposed to malaria, dengue fever, and Japanese encephalitis for the first time. Previously, they were protected from these diseases because the insects that carried them could not survive in the relatively cool mountain climates.

In non-tropical areas, a rise in winter temperatures rather than average temperatures is of more consequence to people's health. Winter temperatures are increasing at twice the rate of average temperatures. As Dr. Paul Epstein, a noted expert on the health effects of climate change, stated, "The winter is the most wonderful thing that was ever invented for public health and we're losing it." Winter temperatures do an outstanding job of killing off disease-bearing insects and dangerous germs, and many areas will lose this protection as their winter temperatures become warmer.

SUSTAINABILITY

The winter is the most wonderful thing that was ever invented for public health and we're losing it.

Why is winter so important for public health?

Lower Temperatures

Remarkably, global warming could even cause dramatic cooling in some areas. The reason for this is quite complicated and considerably more research needs to be done to confirm this hypothesis. It is believed that warmer global temperatures may have a dramatic impact on something called the Great Ocean Conveyor (see Figure 20–11). The Conveyor moves great quantities of warm water close to the coast of western Europe by means of the Gulf Stream and North Atlantic Drift ocean currents. Consequently, western Europe has a remarkably mild climate for its latitude.

Warm ocean waters that cool and become denser in the ocean north of Norway drive the Conveyor. Because of their density, they sink far below the surface and start moving southward. This creates a convection cell that draws more warm surface water northward. Many marine scientists theorize that the melting of glaciers in Greenland and extreme northern Canada would reduce the *salinity* (concentration of salt) of surface water in the North Atlantic. The lower salinity, and hence reduced

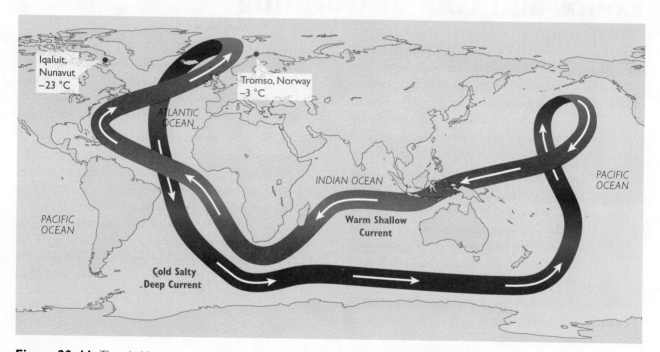

Figure 20–11 The vital importance of the Great Ocean Conveyor has become known only in recent years. The impact of the Conveyor is striking. The coldest month in Tromsø, in northern Norway (latitude 69°N), averages –3°C; while the coldest month in Iqaluit, Nunavut (at 64°N, more than 300 kilometres farther south) averages only –23°C.

density of this water, would reduce, or even eliminate, the downward movement of water, stopping the Conveyor. Without the warmth that ocean currents bring, the climate of western Europe would become dramatically cooler—some scientists are even prepared to say that the cooling would be so intense that a new ice age could occur in northern Europe. Coastal areas of eastern North America, from Florida to Newfoundland, could also experience noticeable cooling.

Human Migrations

Global warming will cause an *unprecedented* (never before seen) growth in the number of environmental refugees. People would have to flee their homelands because of severe environmental changes.

- Some might leave because the land they live on is being flooded by rising sea levels.

- Others might leave because the area where they live has been devastated by tropical storms made more severe as a result of climate change.

- Others might have to migrate because their homelands have suffered a significant reduction in agricultural productivity as a result of rainfall reductions.

Some observers suggest that there are already as many as 25 million environmental refugees in the world, in particular in North Africa, where rainfall levels have declined over the years. Climate change could make this number dramatically increase.

Global Security

In 2007, ten very senior, retired American generals and admirals issued a report on the security implications of climate change. They concluded that precipitation changes, increased hunger, higher sea levels, and large numbers of environmental refugees will contribute to decreased security in the world. They stated that within 30 to 40 years (that is, before 2050) "the chaos that results can be an *incubator* [an environment that provides optimum conditions for the growth of something] of civil strife, genocide, and the growth of terrorism." In particular, they warned of wars being fought over water as areas that are already dry become even drier.

Loops and Global Warming

Of particular concern to those who study global warming is the problem of **positive feedback loops** (see Figure 20–12). These exist when a result of global warming causes even more global warming. At a certain point, global warming and climate changes that have started slowly may begin to accelerate significantly. The following are three examples of critical feedback loops.

- The ability of water to hold dissolved gases is inversely related to temperature. Therefore, as oceans warm they will not be able to hold as much carbon dioxide. The excess carbon dioxide that is released into the atmosphere will cause more global warming that will, in turn, make the oceans warmer and cause even more carbon dioxide to be released.

- The melting of ice caps and sea ice reduces Earth's *albedo* (reflective power), as highly reflective ice and

snow are replaced by rock, soil, and open water. Their darker surface will absorb more solar radiation and ultimately reradiate more heat back into the atmosphere. This will, in turn, cause more melting of ice and snow, further reducing the albedo.

- Higher temperatures will cause permafrost to melt in areas of northern Canada, Alaska, and Siberia. The previously frozen muskeg in these vast areas contains enormous amounts of organic material that has not decomposed because of the low temperatures. If the permafrost thaws, this material will be able to break down, and vast quantities of methane and carbon dioxide will be given off—increasing the greenhouse effect and causing even more permafrost to melt.

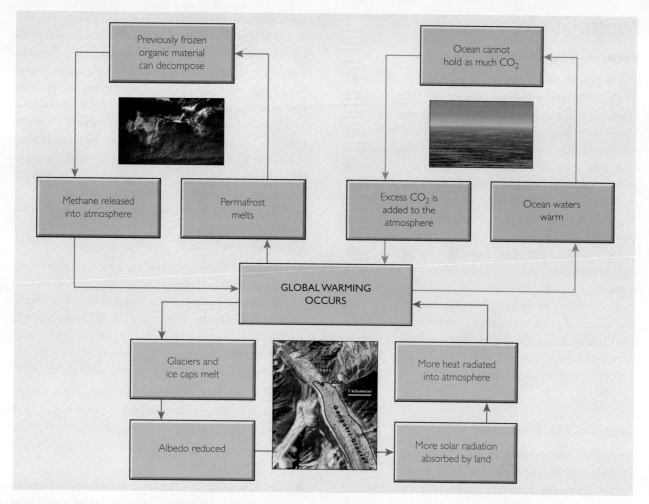

Figure 20–12 The existence of a number of positive feedback loops (these are only some of the more important ones) threatens to accelerate global warming in the future.

Politics of Climate Change

In simplest terms, the issue of climate change can be divided into two parts: the *science* of global warming and the *politics* of global warming.

Rio Conference, 1992

Although the first research on climate change was published in the 1970s, it was not until the early 1990s that the issue moved from the scientific world into the political forum. The politics of climate change began at the UN Conference on Environment and Development held in Rio de Janeiro in 1992. Perhaps the most important achievement of the conference was the creation of the United Nations Framework Convention on Climate Change (UNFCC). It was called a "framework convention" because it provided only a basic outline for the international efforts that would be required to prevent climate change. The UNFCC's objective was "to achieve... stabilization of greenhouse gas concentrations in the atmosphere at a level that would prevent dangerous anthropogenic interference with the climate system." The details of how this should be accomplished were to be worked out at later international conferences, in particular, in Kyoto, Japan, in 1997.

Kyoto Conference, 1997

Kyoto—The Promise

The **Kyoto Protocol,** the treaty produced at the Kyoto Conference, was meant to be only the first step in a long and contentious battle against climate change. There were two reasons for this. First, scientists had predicted that a complete solution would require emissions reductions of 60 to 70 percent. Politically and technologically, reductions of this magnitude were impossible at this early stage of the process. Second, Kyoto applied only to the rich nations of the Old Core along with Russia and a number of countries in eastern Europe. Carbon emissions from the rest of the world were to be tackled at a later conference. The agreement acknowledged that developed nations had caused most of the problem so far and that they had the financial and technical resources to reduce emissions (see Figure 20–13). The target date for reforms was 2012, although substantial progress was to occur by 2005. A more comprehensive treaty was to replace Kyoto for the years after 2012.

Kyoto—The Problems

It soon became apparent, though, that most developed countries lacked the political will to make the economic and social changes needed to significantly reduce greenhouse gas emissions based on their 1990 levels.

Domestic politics also played a significant role in the overall failure of Kyoto. For example, the US signed on to Kyoto while Bill Clinton was president (even though he realized that he could not get the treaty ratified by the Senate). Eight years later, shortly after assuming office in 2001, President George W. Bush announced that the US was withdrawing its support for the Kyoto Protocol. This was a serious blow since the US was, at that time, the largest producer of greenhouse gases in the world and also the most influential country in the world. Similarly, in Canada, the new Conservative government that was elected in 2006 and led by Stephen Harper withdrew Canada's support for Kyoto. On the other hand, in 2007, an Australian government that opposed Kyoto was replaced by one that supported it.

The results of Kyoto have been unimpressive to say the least. An examination of the results achieved by the G8 nations illustrates the problem (see Figure 20–14).

- The US, Italy, and Japan, each with reduction targets in the 6 to 8 percent range, have seen significant increases in greenhouse gas emissions. (It is important to remember that since the US did not ratify Kyoto, it has no responsibility under international law to meet its target. This is not the case for the other G8 members who are parties to the treaty.)

- Russia's emissions declined by more than 30 percent, but this was largely because of the closure of many large, heavily polluting, industrial installations after the collapse of the communist system in the Soviet Union.

- The European Union had an overall Kyoto target of an 8 percent reduction. Individual targets were then established within the EU. Germany, Britain, and France have significantly reduced emissions. Britain and France have, in fact, reached their Kyoto targets.

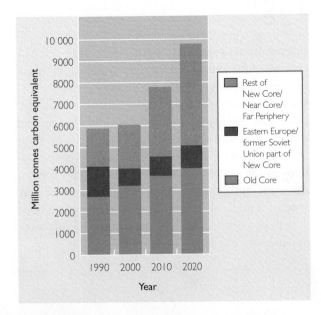

Figure 20–13 Projected global CO_2 emissions, 1990–2020

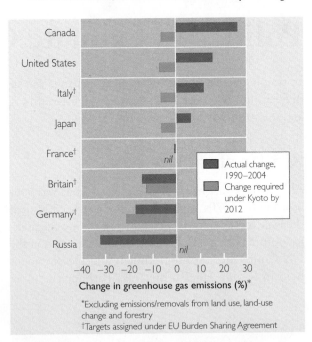

Figure 20–14 Some G8 members have done a much better job of battling climate change than others.

- Canada has had, by far, the greatest increase in emissions. Instead of a 6 percent reduction, we have had an increase of 27 percent! This increase has occurred for several reasons:
  - Population has increased.
  - Wealth and consumption have increased.

- No serious political will has existed to pass laws that would significantly reduce emissions.
- The Canadian public has not been sufficiently concerned to make lifestyle choices that would dramatically cut emissions.
- Canada's resource industries, in particular the oil sands of northern Alberta, have grown significantly to meet international demand.

What's Next Politically?

Bali Conference, 2007

Bali—The Promise

In the extended drama that is the climate change debate today, we have seen only the first few scenes of the first act. Almost 12 000 delegates, from more than 180 countries, met at the Bali Conference in 2007 to agree on the terms of the new treaty that would replace the Kyoto Accord in 2012. For several reasons, Bali would be much more important than Kyoto.

- Much more was known scientifically about what was happening to the climate and about the impacts that these changes would have on the human race.
- The Bali agreement was to be much more comprehensive than Kyoto and would involve all the world's nations, including the dramatically growing economies of China, India, and other New Core countries. In fact, in the lead-up to Bali it was learned that China's greenhouse gas emissions had come to exceed those of the US.

WORKING IT OUT   READING BETWEEN THE LINES

Diplomatic language is carefully chosen to get the idea across while avoiding wording that could be seen as harsh or controversial. This means that a diplomatic *communiqué* (statement) should be read very carefully. Consider the following. On the left is a leak of part of the proposed joint communiqué to be issued by the leaders of the G8 nations after their meeting in 2007. (Final communiqués are typically written before such meetings even start, by the way.) On the right is what the American government wanted instead.

Questions

1. The alternative wordings contain two major differences in beliefs between the EU and the US on climate change. What are these and what words are used to express each?

2. Rewrite each statement in your own words in a way that makes the intent of each more clearly understood.

Draft communiqué (largely EU-based)	American replacement
We firmly agree that resolute and concerted international action is urgently needed in order to reduce global greenhouse gas emissions... To this end we will. . .send a clear message on the further development of the international regime to combat climate change.	Addressing climate change is a long-term issue that will require global participation and a diversity of approaches to take into account differing circumstances.

Figure 20–15 Can you "read between the lines"?

- There seemed to be more flexibility on the part of the American government, since it had at least stopped denying the existence of anthropogenic climate change.

Bali—The Problems

Negotiations at the Bali Conference were heated to say the least. To understand why, it is important to understand the positions of two major groups of nations.

- **EU and its allies.** The EU has always taken climate change more seriously than any other of the world's major economic "players." The EU and its climate change allies proposed that countries should agree to greenhouse gas reductions based on scientific recommendations—that is, based on 1990 greenhouse gas levels, cuts of 25 percent to 40 percent should be made by 2020.

- **US and its allies.** The US, Japan, Russia, Canada, and other APEC (Asia-Pacific Economic Cooperation) members wanted to go in a different direction with respect to climate change. Their approach was much less rigorous than that of the EU. It was based on four principles:

Aspirational goals. Rather than setting fixed targets, the US and its allies wanted *aspirational goals.* This means that countries agreed "to aspire" to reach targets rather than be required to reach them under international law.

Energy intensity reduction. The EU and Kyoto approaches focus on absolute reductions in emissions compared to those of earlier years. APEC takes a different approach. By 2030, the US and its allies would like to see a 25 percent improvement in **energy intensity**. This term is best understood with a specific example. Suncor is one of the major producers of synthetic oil from the Alberta oil sands and is an environmental leader in the field. Figure 20–16 indicates that Suncor has reduced the amount of greenhouse gas emissions from its oil sands operations by 51 percent between 1990 and 2006. This is true if we look at emissions *on an energy intensity basis*—that is, in terms of tonnes of emissions for each cubic metre of oil produced. In contrast, Figure 20–17 shows the total amount of emissions from Suncor's oil sands operations. The difference is striking and is the basis for much of the criticism of the energy intensity approach.

Flexible national approaches. The US and its allies also accepted the principle that different countries would take different approaches to meeting emission reduction goals. For example, China would like to be able to claim credit for the impact that the One Child Policy has had on reducing its greenhouse gas emissions.

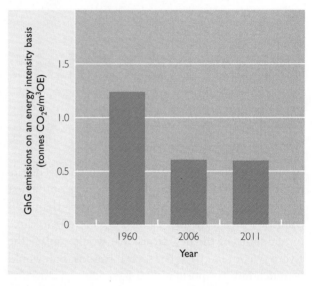

Figure 20–16 Suncor has done an impressive job of reducing the amount of greenhouse gases from its oil sands operations on a per-cubic-metre-of-oil basis. The units of this graph deserve comment. *Tonnes CO_2e/m^3OE* means tonnes of carbon dioxide equivalent produced from each cubic metre of oil equivalent. This takes into account all greenhouse gases including carbon dioxide, methane, and nitrous oxide.

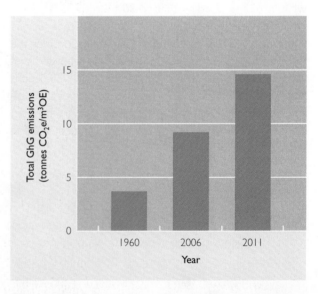

Figure 20–17 An entirely different picture emerges if we examine the total greenhouse gas emissions from Suncor's operations.

Increase in forest cover. They also agreed to an increase in forest cover of at least 20 million hectares. This increase in the size of this carbon sink would remove the equivalent of about 11 percent of the world's carbon emissions (as of 2004).

Canada's climate change policies have been rather fluid in recent years. The Liberal government, in power from 1993 to 2006, signed on to Kyoto, but did little to ensure that targets would be met. The Liberals were replaced by a minority Conservative government in 2006 that had even less interest in passing dramatic regulations to control climate change. The new government found itself in a politically difficult position. On one hand, a large majority of Canadians wanted something done about climate change. On the other, the base of Conservative support was in oil-rich Alberta whose rapidly growing oil sands industry was the biggest (and fastest-growing) source of greenhouse gas emissions in the country. Stringent carbon emission limitations would hit Alberta and its economy hard.

The Conservative government was more comfortable with the flexible APEC approach than with the strict standards of Kyoto. At Bali, Canada frequently won the "Fossil of the Day" award—given as a show of disapproval by environmental groups—because its policy was seen as a significant roadblock to developing a strong, new treaty.

The final agreement from Bali was a compromise, the success of which cannot be determined for a number of years. A new treaty "with teeth" that would commit countries to specific actions was not possible—the US and its powerful group of allies were not prepared to go that far. Instead, there was agreement on a "road map" for further discussions in 2008 and 2009. These discussions would be between two groups. The first group includes the 37 nations that had agreed in the Kyoto Accord to reduce emissions—this group includes Canada but not the US, since the US did not ratify Kyoto. This group would attempt to agree to further reductions and would be "guided by, but not bound to" the EU's goal of 25 to 40 percent reductions (compared to 1990) by 2020. It is interesting to note that at Bali, Canada's delegation had tried to have these numbers dropped from the agreement.

The second group includes all the nations of the world, including those in the first group, along with major emitters like the US and the BRIC nations (**B**razil, **R**ussia, **I**ndia, **C**hina). This larger group has the difficult task of finding the common ground needed for the kind of agreement that proved so impossible to reach at Bali and in other climate change negotiations.

Many contentious issues must be settled. These include

- What emissions limitations should be applied to countries with emerging economies? How should these limitations be related to those of developed countries?

- Are there emissions-limitation approaches that are unique to poorer countries?

- What sort of compensation should developing countries get for actions that harm their economies but help reduce global warming (for example, if they do not cut large tracts of rainforest to maintain carbon sinks)?

- What assistance should be provided to poorer countries that suffer climate-change-related damage, such as drought, severe storms, loss of land to rising sea levels, and shortages of drinking water?

A key ingredient in evaluating the progress of these talks can be found in a guideline agreed to in Bali. Countries are to take "measurable, reportable, and verifiable nationally appropriate" steps to fight climate change. To understand the significance of this statement, look carefully at each of the terms. To decide whether Bali was a success or failure will depend on the discussions that occur from the "road map" and whether a new international climate change agreement "with teeth" emerges.

The "Governator's" Role in Fighting Climate Change

You may well ask why the state of California deserves attention here, separate from that given to the US (see Figure 20–18). The reason is that this giant state (with a population and economy larger than Canada's) is taking a dramatically different route than the US federal government and is providing a North American model for aggressive climate change policies. Governor Arnold Schwarzenegger is proposing that his state reduce its emissions to 2000 levels by 2010; to 1990 levels by 2020; and to 80 percent below its 1990 levels by 2050. As part of this reform, California has passed legislation that requires cars sold in the state to reduce their greenhouse gas emissions by 30 percent by 2016.

To achieve this dramatic goal, Schwarzenegger is proposing that emissions be cut on a "full-cycle" basis. Consider the example of the oil industry. If emission cuts were to be applied only to activities carried out within California, the easiest way for a company to reduce its emissions would be to close its oil wells and refineries in California and bring in gasoline and other products from other jurisdictions that did not have such strict emission standards. To prevent this from happening, California will count the carbon emissions at all stages of the production and distribution process—even if this happens outside the state. For example, oil companies operating in California might be trying to decide whether to buy crude oil from Mexico or Canada's oil sands. They would have to consider the amount of carbon emissions in each case before deciding which oil to buy. Producers in Canada (and Mexico) would have to reduce their emissions or lose this huge market. As a result, California's policies would have an impact far beyond its borders.

There are other reasons why Schwarzenegger's climate change policies are having a significant impact outside the state. More than 20 other states have adopted (or plan to adopt) at least some of the California automotive standards for fuel economy and emissions reduction. There is some possibility that Canadian provinces, led by Ontario and British Columbia, may follow suit. Also, the size of the market in California means that manufacturers have a choice. They can make two models—one for California and a

different one for the rest of the country, which is costly and inefficient—or they can sell the same, climate-change-fighting model everywhere.

What may be happening in the US is an "end run" around the inaction of the federal government. In addition to the actions of California and its state allies, the mayors of many of the largest cities in the country are providing leadership in the fight against climate change. A future American president, elected on an environmental platform, may find it relatively easy to piggyback on the California reforms. The result is that the US could end up becoming a leader in fighting climate change.

Figure 20–18 This 2006 cartoon, showing California Governor Schwarzenegger and US President Bush, illustrates the enormous disconnect in the United States over climate change.

Possible Solutions to the Climate Change Problem

Once there is agreement on the need to fight climate change, the next step would be to decide on the best way to do it. There will not be one solution to the threat we face. Rather, there will be a complex set of solutions—economic, political, technological, and lifestyle-related. The great challenge will be to solve the problems with the minimum amount of economic and social disruption. Certainly individuals can (and should) make lifestyle changes that will reduce the impact that they have on climate change, but more will be needed. Broadly speaking, three different approaches are being considered.

Cap and Trade System

There are several steps in setting up and using a **cap and trade system**.

1. First is the creation of a cap on greenhouse gas emissions by a regulating body. For example, a national government might decide that the emissions from a particular industry have to be reduced by 20 percent.

2. Responsibility for this reduction is then divided among all of the companies in this industry. It is likely that different cuts would be required of

different companies based on their existing efficiency. This would reflect the fact that some companies are already emitting fewer greenhouse gases on an energy intensity basis.

3. Companies can meet their obligations in one of two ways.

   a) A company could reduce its emissions enough to meet its targets. If it exceeded its target, it could sell the rights to emit greenhouse gases in a market something like a stock market or commodity exchange. Such exchanges already exist but are still quite small.

   b) If a company could not meet its target or decided it was too costly to do so, it could buy the rights to emit more on the emissions exchange. If many companies had exceeded their targets, this would be relatively inexpensive; if not, emissions credits might be very expensive, and it would be cheaper to actually reduce emissions.

4. The cost of cutting emissions or buying emissions credits would be passed on to customers of the companies—for example, on your electricity bill or at the gas pump. The higher costs for the things we buy would encourage us to use less.

Carbon Tax

There are several steps in setting up and using a **carbon tax** system.

1. The amount of emissions created by the production of every product and service would have to be determined. For example, there would be an emissions amount assigned to a chocolate bar. This number might appear on the label like the nutrition summary that we now see.

2. Next, a dollar amount (the tax rate) would be assigned to each tonne of greenhouse gas emissions. The amount would have to be high enough to encourage conservation so that emissions would be significantly reduced. For example, let's assume that

   a) A family uses 1000 kilowatt hours (kWh) of electricity each month.

   b) Electricity costs 12¢ per kWh, or $120 per month.

   c) Using this amount of electricity results in the emission of about 69 kilograms of CO_2. (The amount of emissions in a particular location would depend on the mix of electrical generation methods used.)

   d) If a tax of 1¢ per kWh was imposed, the monthly electricity bill would rise by ($0.01 × 1000) $10 per month. Do you think that this level of carbon tax would be high enough to encourage people to cut electricity use and, as a result, cut emissions? If not, the tax would need to be higher.

3. The money raised by a carbon tax could be used to reduce other forms of taxation like income taxes and sales taxes.

Geo-engineering

Geo-engineering is a blanket term used to describe a wide range of technological solutions to the problems of climate change. Geo-engineered solutions focus on reducing the input of solar radiation into the atmosphere and on dealing with excessive greenhouse gases once they have been produced. Some solutions seem quite practical, with current technologies.

■ **Geological sequestration** (the act of locking away). This approach seems closest to being put into large-scale use and may be of particular value in reducing carbon dioxide emissions from Alberta's oil sands. The principle is simple. Carbon dioxide would be collected from a source (for example, a coal-fired generating plant or oil sands conversion plant) and shipped through a pipeline to an area with suitable geology (see Figure 20–19). Here it would be pumped into the ground below a layer of impermeable rock

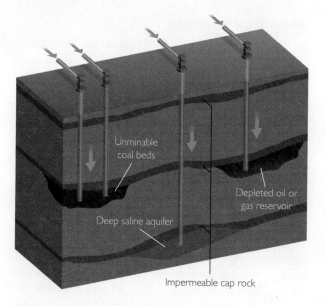

Figure 20–19 Carbon sequestration could become a major weapon in the battle against climate change.

where it would be trapped indefinitely. (Unlike other geo-engineering schemes, the technology to do this is not entirely new. Natural gas and water are routinely pumped back into rock strata to increase oil production.)

- **Iron fertilization of the oceans.** This proposal suggests that instead of planting trees as a carbon sink, we should fertilize the growth of plankton in the world's oceans. Many parts of the ocean do not have enough iron for optimum plankton growth. Sprinkling finely powdered iron in these areas would dramatically increase the density of plankton. Extra plankton would remove a great deal of carbon dioxide from the atmosphere.

- **Increasing the earth's albedo.** An increase of the earth's albedo of between 1.5 percent and 2 percent would balance the increase of the earth's temperature caused by greenhouse gases because more solar radiation would be reflected into space. One group has suggested that this could be done by blasting fine droplets of seawater, by a fleet of 50 to 100 ships, to create banks of reflective, low-lying clouds. This would require about ten kilograms of water per second. These ships would operate in polar regions in the summer, moving from Arctic to Antarctic waters and back each year.

- **Sending carbon dioxide into space.** Much further from even being tested is a proposal by a Canadian physicist, Alfred Wong, to use the earth's magnetic field in the Arctic to transport excess carbon dioxide into space.

Geo-engineering solutions can be evaluated by considering several factors.

- The idea has to work. Many geo-engineering solutions sound wonderful but exist only in the creator's mind. Much research and testing would need to be done, and time is limited.

- Side effects would have to be minimal.

- The solution has to be scalable—it must be able to cope with ever-increasing amounts of greenhouse gases.

- It has to be cheaper than just reducing greenhouse gases emissions at the source.

Geo-engineered solutions to climate change often appeal to people because they do not require significant lifestyle changes by ordinary citizens, nor operational changes by companies (except for carbon sequestration). The problem is solved by "someone else, somewhere else." These solutions are also popular among those who are not fully committed to the idea that climate change is a major problem that will require a concerted, global effort to solve. None of these technological solutions are available now (nor will be soon). They would postpone society having to do anything until some time in the future while various geo-engineered solutions are developed and tested. Many experts suggest that we do not have the luxury of waiting.

Climate Change and You

Ultimately, what will happen with climate change comes down to you—and more than six billion other "yous" who share our planet. No matter what...

You will have to deal with the impacts of climate change. These will vary enormously.

- Canada may accept large numbers of climate refugees, which will change the size and composition of the population.

- There may be more severe natural hazards.

- There may be more wars and other conflicts.

You will pay the cost of fighting climate change.

- Food products may be more expensive.

- A cap and trade system will increase the cost of the products you buy (though it will be hidden in the price).

- A carbon tax would be more obvious to you. It might be listed on your bill in the same way that PST and GST are now.

- The cost of geo-engineered solutions would be paid for by governments, hence higher taxes; or paid for by companies, hence higher prices.

- The cost of building sea walls around coastal cities would be passed on to all citizens of the country.

You will be exposed to different lifestyle options.

- Climate change will create (and destroy) various career options.

- We will have to change our attitudes toward consumption—switching to more efficient light bulbs is only a start.

- Your recreational interests may have to change.

- Big SUVs and powerful sports cars will become a thing of the past.

You will have to decide what political party to support based, at least partly, on the climate change policies they support.

Chapter Questions

Knowledge and Understanding

1. **a)** In your own words, explain Malcolm Gladwell's idea of "tipping points." Include the following in your answer: the law of the few, stickiness, power of context, and early and late majority stages.

   b) How does the idea of tipping points apply to climate change?

2. Summarize how the greenhouse effect works, the chemicals involved, and how the production of anthropogenic greenhouse gases increases temperatures.

3. **a)** Define carbon sink, carbon source, and fixed carbon.

   b) Draw a simplified sketch of the carbon cycle, focusing on identifying the sinks, sources, and processes that create and release fixed carbon.

4. **a)** What is a feedback loop? Give a definition, not an example.

   b) Describe, in your own words, how one of the feedback loops mentioned in this chapter works.

   c) Describe an example of a feedback loop, other than the ones given in this chapter, that contributes to global warming. Use a diagram to explain your description.

5. **a)** How successful was the Kyoto Protocol in reducing climate change?

   b) Why is this the case?

6. What is meant by the term "energy intensity?" Why is this a fundamentally important concept in the fight against climate change?

7. Compare the EU approach to fighting climate change to the APEC approach. In your answer, consider at least the following: what countries support each approach, what are the similarities between each, and what are the differences?

8. Create a timeline to show both international efforts to fight climate change and how Canada's policies regarding climate change have changed over the years.

9. **a)** In what ways was the Bali conference a success for those who wanted to fight climate change? In what ways was it a failure?

   b) Why were these results virtually inevitable?

Thinking

10. **a)** Identify at least six cities, on at least three continents, that are located barely above sea level and would be threatened by rising sea levels. You may want to check an atlas if you are not sure of these.

    b) Why is it common for large cities to be located in such areas?

11. This chapter mentioned three reasons why environmental refugees are created. For each of the three reasons, give examples of environmental refugees, and name the countries affected.

12. **a)** Briefly summarize the impacts that global warming will have on the earth. In your summary, do not forget to include the impacts that are part of feedback loops.

    b) Describe how significant each of these impacts will be on Canada compared to the world in general.

    c) On balance, will Canada be affected by global warming to a greater or lesser extent than most countries?

    d) Will the impacts, on balance, be positive or negative for Canada?

13. **a)** What was your reaction when you learned (in this chapter or previously) that Canada had done the least well of any of the G8 nations in meeting its Kyoto commitments?

    b) Why do you think you had this reaction?

    c) Give two reasons why Canada did so poorly in reducing its greenhouse gas emissions.

14. **a)** Owners of large Hummer SUVs have reported that their vehicles have been vandalized, that they are subject to rude gestures when they are driving, or that people openly criticize them. Why might this be happening?

    b) Are such actions ever justified?

15. The Green Party of Canada thinks that there should be a 12 cents per litre carbon tax on gasoline. Would you support such a tax? Why or why not?

Communication

16. What can you do in your own life (and your family's life) to contribute to a reduction in the greenhouse gases that you emit?

17. Imagine that you are a speechwriter for a major politician in Canada or another country. The politician you work for tends to support whichever side of an issue the polls suggest the public favours. The problem is that polls on climate change are evenly split between those who support the EU approach and those who support the APEC approach. Your politician, wants two speeches—one in support of each approach. Each speech should take no more than one minute to deliver and strongly support why each approach makes the most sense for the country. Start writing!

18. There was a common expression from the 1970s, *"If you are not part of the solution, you are part of the problem."* Organize a round-table discussion group to reach a consensus on short-term and long-term ways to reduce greenhouse gases.

Application

19. If you are reading this question before the Copenhagen Conference in 2009, answer question a). If you are reading it after the conference, answer question b).

a) What has happened to the Bali "road map" negotiations since this book was published? In your answer, consider the amount of progress that has been achieved by both groups of countries.

b) From what you have read, did the Copenhagen Conference produce a climate change treaty that is both fair and likely to have a significant impact on climate change? If a treaty was signed at this conference (or afterward), has it been ratified by major climate change players like the US, EU nations, BRIC nations, Japan, and Canada?

20. a) In your own words, summarize the three different approaches to climate change: cap and trade, carbon tax, and geo-engineering.

b) What is your personal reaction to each of these approaches? Which one(s) do you think have the best potential for curbing climate change?

21. The effects of climate change, along with the reforms needed to minimize the amount of climate change that does occur, are likely to be central themes for the remainder of your life. Work with a partner to prepare a summary of each of these aspects of life in Canada in the 21st century. One person should focus on the effects of climate change and the other on reforms. You should consider the nature of the effect/reform, along with how significant it will be and when it will have its greatest impact. Your teacher will tell you what kind of product you are to create. **S**

UNIT 5 CONFLICT AND COOPERATION

What do you see here? These soldiers may be under the control of a warlord who is threatening a neighbour. Or they may be UN peacekeepers providing security in a conflict-ridden country. In this case, it is the latter. These peacekeepers in Haiti are waiting for orders.

CHAPTER 21

An Introduction to Geopolitics

Key Terms

geopolitics
nation state
global village
sovereignty
ideology
democracy
authoritarian
nationalism
communism
Cold War
imperialism
containment
sphere of influence

What does this image of a military parade tell you about the societies in which these events are held? How might the policies of these societies balance with international organizations such as the UN Security Council, shown below?

Key Questions

By the end of this chapter you will be able to answer the following questions.

■ What is the meaning of the term "geopolitics"?

■ How did Canada's border come into being?

■ What are the characteristics of a nation state?

■ What are the differences between the ideologies of democracy and authoritarianism?

■ How did the Cold War shape international relations during the last half of the 20th century?

■ Is the world becoming more democratic?

What Is Geopolitics?

Generally speaking, politics is the administration and management of state affairs. More specifically, politics is the decision-making process of government. A multitude of geographical factors come into play when governments make decisions on issues such as determining their borders, resolving international conflict, forming military alliances, striking trade agreements, developing and protecting natural resources, or controlling access to sea and air routes. Population size, topography, climate, economy, resource base, and unique environmental characteristics will influence many political decisions.

Geography often directly influences a political decision. For instance, to provide economical telephone, radio, and TV links across Canada's vast area, the Canadian government decided to develop a non-military satellite communications system. At other times, a political decision will directly affect geography. For example, Canada passed legislation to restrict the release of airborne pollutants that acidify lakes. The interplay of geography and politics, on either a national or international level, is known as **geopolitics**. This chapter introduces some basic concepts that will help you analyze geopolitical issues.

The Nation State

The **nation state** is comparatively new in recorded history. The concept originated in Europe during the Renaissance (late 1400s to early 1600s). It evolved as historical events, such as the French and American revolutions, changed people's views on how they wished to be governed. Prior to the Renaissance, the concept of an independent nation ruled by a government that controlled events within clearly marked boundaries did not exist. Political power usually resided in the hands of a single ruler (or dynasty) who exercised control over various groups of people living within loosely defined borders. Examples include the empires of Alexander the Great, Genghis Khan, ancient Rome, and the Katsina Kingdom in what is now northern Nigeria.

Nation State Formation

Most nation states were created between 1900 and 1999 (see Figure 21–1). Many of them resulted from the decolonization of Africa, Asia, the Caribbean, and the Middle East after World War II. In the 1990s, a number of new nation states were established when the Soviet Union broke up.

Time Period	Asia and Oceania	The Americas	Central, Eastern, Southern Europe	Central, Southern Africa	Middle East, North Africa	Northwest, Western Europe	Total
Pre-1000	0	0	0	0	0	3	3
1000–1599	2	0	1	1	1	7	12
1600–1799	3	1	0	0	0	3	7
1800–1899	2	20	2	1	0	4	29
1900–1950	12	1	6	1	6	5	31
1951–1975	11	7	0	40	10	2	70
1976–1999	13	6	15	5	1	0	40
2000 +	1	0	1	0	0	0	2
Total	44	35	25	48	18	24	194

Figure 21–1 Historical and regional pattern of nation-state formation. As of 2008, East Timor (2002) and Kosovo (2008) were the only new nations to have been created in the 21st century.

The Role Played by National Sovereignty

A nation state is more than just a political entity. It is a sizable group of people who have adopted a unique common identity as fellow citizens, and who live together under one government within a certain geographical area. One nation state is set apart from another nation state by its history, language, customs, religion, ethnic composition, and unique sense of community.

A nation state has political autonomy, that is, it is able to create policies and enforce laws within its borders without interference from other states. In other words, the nation state has **sovereignty**. Sovereignty is a legal concept that, according to international law, recognizes that the authority of a state is not subject to legal control by any other state (see Figure 21–2).

The extent of the sea ice in Canada's Arctic region is diminishing as a result of climate change. Since transit through the Northwest Passage may become a reality as a result, a number of countries, among them the United States and Russia, consider this passage to be international waters as opposed to Canadian territorial waters (see Figure 21–3). Canada's sovereignty is currently being challenged in the Arctic. You can read more about the conflicting claims surrounding Arctic Ocean sovereignty in Chapter 22.

The sovereignty of one nation state is differentiated from that of another by a border. Borders mark the limit of a nation's laws and security, and at the same time, brand a specific geographical area with a national identity. When the armed forces of one country cross the border of another without being invited to do so, they threaten that country's national sovereignty. A threat to national sovereignty often results in an armed clash.

In the mid-1990s, the United Nations (whose members are sovereign nations) voted against becoming

Figure 21–3 The Coast Guard icebreaker *Terry Fox* sits in the waters of Lancaster Sound, Nunavut, at the eastern gates of the Northwest Passage.

involved in the internal conflicts in the former Yugoslavia. Even though the UN knew that genocide was occurring, it felt that Yugoslavia's sovereignty could not be breached. National sovereignty became a factor in the UN's failure to protect people from human-rights abuses. This was ironic since the UN Secretary-General had stated in 1991 that governments could no longer hide behind the barrier of national sovereignty and "massively...violate" the human rights of their citizens.

GLOBALIZATION

Globalization has given rise to a number of forces that are weakening the concept of national sovereignty.

Is the weakening of national sovereignty a good or bad thing?

Globalization has given rise to a number of forces that are weakening the concept of national sovereignty. For instance, high-tech communications systems have allowed people from many countries to communicate as though they lived in the same neighborhood, or in a **global village**. Furthermore, national governments have a limited ability to control (that is, exert sovereignty over) the Internet and other communications technologies.

Agreements such as NAFTA (the North American Free Trade Agreement) and ASEAN (Association of Southeast Asian Nations) have created trading blocs in which national borders do not limit the movement of goods. Most countries of the European Union use a single currency, the euro, and have done away with border checkpoints. Suggestions have been made that Canada, the US, and Mexico should also have a common currency. Western viewpoints have been transported the world over and have eroded cultural differences, making it difficult for countries to retain their national character.

Figure 21–2 As a sovereign entity, a country decides who is allowed in, who is kept out, who is entitled to work there, and how long a visitor can remain within its borders.

HOW BORDERS BECOME BORDERS

Borders are sometimes based on easily recognizable natural features such as shorelines, rivers, lakes, deserts, swamps, and mountain ranges. If a mountain range acts as a boundary, the actual border often follows the height of land that separates the drainage basins on either side. This is the case with the Andes mountain range that separates Chile from Argentina. In other cases, borders may be arbitrary, that is, determined purely on the basis of someone's point of view or purpose. European powers in colonial Africa frequently imposed arbitrary borders as they pieced different territories together to make colonies. Because they divided or united different cultural groups without consideration for the possible consequences, they gave rise to conflicts that continue to this day. For example, Nigeria was given borders that did not take into account tribal and linguistic groups in these areas. As a result, the country has experienced civil war and several tribal-based coups over the years.

Sometimes borders are determined as a result of negotiations between the countries concerned. In 1846, the US stated that it had a better claim than the British to the Oregon Territory and a part of present-day British Columbia, even though the two countries had been jointly occupying the area since the early 1800s (see Figure 21–4). The annexation, or takeover, of the Oregon Territory was seen by some Americans as part of their "Manifest Destiny," in which the US had a mission to expand and spread its form of democracy to all parts of North America. Many US citizens, wishing to set the border at 54°40'N latitude, took up the slogan "Fifty-Four Forty or Fight." Rather than fight, the two countries negotiated the border at the 49th parallel in 1848.

1. How would Canada and the US be different if
   a) the US got what it claimed in 1846?
   b) Great Britain got what it claimed?

2. Research other border disputes between Canada and the US and explain how they were resolved.

3. Sometimes arbitrary borders do not work very well. Take the case of Point Roberts, Washington (see Figure 21–5). What problems do residents of Seattle, Washington, face if they want to visit friends and relatives in Point Roberts?

4. What problems do residents of Point Roberts face?

5. Would it be easier if Point Roberts became part of Canada? Is this likely to happen? Explain.

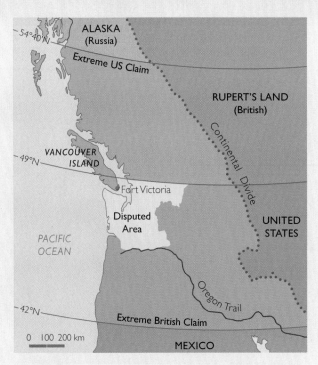

Figure 21–4 The US and Great Britain had territorial and commercial interests, especially in the fur trade, in the Oregon Territory. Each country made territorial claims.

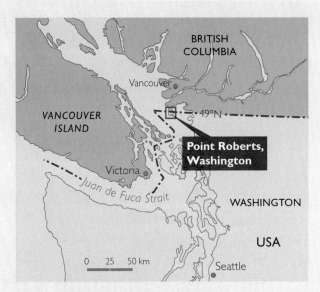

Figure 21–5 Point Roberts, Washington: a geopolitical oddity

Research the answers to the following questions.

6. Canada's border with the US is based on physical features, geopolitical decisions, and grid lines (see Figure 21–6). Borders between countries are often flashpoints for disputes. Examine Figure 21–6 and explain the reason for each of the numbered parts of the border, and name the boundary.

7. Research the history of the border between France and Germany since the late 1800s.

a) Why has the border changed position throughout history?

b) Why is the border located where it is today?

8. Examine the causes, impact, and current status of the following border disputes:

a) between China and India

b) between India and Pakistan

c) between two other countries (for example, Ethiopia and Somalia, Ethiopia and Eritrea)

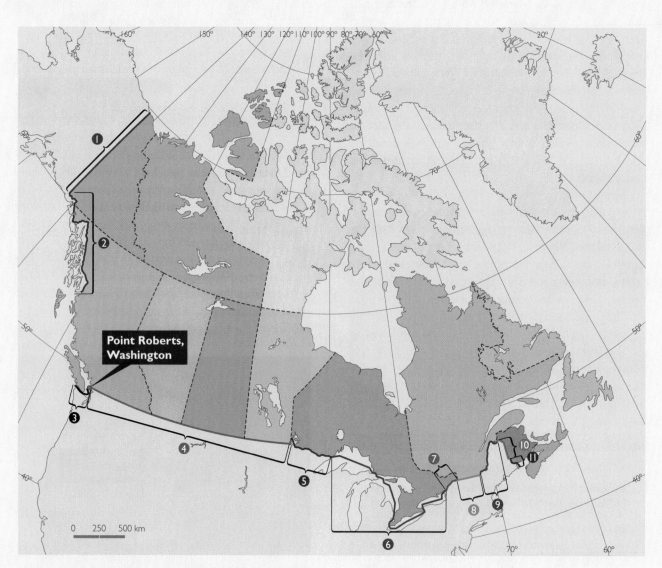

Figure 21–6 Different sections of the border between Canada and the US were established over time by political authorities using a number of techniques and dispute mechanisms.

What Is an Ideology?

An **ideology** is a set of ideas and beliefs that a nation uses as the basis for its way of life, its political and economic systems, and its social goals. A political system may be based upon one ideology or a combination of ideologies.

A country's political system cannot always be determined by examining its name. For instance, one would never guess from the name that the People's Republic of Korea (North Korea) has been ruled since its creation by a father and son who have been treated more like monarchs than leaders of a supposedly *egalitarian* (meaning all people have equal rights) communist state.

Although today's nation states have ideologies based on their unique history and experience, each subscribes to one of two basic ideologies: democracy or authoritarianism (see Figures 21–7 and 21–8).

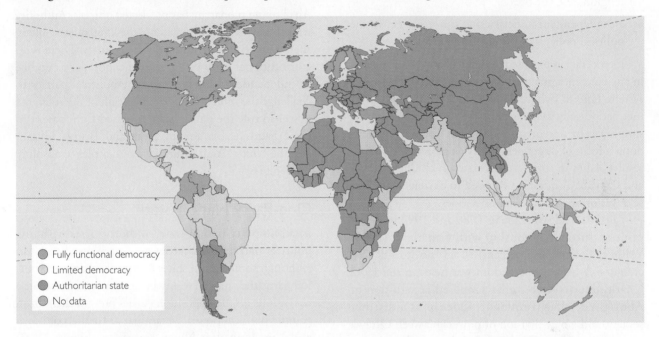

Figure 21–7 In 1976, there were 42 fully functional democracies, 49 limited democracies, and 68 authoritarian states.

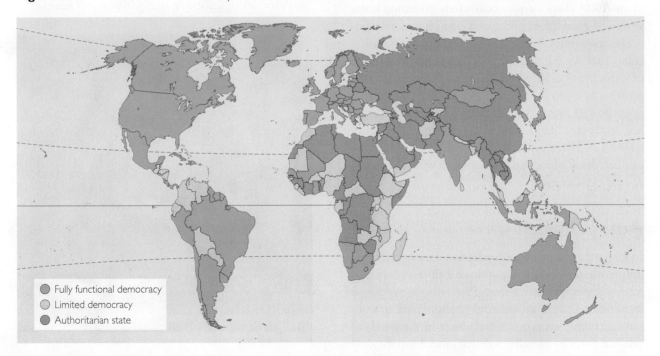

Figure 21–8 In 2007, there were 90 fully functional democracies, 58 limited democracies, and 45 authoritarian states. What changes over the years are evident from the 1976 and 2007 maps?

Democratic States

In a representative **democracy**, citizens exercise political power by electing officials who govern in accordance with their wishes. Essential features of democracy include

- a decision-making system based on the rule of the majority of citizens
- accountability of the government to the electorate
- guarantees for the freedoms of expression, assembly, religion, and the press
- an independent judiciary that is not subject to the political policies of the government in power

Democracy is practised in different ways. The Greeks in ancient times practised direct democracy. Under this system, citizens (who did not include women or slaves) met periodically to make political decisions, and gave a simple yes or no vote to a question. Today, a referendum, a form of direct democracy, is sometimes used to resolve issues in some nation states, including the US and Canada. A question is posed to citizens who then vote yes or no, and the majority rules.

Quebec held referenda in 1980 and 1995 to determine its future relationship with Canada; in 1995, a slim majority (50.6 percent) voted "no" to full sovereignty. A federal referendum was held on the 1992 Charlottetown Accord that proposed recognition of Aboriginal self-government, Quebec as a distinct society, and a new division of powers between Ottawa and the provinces. (The accord was rejected.)

In 2007, there were approximately 90 nation states with well-established political systems based on democratic principles. There were an additional 58 nation states that were limited democracies. Limited forms of democracy exist where the armed forces are in a position to assert control if the democratically elected government moves in a direction that the military leaders do not like. This was the case in Fiji in 2006, when a military coup removed the elected prime minister from office and replaced him with an interim military government.

Authoritarianism

In 2007, there were 45 **authoritarian** nation states that limited the political participation of their citizens. These states often stifle dissent from those who speak out in an effort to change the political system. Political, military, and religious power usually rests in the hands of one individual or a small group that often heads the only political party allowed in the country. Many states, but particularly authoritarian states, often rely on stirring up

nationalism, an extreme devotion to the country, in order to obtain the loyalty and support of their citizens.

A number of freedoms that Canadians take for granted are usually missing in authoritarian states. These may include equality before the law, the freedoms of speech and association, and the freedom to create opposition parties. Authoritarianism may take the form of an absolute monarchy, a one-party nation state, or a military-run state.

Absolute Monarchy

An absolute monarchy has no elected officials. Authority rests entirely with the monarch—the king, queen, sultan, sheikh, or emir, depending on the country. There is no constitutional form of government, popular assembly, or independent judiciary, nor any political parties to challenge the monarch. Upon the death of the ruler, the power to rule the nation state is passed from parent to child. Saudi Arabia, Jordan, Swaziland, Brunei, Oman, and the United Arab Emirates are examples of absolute monarchies.

One-Party Nation State

In a one-party nation state, authority rests with one political party; other parties are not allowed to exist. Although some nation states have more than one political party, they may in reality be one-party states because restrictions on the opposition parties prevent them from gaining political power. Muammar al-Kadhafi of Libya and Kim Jong-il of North Korea (see Figure 21–9) are examples of leaders of one-party nation states.

Figure 21–9 Kim Jong-il became the leader of North Korea in 1994.

Military Authoritarianism

In a military-run state, the power to govern rests in the hands of one or more military leaders who refuse to give up power or have seized power from an elected government. In 1990, for example, the existing military government of Myanmar (formerly called Burma) refused to relinquish power after the main opposition party won the election. Since that time, the military government has suppressed all opposition and wielded absolute power. In 2007, thousands of monks and their supporters participated in pro-democracy marches against the military government. The government cracked down on the protestors with lethal force, resulting in a number of deaths and injuries.

Since 1960, more than 50 states in Latin America and central and southern Africa have experienced at least one military *coup d'état* (illegal seizure of power). In some countries, such as Algeria, Chile, Indonesia, Mozambique, Thailand, and Iraq, the military plays an influential role in running the country even though it doesn't form the government.

Religious Nation State

In a religious nation state, spiritual leaders whose religious beliefs form the political framework hold political power. Iran is an example of a religious nation state. The spiritual leaders in Iran provide guidance to the political parties, whose policies are formulated according to Islamic religious law (Shari'ah). Shari'ah is regarded as the expression of divine will and is concerned not only with people's ethical standards of behaviour, but also with what they are bound by law to do. In this latter sense especially, Iran is very different from both Western democracies and other Islamic nation states whose citizens formulate the laws through their elected representatives.

Afghanistan between 1996 and 2001—when it was under the rule of the Taliban—is an example of a nation state in which extreme religious beliefs dominated the political process. Television and non-religious music were illegal, and it was against the law for women to work, or attend school. It was also illegal for women to appear outside the home without being completely covered. Men were required by law to wear beards. Many Muslims considered this a mistaken interpretation of Shari'ah, and in most countries where Islam is the state religion, Shari'ah has been interpreted in a way that permits a modern lifestyle.

Communist States

Communist ideology is based on the writings of 19th-century German social scientists Karl Marx and Friedrich Engels, who believed that the ruling class should be overthrown by the working class. The result of such a revolution would be a classless society in which citizens would collectively own all land, capital, and means of production. Many nation states have called their governments "communist," but true communism as described by Marx and Engels has never been achieved. Instead, the **communism** that developed from this ideology saw one-party states in which the Communist party held power through the use of propaganda, state-controlled education, and secret police. Public criticism of the government was not permitted and the rights of the state took precedence over those of the individual.

After World War II, the Soviets set up communist governments in Eastern Europe. Communist nation states later developed in China, North Korea, North Vietnam, Albania, Yugoslavia, and Cuba. In each case, strong leaders ran the country as dictators. Countries that are controlled by Communist parties under a single-party system today include the People's Republic of China, Cuba, Laos, North Korea, and Vietnam. China, Laos, and Vietnam, however, are no longer true communist states because they allow varying degrees of private ownership.

Geopolitics and Conflict

Between the mid-1940s and the end of the 1980s, international politics was shaped to a large extent by the intense rivalry, distrust, and suspicion between two groups of countries and their differing political ideologies. These were the democratic capitalist US and its allies, and the communist Soviet Union (USSR) and its allies. The US and the Soviet Union were known as superpowers. Countries that were not formally committed to either group, or power bloc, were known as neutrals. If they were part of what was known at the time as the Third World (developing countries), they were called non-aligned nations.

The Cold War

The term **Cold War** was used to describe the fact that relations between the two power blocs had deteriorated to the point of war, but without the actual occurrence of fighting. This situation was essentially the result of the basic incompatibility of the democratic and communist ideologies, combined with the international politics of power. The democratic countries charged the communist countries with spreading communism by *fomenting* (stirring up) revolution in unstable regions. The communist countries accused their rivals of **imperialism**—trade with, and exploitation of, developing countries through political and military pressure without assuming direct political control. To some degree, both charges were true, as each power endeavoured to enlarge its influence throughout the world (see Figure 21–10).

After World War II, **containment** became the foreign policy of the democratic states. The object of this policy was to stop the expansionism of the Soviet Union (and communism) by containing it within its current geographical boundaries. The Marshall Plan, discussed in Chapter 13, and the formation of the NATO military alliance were used to stop Soviet expansion in Western Europe.

During the Cold War, each of the two superpowers had its own **sphere of influence**, an area over which it exerted economic, military, and political influence. The US sphere of influence was in the Americas and the Soviet sphere of influence was in Eastern Europe.

Figure 21–10 During the Cold War, May Day celebrations in Moscow's Red Square were seen by the West as an attempt to demonstrate the superiority of the communist ideology.

There was an understanding that one superpower would not interfere in the other's sphere of influence. This changed in 1962 when the Soviet Union encroached upon the US sphere of influence by placing nuclear missiles in Cuba. Fortunately, a standoff between the two sides was defused before nuclear war broke out.

Rather than risk nuclear war again by facing each other directly, the superpowers began to compete in other ways. They supplied foreign aid, including technological assistance and military support, to non-aligned countries around the world. Where civil war occurred during the 1970s and 1980s (for example, in Angola, Mozambique, and in the Somali–Ethiopian War), each superpower provided money, weapons, military advisers, and sometimes *proxy* (substitute) troops from other countries to the side it supported. In effect, each superpower was trying to enlarge its sphere of influence without a direct confrontation. An example of proxy troops was the deployment of 1900 Cuban troops to support the pro-communist faction in Angola

One of the most visible competitions between the Cold War combatants was the "space race" of the 1960s. At the time, successful space exploits were viewed as demonstrations of the superiority of one political ideology over another. In fact, Cold War geopolitics was the most significant factor behind the race to the moon. Since the Soviet Union had been the first to launch a satellite and to send a human into space, the US was determined to put the first person on the moon. It spent huge amounts of money developing its space program, and when it succeeded in its goal in 1969, the geopolitical victory was monumental. Today, China is developing its space program and plans to travel to the moon to demonstrate, among other things, the superiority of its own political ideology.

After the Cold War

The Cold War gave way to détente, a relaxation of tension between democratic and communist nations, because they realized that nuclear war would probably end in disaster for both sides (see Chapter 25). With the breakup of the Soviet Union in 1990, the Cold War became a thing of the past. The former Soviet states adopted various forms of government, abandoning the command economy, in which the government controlled the supply and price of goods, in favour of free market economies in which the price of goods is determined by supply and demand. Communist China realized that a certain amount of private enterprise would boost its economy, and that some increase in personal freedoms did not necessarily threaten its power.

GLOBALIZATION

China sees globalization as the key to its economic development.

Why does China see globalization in this way?

China sees globalization as the key to its economic development. It has allowed private ownership of many businesses, including large, previously state-owned enterprises, such as the state oil company. It has encouraged corporations from around the world to open manufacturing plants and offices. As of 2006, 450 firms of the Fortune 500, the top 500 US public corporations, had invested in China. Relations between communist and non-communist countries had improved as the desire for increased trade grew and took precedence over political rivalry.

The end of the Cold War, however, did not bring an end to geopolitical conflicts. In 1990, the Gulf War erupted when Iraq invaded Kuwait. In 2001, the war in Afghanistan to remove the Taliban began. In 2002, Canada joined this war as part of a NATO mission. A second Gulf War occurred in 2003 when a US-led coalition invaded Iraq to remove Saddam Hussein. Major civil wars raged in Africa throughout the 1990s and into the 21st century; those in Sierra Leone and the Democratic Republic of Congo, the Darfur region of Sudan, Somalia, and Uganda displaced millions of people and also involved many neighbouring countries. India and Pakistan continued to dispute ownership of the Kashmir region, and there are fears that nuclear weapons might be used in this conflict. Reports of geopolitical issues such as international disputes over trade policies, environmental degradation, migration, human rights, and Aboriginal self-determination have filled the news, and no doubt will continue to do so.

Chapter Questions

Knowledge and Understanding

1. a) Define the term "geopolitics." Provide an example.

   b) Define the term "politics." Provide an example.

   c) Explain how geopolitics differs from politics.

2. What does the term "political sovereignty" mean?

3. How does the modern nation state differ from earlier empires or kingdoms?

4. Why is the UN reluctant to get involved in internal conflicts? Why is this reluctance problematic?

Thinking

5. What role did geography play in the relationship between the US and the Soviet Union during the Cold War?

6. Examine an area of the world where there is a dispute over a border. Determine

   a) how and when the borders were created

   b) what geopolitical problems have arisen

   c) the arguments put forward by each side

   d) the current status of the dispute

7. a) Examine the maps in Figures 21–7 and 21–8. Describe the changes that have occurred in the type of governments for the following regions:

   i) South America

   ii) Africa

   iii) Eastern Europe and former Soviet Union

   iv) Southeast Asia

   b) What general global trend do you think is occurring? What reasons may account for this trend?

8. Research the different ways that countries use nationalism to obtain the support of their citizens.

9. Demonstrate how charismatic politicians use this feature of their personality to gain and hold power.

10. Why does China see globalization as key to its economic development?

11. A few nation states, Canada among them, comprise people from many parts of the world, who have different traditions, religions, and languages.

    a) Name a state, other than Canada, that views this kind of diversity as a strength. Describe how diversity is seen as a strength.

    b) Name a state where diversity has led to conflict. How has diversity caused conflict?

Communication

12. Many organizations opposed to globalization feel that agreements such as NAFTA and rulings of the WTO threaten national sovereignty. Is national sovereignty threatened by globalization? In a group, prepare a presentation that fully supports your point of view. **G**

13. Research a country that has an authoritarian government. Convey the following information in a chart, table, or other graphic representation:

    a) the person or group who leads the country

    b) how they came to power

    c) how they retain power

    d) major domestic and international policies

    e) relations with other countries

    f) the nature of any opposition parties or groups

14. If you lived in an authoritarian state, what aspects of life there would be most distressing to you? How do you think you would cope with such a situation? Explain.

Application

15. Quebecois who support separatism feel that Quebec meets the criteria for being a nation state and should therefore separate from Canada. Do you think that Quebec meets the criteria for a nation state? Explain your answer.

16. Sovereign nations control what happens within their boundaries without interference from other countries. In what situations is it acceptable for a country (or group of countries) to interfere in another's sovereignty? Explain your point of view.

17. Research and write a report that traces the development of the African Union (AU) since the 1960s.

    a) What are the goals of the AU?

    b) What current issues does the AU face?

    c) To what extent can the AU be called the "United States of Africa"?

CHAPTER 22

Conflict in the 21st Century

Key Terms

weapons of mass destruction (WMD)

armed conflict

hard power

soft power

asymmetric warfare

proxy war

peace dividend

caliphate

Canadian soldiers in Kandahar province, Afghanistan, in 2008 (right). This NATO mission marks the first serious combat for the Canadian army since the Korean War in the early 1950s. The New York Philharmonic Orchestra visited North Korea in 2008 (below). Only time will tell if this visit will help break down the walls around Korea, the most isolated, nation.

Key Questions

By the end of this chapter you will be able to answer the following questions.

■ Why is there a conflict over control of the Arctic Ocean basin?

■ What is the difference between soft power and hard power?

■ What are the main causes of conflict?

■ What is asymmetric warfare and why is it important today?

■ In what parts of the world do most conflicts occur?

■ Will different visions of globalization lead to more or less conflict?

Conflicts are complex, and all too common. Not to treat the subject lightly (in fact, the purpose of this exercise is exactly the opposite), but it is time for you to play "Name That War!" Identify the war, or other conflict, that could be associated with each of the following comments.

1. "We are fighting to stop the spread of **weapons of mass destruction** (**WMD**) from this country to others." WMD include nuclear, chemical, and biological weapons.

2. "We are fighting to protect the sanctity of our religion from non-believers."

3. "We are fighting to ensure the smooth flow of the oil that our country needs."

4. "We are fighting to remove a dictator from power who has killed many thousands of his own people."

5. "We are fighting to protect our culture from the immoral culture of the Western world."

6. "We are fighting to drive the invaders from our homeland."

How did you do? Check your answers on page 363.

Nature of Conflict

The dictionary defines conflict as "… a struggle or clash between opposing forces, ideas, or interests." Adversarial states exist at all levels and in all places. For example, one might exist between you and your geography teacher over whether or not you can get an extension on the due date for your major paper. One would assume that this conflict could be resolved peacefully, but unfortunately this is not always the case with conflicts on the global stage. There, conflicts have one of three outcomes:

■ A solution is found that is acceptable to all parties.

■ The parties learn to live peacefully (if often grudgingly) in "an adversarial *state*" without the need to proceed to "adversarial *action*."

■ Some conflicts, unfortunately, worsen to the point where they become **armed conflicts**, in which each side uses force to achieve its goals.

In this chapter, you will look at conflict from a theoretical perspective. You will also examine the positive and negative aspects of the relationship between conflict and globalization, and learn about the specific characteristics of a number of conflicts. You will be able to apply the knowledge you gain in this chapter to better understand the conflicts that are occurring around the world.

GLOBALIZATION

The impact that climate change is having on ice conditions in the Arctic basin has sparked greater interest in the region from nations that border the Arctic Ocean.

Why are changing climate conditions so critical here?

A Conflict Over Arctic Ocean Sovereignty

For centuries, explorers tried to find the "Northwest Passage" between western Europe and East Asia that would be thousands of kilometres shorter than the southern routes around Africa and South America. Until recently, the Northwest Passage was only of theoretical interest because difficult ice conditions made the trip impractical and unpredictable. Now, however, with the dramatic melting of sea ice as a result of climate change, sea routes through the Arctic Ocean have become a possibility. (The summer of 2007 marked the first time in recorded history that the Northwest Passage was entirely ice-free.)

Also, geographers (and oil companies) estimate that as much as 25 percent of the world's undiscovered oil and gas may lie under the Arctic Ocean. The impact that climate change is having on ice conditions in the Arctic basin has sparked greater interest in the region from nations that border the Arctic Ocean. The result was that, in 2007, a conflict loomed over control of the Arctic Ocean basin.

Conflicting Claims

Several events occurred within a few weeks during the short Arctic summer of 2007 to bring this conflict to the attention of the world.

■ The Russian government claimed to have sent an expedition to plant their flag on the bottom of the ocean at the North Pole (see Figure 22–1). This was done to promote Russia's claim of ownership of the sea floor between its coast and the Pole.

- Denmark and Canada stated that they may have overlapping claims to the seabed between Greenland and Ellesmere Island and the North Pole.

- Prime Minister Stephen Harper announced that Canada would build a deep-water port and military training base at the site of an abandoned mine at Nanisivik at the northern tip of Baffin Island. He also announced that Canada would build six armed, ice-reinforced Arctic patrol vessels. (These vessels would be about 100 metres long and have missile-launch capabilities, helicopters, and deck guns. They would not be able to operate in the heaviest ice of the Arctic. Why might the government have decided not to build ships capable of operating in heavier ice conditions?)

- Denmark and the United States each sent expeditions into the basin to do research to learn more about the undersea geography of the area.

- The US and other countries maintain that the Northwest Passage is in international waters. (Note that there is not one specific Northwest Passage. The best route through the islands in the late summer depends on the specific ice conditions that develop that year.) Canada vigorously opposes this claim (one reason for building the northern patrol ships) and counters that all ocean areas inside the 200-nautical-mile (370-kilometre) limit are part of Canada's Exclusive Economic Zone (EEZ). Under the law of the sea, the EEZ is a zone in which a state has special rights over exploration and use of marine resources (see Figure 22–2).

Solving This Conflict

The United Nations Law of the Sea Convention is a treaty that deals with oceanic territorial claims. The

Figure 22–1 This image from a Russian video, apparently showing a Russian flag being placed on the bottom of the sea at the North Pole, raised the suspicions of a 13-year-old Finnish boy. He checked his DVD collection and realized that the footage had been lifted from the 1997 film, *Titanic*. Observers also wondered, since the Russians had said they used two submersibles, who took the video. As a result of this disclosure, it was not altogether clear whether the Russians had actually placed their flag on the sea bottom at the North Pole.

provisions of the Convention include the process to be used for "staking" territorial claims in the Arctic basin. Nations have only ten years after *ratifying* the treaty to launch their claims. (A treaty is ratified when it is confirmed by a country's government.) By this rule, Russia has until 2009 to launch its claims, Canada has until 2013, and Denmark until 2014. As of 2008, the US had not ratified the treaty but may do so to support its own claims.

It is virtually impossible that you will be called on to fight in a war to protect Canada's Arctic *sovereignty* (controlling power). The overriding reason for this is that Russia, Canada, the US, and Denmark—all Core nations—are inclined to accept international treaties and negotiation as the best way to prevent and solve conflicts. Supporters of globalization point out that most of the world's serious conflicts occur in regions where globalization, and the acceptance of the rule-of-law, is not well established, namely, in Near Core and Far Periphery nations.

Figure 22–2 National borders at sea are determined in two ways. In general, a country can claim an economic interest up to 200 nautical miles (370 kilometres) from shore. If the offshore zones of two (or more) countries overlap, then an equidistant border is used.

Map legend:
— Agreed national borders
--- Equidistant borders
— 200-mile line
Typical shipping routes:
- - Northern Sea Route
- - Northwest Passage
⊘ Russian-claimed territory
● Lomonosov Ridge
◉ Summer sea-ice extent

The Role of Hard and Soft Power in Conflicts

We are all very familiar with **hard power**. Far too often, on our television screens and the Internet, we see coverage of armed conflict and violent terrorism. The role played by hard power in conflict is well understood, but this is not the only option for resolving conflicts. **Soft power** can also be used at much less human and financial cost. But what exactly do we mean by soft power? Figure 22–3 compares soft power and hard power. Some comments about the terms included in the diagram will aid your understanding.

- **Co-option** is the process by which potential opponents become closely tied to one another long before an actual conflict occurs. France and Germany fought each other in four devastating wars between the early 1800s and the 1940s. After World War II, leaders on both sides wanted this never to happen again. The creation of the European Union co-opted one country to the other and dramatically reduced the possibility of a future war.

- **Public diplomacy** is a process that aims to create an ongoing positive image of a country in the minds of citizens of other countries. Countries believe that a positive image may prevent conflicts from emerging. There are many formal and informal ways in which public diplomacy is carried out. Russia's placement of its flag on the seabed under the North Pole, plus the video that was made to publicize the event, is an example (though in this case, not a very successful one) of public diplomacy.

- **Government diplomacy** involves international negotiations that take place through formal government channels. Countries use government diplomacy to prevent conflict, or at least to settle disputes if they cannot be prevented. In all likelihood, the dispute over the Arctic Ocean basin will be settled by government diplomacy.

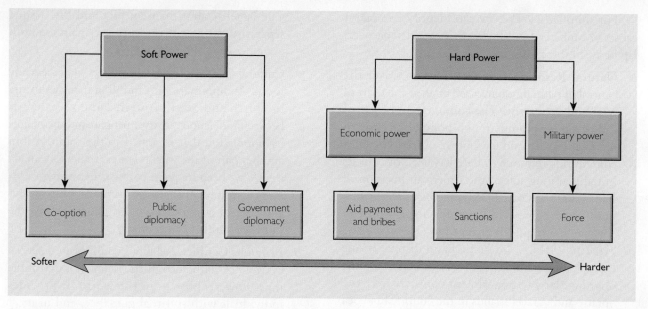

Figure 22–3 Governments can influence the outcome of conflict, and even prevent it through the use of various types of hard and soft power.

■ **Aid payments and bribes** are often used as tools in a dispute. Often, wealthier countries will provide a variety of financial incentives to poorer countries to gain their support. Both sides in the Cold War (the US and Russia) followed this policy, and many countries do the same today.

■ **Sanctions** are measures taken by countries or international organizations (such as the UN or NATO) against countries to force them to change policies. Sanctions take many forms, for example, financial sanctions, whereby one country may freeze the assets of another (or the assets of a government leader). If financial sanctions are not enough, military sanctions may be applied. For example, in 1991, after the Gulf War, the US, the United Kingdom, and France imposed "no-fly zones" over more than half of Iraq. Iraqi aircraft were not allowed to enter these zones.

■ **Force** is the ultimate expression of hard power; the kind of force depends on the particular situation. Most wars in the past, such as the two World Wars, involved military forces that were of comparable strength. In the modern world though, armed conflicts often pit a militarily strong combatant against a much weaker opponent. This is known as **asymmetric warfare**. In asymmetric warfare, the weaker side fights with whatever weapons are at hand, often car bombs, suicide bombers, and *improvised explosive devices* (IEDs). (IEDs are bombs built from whatever materials are available, for example, the explosive head of an artillery shell and a detonator used in mining. They are often buried next to roads and set off by contact or by the use of a cellphone.) The weaker side hopes that the more powerful, conventional force will not be able to respond effectively to this sort of attack and that public support will diminish. This type of warfare has been the norm in both Iraq and Afghanistan in recent years.

GLOBALIZATION
In the modern world, though, armed conflicts often pit a militarily strong combatant against a much weaker opponent. This is known as asymmetric warfare.

Do you think that asymmetric warfare is much more common now than in the past? Why or why not?

Causes of Conflict

The number of conflicts in the world at any given time varies and, to some extent, depends on one's particular definition of "conflict." In 2007, there were about 40 ongoing conflicts worldwide. Africa and the Middle East are typically the most war-torn regions.

You can learn more about current conflicts, and find an overview of conflicts between 1900 and 2001, at the link on our Web site.

For simplicity's sake, we can identify five major causes of conflicts. In reality there is considerable overlap between these causes.

- **Natural Resource Conflict.** Disputes over the control of natural resources are often at the heart of wars and civil strife. The combination of global industrial development and population growth increases the demand for finite resources. The most contentious resource to date has been oil. (In its initial planning stages, the American invasion of Iraq in 2003 was called *Operation Iraqi Liberation*—until someone noticed the unfortunate acronym. The name was quickly changed to *Operation Iraqi Freedom* [OIF].) The Arctic basin dispute is one example of a natural-resources conflict, as are the ongoing, largely non-violent conflicts over the Spratly and Paracel Islands in the South China Sea (see Figure 22–4). Many observers suggest that in the years to come, conflicts over water will become even more important than conflicts over oil and other resources.

- **Territorial Conflict.** Conflict often arises when two or more groups wish to control the same territory.

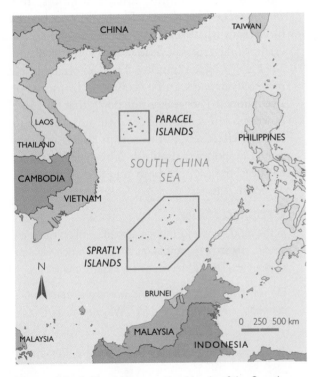

Figure 22–4 The 100 or so tiny islands of the Spratly Islands (the total area is less than five square kilometres) are claimed in total or in part by China, Taiwan, Vietnam, Malaysia, and the Philippines. Similarly, China, Taiwan, and Vietnam claim the tiny Paracel Islands group. In both cases, their claims are based on the belief that significant oil reserves exist there.

The Israeli–Palestinian conflict and the Basque separatist movement in northern Spain are both examples of territorial conflicts.

- **Cultural Conflict.** Cultural conflicts can take many forms. An important one, found in many countries in North and South America and Oceania, is between indigenous (native) peoples and the majority population that migrated to the country from another part of the world. For example, in Canada there have been frequent conflicts between government and Aboriginal groups over ownership of land and control of resources. (This illustrates how the causes of conflict can overlap.)

- **Religious Conflict.** Religious conflicts are a special category of cultural conflicts. Religion is one of the most powerful forces in the world. It provides individuals with spiritual guidance, and in most countries forms the basis for *secular* (non-religious) law. It unites people through common beliefs and experiences. It can also divide them and become the cause of deadly conflicts. Religious conflicts are common in many parts of the world—for example, the "Irish Question," as it was known, pitted Catholics against Protestants for more than 300 years. Much of the violence in Iraq since 2003 has been between Sunni and Shiite Muslims.

- **Global Geopolitical Conflict.** Often conflicts within a particular country are little more than localized versions of global rivalries. This was best seen during the Cold War when **proxy wars** ("proxy" means acting on behalf of another) were fought between the West and the Communist bloc largely because a direct conflict between the Soviet Union and the US could too easily have led to a devastating nuclear war. From the 1950s to 1980s, many civil wars and insurgencies in Africa, Asia, and Latin America were fought by one faction supported by the US, and the other supported by the Soviets. Less frequently, proxy wars actually involved one of the two superpowers. Good examples of this type of conflict were the Vietnam War, when Soviet proxies (the North Vietnamese and Viet Cong) fought the US; and the Afghan war in the 1980s, when American proxies (the mujahedeen—Islamic guerilla fighters) fought the Soviet Union (see Figure 22–5).

Rarely do the causes of a conflict fit into only one of these categories. For almost every dispute, there is a combination of causes. For example, the Afghan–Soviet war had all five causes.

- **Natural Resource Conflict** → Although natural resources were certainly not the most important reason for the Soviets' interest in Afghanistan,

Figure 22–5 This Mujahedeen fighter in Afghanistan is holding a portable ground-to-air missile. These missiles did much to ensure the defeat of the Soviets in this proxy war since their use dramatically reduced the Soviets' ability to use their attack helicopters and other aircraft. The Americans did not realize that many of the fighters they supported, including Osama Bin Laden, would later become their enemies and that some of the weapons the Americans had provided would be used against them.

the country does have a wide range of valuable mineral and energy resources.

■ **Territorial Conflict** → The Soviet Union wanted land access to the Indian Ocean. By having a *puppet state* (where one country is controlled by another) in Afghanistan, the Soviets would have made an important step in achieving this access. Most Afghanis, not surprisingly, wanted the foreigners out of their country.

■ **Cultural Conflict** → Most Afghanis opposed the modernity that the Russians brought to their country.

■ **Religious Conflict** → Although there were many Muslims in the Soviet Union, the Soviet military was seen as a great threat to Islam. Such a threat was totally unacceptable in a country with very traditional beliefs and powerful religious groups.

■ **Geopolitical Conflict** → To the Soviets, control of Afghanistan provied an opportunity to expand their sphere of influence in an important direction—toward the Indian subcontinent and Iran. To the Americans, Afghanistan was an opportunity to give the Soviets a "bloody nose" at little obvious cost to the US.

CASE STUDY — Examples of Conflict in the World

In this case study, you will have the opportunity to do Web research on one conflict and to learn about other conflicts from your classmates.

What You Will Do

• You will work in groups. Your teacher will let you know the size of each group and how many groups there will be.

• Each student will research one conflict. It is a good idea to coordinate your research with other students, either in your group or in others. For example, if one person finds a really good Web resource, then others might benefit from it too.

• Each student will present his or her findings to the group. Presentations should be seven to ten minutes long.

• The group will choose its best presentations. (The number of presentations will depend on the number and size of the groups. Your teacher will provide details.) Group members will offer suggestions on how each presentation could be made even better.

• In turn, each group's chosen presenters will give their presentation to one other group.

Choosing a Conflict to Study

There is no shortage of conflicts in the world that could be researched and presented. You may focus on any international or internal conflict in the post–World War II era, the cause of which relates to the section entitled "Causes of Conflict" above. You may choose a conflict that has been resolved or one that is ongoing; you can learn something from either situation. A list of suggestions follows, but you are also encouraged to choose one that is not listed. Check with your teacher before proceeding to ensure that your choice is suitable and that you will be able to find sufficient information in your research. (Check the list of conflicts at the link provided on our Web site.)

Conflicts You Might Study

Conflicts in **bold italic** were ongoing as of the beginning of 2008; those in *italic* had reached a resolution.

- *US and Iraq*—The US fought Iraq twice, first in the early 1990s, and a second time beginning in 2003.

- *Rwandan genocide*—In only 100 days in 1994, 800 000 people were killed while the world did nothing.

- *Israeli–Palestinian conflict*—This has been the world's most notorious conflict "hot-spot" since 1947.

- *Cyprus*—An uneasy truce between Cyprus' Greek majority and Turkish minority has existed on this small island for decades. People live peacefully, but an enduring solution to the conflict remains elusive.

- *Fight against "narco-terrorism" in Colombia*—This complex conflict involves a civil war and the production and distribution of cocaine.

- *Battle against apartheid in South Africa*—For almost 50 years, people inside and outside South Africa fought for an end to institutionalized racism in South Africa (see Figure 22–6).

- *Darfur*—Ethnically-based killings in this part of Sudan, starting in 2003, have reminded many of what happened in Rwanda a decade earlier.

- *Northern Ireland*—Violent religious conflict in Ireland occurred for centuries, but ended in the North only at the beginning of the 21st century.

- *Afghanistan*—The fight against the Taliban and al-Qaeda in Afghanistan marked the Canadian army's first combat role since the Korean War.

- *Former Yugoslavia*—Civil conflict broke out when Yugoslavia broke up in 1990. Eventually a NATO force intervened.

Figure 22–6 South Africa's apartheid system rigidly defined an individual's rights on the basis of their racial group.

Figure 22–7 In 2007, Buddhist monks were prominent in protests against the military government of Myanmar. These protests were brutally suppressed by the government. Many lives were lost.

- *Myanmar*—A brutal military government has maintained control in Myanmar (Figure 22–7).

- *Civil war in Chad*—Chad experienced 15 years of civil war that began in 1965. The war was followed by an unstable peace accord.

How You Will Do It

The Internet has a vast range of resources that you can use for your research. You should use at least five sites to collect research; be very aware of the bias you encounter. Be sure to keep a complete bibliography of your research. In your presentation, you should include several features:

- Provide the context for the conflict, that is, the geographic situation and historical elements within which the conflict developed. This may include the possible threats that each party in the conflict sees in the other. This is different from the specific causes of the conflict.

- In the previous section of this chapter, you learned five reasons why conflict occurs. In your presentation, describe the particular combination of reasons that led to your conflict. Some reasons will be more important than others. Indicate this in your presentation.

- Discuss the important events of the conflict. Be careful not to focus on events that might be interesting but unimportant. An important event is one that made the conflict considerably more serious or less serious.

- Elaborate on the roles played by major "actors" inside and outside the conflict zones. These people may have made the conflict worse or helped resolve it.

- Indicate the impact of the dispute on other countries, for example, migrations, geopolitical considerations, or economic impact on a local/regional/global scale.

- Discuss the possible role played (or that could be played) by Canada or individual Canadians in resolving the conflict.

- If the conflict has been resolved, how did it come about? If it is ongoing, what is being done to end it and how successful are these efforts?

The Costs of Conflict

Every gun that is made, every warship launched, every rocket fired represents, in the final analysis, a theft from those who hunger and are not fed, who are cold and not clothed.

—President and former General
Dwight D. Eisenhower

The costs of conflict can be reckoned in many different ways. Most often we think about the people who are killed in conflicts, but it is critical to consider other costs as well. Thousands of people are wounded each year in both major and minor conflicts. Even after conflicts are supposedly over, people can be killed or injured. Even today, farmers in northern France and Belgium are killed when their ploughs strike World War I artillery shells and other munitions that are still deadly after almost a century (see Figure 22–8). Thousands are also killed or maimed by anti-personnel land mines each year in many parts of the world. Most of these mines are left over from earlier conflicts but, like the bombs in France, remain dangerous for many years. Most at risk are farmers tending their fields and children playing.

Conflict also has enormous social and economic costs. As Eisenhower suggested above, the enormous amount spent on the world's military is money not spent on economic and social development for the world's people. Nowhere is this more obvious than in Africa. Many observers have suggested that the most important reason this continent lags behind the rest of the world in so many ways is because of the prevalence there of armed conflicts of many types.

Because a country's "economic pie" is only so big, governments must decide whether to spend their money on "guns" (its military) or "butter" (social programs and development). ("Guns or butter" is a commonly used metaphor for the choice that Eisenhower talked about.) Many governments have large militaries and spend a

Figure 22–8 Sheep are used to cut the grass at the Vimy Ridge memorial in France because it is too dangerous for people to walk over much of the battlefield; live munitions from this battle, fought in 1917, surface each year.

significant proportion of their budget on defense purchases such as armaments. In this section we will investigate why.

Armaments obviously vary enormously in cost and function. The F-35 Joint Strike Force fighter plane (see Figure 22–9) is to come into service in 2011 and will cost between US$48 million and US$63 million each, depending on the particular version chosen. At this price, the F-35 is a weapon that will be bought primarily by Core countries. Canada is a junior partner in the development of this plane and may order as many as 80 planes to replace our aging CF-18s, the first of which came into service in 1984.

At the other extreme, in terms of purpose, sophistication, cost, and market, is the *ubiquitous* (found everywhere) AK-47 assault rifle (see Figure 22–10). Remarkably (and many would say, sadly), more than 100 million of this weapon have been made since its introduction in 1949. It was originally made in the Soviet Union and has since been manufactured in about 20 countries including China, Egypt, the US, and Pakistan. The fact that it is simple to use and maintain, inexpensive, and rugged has made the AK-47 the most popular weapon in dozens of conflicts, in particular in Asia and Africa. In recent years, used AK-47s could be bought in countries like Somalia, Democratic Republic of the Congo, and Ethiopia for between US$30 and US$125 each.

Figure 22–10 This button shows details from the flag of Mozambique. It indicates the iconic role of the AK-47 in Periphery conflicts. The three symbols chosen to represent the country are a hoe (agriculture), a book (education and law), and the AK-47.

Figure 22–9 The F-35 fighter plane is typical of the costly technology that is central to the military operations of Old Core, and increasingly, New Core countries.

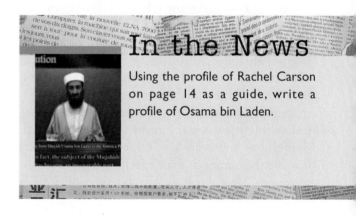

In the News

Using the profile of Rachel Carson on page 14 as a guide, write a profile of Osama bin Laden.

WHICH COUNTRIES ARE THE MOST MILITARISTIC?

One definition of "militaristic" is "having aggressive military preparedness." Using this definition, why would a country choose to be militaristic? There are two obvious reasons. Often they exist together.

- The country's government feels that the safety of its people is at risk, either because of hostile neighbours or internal threats.

- The government feels that the best way to solve its conflicts is by the use (or threat of use) of hard power rather than soft power.

In 2005, the nations of the world spent about US$741 billion on military expenditures. This is an improvement from the Cold War peak of US$1.3 trillion in 1985. This reduction in military spending has been called the **peace dividend**. The peace dividend is being eroded today by events such as spending on wars in Iraq and Afghanistan and the significant growth in military spending by China and many of the countries in southern and western Asia. There are other ways of looking at military spending. World military spending amounts to about 2 percent of the gross world product and is about US$142 for each person on Earth.

Interpreting statistical data and clearly expressing what you have learned are vital skills for geographers and professionals in many other fields. In the following exercise, you will have a chance to practise these skills.

 For the online source mentioned in question 2 c), check the link on our Web site.

Questions

1. Consider the information given in Figure 22–11. The data in these tables provide varying perspectives on the commitments that nations make to their militaries. Note that Canada is included for comparison's sake. Your job is to summarize what each table tells you about this subject. Consider such factors as the area and population of the countries, the size of their economies, and their geopolitical situation.

2. To what extent do conflicts influence military spending and the size of a country's military?

   a) Choose any three of the ongoing conflicts mentioned on page 356.

   b) Identify the countries that are involved in this conflict.

   c) Consult the online source of the data we have been using and determine if these countries have military commitments (size or cost) that are significantly larger than average.

Total Military Personnel	Military Personnel as % of Population	Military Expenditures (US$ billions)	Military Expenditures Per Capita (US$)	Military Expenditures as a % of GDP on a PPP Basis
1. China 3 755 000	1. North Korea 5.8	1. US 277	1. Israel 1429	1. Oman 11.2
2. India 3 047 000	2. Eritrea 4.6	2. China 56	2. Singapore 1010	2. Eritrea 10.4
3. US 1 546 000	3. Singapore 3.9	3. France 47	3. US 936	3. Ethiopia 9.9
4. Russia 452 000	4. Brunei 2.9	4. Japan 40	4. New Caledonia 888	4. Afghanistan 9.1
5. North Korea 1 295 000	5. Bahrain 3.0	5. Germany 39	5. Brunei 885	5. Mali 8.6
6. Pakistan 921 000	6. Israel 2.5	6. UK 32	6. Kuwait 842	6. Israel 7.6
7. Egypt 799 000	7. Lebanon 2.4	7. Italy 20	7. Qatar 838	7. Saudi Arabia 7.3
8. South Korea 693 000	8. Syria 2.2	8. Saudi Arabia 18	8. Oman 807	8. Jordan 6.8
9. Brazil 673 000	9. Laos 2.2	9. Brazil 13	9. France 767	9. Burundi 6.4
10. Turkey 617 000	10. Jordan 2.0	10. South Korea 13	10. Bahrain 764	10. Iran 6.0
58. Canada 71 000	132. Canada 0.2	17. Canada 8	30. Canada 240	126. Canada 0.8

Figure 22–11 Country rankings, 2005: military personnel and expenditures

A Clash of Civilizations
or a Clash of Globalizations?

As the 1990s began, most of the world's citizens looked toward the future with a sense of hope. The Cold War was over and the world seemed to be a much safer place without the looming threat of a nuclear war that had existed for so long. The Cold War had been the fundamental geopolitical reality from the end of World War II until 1990 and directly or indirectly underlaid most of the conflicts of that time. No one—politicians, military leaders, and ordinary citizens alike—really knew what the future might bring. Two books were published within a few years of each other that presented very different visions for the future (see Figure 22–12).

Francis Fukuyama's book was written in response to the end of the Cold War and the collapse of the Soviet Union. It proclaimed a view of the future that was nothing less than a victory for globalization that was clearly based on the principles of Western political and economic liberalism. To dramatize the importance of this revolutionary development, he proclaimed that this was the "end of history" as it had been known for centuries.

For the first five years after its publication, Samuel P. Huntington's book received little attention outside the academic community. Not surprisingly, this changed dramatically in the weeks and months after the 9/11 attacks, in particular because Huntington had written about the potential for conflict between the Western and Islamic civilizations. The question became whether Huntington's work was, in fact, an accurate prediction of the nature of conflict in the 21st century. As you might expect, this issue is controversial and critically important.

Most people would say that the growth of globalization in the world has reduced the possibility of conflict—you might remember the "Golden Arches Theory of Conflict Prevention" mentioned in Chapter 2. In fact, some observers have even suggested that globalization should be spread by the use of hard power in extreme cases. (You can learn more about this view in the book, *The Pentagon's New Map: War and Peace in the Twenty-First Century* by Thomas P.M. Barnett.) The invasion and occupation of Iraq, albeit botched in the execution, can be seen as an attempt to use hard power to bring globalization forcefully into this part of the world.

There is one large "BUT" that must accompany the assertion that globalization reduces conflict, and that is that the values encompassed in globalization must be at least marginally acceptable by those who are being globalized. This is not always the case.

Francis Fukuyama	**Author**	Samuel P. Huntington
The End of History and the Last Man	**Key work**	*The Clash of Civilizations and the Remaking of the World Order*
1992	**Year of publication**	1996
History was "ending" in the sense that major conflict in the future was unlikely because the world was moving toward the universal acceptance of Western liberal democracy as the "final form of human government."	**Thesis**	Conflicts in the world would no longer be based on ideology and economics as in the past, but on cultural differences. Huntington identified nine "civilizations" (see Figure 22–13) and suggested where conflicts and alliances are most likely (see Figure 22–14).
Globalization contributes to fewer conflicts—i.e., the more we have in common, the less we have to fight about.	**Relationship to globalization**	Globalization contributes to more conflict—i.e., globalization is overwhelmingly a Western civilization-centred trend and, as such, is seen as a threat to other civilizations.

Figure 22–12 Fukuyama's and Huntington's conflicting ideas set off a debate over the future of conflict in the world.

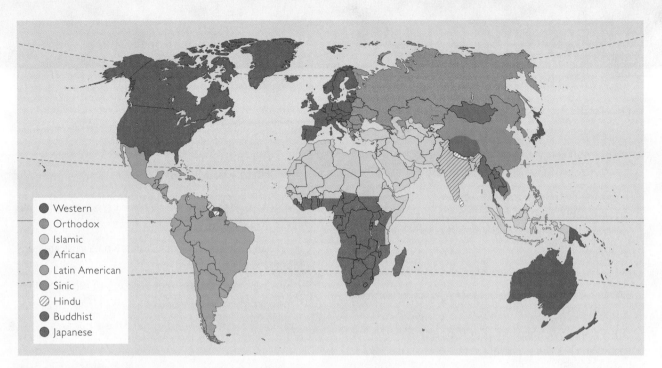

Figure 22–13 Huntington identified nine "civilizations" that he thought would dominate the world's affairs in the post–Cold War era. He believed that the Buddhist civilization did not qualify as a major world civilization. This map does not show what Huntington called "lone countries" and exceptions. The two most important lone countries are Turkey and Ethiopia.

In considering the role that globalization plays in the conflict between Western countries and radical Islamic elements, some observers have taken one more step. They suggest that what is actually happening is a "battle of globalizations" between the Western idea of globalization and a separate vision of Islamic globalization. Osama bin Laden, in a 2007 video addressed to the people of the West, mentioned this directly:

> *The capitalist system seeks to turn the entire world into a fiefdom of the major corporations under the label of "globalization."*

> *And Iraq and Afghanistan and their tragedies; and the reeling of many of you under the burden of interest-related debts, insane taxes, and real estate mortgages; global warming and its woes; and the abject poverty and tragic hunger in Africa: all of this is but one side of the grim face of this global system.*

According to Huntington and others, an Islamic globalized world would extend from the Atlantic coast of North Africa to Indonesia. Within this region, Islamic values and beliefs would dominate rather than Western ones, which are often regarded as decadent and immoral. Carried to its extreme, this Islamic globalization would lead to the creation of a modern **caliphate**—a transnational state based on Islamic belief and traditions that would be powerful enough to oppose the cultural,

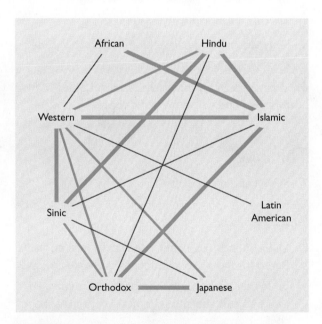

Figure 22–14 Thick blue lines indicate a significant potential for conflict. Thinner blue lines represent a lesser potential for conflict. Brown lines represent the potential for alliances between civilizations. No line between two civilizations indicates no significant interaction between them.

economic, military, and political forces of the West. Only time will tell whether this clash of globalizations will be lessened or become more significant.

Chapter Questions

Knowledge and Understanding

1. Research the role played by each of the following in world conflicts: AK-47s, the 82nd Airborne, Suicide Bombers, and Coca-Cola. See if you can identify a second "conflict connection" for one of these items.

2. a) Indicate the differences in meaning among the following terms: adversarial state, adversarial action, and active conflict.

   b) Give an example of each of these in the world.

3. a) What is the difference between soft power and hard power?

   b) What advantages does soft power have? What disadvantages does it have?

   c) What advantages does hard power have? What disadvantages does it have?

4. a) What is asymmetric warfare?

   b) Where is this occurring in the world today?

   c) Why is its use not at all surprising?

5. Why would Mozambique have chosen to include an AK-47 on its flag?

6. What is meant by the phrase "guns or butter?" Why is this a key question in the world today?

Thinking

7. a) What is public diplomacy?

   b) Give three specific examples of how this can be accomplished.

8. a) Diamonds have been used to finance conflicts. Research where "blood diamonds" were/are an issue.

   b) What reforms has the diamond industry instituted to assure its customers that it is not supporting a bloody conflict?

9. In 1995, a World Bank official stated that wars in the 21st century would be fought over water. Why is this likely to be the case? What can be done to reduce the likelihood of this happening?

10. What controls, if any, do you think should be placed on weapons manufacturing and trade in the world? Explain your reasoning in two to three well-reasoned paragraphs.

11. a) Huntington identified the possibility for conflict between the following pairs of "civilizations."
    - Western and Islamic
    - Hindu and Islamic
    - Orthodox and Islamic
    - Hindu and Sinic
    - Sinic and Western
    - African and Islamic

    Give an example of a conflict that would illustrate each of these.

    b) How might Western globalization tend to reduce these conflicts?

    c) How might it tend to expand these conflicts?

Communication

12. a) The Internet is being used as a method of public diplomacy by a variety of revolutionary organizations—including many that have been accused of using terrorist methods. Why would these groups have chosen to do this?

    b) Why could the use of the Internet be considered a type of asymmetric soft power?

    c) Give the URL of at least one of these revolutionary organizations and briefly indicate what kind of information is included on the site.

Application

13. a) A number of revolutionary groups raise money from their expatriates around the world. Some countries have banned fundraising by such groups because of their terrorist activities. How should Canada deal with fundraising by such groups?

    b) What danger is there in having such restrictions? What danger is there in not having such restrictions?

14. You are a newspaper reporter who is investigating a dispute between an indigenous group and the government of a country, province, or state. (There are many examples in Canada, the US, Australia, Brazil, and other countries.) Write a short report about the dispute of your choice in which you examine the key issues, how they are being addressed, and the current status.

15. Land mines are used in many conflicts around the world. Research the issues surrounding their use under the following headings:

a) Why and how land mines are used

b) Countries in which land mines are used (How many are in each?)

c) Impact of land mines on
   i) people
   ii) the economy
   iii) the environment

d) Global efforts to remove land mines

e) Countries that have not signed the treaty banning land mines (What are their reasons for not signing?)

f) Ways of persuading countries that have not signed the treaty to stop producing and using land mines

16. The Nuclear Age Peace Foundation asks the question "What if we had a concept of security that was not conceived of by the military ... [but] in terms of food, a clean environment, healthcare, education, and other simple ways to improve the human condition?" Do you think this concept is viable? If so, explain how it could be implemented. If not, explain your views. **G**

17. One Nobel laureate has stated that "The poor are crying out for schools and doctors, not guns and generals." Using the military expenditures data from this chapter and by researching costs to eliminate the global social, environmental, and economic issues of today such as poverty, the need to increase food production and prevent malnutrition, the provision of clean water for everyone, and the elimination of illiteracy, compare the costs and explain how this comparison may validate this statement.

Answers to Quiz page 350

All of the statements have been tied to the war in Iraq (from one side or the other) that started with the American invasion in 2003. You may have other, equally correct answers as well—for example

- #2 could refer to the Crusades between 1095 and 1291 (and could have been said by either side in the conflict)

- #3 could apply to the Japanese invasion of the Dutch East Indies in the days following the Pearl Harbor attack

- #4 could be used to describe World War II from the Allied side

- #5 could be applied to the war in Afghanistan (from the perspective of the Taliban)

- #6 could apply to literally hundreds of conflicts over many centuries

CHAPTER 23

The Globalization of Terrorism

Key Terms

terrorism
state terrorism
state-sponsored terrorism
chemical terrorism
bioterrorism
nuclear terrorism
War on Terror
counterterrorism
civil liberties

A woman attends a memorial service in New York City (right), held in remembrance of the 2792 people killed at the World Trade Center on September 11, 2001. (Left) In 1988, the US government labelled Nelson Mandela a terrorist. Less than a decade later he was the president of South Africa and a Nobel Peace Prize winner shown with co-winner F.W. de Klerk. Had he changed, had the situation changed, or had perceptions of him changed?

Key Questions

By the end of this chapter you will be able to answer the following questions.

■ How can terrorism be defined, and why does the specific definition matter so much?

■ Is terrorism becoming more or less common in the world?

■ What are the reasons behind terrorist attacks?

■ How are terrorist threats changing?

■ How can governments fight terrorism?

■ Are you prepared to give up some of your civil rights to combat terrorism?

What Exactly Is Terrorism?

On September 11, 2001, hijackers crashed two airplanes into the twin 110-storey towers of the World Trade Center in New York City. A third plane hit the Pentagon in Washington, DC; a fourth crashed in a field in Pennsylvania. About 3000 people were killed, and the immediate economic loss was estimated at more than US$150 billion. The attacks, now known almost universally as "9/11," were directed at symbols of American power and the Western world's economy. They were linked to an extremist Islamic group called *al-Qaeda*. The events of 9/11 brought **terrorism** to the attention of the world to a degree never seen before. But while terrorism is news, there is nothing new about terrorism. It has existed for centuries—the word was first used to describe some of what was happening during the French Revolution.

WORKING IT OUT

THE PROBLEM OF DEFINING "TERRORISM"

Surprisingly, there is no generally accepted definition of the word "terrorism." In fact, multiple definitions can exist even within the same government. As well, definitions evolve over time. The specific content of the definition matters a great deal since it determines which acts really are terrorism and, to a considerable extent, what governmental (or inter-governmental) responses are appropriate.

1. How would you define terrorism?

2. Work in a group of three to four students to study the definitions below, and then answer the questions that follow.

   • In 1937, the League of Nations declared terrorism to be *all criminal acts directed against a State and intended . . . to create a state of terror in the minds of particular persons . . . or the general public.*

At first glance, this may seem like a reasonable definition, but by many standards, it is inadequate in several respects. Consider the following issues.

   • Terrorists often target not just governments, but also individuals and companies (as in 9/11), religious groups, and groups who oppose governments.

   • This definition also ignores the fact that the threat of violence can be almost as effective as an actual attack.

   • Lastly, how can we define "criminal"? An action that might be considered criminal by some may be viewed as a legitimate protest by others.

Other definitions of terrorism:

   • [Activities] *directed toward or in support of the threat or use of acts of serious violence against persons or property for the purpose of achieving a political objective within Canada or a foreign state.* —Canadian Security Intelligence Service (CSIS)

   • *Terrorism is violence, or the threat of violence, calculated to create an atmosphere of fear and alarm. These acts are designed to coerce others into actions they would not otherwise undertake, or refrain from actions they desired to take. All terrorist acts are crimes. Many would also be in violation of the rules of war if a state of war existed. This violence or threat of violence is generally directed against civilian targets. The motives of all terrorists are political, and terrorist actions are generally carried out in a way that will achieve maximum publicity. Unlike other criminal acts, terrorists often claim credit for their acts. Finally, terrorist acts are intended to produce effects beyond the immediate physical damage of the cause, having long-term psychological repercussions on a particular target audience. The fear created by terrorists may be intended to cause people to exaggerate the strengths of the terrorist and the importance of the cause, to provoke governmental overreaction, to discourage dissent, or simply to intimidate and thereby enforce compliance with their demands."* —Memorial Institute for the Prevention of Terrorism

   • *The calculated use of violence or threat of violence to attain goals that are political, religious, or ideological . . . through intimidation, coercion, or instilling fear.* —US Army

- *. . . Premeditated, politically motivated violence perpetrated against non-combatant targets by subnational groups or clandestine agents, usually intended to influence an audience.* —US National Counterterrorism Center (NCTC) (Non-combatant means civilians and unarmed military personnel, and subnational means existing within a nation.)

  a) Examine each of these definitions. One is much longer than the others. Is this length justified? Which comes closest to your understanding of what terrorism is?

  b) What specific elements of the definition you selected in part a) make it appealing to you?

  c) Are any elements missing from this definition?

3. Now that you have seen how the "experts" define terrorism, revisit your original definition. Consider that a definition of terrorism might include the following considerations.

   - Must there be actual violence, or is the threat of violence enough?

   - Must there be intent to have a psychological impact and to inspire fear?

   - Must there be a political purpose for the action?

   - Must it be aimed at non-combatants?

   - Must the action be illegal? Note that this is not as obvious as it might seem at first. If an action is taken by a government against its opponents, it would generally be considered legal unless it breaks some accepted standard of international law.

   Use this framework to rewrite your own definition of terrorism. Use your own words rather than trying to make it sound formal and legalistic.

4. Compare your definition to those of the members of your group. Based on this comparison, modify your definition if you think that you can make it clearer.

5. Consider three events that have been described as "terrorism" by the media or by governments. Does each of these events qualify as terrorism according to your definition? If not, in what respect does it not? Does this mean that your definition is inadequate or that the event might not be terrorist in nature? Explain.

Geography of Terrorism

There are vitally important geographic dimensions to terrorism. Global patterns of terrorism can be mapped and analyzed in terms of the events themselves, their causes, and the responses that occur. As well, certain nations harbour terrorists, or even sponsor terrorist acts against their own people or other countries. The causes of terrorism often have geographic origins, too. Geopolitics, globalization, economic disparity, and variations in religion and culture are all central to the study of terrorism.

GLOBALIZATION

There are vitally important geographic dimensions to terrorism. Global patterns of terrorism can be mapped and analyzed...

What unique perspectives can geographers bring to the study and elimination of terrorism in the world?

Global Patterns of Terrorism

Modern terrorism began in 1968 when an Israeli airliner was hijacked by Palestinian terrorists. Modern terrorism is distinctive from earlier terrorism in two major ways. The first distinction is that terrorists have a clearer understanding of the vital role that mass media can play in their struggle. For example, terrorists today use the Internet to gain publicity, attract support, and spread fear. The second distinction is that, in comparison to earlier forms of terrorism, little care is taken in modern terrorism to avoid death and injury to ordinary people. Before 1968, it was normal for a terrorist group to warn authorities about the placement of a bomb. Today, warnings are seldom given, and bombs are often placed to cause the maximum number of deaths.

Each year, hundreds of terrorist acts occur on all continents. Most get little attention outside the local area where they occur (see Figure 23–1) because they cause no deaths and little damage. When most of us think about terrorism, we think about the major incidents that get a great deal of global attention. Some of the most significant terrorist attacks, since the beginning of the 1980s, are shown in Figure 23–2.

Figure 23–1 This is an "incident profile" for a typical terrorist attack—the kind that gets little, if any, international attention. This report is part of the world's most extensive database of terrorist groups and activities.

Where is terrorism happening today? In far too many parts of the world! The Memorial Institute for the Prevention of Terrorism (MIPT) was established in 1995 after American terrorists blew up a federal office building in Oklahoma City. The MIPT's Terrorism Knowledge Base lists hundreds of terrorist groups, but many of these are inactive or so tiny that they can be ignored. An example of an inactive group is the *Irish Republican Army (IRA)*. The IRA fought the British government for decades before deciding to work peacefully in the political arena to achieve its goals. An example of a tiny group is a Greek one called *Consciously Enraged* that firebombed a bank in 2003 but has not since resurfaced. A significant number of terrorist groups are well known because they have made numerous attacks and killed and wounded large numbers of people. Figure 23–3 provides an overview of the worst of these.

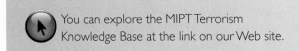

You can explore the MIPT Terrorism Knowledge Base at the link on our Web site.

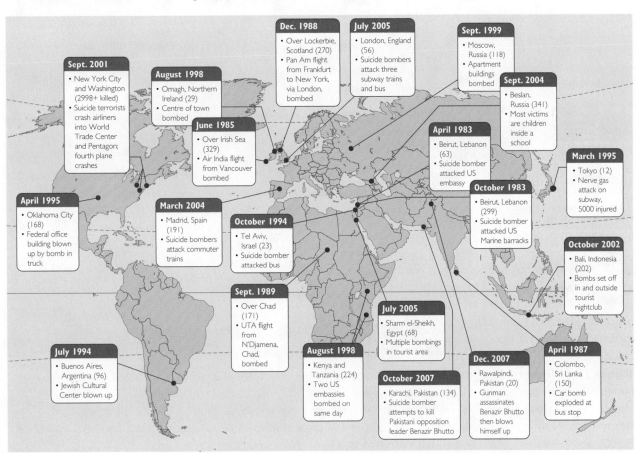

Figure 23–2 Significant terrorist attacks have occurred all over the world. This map focuses on specific attacks that received a great deal of international attention.

Terrorist Organization	Incidents	Deaths	Focus area(s)	Characteristics
Africa				
Armed Islamic Group	64	506	**Algeria**, *France*	• seeks Islamic republic in Algeria
Lord's Resistance Army	33	500	**Uganda**, *Sudan, Congo DR*	• seeks overthrow of Ugandan government; Christian
Asia				
Abus Sayyaf Group*	58	197	**Philippines**	• seeks overthrow of government; Islamic
Communist Party of India – Maoist	219	318	**India**	• seeks independence for area of India bordering Nepal; secular
Communist Party of Nepal – Maoist	403	174	**Nepal**	• seeks to overthrow the government; secular
Liberation Tigers of Tamil Eelam (LTTE) (Tamil Tigers)	233	700	**Sri Lanka**	• seeks an independent Tamil state in Sri Lanka; secular
New People's Army	85	77	**Philippines**	• seeks overthrow of government; communist
Taliban*	418	990	**Afghanistan**	• seeks to return a rigid, Islamic government to the country; some bases in Pakistan
United Liberation Front of Assam	129	107	**India**	• seeks independence for Indian state of Assam; secular
Europe				
Basque Fatherland and Freedom (ETA)	418	64	**Spain**	• seeks separate state for Basque people; secular
Fronte di Liberazione Naziunale di a Corsica	156	1	**France**	• seeks independence for Corsica; secular
Riyad us-Saliheyn Martyrs Brigade*	11	514	**Russia**	• seeks separate Islamic state in Chechnya and nearby areas of Russia; Islamic
North America				
Anti-Castro Cubans	211	87	**Cuba**, *United States*	• opposes the Cuban regime, based in the US; anti-communist
Earth Liberation Front	62	0	**United States**, *Canada*	• environmental activists who use violence; secular
South America				
National Liberation Army (Colombia)	296	189	**Colombia**	• seeks overthrow of current government; socialist
Revolutionary Armed Forces of Colombia (FARC)	648	697	**Colombia**	• seeks to establish communist state; closely tied to coca-growing and cocaine distribution
Shining Path	141	140	**Peru**	• seeks overthrow of state or at least control of coca-growing areas of Peru; communist

Figure 23–3 These terrorist groups were chosen based on three criteria: they had to be active at the end of 2007 and had to have either carried out at least 50 attacks or killed at least 500 people between 1968 and 2007. With one exception, all of these groups focus on one country or even just a region within a country. The exception is al-Qaeda, which in some ways can be seen as a "transnational" terrorist organization. Al-Qaeda has a reported membership of some 50 000 people, while most terrorist groups have, at most, a few hundred members.

*Links with al-Qaeda

Under Focus Area: Bold type indicates primary location of activity; italic type indicates secondary location.

Terrorist Organization	Incidents	Deaths	Focus area(s)	Characteristics
Middle East				
Al Aqsa Martyrs Brigade	126	22	**Israel**, West Bank, Gaza	• opposes Israel and some Palestinian organizations; secular
Al-Qaeda	32	3464	**65 nations** – Islamic world, Western Europe, United States	• has carried out attacks in 13 countries with the largest number in Saudi Arabia; Islamic
Al-Qaeda Organization in the Land of the Two Rivers*	215	1888	**Iraq**	• opposes American occupation and Iraqi government; Islamic
Ansar al-Sunah Army	95	620	**Iraq**	• opposes American occupation and Iraqi government; secular
Hamas	581	603	**Israel**, West Bank, Gaza	• opposes Israel and some Palestinian organizations; Islamic
Hezbollah	179	836	**Lebanon**, Israel	• opposes Israel; Islamic
Islamic State of Iraq	127	541	**Iraq**	• opposes American occupation and Iraqi government; Islamic
Kurdistan Workers' Party (PKK)	111	53	**Turkey**	• seeks an independent Kurdish state in southeast Turkey; bases in Turkey and Iraq; secular
Mujahedeen Shura Council	85	379	**Iraq**	• umbrella group of Sunni Islamic groups opposed to American occupation and Iraqi government
Palestinian Islamic Jihad (PIJ)	257	213	**Israel**, Lebanon, Syria, West Bank, Gaza	• opposes Israel and some Palestinian organizations; Islamic

Is Terrorism Increasing or Decreasing?

It is not possible to give a clear answer to the question in the heading above. Perhaps the best possible answer is to say that it depends on what statistics you use to measure terrorism. This, in turn, depends on what definition is used to decide whether an event qualifies as terrorism. Consider the two graphs in Figure 23–4. Both sets of incident numbers and fatalities come from respected American organizations, the National Counterterrorism Center (NCTC), a branch of the American government, and the MIPT Terrorism Knowledge Base (TKB), a private think tank—and yet, since 2005, they present completely different data. Each is trying its best to accurately identify the extent of terrorism in the world but the results are completely different. According to the TKB, the frequency of terrorist incidents has been relatively stable with a decline from a peak in the 1980s. (Obviously the number of fatalities peaked in 2001 because of the 9/11 attacks.) On the other hand, the NCTC statistics show a massive increase in attacks and fatalities starting in 2005.

The reason for this difference is surprisingly simple, but very important. Before 2005, both organizations counted only incidents of international terrorism. This meant that terrorist acts involving attackers and victims within one country were ignored. The problem with this limitation can be seen in one incident. In 2004, Chechen terrorists bombed two Russian airliners that crashed within minutes of each other. One plane had one Israeli citizen on board (along with dozens of Russians), and the other had only Russians onboard. The first plane attack was counted as international terrorism; the second was not. Clearly both were acts of terrorism.

There are other differences between the definitions that tend to make the NCTC numbers higher, but what is clear is that one has to relate the numbers to the definitions being used. A significant problem comes with how these statistics are used by politicians and by the media. If a politician or newspaper columnist uses the statistics generated by the NCTC to state that terrorism is increasing, it is misleading since the NCTC changed the terrorism definition it used.

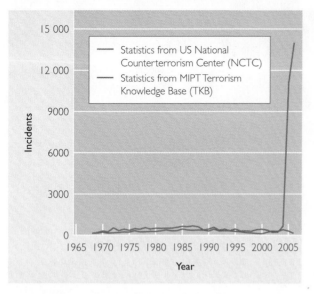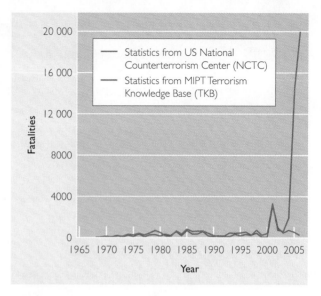

Figure 23–4 Interpreting terrorism statistics is tricky. The NCTC trend lines on these graphs would suggest a massive increase in terrorism starting in 2005—but this increase is not seen in the TKB lines. Both of these sources counted only "international" terrorism statistics until 2004 and hence had similar statistics (there were other differences between definitions, too). Starting in 2006, the NCTC counted national terrorism as well.

Objectives of Terrorism

It is important to remember that terrorism is not a goal; it is a method used to achieve a goal. It is one aspect of *asymmetric warfare*. (Asymmetric wars, as seen in Chapter 22, are fought between opponents with dramatically different levels of conventional military technology and power. The weaker opponent will often resort to tactics that the stronger opponent might well describe as terrorism.) Terrorism is carried out for a variety of reasons. Depending on the circumstances, one or more of the following objectives may apply.

- A terrorist group may be trying to attain a specific goal, such as overthrowing a government, forcing a foreign army to leave a country, obtaining money to support its activities, or forcing the release of imprisoned colleagues.

- Terrorists try to cause widespread fear and anxiety, hoping to break down the normal social order of the targeted population and thus improve their chances of achieving their goal.

- Terrorist leaders may want to provoke the target government to overreact and introduce excessively harsh counterterrorism measures. By doing this, they hope to make a majority of the population oppose the government.

- Governments may use terrorist methods to force obedience from the general population. (This type of terrorism is called **state terrorism**, which is also known as institutional terrorism. Note that according to some definitions of terrorism, it is not possible for a government to be guilty of terrorism. The NCTC definition, for example, explicitly states that only "sub-national groups" and not nations can be guilty of terrorism. Most definitions of terrorism, however, do provide for the existence of state terrorism.)

State Terrorism

The particular terrorist acts that governments use vary from country to country. In some cases, political opponents are murdered. Elsewhere, torture is used to intimidate opponents and to obtain information from them. In some countries, those who threaten the government just disappear (see Figure 23–5). The uncertainty of their fate merely adds to the terror for families and political associates of the "disappeared."

The use of state terrorism has declined considerably since the 1980s because many countries in Latin America, Africa, eastern Europe, and Asia now have governments that are more inclined to respect human rights. In Myanmar and some other countries, governments continue to use repressive measures against their opponents. The US government has been accused of using torture—clearly a form of terrorism—in its battle against terrorists in Iraq, Afghanistan, and elsewhere.

In another form of institutional terrorism, a country that does not actually commit terrorist acts may instead provide a safe haven for terrorist groups. This is **state-sponsored terrorism**. An example is the role played by Afghanistan in hosting the leadership and training facilities of al-Qaeda, the terrorist group responsible for the 2001 attacks on the United States. Other countries that have a record of harbouring terrorists include Iran, Syria, Libya, and North Korea. In the past, the US has been accused of supporting regimes that were guilty of terrorism or of sponsoring terrorism, for example, by providing financial and military aid to countries such as Argentina and Chile when they were guilty of state terrorism.

Figure 23–5 Members of the group Mothers of Plaza de Mayo comfort each other as they participate in the 19th annual Resistance March in the main square of Buenos Aires, Argentina. The march is held every year to demand an accounting for the 30 000 people who disappeared during the armed forces' "dirty war" against alleged subversives between 1976 and 1983. The last march was held in 2006. (In 1999 the organization was awarded the UN prize for peace education.)

Motivations for Terrorism

Human motivation is often complex, and a wide variety of reasons might draw someone to join a terrorist group. However, three types of motivation are often suggested. In most cases, various combinations of these motivations may be at work.

- **Rational motivation**. These terrorists may have considered other methods of reaching a particular goal but abandoned them because they were not effective. Instead they choose to employ asymmetric warfare to achieve their goals.

- **Psychological motivation**. Terrorists with this motivation feel a sense of purpose in their lives that did not exist before. They are "true believers" in their cause and do not consider the possibility that they might be wrong in either their goals or their methods. They consider their opponents to be evil, and this belief makes it easier to use violence against them. Terrorists who are psychologically motivated have absolute beliefs; hence, disagreements within the group are not readily accepted. The result is that terrorist groups built on this type of motivation frequently splinter into smaller and smaller factions. For example, when the main leaders of the IRA chose (for rational reasons) to end their terrorist activities and negotiate a settlement with the British government, a number of splinter groups, such as the *Real IRA* and *Continuity IRA*, broke away because they wanted to continue to use violence.

- **Cultural motivation**. People may join terrorist groups out of fear that their most important cultural or religious values are under threat. To some, terrorism in defence of one's culture or faith is not only acceptable, it's a duty. It is important to remember that while a few members of a cultural or religious group may adopt terrorist tactics, the vast majority of those who share the culture or faith do not support such tactics.

Freedom Fighter or Terrorist?

There is an old expression that says a lot about the nature of terrorism: "One person's terrorist is another person's freedom fighter." A violent act can be seen by one person as a terrorist act, while to another it is a necessary step to achieve liberty or to protect one's religion or culture. Consider the following examples:

- In 1988, the US *Vice President's Report on Terrorism* included a list of groups that the government considered to be terrorist. One of these was the *African National Congress* (ANC), which had fought for years against the *apartheid* (racial separation) policies of the government of South Africa. The jailed leader of the ANC, Nelson Mandela, was also considered to be a terrorist. Only five years later, Mandela won the Nobel Peace Prize for being the person most responsible for the peaceful transition of South Africa from the racist apartheid regime to the democratic government that exists today. In 2001, in recognition for his contributions to world peace, he became only the second foreigner to be given honorary Canadian citizenship.

- Mandela was not the first person formerly labelled a terrorist to win the Nobel Peace Prize. In 1978, Israeli President Menachem Begin won the award in recognition for his efforts to establish peace between his country and Egypt. Begin first came to public notice in the 1940s as the leader of an anti-British terrorist group called the *Irgun*. The Irgun was best known for its bombing of the King David Hotel in Jerusalem, an attack that resulted in the deaths of 91 people. Similarly, Yasser Arafat, founder of the *Palestinian Liberation Organization* (PLO), was often called a terrorist leader, but he shared the

Nobel Peace Prize in 1994 with Shimon Peres and Yitzhak Rabin of Israel for their efforts to create peace in the Middle East.

- In the early 1950s, Jomo Kenyatta was the leader of a group in Kenya called the *Mau-Mau*. To destabilize the British colonial government, the Mau-Mau attacked the isolated farms of European settlers. More than 30 of these settlers were brutally murdered in a fashion that was clearly designed to create terror. During this time, Kenyatta was described in British newspapers as a "terrorist leader." A decade later, when he was negotiating Kenya's independence from the British, these newspapers called him a "nationalist leader." Years later, as the highly respected president of Kenya, he was frequently called on to help solve problems in other parts of Africa. During this time, the same newspapers that had called him a "terrorist" described him as the "father of his country" and the "elder statesman of Africa."

In all cases, terrorism is a relative concept. Individual perceptions and changing geopolitical realities affect how the violent actions of groups and individuals are interpreted. Consider the case of Osama Bin Laden. In the 1990s, he was one of the idealistic young Muslims who went to Afghanistan to fight against the "godless" Soviet occupiers of that Islamic country. To people and governments in the West, he was one of the "good guys" and worthy of moral and financial support. Now, in the West, he is widely considered one of the worst villains of modern times, but from his perspective, little has changed. He continues to fight for his faith against powerful, foreign forces that he sees threatening it, using whatever methods are available to him and his allies.

Changing Nature of Terrorist Threats

In the past, most terrorism has involved conventional weapons such as guns and bombs. While these threats are still widely used, the greatest fear today is of even more dangerous weapons.

Biological and Chemical Threats

The threat posed by **chemical terrorism** became a reality in 1995 in Tokyo. An extreme religious cult, *Aum Shinrikyo*, released a nerve gas called sarin into the subway. The method of delivery was simple. While holding their breath, cult members dropped small plastic bags containing sarin onto a train platform, broke the bags by stepping on them, and then ran away before the gas spread. Twelve people died and more than 5000 were injured. The Aum Shinrikyo attack proved that a small group could acquire and successfully use a chemical agent for terrorism.

In the weeks after the 9/11 attacks on the US, letters containing anthrax spores were mailed to American media outlets and government offices. It seemed that the age of **bioterrorism** had begun, since anthrax is a potentially deadly disease. (No one was ever charged in connection to the anthrax attacks.) The anthrax attacks engendered widespread concern, and Canada, as well as many other countries, took steps to build up supplies of antidotes to biological weapons.

Nuclear Threats

Perhaps the ultimate terrorist threat is **nuclear terrorism**. The death and destruction that an act of nuclear terrorism could cause would greatly exceed that of any previous attacks. The mere threat of a nuclear attack accomplishes the terrorists' goal of creating fear and uncertainty. Four main forms of nuclear threat exist.

- A terrorist group could buy an atomic bomb. There is evidence that both Aum Shinrikyo and al-Qaeda attempted to purchase a nuclear device in the former Soviet Union in the early 1990s. The proliferation of nuclear weapons in countries like Pakistan and North Korea increases the risk of an atomic bomb falling into terrorist hands. For example, in the mid-1990s a senior Russian security official claimed that, after the breakup of the Soviet Union, 84 nuclear "briefcase" bombs could not be accounted for. These bombs were small enough that they could be carried for short distances in a backpack and yet could kill as many as 100 000 people. This threat has likely declined since these bombs have an operational life span of only five to ten years.

- A terrorist group might attempt to build its own nuclear weapon. While this undertaking would require enormous financial and scientific resources, experts say that it is not impossible. There is evidence that al-Qaeda, after failing to buy an atomic bomb, tried to buy enough weapons-grade uranium or plutonium on the black market to make one.

- Terrorists who do not have the technical ability to make a real atomic bomb could build a *hybrid bomb* (called a dirty bomb) in which high explosives are used to spread dangerous radioactive materials over populated areas. While the damage from an attack of this type would be much less than from a standard nuclear weapon, the likelihood of a terrorist group acquiring such a weapon is greater. Not only would it be technically much less difficult to build, high-grade nuclear materials are not needed—wastes from a nuclear power plant could be used, for example.

- Nuclear terrorism could involve blowing up a nuclear power plant to release the massive amount of radioactive materials inside. This might prove a more difficult task than it would seem. In one test, a fighter jet flown at subsonic speeds into a section of a reactor building wall caused only minor damage on impact. The damage did not destroy the wall's integrity.

Did You Know?

The use of fuel-laden airliners against New York and Washington has been described as a novel, "high-concept, low-tech" approach to terrorism. Authorities are concerned about the use of a variety of novel methods of terrorism in the future.

Fighting Terrorism—Is a "War on Terror" Possible?

People must feel safe as they go about their lives: going to school, working, travelling, and raising children. This was made particularly clear in the Old Core countries after the attacks on 9/11. The response of the American government was to declare a "**War on Terror**." This concept can be seen as problematic since "terror" is a methodology and not an enemy. Wars either end by negotiation, by surrender, or by the complete destruction of one combatant by the other; any of these is very difficult in this current "war." There is no opponent nation to negotiate with and the goal of capturing or killing all of the terrorists that might exist is impossible. In fact, there is considerable evidence that the War on Terror has, in fact, increased the number of terrorists or potential terrorists.

Containing the threat of terrorism involves the process of **counterterrorism.** Counterterrorism can occur at a number of levels. Efforts can be made to interfere with the planning and organization of terrorism. Such efforts include maintaining a network of spies to uncover terrorist plots. This strategy is not easily achieved, since it requires agents who are willing and able to work undercover, perhaps for years, in dangerous conditions. More routine is the use of electronic surveillance, for example of long-distance phone calls and emails. Fighting terrorism in these ways can also produce concerns about the invasion of privacy and interference with freedoms of speech and association.

In some cases, especially when terrorism is an internal or domestic problem, arrests may be possible. Sometimes, a settlement may be negotiated between the perpetrators and the government. In extreme cases, the possibility of assassinating terrorists might be considered. Since killing by government is illegal in most countries, the question again is, how willing are we to compromise the principles by which we live in order to gain a feeling of enhanced security?

The War on Terror employs these conventional counterterrorism methods but also includes an additional, highly controversial, approach. In response to the 9/11 attacks, the US, with the support of many of its NATO and other allies, including Canada (see Figure 23–6), decided to launch a military attack against Afghanistan in an attempt to eliminate both the leadership of al-Qaeda and the Taliban government that had sponsored the terrorists. The initial attack on Afghanistan proved highly successful as it matched the most powerful military forces in the world against a relatively poor country with limited military resources. What followed, though, has been a *protracted* (long) phase of asymmetric warfare, something that the Taliban and their al-Qaeda allies are very good at. At the same time that military action is occurring, the Western allies are trying to help build an effective and widely respected Afghan government and provide various forms of development assistance. While the initial war was short, this phase of the struggle is likely to last for many years. (No one is forgetting that Afghanistan has a history of being a graveyard for powerful invading foreign forces. In 1842, only one member of a British force of 4500 survived a retreat from Kabul; in the 1980s, the powerful Soviet army was defeated by the Afghans.)

After Afghanistan, the question became "What next?" Were other countries that harboured and supported terrorists to be attacked? In 2002, President George W. Bush identified an "axis of evil" that consisted of North Korea, Iraq, and Iran as potential targets in the war against terrorism. Then in 2003, the US, with considerably less international support than in 1991 or in Afghanistan, invaded and occupied Iraq. Critics of this war pointed out that there was little evidence to support the contention that Iraq was a hotbed of terrorism.

Figure 23–6 In April 2007, a gunner with the Royal Canadian Horse Artillery (RCHA) fires a 155-mm howitzer in support of front line troops during a mission in Helmand Province, Afghanistan.

Major terrorist campaigns require significant funding. At least some of this funding has come from expatriates in countries like Canada, the US, and the European Union. For example, there is evidence that money has been raised in Canada for terrorist groups in countries such as Ireland, Sri Lanka, and Afghanistan. Careful monitoring of international banking systems can limit the flow of such funds. Globalization both aids and hinders this measure. Because of financial globalization, immense sums of money move around the world each day. Support to terrorist organizations can be hidden in this traffic. At the same time, however, technological globalization makes it easier for authorities to track these transactions.

Another approach in combatting terrorism is to provide better protection for likely targets of attack. Increasing airport security is an obvious example that you might have experienced: others are ensuring adequate protection of nuclear power plants, city water systems, and major sports facilities. Two problems emerge with this approach: is it possible to protect all potential targets? And is society prepared to accept the cost of this protection and the resulting disruption of normal activities?

Concerns have been, and are being, expressed about anti-terrorist laws that have been introduced in many countries in response to various threats. Typically, these laws suspend some of the **civil liberties** that we take for granted, for example, strict limits on how long a person can be held by police without charges being laid,

or when wiretaps can be used. For some, the loss of civil liberties is acceptable in return for a higher level of security. For others, the protection of hard-won civil liberties is paramount. An additional concern is that innocent members of particular ethnic or religious groups might be deprived of their rights for no reason other than the fact that they are members of that faith or may have an appearance similar to members of a terrorist group.

Eliminating the Conditions in Which Terrorism Grows

Many feel that the best way to eliminate the problem of terrorism is to remove the conditions that cause it to develop in the first place. For example, if people feel that they have a legitimate way to address their grievances, few will feel the need to resort to terrorist tactics. It may be difficult to remedy the conditions that cause terrorism as they are varied, serious, and often seem *intractable* (not easily solved). As you read about the wide range of economic, social, geopolitical, and even environmental issues that are investigated in this book, think about how they may have contributed, to a greater or lesser extent, to the growth of terrorism. Our ultimate success in eliminating terrorism may be directly related to our success in eliminating these core causes of the problem.

Chapter Questions

Knowledge and Understanding

1. All terrorist acts are crimes, but not all crimes are terrorist acts. Explain this difference.

2. What role do mass media (television, newspapers, the Internet) play in terrorism today? Answer this question both from the perspective of terrorist organizations and from the perspective of those who fight terrorism.

3. Describe the difficulties faced by governments who are trying to fight terrorism.

4. Using specific examples, describe some of the circumstances that might motivate terrorists.

Thinking

5. **a)** Using specific examples, explain the difference between a freedom fighter and a terrorist. Why is it sometimes difficult to make this distinction?

   b) Who might consider Osama Bin Laden to be a freedom fighter? Explain.

6. Discuss the statement, "It is impossible to have a war on terror."

7. In 2007, Canada's *Auditor General* (the person in government whose job it is to assess how effective parts of the government are in meeting their responsibilities) stated that the federal government was not doing enough to secure Canada's borders or to prevent undesirable people from entering Canada. Why is this not surprising? What steps could be taken to make Canada's borders more secure? What costs would be associated with increased border security?

Communication

8. Prepare for a debate on one of these topics. Your teacher will let you know which side to argue in the debate.

   a) Resolved—That the concept that one person's terrorist is another person's freedom fighter is morally unacceptable.

   b) Resolved—That governments should use all the means at their disposal to deal with terrorism, even if this involves the restriction of constitutionally protected civil rights.

Application

9. How does terrorism affect your life? Suggest the ways in which the growing concern about terrorism since 9/11 has had an impact on the life you lead compared to someone your age living in Canada on September 10, 2001.

10. It was suggested in this chapter that the ultimate solution to the problem of terrorism is the elimination of the underlying conditions that encourage people to adopt terrorist methods to achieve their goals. Work with a partner to identify a terrorist-related problem (and suggest a solution) in each of the following areas: cultural globalization, economic globalization, political globalization, and environmental sustainability.

11. Investigate the following aspects for one of the terrorist groups shown in Figure 23–3. A good starting point is the MIPT TKB Web site, mentioned in the Weblink on page 367. With your teacher's approval, you may choose another group to research.
    - motivation and purpose of the group
    - membership characteristics (who joins, how many members are there)
    - location—including country, region
    - types of terrorist acts carried out and purpose of the attacks
    - response of the state
    - impact of the group's activities **G**

CHAPTER 24

Toward 2050—Changing Global Power Structures

Key Terms

rule set

MAD—Mutually Assured
Destruction

Political Islam

isolationist

unilateralist

intellectual property

Rome existed as both a republic
and an empire for more than
1000 years. Jerash in Jordan
(right) is the best-preserved
Roman site in the Middle East.
During nearly four centuries of
occupation in Britain, the Romans
built a network of roads (one is
shown below).

Key Questions

By the end of this chapter you will be able to answer
the following questions.

■ What combination of factors contributes to the rise and fall
of a world power?

■ What uses were made of hard power and soft power
during the Cold War?

■ How might globalization contribute to (or reduce)
the influence of a world power?

■ To what extent will sustainability issues be reflected
in the distribution of world power by 2050?

■ What countries/regions will dominate the world by 2050?

World Power Structures Today and Tomorrow

The first volume of *The History of the Decline and Fall of the Roman Empire* by Edward Gibbon appeared in 1776. Eventually, six volumes were published, and it remains in print today. Gibbon's work was the first to analyze in detail why a major world power declined and fell. Rome was not the first great world power to fall from prominence and certainly will not be the last. Figures 24–1 and 24–2 show just two examples of dominant world powers of the past that, like Rome, saw their great empires disappear.

Figure 24–1 The Mongol Empire was the largest *contiguous* (in one piece) empire in history. It opened contacts between eastern Asia and Europe and united China for the first time. Immense at its peak in the mid-1200s, it survived almost two centuries.

Figure 24–2 This stamp shows the British Empire at its peak at the end of the 19th century. It was the most extensive empire in world history and spread the English language and British traditions of government, education, and law throughout much of the world.

When you think about the rise and fall of world powers, several questions should come to mind:

- What special set of conditions allows a state, sometimes quite small like Britain, to expand its influence to the point where it becomes a major world power?

- How does a world power (or empire) eventually lose its influence? To what extent is this determined by what happens inside or outside the country?

- What will the world's power structures be like in 50 years?

The end of World War II marked an important watershed in the history of world power structures. The devastation of the war had not only affected the defeated nations, Germany and Japan, but it had also dramatically weakened two of the victors, Britain and France. Two aspiring imperial powers and two long-term imperial powers were no longer in the race to be dominant countries in the world.

Only two superpowers remained—the United States and the Soviet Union. The result was the Cold War, which threatened the world with nuclear annihilation for close to 40 years. The Cold War involved the use of hard power and soft power by both sides in an attempt to expand each power's influence in the world at the expense of the other. The application of hard power can be seen in several wars involving the superpowers (such as the Korean War, Vietnam War, and Afghan–Soviet War) and in numerous proxy wars (see Chapter 22). It can also be seen in the massive military spending by both sides.

The use of soft power was less obvious, but often just as important. Negotiations and discussions at international forums such as the UN, and relationships developed at international sporting events and through development assistance, are examples of soft power. The UN provided a polite "battleground" for the Soviet

Union and its allies, and the US and its allies. Each tried to make its case and gain support from the many "non-aligned" UN members. The Olympics were also highly politicized at this time. More than 60 nations, led by the US, and including Canada, boycotted the Moscow Olympics in 1980 to protest the Soviet invasion of Afghanistan. In retaliation, the Soviet Union led a boycott, with more than a dozen nations, of the Los Angeles Olympics in 1984, citing "chauvinistic sentiments and an anti-Soviet hysteria being whipped up in the United States."

By the end of the 1980s, the Soviet Union had lost the Cold War. The cost of competing militarily with the US combined with the inefficient Communist economy had almost bankrupted the Soviet Union, and its allies. People in these countries wanted their futures to take a different direction; the Soviet Union as we knew it, split up and ceased to exist. As a result, the world now has only one superpower—the US. Numerous commentators have suggested that the US is now, in three important ways, the most dominant power in history. Never has a country had such a truly worldwide sphere of influence. At the same time, no country has ever had the ability the US has to project its soft and hard power to every part of the world. Also, no world power has ever experienced the complete absence of a peer, or even a near-peer, rival. While no rival to the US exists today, in this chapter you will investigate the extent to which this may change within your lifetime.

GLOBALIZATION

While no rival to the US exists today, in this chapter you will investigate the extent to which this situation may change within your lifetime.

How might such a change alter the lifestyle of the average Canadian?

A New World Needs New Rules

The world was left with the job of defining a new **rule set** for the post–Cold War era. A rule set can be defined as *a collection of rules that delineates how an activity should unfold.* The rule set for different sports or games, for example, is unique. The rule set for hockey is very different from that for tennis. A hockey game or tennis match can be played successfully because those involved know and agree to use the appropriate rule set specific to that sport.

Rule sets exist in international relations as well. A Cold War rule set developed that those on both sides understood and respected. Perhaps the most obvious and fundamental rule was the existence of **Mutually Assured Destruction** (**MAD**). Each side realized that if it used nuclear weapons, the nuclear strikes that would follow would destroy both sides (see Figure 24–3).

At the end of the Cold War, many of the old rules no longer applied, and a new rule set had to be developed. For the most part, this does not happen by discussion around a table in Geneva or at the UN. Instead, it evolves as a result of the actions by nations and sub-national groups (like al-Qaeda) and the response of others to those actions. This process can be demonstrated by what has happened since the al-Qaeda terrorist attacks on the US in 2001. The response to these attacks included the US attack on Iraq and NATO involvement in Afghanistan. Canada chose to actively support military action in Afghanistan but not to do so in Iraq. These differing decisions were made based on how the Canadian government interpreted the new rule set that involved dealing with terrorism.

Figure 24–3 This is the *Tsar Bomba* (King of Bombs), the largest nuclear bomb ever made. It was built in 1961 by Soviet scientists and had the power of 100 million tonnes of TNT. During the Cold War, the Soviets and Americans competed to have the most bombs, the biggest bombs, and the best delivery systems, even though MAD meant that these would never be used. All of this was the result of the rule set of the day.

WHO WILL BE THE WORLD'S GREAT POWERS BY 2050?

What do you think your life will be like in 2050? How will world economic, political, and military power structures influence your life? It is fascinating to think about how the world will change between now and then. In this exercise you will consider how the world's power structures might evolve.

Once you have an understanding of today's rule set and the factors that will influence its future evolution, you can start to think about the world's power structures in 2050. To do this, you will look at a number of countries/regions that will likely continue to be dominant world powers or that may become dominant powers by 2050. Our "nominees" for major world powers in 2050 come from the Old Core (Canada, the EU, Japan, and the US), the New Core (the BRIC countries: Brazil, Russia, India, and China) and one composite region that we will call "**Political Islam**," which exists in the New Core (a bit), Near Core (a lot), and the Far Periphery (to some extent.) (See Figure 24–4.) (Note that in the descriptions below we will use the word "country" to refer to both individual countries and to our two regional groupings—the EU and Political Islam.)

You should work on this activity in a group with two to three classmates to discuss the factors that contribute to a country becoming a dominant power and what conclusions you wish to draw from your analysis. We will use Canada to demonstrate how you should approach this task.

The rule set for international relations is constantly evolving as conditions change. The new rule set for the 21st century must take into consideration several important factors.

- Dealing with globalization of all types. By most measures, globalization has had (and will have) many benefits, but the spread of globalization has also caused serious problems.

  - Some people and some countries have benefitted economically far more than others. Can the overall benefits of economic globalization be sustained while ways are found to protect those people hurt by freer trade and by the global movement of jobs and investment?

  - Can individual cultures be protected in a world increasingly dominated by the cultures of the Old Core, especially that of the US?

  - How and to what extent can countries and regions choose to "opt out" of aspects of globalization that they find unacceptable?

- Encouraging a move to sustainable practices on a global basis, without causing undue economic dislocation for people in both rich and poor countries.

  - In particular, how can the living standards of those outside the Old Core be improved substantially without causing increased greenhouse gas emissions, pollution of all types, and resource depletion?

  - To what extent can residents of Old Core countries live much more sustainably and still enjoy a lifestyle comparable to what they have had?

- Coming to terms with the predominant role of the US, both in terms of it being the only superpower and its having a truly global reach.

  - Not only does the rest of the world have to come to terms with the dominance of the US, but so too do the American people. While some Americans relish their dominant role in the world, others have little interest in it and want to pull back to a more **isolationist** stance—for example, by avoiding foreign wars, by dramatically reducing legal, and especially illegal, immigration, and by erecting more trade barriers.

Figure 24–4 Here are our "nominees" for the world's great powers in 2050.

What You Will Do

Determine how the world's power structures might evolve.

1. Examine the **country statistics** and the **Five Things You Should Know** pointers.

2. Gather **additional information** by doing your own research on each country.

3. Evaluate the information you gather from these sources and summarize your findings in "Evidence" under the most appropriate heading.

4. Analyze the evidence to reach a "Verdict."

5. Categorize the nominees and identify relationships.

Note: Obviously, the conclusions you draw will be somewhat speculative in nature. Do not be afraid to explain the conditions needed for your prediction to come true, or to suggest alternative outcomes for a particular country, based on different assumptions of what might happen.

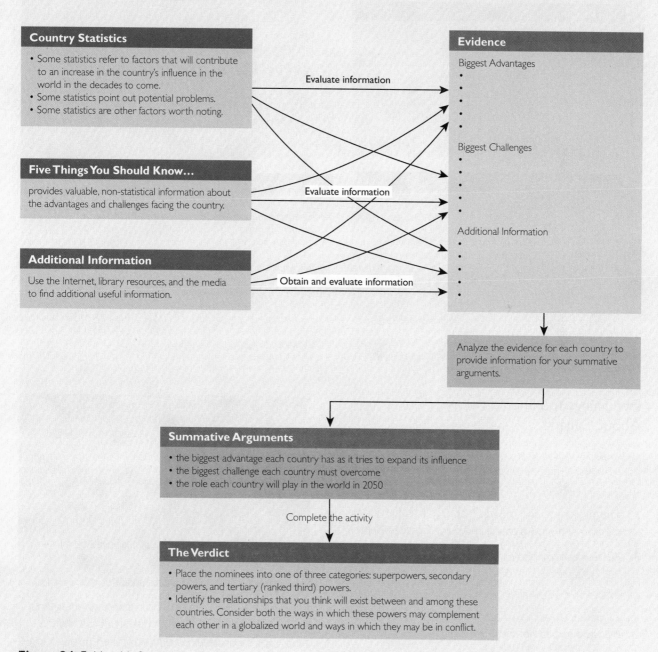

Country Statistics

- Some statistics refer to factors that will contribute to an increase in the country's influence in the world in the decades to come.
- Some statistics point out potential problems.
- Some statistics are other factors worth noting.

Five Things You Should Know...

provides valuable, non-statistical information about the advantages and challenges facing the country.

Additional Information

Use the Internet, library resources, and the media to find additional useful information.

Evaluate information

Evaluate information

Obtain and evaluate information

Evidence

Biggest Advantages
-
-
-
-
-

Biggest Challenges
-
-
-
-

Additional Information
-
-
-
-

Analyze the evidence for each country to provide information for your summative arguments.

Summative Arguments

- the biggest advantage each country has as it tries to expand its influence
- the biggest challenge each country must overcome
- the role each country will play in the world in 2050

Complete the activity

The Verdict

- Place the nominees into one of three categories: superpowers, secondary powers, and tertiary (ranked third) powers.
- Identify the relationships that you think will exist between and among these countries. Consider both the ways in which these powers may complement each other in a globalized world and ways in which they may be in conflict.

Figure 24–5 Use this flowchart to help you complete this activity. Now read the Canadian example. It will help you get started.

Old Core

"*The proximity and economic, cultural, and military power of the United States play a remarkably important role in defining Canada.*"

The People

• Population	33 400 000
• Population density	3 people/km^2
• Total fertility rate	1.6 children/woman
• Life expectancy	80.3 years
• Population over 65	14%
• Population growth rate	+0.87%
Natural increase	+0.29%
Net migration	+0.58%
• Infant mortality rate	4.7%
• Literacy rate	99%

Energy Resources

• Oil	
Net trade	+1.71 t/per capita/yr
R/P ratio	15 (conventional)
	and 142 (oil sands)
• Natural gas	
Net trade	major exporter
R/P ratio	9
• Coal	
Net trade	major exporter
R/P ratio	105

The Land

• Area	9 984 670 km^2
• Land use	
Farmland	5.2%
Other:	94.8%

The Economy

• Total GDP	US$1.09 trillion
• Total GDP PPP	US$1.18 trillion
• Per capita GDP PPP	US$35 700
• GDP growth rate	+2.8%
• Composition of GDP	
Agriculture	2.3%
Industry	29.2%
Services	68.5%
• Current account balance	+US$21 billion (1.9% of GDP)
• GINI index	33
• Public debt as %GDP (Trend)	65% (↓)
• Trade balance	+US$52 billion (4.8% of GDP)
• Export partners	US (82%), UK (2%)
• Import partners	US (55%), China (9%)
• Internet users	66%

The Military

• Size of military	59 000 (0.2% of population)
• Spending on military	US$7.9 billion
• Spending per capita	US$240
• Spending as percentage of GDP	0.8%

Figure 24–6 Canada statistics

Five Things You Should Know About Canada

1. Canada (see Figure 24–6) is fortunate to have a remarkable natural resource base for a country with such a relatively small population.

2. The proximity and power (economic, cultural, and military) of the US is critical in defining Canada's identity.

3. Because of expanding oil sands developments (see Figure 24–7), Canada is one of the world's worst offenders in the production of greenhouse gases.

4. Climate change may affect Canada less severely than many other parts of the world.

5. Canada has been one of the most successful Old Core countries in accepting and integrating immigrants. Immigrants have added to a highly educated and skilled population.

Figure 24–7 Perhaps Canada's greatest advantage in the 21st century will be its rich resource base, like the Alberta oil sands development shown here, in a world that will increasingly be in need of all manner of raw materials. The lure of resource-related jobs will be so strong that you may end up living in a part of Canada far from Ontario.

The Evidence

These are the kind of observations you should make for each country.

Biggest Advantages

1. Canada's population is similar to that of most of the Old Core countries but generally somewhat healthier. Our ability to attract highly skilled immigrants makes up for the fact that our natural rate of increase is low and dropping since our total fertility rate is much below replacement level. We will likely have something close to zero population growth by 2050. Also, skilled immigrants will likely be harder to find than now as New Core countries grow economically and competition for immigrants becomes more intense.

2. The oil sands mean that we have a substantial amount of oil for domestic use and for export. A problem with oil sands development is the massive production of greenhouse gases. A solution for this is being sought.

3. The Canadian economy is strong and growing. Our rich fossil fuel, mineral, and forest resources suggest solid future growth. Canada's GDP growth rate is 2.8 percent. This may seem small compared to China's 11.1 percent, for example. However Canada's growth rate yields an increase in the per-capita GDP of about US$1000, while China's only increases its per-capita GDP by US$866.

4. Canada's positive current-account balance is a sign of a very healthy economy—more money is coming into the country each year (primarily from trade, travel, and investments) than is leaving.

5. Our Gini index shows that income is relatively evenly distributed across the population compared to the income distribution in most countries.

6. Canada's federal government has paid down the public debt significantly by running surpluses for many years.

7. Our positive trade balance reflects increasing demand for our resource products.

Biggest Challenges

8. We have relatively small natural gas reserves and under NAFTA rules are required to treat the American market like the Canadian market—that is, we cannot arbitrarily cut exports to the US. New reserves must be found and alternatives to natural gas (for example, for home heating) must be put in place.

9. Canada has limited amounts of farmland and imports large amounts of food from all over the world (Figure 24–8).

10. Our dependence on the American market is worrisome since poor economic conditions there have a great impact in Canada.

Additional Information

11. Whether Canada's limited spending and reliance on its military is a good thing or a bad thing depends largely on your view of the role of hard power in achieving peace and stability in the world—and whether you think Canada can make a meaningful contribution in this type of endeavour.

12. Additional evidence can be found in the "Five Things You Should Know . . ." section or from your own knowledge and research.

The Verdict

Biggest Advantage—There will be an increasing demand in the future for Canada's immense natural-resource wealth.

Biggest Challenge—Canada does not have a large enough population to compete in the "big leagues" of world economic, political, and military power.

Conclusion—It is highly unlikely that Canada will be one of the most important world powers by 2050 or even a secondary power. Most likely we will be a tertiary world power—still important, but rarely thought of in world-power politics. Three things stand in Canada's way. Our population is just too small—less than one-third that of the next-smallest country on our list, Japan. Our relationship with the US will make it difficult for Canada to emerge as an independent centre of world power. Finally, there doesn't appear to be a desire to become a major world power.

Figure 24–8 Why would Canada's potential to be a dominant power in 2050 be reduced by the fact that we import much of the food we eat?

EUROPEAN UNION

"The EU consists of richer Old Core countries in the west and poorer New Core countries in the east."

The People

- Population — 490 430 000
- Population density — 113 people/km^2
- Total fertility rate — 1.50 children/woman
- Life expectancy — 78.7 years
- Population over 65 — 17%
- Population growth rate — +0.16%
  - Natural increase — 0.0%
  - Net migration — +0.16%
- Infant mortality rate — 4.8%
- Literacy rate — 99%

Energy Resources

- Oil
  - Net trade[1] — −1.14 t/per capita/yr
  - R/P ratio — 8
- Natural gas
  - Net trade[1] — major importer
  - R/P ratio — 13
- Coal
  - Net trade[1] — little external trade
  - R/P ratio — 63

The Land

- Area — 4 324 782 km^2
- Land use
  - Farmland: — na (varies by country)
  - Other: — na

The Economy

- Total GDP — US$13.74 trillion
- Total GDP PPP — US$13.08 trillion
- Per capita GDP PPP — US$29 900
- GDP growth rate — +3.2%
- Composition of GDP
  - Agriculture — 2.1%
  - Industry — 27.3%
  - Services — 70.5%
- Current account balance — varies country to country
- GINI index — 31
- Public debt as %GDP (Trend) — varies country to country
- Trade balance[1] — −US$136 billion (1.0% of GDP)
- Export partners[1] — US (23%), Switzerland (8%)
- Import partners[1] — US (14%), China (13%)
- Internet users — 53%

The Military

- Size of military[2] — 2 184 000 (0.4% of population)
- Spending on military — US$183 billion
- Spending per capita — US$373
- Spending as percentage of GDP — 1.3%

[1] Refers to trade outside the EU only
[2] Total of the military of all members

Figure 24–9 European Union statistics

Figure 24–10 The economy of the EU relies on costly labour compared to most of the world. As a result, the products and services it sells to the world must reflect a high degree of intellectual capital and creativity to command a high price. This is equally true in high fashion, auto design, and international banking.

Five Things You Should Know About the European Union

1. The EU (see Figure 24–9) consists of richer Old Core countries in the west and poorer New Core countries in the east. The addition of these eastern countries to the EU has provided a source of lower-cost labour.

2. Considerable uncertainty exists in the EU about whether further integration is desirable.

3. There is also uncertainty about further expansion of the EU, particularly the possible admission of Turkey into the union. The addition of a secular Islamic country that is mostly in Asia has proven to be very controversial.

4. The EU remains a global style leader, whether in fashion (see Figure 24–10), cars, or interior design.

5. Considerable immigration to the EU will be necessary in the decades to come to maintain population levels and economic growth. Many EU residents do not welcome increased immigration.

"Much of Japan's 'economic miracle' in the 60+ years since the end of World War II had been based on its ability to bring new technologies into the marketplace."

The People

• Population	127 433 000
• Population density	337 people/km²
• Total fertility rate	1.61 children/woman
• Life expectancy	80.3 years
• Population over 65	17%
• Population growth rate	−0.09%
Natural increase	−0.09%
Net migration	0.0%
• Infant mortality rate	2.8%
• Literacy rate	99%

Energy Resources

• Oil	
Net trade	−1.98 t/per capita/yr
R/P ratio	minimal reserves and production
• Natural gas	
Net trade	major importer
R/P ratio	limited
• Coal	
Net trade	major importer
R/P ratio	268 (reserves are not economically recoverable at this time)

The Land

• Area	377 835 km²
• Land use	
Farmland:	12.5%
Other:	87.5%

The Economy

• Total GDP	US$4.88 trillion
• Total GDP PPP	US$4.22 trillion
• Per capita GDP PPP	US$31 100
• GDP growth rate	2.2%
• Composition of GDP	
Agriculture	1.6%
Industry	25.3%
Services	73.1%
• Current account balance	+US$174 billion (3.6% of GDP)
• GINI index	38
• Public debt as %GDP (Trend)	176% (↑)
• Trade balance	+US$66 billion (1.4% of GDP)
• Export partners	US (23%), China (14.3%)
• Import partners	China (21%), US (12%)
• Internet users	69%

The Military

• Size of military	237 000 (0.2% of population)
• Spending on military	US$39.5 billion
• Spending per capita	US$310
• Spending as percentage of GDP	0.8%

Figure 24–11 Japan statistics

Figure 24–12 This concept car, the Nissan Pivo-2, reflects the world leadership that Japan has consistently demonstrated in bringing advanced technologies into the consumer market. This car is electrically powered and does not have a designated front or back—the passenger compartment rotates as needed.

Five Things You Should Know About Japan

1. Japan (see Figure 24–11) is a very rich country that has seen relatively slow economic growth for more than a decade.

2. Much of Japan's "economic miracle" in the more than 60 years since the end of World War II has been based on its ability to bring new technologies into the marketplace. This has occurred in widely diverse industries—electronics, automobiles (see Figure 24–12), and shipbuilding.

3. Very few migrants move to Japan and many of those who do have great difficulty integrating into the society. This is a great problem in a country whose population is aging and starting to decline in size.

4. After the destruction that militarism brought to Japan in World War II, the country finds itself torn over what role the military should play.

5. Japan has relatively few natural resources and must import oil and most other raw materials to keep its economy healthy.

Old Core

"The US is the world leader in theoretical and applied scientific research. This fact is fundamental to the future economic health of the country."

The People

• Population	301 140 000
• Population density	31 people/km²
• Total fertility rate	2.09 children/woman
• Life expectancy	78.0 years
• Population over 65	13%
• Population growth rate	+0.89%
Natural increase	+0.59%
Net migration	+0.30%
• Infant mortality rate	6.4%
• Literacy rate	99%

Energy Resources

• Oil	
Net trade	−2.02 t/per capita/yr
R/P ratio	12
• Natural Gas	
Net trade	major importer
R/P ratio	11
• Coal	
Net trade	major exporter
R/P ratio	234

Figure 24–13 United States statistics

Figure 24–14 This statue stands in front of the New York Stock Exchange. What is the connection between a bull and the stock market?

The Land

• Area	9 826 630 km²
• Land use	
Farmland:	18.2%
Other:	77.8%

The Economy

• Total GDP	US$13.16 trillion
• Total GDP PPP	US$13.06 trillion
• Per capita GDP PPP	US$43 800
• GDP growth rate	2.9%
• Composition of GDP	
Agriculture	0.9%
Industry	20.4%
Services	78.6%
• Current account balance	−US$862 billion (6.6% of GDP)
• GINI index	45
• Public debt as %GDP (Trend)	65% (↑)
• Trade balance	−US$845 billion (6.4% of GDP)
• Export partners	Canada (22%), Mexico (13%)
• Import partners	China (16%), Canada (16%)
• Internet users	69%

The Military

• Size of military	1 336 000 (0.4% of population)
• Spending on military	US$276.7 billion
• Spending per capita	US$919
• Spending as percentage of GDP	2.1%

Five Things You Should Know About the United States

1. The US (Figure 24–13) is the world leader in theoretical and applied scientific research. This is fundamental to the future economic health of the country.

2. The world's financial markets are focused on New York City (Figure 24–14). Also, more of the world's largest corporations have their homes in the US than anywhere else.

3. The US has been criticized, both domestically and from abroad, for following a too **unilateralist** foreign policy—that is, for not being willing to work cooperatively with other nations to solve problems. This can be seen in their failure to ratify treaties like the Kyoto Protocol on climate change, the Ottawa Treaty to restrict the use of land mines, the UN Law of the Sea Convention, and the UN Convention on the Rights of the Child.

4. Many regions of the US face significant water shortages. This includes the rapidly growing southwestern regions of the country.

5. The US military has over 700 military bases in more than 36 countries around the world.

"Brazil has shown little interest in being a global power (except in soccer of course). Instead it prefers to be the dominant country in South America."

The People

• Population	190 011 000
• Population density	22 people/km^2
• Total fertility rate	1.88 children/woman
• Life expectancy	72.2 years
• Population over 65	6%
• Population growth rate	+1.01%
Natural increase	+1.04%
Net migration	−0.03%
• Infant mortality rate	27.6%
• Literacy rate	89%

Energy Resources

• Oil	
Net trade	−0.01 t/per capita/yr
R/P ratio	18.5
• Natural gas	
Net trade	minor importer
R/P ratio	30
• Coal	
Net trade	minor importer
R/P ratio	>500

The Land

• Area	8 511 965 km^2
• Land use	
Farmland:	7.8%
Other:	92.2%

The Economy

• Total GDP	US$967 billion
• Total GDP PPP	US$1.66 trillion
• Per capita GDP PPP	US$8800
• GDP growth rate	3.7%
• Composition of GDP	
Agriculture	8%
Industry	38%
Services	54%
• Current account balance	+US$14 billion (1.4% of GDP)
• GINI index	57
• Public debt as %GDP (Trend)	50% (↓)
• Trade balance	+US$46 billion (4.8% of GDP)
• Export partners	US (18%), Argentina (9%)
• Import partners	US (21%), Argentina (8%)
• Internet users	22%

The Military

• Size of military	288 000 (0.2% of population)
• Spending on military	US$14.4billion
• Spending per capita	US$76
• Spending as percentage of GDP	1.5%

Figure 24–15 Brazil statistics

Five Things You Should Know About Brazil

1. Brazil (see Figure 24–15) is the world leader in the production of ethanol (principally from sugar cane) for use as a motor vehicle fuel.

2. Brazil has major problems with deforestation in the immense Amazon Basin.

3. Brazil has shown little interest in being a global power (except in soccer, of course). Instead, it prefers to be the dominant country in South America.

4. Brazil is the fifth-largest country in the world and has the fifth-largest population. Its economy is ranked ninth on a GDP PPP basis.

5. Poverty (see Figure 24–16), urban violence, and enormous economic disparities are major problems in Brazil.

Figure 24–16 Brazil has one of the highest Gini indexes in the world, indicating a huge gulf between rich and poor. This *favela* (slum) is in São Paulo, Brazil.

"Men in Russia live almost 14 years less than women. Life expectancy for men is only 59 years."

The People

• Population	141 378 000
• Population density	8.3 people/km²
• Total fertility rate	1.39 children/woman
• Life expectancy	65.9 years
• Population over 65	15%
• Population growth rate	−0.48%
Natural increase	−0.76%
Net migration	+0.28%
• Infant mortality rate	11.1%
• Literacy rate	99%

Energy Resources

• Oil	
Net trade	+1.78 t/per capita/yr
R/P ratio	22
• Natural gas	
Net trade	major exporter
R/P ratio	78
• Coal	
Net trade	major exporter
R/P ratio	>500

The Land

• Area	17 075 200 km²
• Land use	
Farmland:	7.3%
Other:	92.7%

The Economy

• Total GDP	US$734 billion
• Total GDP PPP	US$1.75 trillion
• Per capita GDP PPP	US$12 200
• GDP growth rate	6.7%
• Composition of GDP	
Agriculture	5.3%
Industry	36.6%
Services	58.2%
• Current account balance	+US$105 billion (14.3% of GDP)
• GINI index	40.5
• Public debt as %GDP (Trend)	8% (↓)
• Trade balance	+US$146 billion (19.9% of GDP)
• Export partners	Netherlands (12%), Italy (9%)
• Import partners	Germany (14%), China (10%)
• Internet users	18%

The Military

• Size of military	1 520 000 (1.1% of population)
• Spending on military	na
• Spending per capita	na
• Spending as percentage of GDP	na

Figure 24–17 Russia statistics

Five Things You Should Know About Russia

1. Russia (see Figures 24–17 and 24–18) has immense mineral, fossil fuel, and forest resources. As well, Russia has enormous freshwater resources, although most of these are far from population concentrations.

2. Men in Russia live almost 14 years less than women. Life expectancy for men is only 59 years.

3. The Russian government has become less democratic in recent years after democracy was introduced following the collapse of communism.

4. Russia faces significant problems as its population declines. Russian governments at various levels have been pushing a pronatalist agenda with little apparent success.

5. Russia is rebuilding its armed forces after the collapse of the Soviet Union.

Figure 24–18 Russia has made a significant recovery from the chaos that followed the collapse of the Soviet Union. The growth of its exports of oil and natural gas has been a key factor.

New Core

"India is by far the world's largest democracy. Governing such a large and complex country democratically is an ongoing challenge."

The People

• Population	1 129 866 000
• Population density	343.6 people/km^2
• Total fertility rate	2.81 children/woman
• Life expectancy	68.6 years
• Population over 65	5%
• Population growth rate	+1.61%
Natural increase	+1.66%
Net migration	−0.05%
• Infant mortality rate	34.6%
• Literacy rate	99%

Energy Resources

• Oil	
Net trade	−0.07 t/per capita/yr
R/P ratio	19
• Natural gas	
Net trade	no trade
R/P ratio	34
• Coal	
Net trade	minor importer
R/P ratio	105

The Land

• Area	3 287 590 km^2
• Land use	
Farmland:	51.6%
Other:	48.4%

The Economy

• Total GDP	US$1.09 trillion
• Total GDP PPP	US$4.16 trillion
• Per capita GDP PPP	US$3800
• GDP growth rate	9.4%
• Composition of GDP	
Agriculture	17.5%
Industry	27.9%
Services	54.6%
• Current account balance	−US$10 billion (0.1% of GDP)
• GINI index	32.5
• Public debt as %GDP (Trend)	60% (↑)
• Trade balance	−US$61 billion (5.6% of GDP)
• Export partners	US (17%), UAE (8%)
• Import partners	China (9%), US (6%)
• Internet users	5%

The Military

• Size of military	1 303 000 (0.1% of population)
• Spending on military	US$11.5 billion
• Spending per capita	US$10
• Spending as percentage of GDP	1.1%

Figure 24–19 India statistics

Figure 24–20 India, like China, is two economic "nations" within one country. The majority of the population lives very traditionally in a manner that would be common in a Far Periphery country. A signficant minority lives in a modern, affluent Old Core environment. This movie theatre would not exist in most rural areas of India.

Five Things You Should Know About India

1. India (see Figures 24–19 and 24–20) is by far the world's biggest democracy. Governing such a large and complex country democratically is an ongoing challenge.

2. India has the third-largest military in the world and has had an ongoing border dispute with Pakistan for more than 60 years. This is particularly worrisome since both countries have nuclear weapons.

3. India has a number of rapidly growing, medium-sized transnational corporations that are expanding their operations beyond the country's borders.

4. India's development is being accomplished with little regard for sustainability—for example, immense numbers of small cars and trucks are being built that lack modern anti-pollution devices.

5. Although Hindi is the official language and English is used extensively in business, India's more than one billion people speak over 1600 dialects.

"China has dramatically increased spending on its military. In the past the Chinese military (in particular the army) was immense but lacked sophisticated weaponry. That is changing dramatically."

The People

• Population	1 321 851 888
• Population density	137.8 people/km^2
• Total fertility rate	1.75 children/woman
• Life expectancy	72.9 years
• Population over 65	8%
• Population growth rate	+0.61%
Natural increase	+0.65%
Net migration	−0.04%
• Infant mortality rate	22.1%
• Literacy rate	91%

Energy Resources

• Oil	
Net trade	−0.13 t/per capita/yr
R/P ratio	12
• Natural gas	
Net trade	no trade
R/P ratio	42
• Coal	
Net trade	minor exporter
R/P ratio	48

Figure 24–21 China statistics

The Land

• Area	9 596 960 km^2
• Land use	
Farmland:	16.1%
Other:	83.9%

The Economy

• Total GDP	US$2.527 trillion
• Total GDP PPP	US$10.21 trillion
• Per capita GDP PPP	US$7800
• GDP growth rate	11.1%
• Composition of GDP	
Agriculture	11.9%
Industry	48.1%
Services	40.0%
• Current account balance	+US$179 billion (7.1% of GDP)
• GINI index	44
• Public debt as %GDP (Trend)	22% (↑)
• Trade balance	+$196 billion (7.8% of GDP)
• Export partners	US (21%), Hong Kong (16%)
• Import partners	Japan (15%), South Korea (11%)
• Internet users	10%

The Military

• Size of military	2 821 000 (0.2% of population)
• Spending on military	US$55.9 billion
• Spending per capita	US$42
• Spending as percentage of GDP	2.2%

Five Things You Should Know About China

1. China has dramatically increased spending on its military (see Figure 24–21). In the past, the Chinese military (in particular its army) was immense but lacked sophisticated weaponry. That is changing quickly. The capability of the Chinese military is still far behind that of the US, but much progress is being made. China also has a major space program.

2. China faces major environmental issues. Urban air quality is far below Old Core standards and the country became the largest producer of greenhouse gases in 2006 (see Figure 24–22). Serious water shortages loom, in particular in the northeastern part of the country.

Figure 24–22 Beijing's air is among the most polluted of any city in the world. People often wear masks to protect their lungs.

3. China has expanded its use of soft power in many parts of the world, including the Far Periphery. Foreign investment is common and likely to increase as China looks to utilize its vast foreign-currency reserves. The expansion of Chinese influence in many parts of the world is related to its need to buy oil and other natural resources to meet the needs of its booming economy.

4. Higher labour costs are on the horizon, and China will not be able to build its economic growth solely on cheap labour. It will have to follow the example of Japan in the 1960s and 1970s and start to manufacture higher-value-added goods that can compete globally for quality and innovation.

5. Lack of respect for international **intellectual property** (creations of the mind, such as music, images, and copyrighted materials) laws will increasingly hamper the growth of Chinese manufacturing. For example, more than ten lawsuits have been launched against Chinese car manufacturers who have copied designs from other countries (see Figure 24–23). Pirating of CDs, DVDs, and computer games is also rampant.

Figure 24–23 Early in Japan's economic recovery from the destruction of World War II, its exports to the West were of poor quality and were often just inferior copies of North American or European products. However, Japan is now known for its high-quality, uniquely Japanese goods. In terms of the merchandise it produces, China today is similar to the post–World War II Japan; an example is shown by the photos above. The car on the left is a Smart Car; the car on the right is a Chinese-made imitation. If China's economy is to prosper in the future, it must continue to follow the Japanese model and produce high-quality goods that are uniquely Chinese.

New Core, Near Core, and Far Periphery

POLITICAL ISLAM

"Unlike the other 'nominees' for future global power, Political Islam is little more than an ideal for some people in the Islamic world who are looking for an alternative to western-style globalization."

The People

- Population (millions)[1]   80/235/65/165/28
- Population density   80/124/39/205/13 people/km^2
- Total fertility rate   2.8/2.4/1.7/3.7/3.9 children/woman
- Life expectancy   71.6/70.2/70.6/63.8/75.9 years
- Population over 65   4.6%/5.7%/5.4%/4.3%/2.4%
- Population growth rate   +1.7%/+1.2%/+0.7%/+1.8%/+2.1%
    - Natural increase   +1.7%/+1.3%/+1.1%/+1.9%/+2.7%
    - Net migration   −0.02%/−0.1%/−0.4%/−0.1%/−0.6%
- Infant mortality rate   29.5 (per 1000)/32.1/38.1/68.8/12.4
- Literacy rate   71%/90%/77%/50%/79%

Energy Resources

- Oil
    - Net trade   major exporter
    - R/P ratio   varies 0 to 80
- Natural gas
    - Net trade   major exporter
    - R/P ratio   varies 26 to >500
- Coal
    - Net trade   negligible
    - R/P ratio   generally >300

The Land

- Area   1.00 million km^2/1.92/1.68/0.80/2.20
- Land use
    - Farmland: 3.4%/18.1%/11.1%/25.3%/1.8%
    - Other: 96.6%/81.9%/88.9%/74.7%/98.2%

The Economy

- Total GDP   US$85 billion/265/194/124/282
- Total GDP PPP   US$334/948/599/438/372
- Per capita GDP PPP   US$4200/3900/8700/2600/13 800
- GDP growth rate   6.8%/5.5%/4.3%/6.6%/4.3%
- Composition of GDP
    - Agriculture   14.1%/12.9/11.0/19.4/3.0
    - Industry   38.4%/47.0/44.9/27.2/63.6
    - Services   47.5%/40.0/44.1/53.4/33.4
- Current account balance   +US$2.7 billion (3.2% of GDP)/ +9.7 (3.6%)/+16.5 (8.5%)/−6.8 (5.5%)/+104.0 (37.0%)
- GINI index   34.4/34.8/43.0/30.6/n.a.
- Public debt as %GDP (Trend) 113(↑)/39(↑)/24(↓)/55(↑)/32(↓)
- Trade balance   −US$12 billion (14% of GDP)/ +30 (11%)/+21 (11%)/−10 (8%)/ +144 (51%)
- Export partners (overall)   Japan/US/EU
- Import partners (overall)   US/China/EU
- Internet users   8%/7%/28%/7%/17%

The Military

- Size of military   448 000 (0.06% of population)/ 297 000 (0.01%)/513 000 (0.08%)/ 612 000 (0.04%)/202 000 (0.07%)
- Spending on military   US$4 billion/1/10/3/18
- Spending per capita   US$52/4/143/18/693
- Spending as percentage of GDP   2.8%/0.9/4.5/3.4/8.2

[1] The population of Moslems in the world has been estimated at about 1.3 billion. Of these, approximately one billion live in the area of "Political Islam."

Figure 24–24 Political Islam statistics

Note: Because of its size and the great variation of nations involved, it is very difficult to come up with a composite, statistical overview of Political Islam. Because of this, statistics for five major representative Islamic nations are included here. These are: Egypt, Indonesia, Iran, Pakistan, and Saudi Arabia. Figures appear in this order in the chart.

Five Things You Should Know About Political Islam

1. Unlike the other "nominees" for future global power, Political Islam (see Figure 24–24) is little more than an ideal for some people in the Islamic world who are looking for an alternative to Western-style globalization (see Figure 24–25). Perhaps it could be seen, in some ways, as something like the EU, except starting from the idea of shared religious values rather than shared location and history.

2. Political Islam (see Figure 24–26), if it came into existence, would extend from the Atlantic Ocean in North Africa to the Pacific Ocean in the southern Philippines. The statistical values given are totals for all the countries of the world in which Muslims are the largest religious group. This is obviously an arbitrary distinction that may not represent this region adequately. For example, Kazakhstan is included even though the percentage of Muslims there is less than 50 percent. India is not included despite the fact that it has more than 150 million Muslim citizens.

Figure 24–25 This scene, from Jakarta, Indonesia, is a visual metaphor for the question facing much of the Islamic world today—how to reconcile the modern, globalized world and a traditional culture.

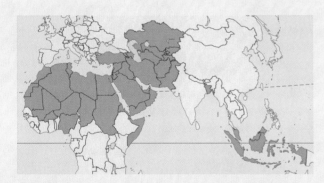

Figure 24–26 The Political Islam region

3. The Islamic world today and in the past has been far from *monolithic* (uniform in character), either politically or religiously. Disputes between Muslim states have been common, as have conflicts between different Islamic groups within countries.

4. The emergence of Political Islam would occur only very slowly and would likely require the emergence of a charismatic leader who could inspire the residents of the many countries in this region to join together around a common cause.

5. Islamic countries typically have high birth rates compared to non-Islamic countries at similar development levels. The result is that these countries have relatively high population growth rates and youthful populations.

Chapter Questions

Knowledge and Understanding

1. What caused the downfall of Britain and France as dominant powers?

2. Describe the use of hard power and soft power during the Cold War.

3. Why is the US described as the most dominant power in history?

4. a) Define "rule set" as it applies to international relations.

   b) Give at least four rules that are part of the post–Cold War rule set.

5. "The new rule set for the 21st century must take into consideration several important factors." What are these factors and why do they matter so much?

6. Conduct research to name the countries in the Political Islam region that have the following characteristics:

   a) all countries with a population over 100 million

   b) the three countries with the largest area

   c) four countries in Africa

   d) five countries in the Middle East

   e) six countries in Central Asia

   f) three countries that have large oil reserves

   g) five countries that are in the Near Core

   h) four countries that are in the Far Periphery

   i) three countries that are in the New Core

7. a) What is intellectual property?

   b) Why is respect for intellectual property important for economic development?

Thinking

8. We started the "World View 2050" exercise with nine nominees. It is highly unlikely that a potential superpower was left off our list of nominees, but it is possible that secondary or tertiary powers might have been missed. Suggest at least one such country and indicate which level of power it will hold in 2050. Explain why you drew this conclusion.

9. a) In this chapter it was suggested that Japan's economy after World War II evolved from producing cheap, poor-quality goods like toys and small electrical appliances to producing competent copies of Western goods like cars and cameras and, finally, to producing innovative products that were often better than those produced in the US or Europe. Why is it logical that a country would follow this sequence of economic development stages?

   b) At what stage is China today? Is there evidence that it is ready to proceed to a higher level of manufacturing sophistication?

10. a) In a few of the country/region profiles there was the suggestion that declining populations would be a problem in the future. What problems does population decline cause?

    b) What advantages might there be for a country that has a declining population?

Application

11. a) Often we can learn useful lessons from what happened in the past. This is certainly the case when we learn why various empires rose and then fell. Choose two of the empires below—one that you have heard of and one that is new to you—and briefly research the reasons why it grew in prominence and why it declined.

    - Almoravid Empire
    - Aztec Empire
    - Dutch Empire
    - Fatimid Empire
    - French Empire
    - Inca Empire
    - Persian Empire
    - Portuguese Empire
    - Songhai Empire
    - Spanish Empire

    b) Suggest a lesson that a modern empire could learn from the history of one of the empires you studied.

12. There is really no right or wrong answer when it comes to predicting which countries or regions will be the most powerful in 2050. Rather, what is important is whether you were able to provide reasoned support for the conclusions that you and your group made in the Working It Out exercise. Your teacher will ask you to meet with students with whom you did not work to compare results. You may find many similarities, but there are likely to be differences as well. In your discussions, understand the basis for these differences. The arguments of other students may make you modify your own world view. If so, how? **G**

CHAPTER 25

Working Together to Build a Better World

Key Terms

Security Council

sanctions

veto

General Assembly

peacekeeping

Economic and Social Council

peacemaking

North Atlantic Treaty
Organization (NATO)

Warsaw Pact

Nobel Peace Prize

The nine imaginary countries at right have different characteristics. In this chapter, you and your classmates will pretend to be leaders of these countries. For decades, most Canadians, along with citizens of other Old Core countries, have enjoyed lives free from want (below). The challenge is to ensure that everyone else has similar lives.

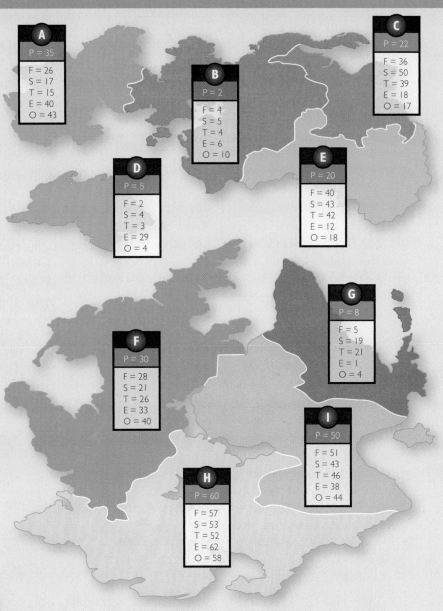

A	
P = 35	
F = 26	
S = 17	
T = 15	
E = 40	
O = 43	

B	
P = 2	
F = 4	
S = 5	
T = 4	
E = 6	
O = 10	

C	
P = 22	
F = 36	
S = 50	
T = 39	
E = 18	
O = 17	

D	
P = 5	
F = 2	
S = 4	
T = 3	
E = 29	
O = 4	

E	
P = 20	
F = 40	
S = 43	
T = 42	
E = 12	
O = 18	

F	
P = 30	
F = 28	
S = 21	
T = 26	
E = 33	
O = 40	

G	
P = 8	
F = 5	
S = 19	
T = 21	
E = 1	
O = 4	

I	
P = 50	
F = 51	
S = 43	
T = 46	
E = 38	
O = 44	

H	
P = 60	
F = 57	
S = 53	
T = 52	
E = 62	
O = 58	

Key Questions

By the end of this chapter you will be able to answer the following questions.

■ How effective is the UN in solving world problems?

■ How is the role of NATO changing?

■ How effective are international treaties in resolving problems?

■ What role do NGOs and individuals play in making a better world?

AN EXERCISE IN COOPERATION

Why is it that ...

- in a world where many go hungry, others are fixated with losing weight?
- in some countries, scientists spend their days inventing new kinds of detergent, while in other countries, there is not enough scientific know-how to improve agricultural productivity?
- in wealthier parts of the world, billions of dollars are spent on cosmetics, while in developing countries, millions die from easily preventable diseases?
- in Old Core countries, skyscrapers are brightly lit all night long, while in the Far Periphery, tens of millions of people live in homes with no electricity?
- in some parts of the world, people live in safe and secure environments, but elsewhere, people live in constant fear for their lives?

Clearly, some of the world's citizens meet their every need and still have money left for luxuries. Others cannot even meet their most basic needs. Do the wealthier peoples of the world understand the difficulties faced by those who live in the Near Core and Far Periphery? Do they care? Should they care? Do you care?

In this activity, you and your classmates will be the leaders of nine countries in a fictional mini-world. Each nation's characteristics are shown on page 395.

The characteristics of the countries are

- *Population (P)*—This value can be compared directly to the other values for a country—for example, a country with a population of 35 requires 35 units of food and 35 units of energy to meet its needs.
- *Food Supply (F)*—the availability of enough food to meet the needs of the country's population
- *Social Development (S)*—the availability of healthcare, education, and other social services
- *Technology (T)*—the availability of modern technologies of all types (for example, communications, electronics, manufacturing, agricultural)
- *Energy (E)*—the availability of energy resources (essentially fossil fuels)
- *Other Resources (O)*—the availability of non-food and non-energy resources in the country

Ensure that your country has enough units of each commodity (food, social development, technology, energy, and other resources) to equal (or exceed) its population. To do this, you must negotiate with the leaders of the other countries to meet your needs. For example, if you have a surplus of energy, but a shortage of food, you may be able to make a trade with a country in the opposite situation (see Figures 25–1a and 25–1b).

Questions

1. a) Did all nine countries meet all of their needs?
   b) If not, which ones were unsuccessful?
   c) Why were they not successful?
   d) How could this situation have been avoided?

2. Is it possible for all of the countries to reach the desired goal? Provide proof for your answer.

3. a) In what ways do the results of this exercise mirror the situation in the world today?
   b) How does this exercise differ from the real world? What do the results of this exercise suggest about the difficulty of solving real international problems?

4. The fictional countries have many similarities to real countries (or, in some cases, regions). Identify which real countries, or regions, these fictional countries may represent.

Country	Population	Food	Energy	Conclusion
A	35	26	40	*Can trade energy for food*
E	20	40	12	*Can trade food for energy*

Figure 25–1a If you have any questions about the rules governing these transactions, check with your teacher. Record all transactions in a form similar to that shown in Figure 25–1b for all the class to see. Name your imaginary country.

Units Transferred	Of Item	From Country	To Country	In Exchange for Units	Of Item	Comments
5	Energy	A	E	7	Food	Trade

Figure 25–1b As a class, use a chart like this to keep track of the success of all "international" negotiations.

Solving Problems in the Real World

The preceding activity illustrates how hard it can be for people to cooperate, even when there is little reason for them not to do so. In the real world, cooperation becomes even more complicated as nations and peoples compete for economic and strategic advantages. In this chapter, you will have an opportunity to consider some of the ways that a variety of organizations and people have worked, and continue to work, individually and together, to build a better world.

United Nations

The United Nations was founded in 1945 as World War II was ending. Government leaders looked back at the causes of the war and realized that one important contributor had been the ineffectiveness of the pre-war League of Nations, the UN's predecessor. The reasons for the creation of the UN could not have been more compelling. Tens of millions of people were dead, and fighting had devastated many parts of the world. The UN had an ambitious agenda, to be sure. It was to maintain international peace and security and promote social and economic development in the world—and it had to do this in a world full of nations, large and small, with conflicting agendas and enormous differences in wealth.

How Successful has the UN Been?

This is a simple question to ask—and a very difficult one to answer. Before attempting to do so, it is vital to remember that the UN is a multi-faceted organization. The most powerful and prominent part of the UN is the **Security Council** because it is the body that can impose **sanctions** on nations that threaten peace (see Figure 25–2). Three types of sanctions can be imposed by the UN:

- Least severe are verbal sanctions. When the UN imposes verbal sanctions, it is voicing the international community's concern about an action taken by an offending country and demanding that the action stop.

- More severe are economic sanctions. All trade with the offending country may be cut off, and any aid that it might otherwise receive is terminated.

- Most severe are military sanctions. Member countries provide appropriate troops to stop the transgressor and help restore peace.

Figure 25–2 Former US Secretary of State Colin Powell addresses the UN Security Council in 2003 looking for support for the upcoming American invasion of Iraq. He did not get it, and the US government proceeded without the support of the UN.

The Council includes five permanent and ten temporary members. The real power lies with the five permanent members: China, France, Russia, the United Kingdom, and the United States. Each of the permanent members has the ability to **veto**—which means to reject—any resolution being considered by the Security Council. All five members must therefore agree before any resolution passes. Since unanimous agreement is difficult to achieve, the Security Council rarely takes meaningful action when peace and security are threatened. This is because far too often one of the permanent powers wishes to protect its interests (or those of its allies). During the Cold War (1945–1989), the Soviet Union used its veto 79 times, more than the other four powers combined. Since the end of the Cold War, the US has used its veto the most, generally to prevent the passage of motions critical of Israel. More recently China has *thwarted* (prevented) actions by the Security Council in countries like Sudan and Myanmar. (In recent years, motions have often not been made in the Security Council if it was known that they would be vetoed.)

The UN **General Assembly** meets each year from September to December and includes representatives from all 192 members of the organization. The General Assembly can also meet in emergency sessions at any time, but rarely does. The Assembly debates and passes many motions, but these tend to be symbolic since only the Security Council has enforcement powers. You might wonder why this is so, but the reason is quite simple. The big powers in 1945 (the permanent members of the Security Council) wanted to ensure that their powers were protected. They did not want to have a situation where the votes of the US and China, for example, were worth no more than those of Tonga and El Salvador. Nothing has changed today. This explains why the permanent membership of the Security Council reflects the powers that won World War II and not the geopolitics of today. There is an obvious need to include countries like India and Brazil in the permanent membership of the Council.

The goals and activities of the UN are certainly not always met with universal approval. International cooperation, a requirement basic to the operation of the UN and to the reduction of conflict in the world, will often require countries to give up some of their national sovereignty. Countries, however, are reluctant to do so. The result is that the UN can become powerless at exactly those moments when a strong and effective UN is most needed. The lead-up to the 2003 Iraq War illustrates this well. The US had decided that it wanted to invade Iraq and wanted the support of the Security Council to do so. The other permanent members of the Council, along with most other nations, wanted to continue to pursue diplomatic solutions to the problem before choosing military action. The US saw this approach as an unacceptable limitation on its national sovereignty and decided to launch its attack without UN approval.

Peacekeeping and Peacemaking

Peacekeeping occurs when the UN (and sometimes other international agencies like NATO, the European Union, and the African Union) provides a force of soldiers, and often police and civilian officials, to maintain order in a country or region that has experienced conflict. A prerequisite for peacekeeping is an agreement, by all the warring parties, to stop fighting and accept the authority of the peacekeepers.

For many years, Canada was a leader in UN peacekeeping. Today, we are much less involved in spite of the fact that the UN is involved in more peacekeeping missions than ever before (see Figure 25–3). There are a number of reasons why the demands for UN peacekeeping have risen so dramatically. Perhaps the most important of these is that so many conflicts are reaching the end stage where peacekeeping is a realistic option.

Organizing major peacekeeping missions is often problematic, especially today when so many peacekeeping operations already exist. In 2008, the UN was trying to organize a major peacekeeping force to reinforce African Union efforts in the troubled Darfur region of Sudan. For several reasons, they were finding

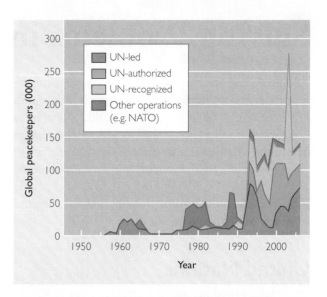

Location	Mission Name	Year of Deployment	Number of Personnel*
Congo	MONUC	1999	22 167
Liberia	UNMIL	2003	18 382
Southern Sudan	UNMIS	2005	13 021
Lebanon	UNIFIL	1978	11 431
Côte d'Ivoire	UNOCI	2004	11 150
Haiti	MINUSTAH	2004	9 524
Kosovo	UNMIK	1999	4 631
Burundi	ONUB	2004	3 142
Ethiopia and Eritrea	UNMEE	2000	2 687
East Timor	UNMIT	2006	1 340
Golan Heights (Israel/Syria)	UNDOF	1974	1 247
Cyprus	UNFICYP	1964	1 069
Afghanistan+	UNAMA	2002	850
Western Sahara	MINURSO	1991	459
Georgia	UNOMIG	1993	419
Middle East++	UNTSO	1948	374
Sierra Leone+	UNIOSIL	2006	298
India and Pakistan	UNMOGIP	1949	113

Figure 25–3 Peacekeeping activities in the world have grown dramatically in recent years, to the extent that the UN is seriously overextended in this regard.

*Includes military, police, and civilians
+Political or peace-building missions
++ Egypt, Jordan, Israel, Lebanon, and Syria

The UN has been considerably more successful in its non-political role. One little-known branch of the UN is the **Economic and Social Council.** This body is responsible for coordinating the economic and social development efforts of the UN. It is responsible for three types of organizations:

- *Functional Commissions*—for example, UN Commission on Sustainable Development, UN Commission on the Status of Women, and UN Forum on Forests

- *Regional Commissions*—for example, UN Economic Commission for Africa, UN Economic and Social Commission for Western Asia

- *Specialized Agencies*—These agencies each focus on a particular aspect of modern life that requires international coordination and cooperation. Some of these organizations existed before the UN came into existence, while others were created by the UN. An example of a specialized agency is the International Civil Aviation Organization (ICAO), which has its headquarters in Montreal. It coordinates safe air travel in the world.

Question

1. How many of the specialized agencies do you know without looking them up? Look at the list below, and try to identify the field within which each organization operates. You do not need to know the exact name of the organization, but if you do, that is a bonus. Hint: You can assume that UN stands for . . . well, you know.

   a) UNICEF   f) UNESCO

   b) IMF   g) ILO

   c) WHO   h) FAO

   d) WMO   i) UPU

   e) ITU   j) UNDP

The correct answers are on page 408. How did you do? If you identified more than four of these you did well. Each of these organizations makes an important contribution to quality of life in the world.

---

it very difficult to do this. One reason is that a large peacekeeping force was needed. Another is that Darfur has a harsh environment in a part of the world that is not readily accessible. This makes the *logistics* of the operation much more difficult. (Logistics is the part of a military operation that deals with the procurement, maintenance, and transportation of equipment and personnel). Also, even if enough troops were available, there was a shortage of more specialized capabilities like heavy-lift aircraft, helicopters, and intelligence capabilities. These highly sophisticated military tools are most commonly used by Old Core armies and air forces; the militaries of these countries are often fully committed to conflicts in Iraq, Afghanistan, and to other UN operations.

The complications of running a large UN peacekeeping operation were well described by former UN Secretary-General Kofi Annan when he said that the UN is the only fire department in the world that must go out and buy a fire engine before it can respond to an emergency. Kofi Annan called for the creation of UN-controlled, multinational military forces in various parts of the world that could respond quickly to an

emergency situation. If such forces had existed in the 1990s, they could have saved hundreds of thousands of lives during the Rwandan genocide, during which 800 000 died in only 100 days. The problem is the absence of political will and financial resources to support such forces.

Peacemaking occurs when UN or other forces must impose peace on warring factions. Peacemaking does not occur nearly as often as peacekeeping because it requires powerful military forces and can be very dangerous. Examples of successful peacemaking efforts include the Korean War (1950–1953) and the First Gulf War (1990–1991). The US has organized and led its own peacemaking efforts in Afghanistan and Iraq with mixed success.

The Bottom Line

GLOBALIZATION

"The UN was not created to take humanity to heaven, but to save it from hell."

What does this suggest about our expectations for the UN?

Assessing the success of the UN is a particularly difficult task. Perhaps it depends most on the expectations that one has of the potential of the organization. Perhaps one of the early UN Secretaries-General, Dag Hammarskjöld, said it best: "The UN was not created to take humanity to heaven, but to save it from hell." Based on this expectation, perhaps the UN has not done badly. While dozens of local wars have been fought since 1945, a third world war has been avoided. Although we cannot say for certain that this was because of the UN, this achievement is a significant one. The possibility of nuclear annihilation was very real in the decades after 1945. (According to US experts, in the 1980s, the Soviet Union had so many nuclear warheads available, that it likely had three targeted against Toronto alone: one at Pearson International Airport, a second at downtown Toronto, and a third at the Pickering nuclear plant.)

The UN's enormous range of commissions and specialized agencies has accomplished a great deal. However, while the UN has had many successes, most experts agree that it needs considerable reform, particularly with respect to the Security Council and General Assembly. Whether this happens will depend entirely on the willingness of nations to give up some of their powers and set aside some of their national interests so that a more effective UN might emerge.

NATO

The **North Atlantic Treaty Organization** (**NATO**) has been a powerful and influential body since it was founded in 1949. NATO was created as a US-led defense and security organization to counteract the threat to western Europe posed by the Soviet Union and its allies. Under the NATO agreement, a threat to any member is regarded as a threat to all. For example, NATO is fighting in Afghanistan, under a UN mandate, because of the 9/11 attacks on the US; al-Qaeda was based in Afghanistan and supported by the government at the time. Originally, NATO consisted of the US, Canada, and ten European states (see Figure 25–4). Later, Greece and Turkey (1952), West Germany (1955), and Spain (1982) joined the alliance. In 1955, the Soviet Union and its allies created a similar military alliance, the **Warsaw Pact**, to counteract NATO.

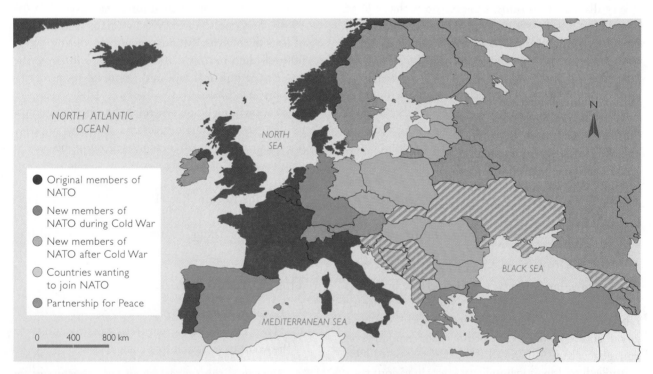

NORTH ATLANTIC OCEAN

NORTH SEA

N

- Original members of NATO
- New members of NATO during Cold War
- New members of NATO after Cold War
- Countries wanting to join NATO
- Partnership for Peace

BLACK SEA

MEDITERRANEAN SEA

0   400   800 km

Figure 25–4 NATO has grown significantly since its founding in 1949. This map shows only the European members of NATO. (Canada and the US are also members.)

From 1949 to 1989, the world's geopolitics were centred around the Cold War (see Chapter 21). Both sides in the Cold War had enormous nuclear and non-nuclear military strength that deterred them from taking overt action against each other. In the case of nuclear weapons, this deterrent was described as mutually assured destruction, or the MAD principle. Neither side was prepared to use its nuclear arsenal because it knew that the enemy had sufficient power to devastate the attacker. Many observers suggest that the main reason the Warsaw Pact and the Communist regime in the Soviet Union collapsed in 1989 was the sheer cost of fighting the Cold War against the much wealthier US and its NATO allies.

With the breakup of the Soviet Union and the dissolution of the Warsaw Pact, NATO had to find a new purpose. In the early 1990s, it reinvented itself because in the "new world order" in which the US was the only superpower, the peace and security of its members were no longer threatened by the Soviet Union and its allies. In fact, East Germany, a former Warsaw Pact nation, had become a part of NATO when it reunited with West Germany in 1990. In 1999, three more former Warsaw Pact nations—Poland, Hungary, and the Czech Republic—became members of NATO, and in 2004, Bulgaria, Estonia, Latvia, Lithuania, Romania, Slovakia, and Slovenia joined. Many countries that used to be part of the Soviet Union or members of the Warsaw Pact have joined NATO. Why do you think they have done so?

NATO has taken an active role as both peacemaker and peacekeeper in Europe and, starting with the war in Afghanistan, outside the borders of Europe. This was demonstrated by its actions in 1995 in Bosnia-Herzegovina, part of the former Yugoslavia. In the early 1990s, after the breakup of Yugoslavia, warring ethnic and religious factions plunged this region into chaos. After the signing of the 1995 Dayton Accord to halt fighting in the region, NATO countries provided 60 000 troops for a one-year implementation force to ensure peace. This was followed by the imposition of a smaller, EU stabilization force that was still in the region in 2008. These forces had many functions, including defusing conflicts, removing land mines, collecting weapons, preventing crime, repairing roads and bridges, and cooperating with NGOs that were providing humanitarian assistance.

Using Treaties to Make the World Better

One of the most important ways of making the world a better and safer place is through the use of treaties between and among nations. Some treaties may deal with issues of local or regional significance, while others involve every country in the world. Treaties can deal with relatively minor, local issues—for example, Canada and the US signed a treaty in 1916 to protect migratory birds. Treaties can also deal with fundamental issues in any number of fields that are of global importance, such as environmental and weapons-control treaties.

The process of treaty-making involves three stages.

■ The first stage is the *negotiation* of the treaty, which may last for years.

■ The second step is the *signing* of the treaty, which often happens soon after negotiations are concluded.

■ The last phase is the *ratification* (formal approval) of the treaty by individual governments, which may also take many years. A treaty does not come into effect until an agreed number of nations have ratified it.

A famous movie from the 1960s (chosen by the International Movie Data Base as the fourth-best movie of all time) is called *The Good, the Bad, and the Ugly.* The title of this movie has become an expression that can be used to describe the degree of success of international treaties.

Treaty-Making: *The Good*

Sometimes treaties work out as well as (or even better than) it was hoped. The Montreal Protocol is an outstanding example of "the Good." It has been described by a former UN Secretary-General as "perhaps the single most successful international agreement to date..." and is frequently held out as the model to be followed for other treaties.

■ *Common name of the treaty*—Montreal Protocol
■ *Formal name of the treaty*—Montreal Protocol on Substances That Deplete the Ozone Layer
■ *Signing and ratification process began*—1987
■ *Entered into force*—1989

- *Number of signatories*—191 nations; not including Andorra, Iraq, Kosovo (not a country until 2008) San Marino, East Timor (not a country until 2002), and Vatican City.

- *Purpose*—To eliminate from use a wide range of chemicals that damage the ozone layer (see Figure 25–5). The reason for doing this was to protect the earth from hazardous amounts of ultraviolet-B radiation that cause skin cancers, reduce oceanic plankton, and damage crops.

- *Features of the treaty*—
  - It was based on sound scientific and economic data.
  - It considered the situations of both rich and poor nations.
  - The success of the treaty (in reducing the use of chemicals that destroy ozone) was to be monitored, and the treaty was to be adjusted in the future as additional data became available.

- *Successes of the treaty*—
  - Requirements of the treaty are generally being well-respected.
  - Ozone destruction has been halted and there is some evidence that ozone levels may be increasing.

- Parties to the treaty were so impressed with the treaty's effectiveness that at a meeting in Montreal in 2007, it was agreed to accelerate the elimination of one category of pollutants (HCFCs) by seven years. (This will also aid in the fight against climate change, as HCFCs are potent greenhouse gases.)

- *Failures of the treaty*—
  - Compared to the successes of the treaty, nothing stands out.

Treaty-Making: *The Bad*

Perhaps the most important of all treaties are those aimed at preventing nuclear conflict. The complex history of nuclear treaties illustrates how difficult it can be for nations to agree to such treaties. There are two types of nuclear weapons treaties: bilateral treaties between the nuclear superpowers, the US and the former Soviet Union; and multilateral treaties designed to stop the spread of nuclear weapons. We will look at the most important of the latter group of treaties—which unfortunately has not had noticeable success in meeting its goals.

- *Common name of the treaty*—Test Ban Treaty
- *Formal name of the treaty*—Comprehensive Nuclear Test Ban Treaty (CTBT)
- *Signing and ratification process began*—1996
- *Entered into force*—Not yet in force
- *Number of signatories*—177 nations have signed the treaty and 140 have ratified it. However, the treaty identifies 44 countries (designated Annex II countries) that were regarded as having (or potentially having) the technical expertise to build nuclear weapons. The treaty comes into force only when all 44 countries sign and ratify the treaty. Of these, only 34 have both signed and ratified the treaty.

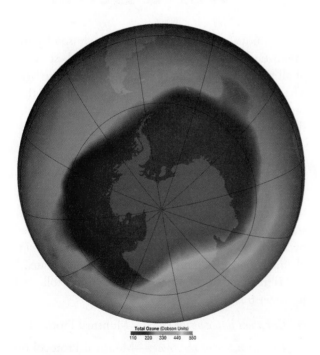

Total Ozone (Dobson Units)
110 220 330 440 550

Figure 25–5 Ozone destruction was greatest in polar areas, in particular over the Antarctic. This map illustrates the "ozone hole" that was getting larger and deeper until, through the Montreal Protocol, international action was taken to repair the damage.

Did You Know?

Since the Test Ban Treaty was opened for signing and ratification, there have been a number of events: China, India, North Korea, Pakistan, Russia, the UK, France, and the US have nuclear arsenals. It is suspected that Israel has nuclear weapons as well. India and Pakistan both tested nuclear weapons in 1998. North Korea conducted one test in 2006. It is thought by some that Iran is developing nuclear weapons. The "father" of the Pakistani nuclear program, Dr. A.Q. Khan, has admitted to selling nuclear weapons technology to Iran, Libya, and North Korea.

- Annex II countries that still need to ratify the treaty: China, Colombia, Egypt, Israel, and the US.

- Annex II countries that still need to sign and ratify the treaty: North Korea, India, Indonesia, Iran, and Pakistan.

- *Purpose*—The treaty prevents countries from doing two things. A country may not test nuclear weapons and it must not support another country's attempt to develop and test nuclear weapons (see Figure 25–6).

- *Successes of the treaty*—

  - Of the 177 nations that have signed the treaty, 140 have ratified it. It has likely discouraged other countries from developing nuclear weapons.

- *Failures of the treaty*—

  - In reality, it would appear that, after many years of negotiations, the CTBT has been an abject failure, since it is unlikely to come into force and countries that decide that they want nuclear weapons will build and test them.

You might wonder why some treaties are considered to be "bad" and others "ugly." Perhaps the most important consideration is how seriously nations approach them. A number of countries have chosen not to sign or ratify the CTBT. This may not be helpful to the cause of world peace, but at least there is a basic honesty to this choice. Other countries have signed but not ratified the treaty, which is a more ambiguous stance. Those countries that have signed but not ratified

> The Bulletin of Atomic Scientists has kept a "Doomsday Clock" since 1947. It measures how close humanity is to destruction—originally because of nuclear weapons and more recently because of environmental problems and non-nuclear technological risks. In early 2008, the clock was at five minutes to midnight. See the link on our Web site.

the treaty can say that since the treaty is not in effect, their actions do not break international law (except by provisions of earlier test ban treaties). The conditions agreed on for the CTBT to come into effect are (and were) probably unrealistic, and for this reason it might be considered a bad example of treaty-making.

Treaty-Making: *The Ugly*

The Kyoto Protocol qualifies as "ugly" treaty-making. Its conditions were agreed to after much negotiation (like all complex, important treaties). Enough nations ratified it that it came into effect. This means that, as of 2005, it became international law. Yet many countries that both signed and ratified the treaty have done little to meet their obligations under the treaty. The Kyoto Protocol contains provisions to punish these countries (by requiring higher emissions cuts later), but there is no indication that any countries will face these punishments.

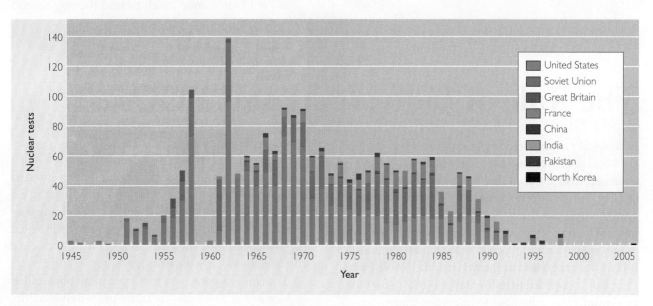

Figure 25–6 Worldwide nuclear testing, 1945–1998. Nuclear testing has become very uncommon since the end of the Cold War. It should have been possible for the CTBT to come into effect and end testing once and for all. What went wrong?

Canada has been one of the worst offenders with respect to Kyoto. The treaty was negotiated, signed, and ratified by Liberal governments that did little to meet our targets. Then, the Conservative government, elected in 2006, indicated that it would attach Canada to an alternative climate change approach called the Asia-Pacific Partnership on Clean Development on Climate.

- *Common name of the treaty*—Kyoto Protocol
- *Formal name of the treaty*—Kyoto Protocol under the United Nations Framework Convention on Climate Change (UNFCCC)
- *Signing and ratification process began*—1997
- *Entered into force*—2005
- *Number of signatories*—175 countries signed; 164 countries ratified, not including Australia and the US
- *Purpose*—To reduce emissions of greenhouse gases in the world to reduce the impact of climate change (see Figure 25–7)
- *Features of the treaty*—
  - Reduction targets were to apply only to 36 advanced nations (called Annex I nations) in the Old Core, Russia, and the eastern European nations of the New Core.
  - Non-Annex I countries needed only to monitor and report their emissions.
  - Kyoto is to expire in 2012, at which time it will be replaced by a new treaty that is to be negotiated between 2008 and 2009.

Figure 25–7 The polar bear has achieved iconic status as a symbol of the dangers of climate change. Why?

- *Successes of the treaty*—
  - It has helped focus attention on the need to fight climate change.
  - Several European countries have significantly reduced their emissions compared to the base year of reference, 1990.
  - It has promoted the establishment of emissions-trading mechanisms and enhanced technologies to reduce emissions.
- *Failures of the treaty*—
  - In general, it is not being respected by major emitters like the US, Canada, and Australia.
  - It has not encouraged sustainable development strategies in major non-Annex I nations.
  - It has not done much to lead the way toward the 2012 climate change treaty.

The Role of Individuals and NGOs

Millions of people and countless organizations all over the world agree that we can do a better job of promoting peace and reducing economic and social disparity. They lobby their governments to support policies and countless organizations that will reduce global conflict and improve the lot of all people. They also give their time and money to support the efforts of *myriad* (a large number) NGOs. In recognition of their efforts, the Nobel Peace Prize is often awarded to individuals and NGOs for their extraordinary contributions to important causes.

The Nobel Peace Prize

In 1859, businessman Jean Henri Dunant witnessed the bloody battle of Solferino, in northern Italy. He was horrified by the battle, and by the chaos that followed as untrained, unprepared people tried to help the wounded and bury the dead. This experience changed his life and the world.

Dunant's response was to write a small book called *A Memory of Solferino*. In it, he proposed that the countries of the world sponsor agencies to care for those who are wounded in war. Within two years, 12 nations had signed a treaty that recognized the neutrality of relief agencies, that had adopted a red cross as a symbol of their work. From this humble beginning developed today's national and international Red Cross and Red Crescent societies.

In 1901, Dunant received the first **Nobel Peace Prize**. The original intent was to award the Prize annually to an individual or group of people who made a significant contribution to world peace.

As of 2007, only one Canadian had received a Nobel Peace Prize (although Stephen Lewis was regarded as one of the favourites in 2007 for his work fighting HIV/AIDS in Africa). Lester Pearson received the Peace Prize in 1957. His contribution to world peace occurred during the Suez crisis in 1956. Not only did Pearson's action defuse an explosive situation, it also established the principle of peacekeeping that was to become a key part of the UN's work in reducing conflict in the world.

Some Nobel laureates receive the award not for what they have accomplished, but for their struggle to promote democracy and human rights by peaceful means against overwhelming odds. One such laureate is Aung San Suu Kyi (see Figure 25–8), who won the prize in 1991. In 1988, as leader of a democratic opposition party in Myanmar, she led a non-violent protest against a military government that often used brutal methods to enforce its policies. Suu Kyi also led a campaign to bring together traditionally hostile regional and ethnic groups in the country. In 1990, her party decisively won a national election, but was not allowed by the military to assume power. As of 2008, she was still fighting for democracy.

Alfred Nobel originally intended that his Peace Prize be awarded to an individual (or individuals). However, it has also been awarded to NGOs. For example, the 1999 award was given to Médecins Sans Frontières (MSF, known in English as Doctors Without Borders). MSF was founded in France in 1971 by a group of physicians and journalists. Their intention was simple—to provide medical aid to those in crisis. Often they do this in conditions of great danger, even when other NGOs are leaving a region because of the risk. MSF helps people regain the dignity and human rights that conflict has taken from them. This requires more than the simple provision of medical aid. MSF's mandate includes a responsibility to challenge governments and non-governmental military forces that deny people their dignity and rights.

Figure 25–8 Aung San Suu Kyi has become a vital symbol of opposition to a repressive government.

This belief contrasts with the approach of most NGOs, which strive to maintain their neutrality.

In recent years, the definition of "peace" has been expanded to recognize efforts that increase environmental sustainability. The first such award was given in 2004 to Wangari Maathai of Kenya who was recognized for her "contribution to sustainable development, democracy, and peace." She had led a movement to have women reforest her country and other African nations that had lost many of their trees as their populations exploded after World War II. (Maathai's award also recognized her role in empowering women in Africa.) In 2007, the Prize went jointly to the Inter-Governmental Panel on Climate Change and former US Vice-President Al Gore for their efforts to combat climate change. Undoubtedly, other environmentally focused selections will be made in the future now that the principle has been firmly established.

Did You Know?

Nobel Prizes are awarded in several scientific disciplines, in economics, and for contributions to peace. They are named for Alfred Nobel, the Swedish discoverer of dynamite. He left a substantial part of his estate to fund the creation of the Nobel prizes.

In the preceding section you were briefly introduced to six winners of the Nobel Peace Prize. Now you will have the opportunity to learn, in a bit more detail, about one other winner of the Prize.

Questions

1. Your teacher will organize the choice of Prize winners that you will research. The idea is for each student to research a different winner so that your class (or classes) can organize a wall display of winners. Lists of winners and information about what they did are readily available online and in libraries.

2. You should create a small poster, no larger than a piece of legal-size paper, that includes at least

a) a brief biography/history of the winner(s)

b) the delay (if any) between the winner's contributions to peace and when the Prize was awarded

c) the field within which the person or organization made their contribution to peace

d) the reasons why the winner(s) was/were chosen (Was it for one action or for work over many years?)

e) a description of the part(s) of the world directly and indirectly affected by the efforts of the winner

f) an analysis of the long-term impact of their efforts

Are World Peace and Social Development Possible?

When the Cold War ended at the end of the 1980s, many people hoped and expected that the world would become a safer place in which to live and that the money and effort used in the Cold War would be put to better use to improve the lives of those in need. Unfortunately, for many reasons, this has not proven to be the case. Why isn't the world a safer place, and why hasn't the peace dividend (see Chapter 22) improved lives? Consider

■ the spread of nuclear weapons and other weapons of mass destruction to more nations

■ a world in which "the rich are getting richer and the poor are getting poorer"

■ cultural globalization, which many see as a threat to their culture and religion

■ the growing choice of terrorism, rather than more peaceful approaches, to achieve reform in the world

■ the US often chooses to go its own way, rather than cooperate with other nations to solve problems

■ expanding populations, increasing industrialization, and growing individual consumption that add to stress on the environment

There is considerable reason for optimism, however. People in every country on Earth are working hard to find solutions to these problems. The key question for the future is whether the influence of these people will increase to the point where their views dominate. What can the average Canadian do? More to the point, what can you do? Perhaps you are already making a contribution. There are many things you can do, really. You are at the stage of your life where you are making many choices about how you will live and what values will be important to you. The most important thing is to learn about how your life interacts with the lives of everyone else on the planet and how the choices you make can contribute to the world being a better place in which to live. Right now you can join an NGO whose goals are important to you. This could be an organization working in international development such as World Vision; it could be a group working to support human rights such as Amnesty International; or it could be an environmentally focused NGO such as the World Wildlife Fund. You might decide that your time is better spent working within your school to provide leadership in one of these areas, or you might choose to lobby for change by contacting local, national, or international leaders.

Chapter Questions

Knowledge and Understanding

1. Examine the United Nations under the following headings:

   a) purpose

   b) role of the Security Council

   c) types of sanctions and their purpose

   d) peacekeeping role

   e) roles played by some of the UN's specialized agencies

2. What are the stages in the treaty-making process? Explain why the very nature of the treaty-making process means that it takes many years for a treaty to come into effect.

Thinking

3. Work in a group of three or four students to investigate the success of the UN. Each student should investigate a different branch of the UN's organization (for example, the General Assembly) or the operation of one of its specialized agencies. Try to identify the following aspects of the body you are studying:

   • What major successes has it had?

   • What major failures has it had?

   • What reforms would be needed to make it more successful?

4. a) Why was the North Atlantic Treaty Organization created?

   b) Why did NATO have to "reinvent itself" after the breakup of the Soviet Union? What did this reinvention involve?

   c) Why has NATO become an active peacemaker and peacekeeper in Europe and Afghanistan?

   d) How might NATO continue to grow and change in the future?

5. a) The Nobel Peace Prize has not been awarded every year. Why do you think the Nobel committee made this decision in the years the Prize was not given?

   b) Predict some of the years when it was not awarded. Do some research to check if you were right.

6. a) The Nobel Peace Prize was given for environmental leadership in 2004 and 2007. How does working toward a more sustainable world contribute to peace in the world?

   b) Do you think that the recognition of environmental leadership is a wise use of the Peace Prize? Can you suggest an alternative approach that the Nobel Committee might follow?

Communication

7. Using data provided by your teacher, create a map to show the pattern of acceptance for the Comprehensive Nuclear Test Ban Treaty. Your teacher will let you know whether you will do this with ArcView GIS software or on a paper base map of the world. Your teacher will also give you questions to answer based on the map you create.

8. Prepare to debate the issue, "Resolved—That the unchallenged military power of the US, working outside the restrictions of the UN, offers the best chance for world peace."

9. Identify a person, a group of people, or an NGO that has not won the Nobel Peace Prize but that you think makes a significant contribution to peace in the world. (Note that you can define "peace" here as you think appropriate.) Your job is to create a formal letter nominating "your" person/people/NGO for the next Prize. You should indicate in some detail the nature of the contribution that warrants this highly prestigious award.

10. Put yourself in the role of a person finishing high school in an Old Core country (this should not be a stretch) and the role of a similar person in a Near Core or Far Periphery country (this might be a tougher task). Consider how the individual choices made by each of these people in the years to come can either contribute to making the world a better place, or make this a more difficult reality to achieve. Your teacher will tell you whether you will be presenting your findings in the form of a five-minute speech, PowerPoint presentation, or illustrated brochure. **G**

Application

11. In 1994, genocide in Rwanda resulted in the deaths of some 800 000 people. Investigate the failure of the UN to prevent this genocide. In what way can this failure be related to the following?

    a) the strategic interests of permanent members of the Security Council

    b) the events that occurred during America's involvement in Somalia a few years earlier

12. Research the role played by one of these organizations in solving world problems:

    • European Union

    • Organization of American States

    • African Union

    • International Monetary Fund/World Bank

    • another international organization or NGO that works to reduce conflict and solve problems in the world

13. **a)** Some people have suggested that Canada can play a special role in solving world problems. What characteristics does Canada have that might contribute to this ability?

    b) What steps could Canada take to make a greater contribution in this regard?

    c) What nations in the world would be natural allies in doing this? Why?

Answers to Working It Out, page 399

a) UNICEF – United Nations Children's (Emergency) Fund
b) IMF – International Monetary Fund
c) WHO – World Health Organization
d) WMO – World Meteorological Organization
e) ITU – International Telecommunications Union
f) UNESCO – United Nations Educational, Scientific, and Cultural Organization
g) ILO – International Labour Organization
h) FAO – Food and Agricultural Organization
i) UPU – Universal Postal Union
j) UNDP – United Nations Development Programme

UNIT 6 QUALITY OF LIFE

"Quality of life" has an enormous range of meanings for people in different circumstances. For this girl in Sudan, it means having a reliable supply of clean drinking water. What does it mean to you?

CHAPTER 26

Globalization of Disease

Key Terms

medical geography

infectious diseases

lifestyle diseases

HIV/AIDS

pandemic

silence, stigma, discrimination, and denial

anti-retroviral drugs (ARVs)

obesity

Body-Mass Index (BMI)

nutrition transition

influenza

H5N1 (bird flu)

This 19th century London, England, water pump marks the spot where a cholera epidemic was stopped by preventing the use of water from an infected well. Dr. John Snow studied the geographic distribution of the epidemic. His original map shows the homes of cholera victims around the infected pump on Broad Street. Non-infected pumps are in blue. (Blue and red dots were added to the original map.)

- Infected pump
- Non-infected pump
- Boundary of infected area
- Homes of people who died (the size of the bars indicates the number of people who died)

Broad Street pump

Key Questions

By the end of this chapter you will be able to answer the following questions.

- Why is there a significant difference in the types of diseases that are most prevalent in rich and poor countries?

- What can be done to minimize the impact of HIV/AIDS in the world?

- Why are people taller and heavier now than in the past?

- Do modern lifestyles really make us unhealthy?

THE GEOGRAPHY OF DISEASE

We don't often think about the geographic distribution of disease—but we should. In fact, there is a branch of geography called **medical geography** that focuses on the distribution of disease (and of healthcare). The simple use of a map by Dr. Snow in the middle of the 19th century (page 410) indicates the power and importance of this often overlooked branch of geography.

In this exercise you will have the opportunity to start to think like a medical geographer. You will do this by considering the nature of various diseases and their link to the Old Core and Far Periphery.

Questions

1. List at least ten diseases that can be fatal or at least cause a serious reduction in one's quality of life. Be sure to include a wide variety of diseases found in different parts of the world.

2. Expand your list by combining it with those of at least two classmates.

3. a) From this expanded list choose five diseases that would, in your mind, be most closely associated with Old Core countries.

   b) Suggest one or more things that can be done to reduce the likelihood of a person suffering from these diseases.

4. a) From your expanded list choose five diseases that would be most closely associated with Far Periphery countries.

   b) Suggest one or more things that can be done to reduce the likelihood of a person suffering from these diseases.

5. a) What differences do you see in your answers to 3. a) and 4. b)?

   b) Why do you think these differences exist?

Infectious and Lifestyle Diseases

In general, diseases can be divided into two groups: **infectious diseases** and **lifestyle diseases**. Infectious diseases such as HIV/AIDS, tuberculosis, malaria, and even diarrhea are most common in the Far Periphery; lifestyle diseases, such as heart attacks, cancer, obesity, and diabetes are most common in the Old Core. The New Core and Near Core fall somewhere in between. New Core and Near Core countries tend to have both groups. Infectious diseases are gradually becoming less of a problem and lifestyle diseases are becoming more of a problem as the country (or region within a country) becomes richer and more like the Old Core. In this chapter, we will look in detail at one infectious disease and one lifestyle disease. From these examples you should be able to make some generalizations about the two groups of diseases.

Infectious Diseases: HIV/AIDS

In Swaziland, one in three adults is infected with the **human immunodeficiency virus (HIV)** or has already developed **acquired immune deficiency syndrome (AIDS)**. HIV/AIDS has reduced Swaziland's life expectancy to less than 34 years. In comparison, the percentage of adult Canadians with this disease in 2003 was only 0.3 percent, or about one person in 334.

In Africa, and to a lesser extent in other parts of the developing world, HIV/AIDS has become a **pandemic**, a disease that affects a large portion of the population in many different countries at any given time. In 2007, it was estimated that 33 million people in the world were infected and that more than two million people died during the year. By 2007, total deaths from AIDS and AIDS-related causes were about 25 million.

It is easier to appreciate the scale of this tragedy if we consider that the death toll in Africa alone is equivalent to a large airplane crash (238 people) per hour—every hour, all year. (We talk of people dying of HIV/AIDS. In reality, most people die of what are termed "opportunistic infections" that can develop because HIV dramatically reduces the ability of the body's immune system to fight infections.)

HIV/AIDS infection rates differ greatly from one part of the world to another. Sub-Saharan Africa has been most affected, but there are great concerns about the spread of the disease in other areas of the world especially eastern Europe, southern Asia, and China (see Figure 26–1).

A Brief History of HIV/AIDS

HIV/AIDS is a relatively new disease. It appears to have spread from chimpanzees to people in Cameroon, with the first AIDS deaths being recorded in 1959. The HIV/AIDS epidemic began "officially" in 1981 when the US Centers for Disease Control and Prevention identified a cluster of cases in Los Angeles. At first, the disease came to be identified with homosexual men and intravenous drug users (those who inject drugs such as heroin). Victims of the disease today come from virtually all groups in society. In much of Africa, more women than men are infected.

In most countries, it was (and to a large extent still is) difficult to talk openly about a disease that is spread primarily through sexual contact. The resulting public silence provides fertile ground for the spread of the virus.

The ignorance and fear surrounding HIV/AIDS has often caused those infected with the virus to be rejected by their community. In an extreme case, an AIDS activist in South Africa named Gugu Dlamini was stoned to death by her neighbours when they discovered that she was HIV positive. An expert from the Centers for Disease Control and Prevention in Atlanta, Georgia, described the societal response to HIV/AIDS in four words: **silence, stigma, discrimination,** and **denial**.

Did You Know?

In 2007, the United Nations dramatically reduced its estimates of the number of HIV/AIDS-infected people in the world—from 39 million to 33 million. This resulted from a recalculation of the number of infected people in India and several African countries. That such a large discrepancy is possible indicates the difficulty of getting accurate statistics about a disease that people are reluctant to talk about.

	People Living With HIV/AIDS, (thousands)	Deaths (thousands)	New Infections (thousands)	Prevalence (% of adults who are infected)
Sub-Saharan Africa	22500	1600	**1700**	**5.0**
Middle East and North Africa	380	25	**35**	*0.3*
South and Southeast Asia	4000	**340**	270	*0.3*
East Asia	800	32	92	0.1
Oceania	75	1	14	0.4
Latin America	1600	58	**100**	0.5
Caribbean	230	**11**	**17**	*1.0*
Eastern Europe and Central Asia	1600	55	**150**	0.9
Western and Central Europe	760	12	**31**	0.3
North America	1300	*21*	46	*0.6*
World	33200	2100	**2500**	*0.8*

Figure 26–1 AIDS statistics, 2007. Values in ordinary print have increased between 2001 and 2007. Values in bold have decreased between 2001 and 2007. Values in italic are unchanged between 2001 and 2007. Many HIV/AIDS experts are very concerned about the spread of the disease in some areas outside sub-Saharan Africa. Which areas are these?

	Ebola hemorrhagic fever	HIV/AIDS
How infection spreads	Contact with infected bodily fluids, from vomiting, bleeding, or diarrhea. Caregivers are at risk unless masks and gloves are carefully used.	Contact with infected body fluids, mainly blood and semen; through childbirth, pregnancy, and breast-feeding
Likelihood of infection when in contact with bodily fluids	Very high	Relatively low for most exposures
Cure available	No	No
Treatment available	Of symptoms only; does not affect the course of the disease	Drugs support immune system that helps body fight off infections
Vaccine available	No	No
Average time between infection and appearance of symptoms	3 to 21 days	AIDS develops 9 to 10 years after HIV infection
Average time between appearance of symptoms and death	10 days	9 months (can range from 2 weeks to 20 years with no treatment)
Mortality rate	50% to 90%	Close to 100% (with no treatment)

Figure 26–2 Comparison of Ebola hemorrhagic fever and HIV/AIDS

HIV/AIDS has been described above as a slow pandemic. It is obviously a pandemic because it affects so many people around the world. It is slow in the sense that, unlike most pandemics, it has been virulent for more than a quarter century and is still expanding in many parts of the world. Let's compare HIV/AIDS to another disease that appears in the news from time to time—Ebola hemorrhagic fever (see Figure 26–2) which kills very quickly.

In many ways, Ebola is a classic example of a horrible disease. It is a favourite plot device of movie writers (the 1996 film *Outbreak* is a good example) because it kills so quickly and in such a horrific fashion. Strangely enough, it is Ebola's very intensity that makes it much less of a threat to people than HIV/AIDS. Someone who catches Ebola either lives or dies. If that person dies, he or she does so quickly, before being able to infect many other people. While the person is sick, the illness is very obvious to others, so they can take precautions to protect themselves. If the person doesn't die, he or she gets better and is no longer infectious. Ebola can be compared to a wildfire that quickly consumes its "fuel" (the people in an area) and as a result quickly burns out.

HIV/AIDS is very different. It does not kill quickly. Infected people can live for many years (sometimes ignorant of their condition) and are capable of infecting others through ordinary activities like having sexual relations or bearing children. Without treatment, almost everyone infected will die of AIDS or AIDS-related causes.

HIV/AIDS in Africa

HIV/AIDS is having, and will continue to have, a profound impact on the world's poorest continent.

- Life expectancies are declining by decades. The AIDS pandemic is ending the population explosion in southern and central Africa in a way that no one could have predicted or wanted.

- Many children are infected with HIV/AIDS by their mothers. For example, more than 70 000 babies per year in South Africa become infected with HIV.

- Millions of children are orphaned each year when their parents die of AIDS. In countries with the highest infection rates, a grandmother may end up trying to look after many children with no one to assist her (see Figure 26–3).

- The pandemic is putting critical pressure on often inadequate African healthcare systems. Most hospital beds are filled with those in the final stages of the disease, mainly because there is nowhere else for them to go. At one point, 80 percent of adult patients and 33 percent of children in the main hospital in Gaborone, Botswana, were in the terminal stages of AIDS.

- The economies and social structures of many countries are being devastated as large numbers of skilled workers die. In one year, 1300 Zambian teachers died of AIDS. This was equal to two-thirds of the number that were trained that year. By 2010, the GDP of sub-Saharan Africa may be cut by as much as 17 percent because of AIDS.

- Unlike most diseases, AIDS usually kills adults in their prime. This fact is dramatically altering the population structures of African countries such as Botswana (see Figure 26–4).

Solving Africa's Problem

HIV/AIDS in Africa is a complex problem that cannot be solved by any one action. In general, the pandemic must be fought in two ways: by reducing the number of new cases and by helping those already infected to live longer with a higher quality of life. To achieve these goals, dramatic measures are needed, both within Africa and in the wealthy Old Core nations that provide the funding needed to fight this terrible disease.

Steps That Need to Be Taken in Africa

- End the silence, stigma, discrimination, and denial associated with the disease. People need to discuss and deal with the ways that people become infected as well as what happens after someone is found to be HIV positive.

- Work toward the "ABC" approach to reducing infection (see Figure 26–5).

Figure 26–3 In much of southern Africa, "single orphans" (one parent dead) and "double orphans" (both parents dead) are common. This grandmother must look after many of her grandchildren who are double orphans.

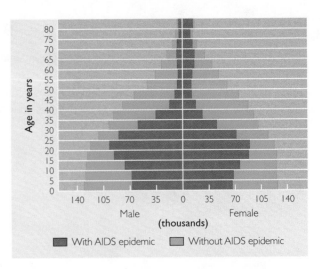

Figure 26–4 HIV/AIDS is dramatically changing the demographic structure of Botswana (shown) and other sub-Saharan nations. In this pyramid, the blue area shows people missing from the country because of the pandemic. Why is the number of children under ten so dramatically reduced? Hint: the explanation is more complicated than it might seem at first glance.

	Stands for	Comment
A	**Abstain**	People are often sexually active at an early age (13 to 15). The first step of the ABCs is to encourage people not to have sex until a much older age. The success of this is directly tied to efforts to empower women to be able to decide if and when to have sex.
B	**Be faithful**	People are encouraged to have only one sex partner. This is important in countries and regions where men migrate to other areas, often for months at a time, to get work. Research has shown that both husbands and wives in these situations frequently find alternative sex partners.
C	**"Condomize"**	Condoms should be used for all sexual activity, even with steady partners. Unprotected sex should only occur when couples are trying to have a baby, and after HIV/AIDS testing.

Figure 26–5 The "ABC" approach to HIV/AIDS is used in many English-speaking countries in Africa. Some people add a "D" to the list—they say that if you ignore the ABCs, you'll Die.

- Empower women in a culture that often permits them to be exploited sexually. Women must feel they can say no to unprotected sex or to having sex at all (see Figure 26–6).

- Treat HIV-positive pregnant women with medications to prevent transmission of the disease to the fetus.

- Implement effective testing and treatment programs (see Figure 26–7). The success of such programs is directly tied to ending the silence, stigma, discrimination, and denial.

- Find better ways to support AIDS orphans and their caregivers and NGOs that look after them.

Steps That Need to Be Taken in Core Nations

- While HIV/AIDS remains incurable, most people in Canada and other Old Core countries who carry the virus can expect to live for many years with a reasonable quality of life, thanks to a range of new and costly pharmaceuticals called **anti-retroviral drugs (ARVs)**. Some of the first people to be treated with ARVs are in good health (except for their HIV infections, of course) after more than 20 years.

- The problem is that ARVs can cost more than $10 000 per year per patient—and this is a recurring cost as long as the person lives. In wealthy countries like Canada, this cost is paid for, or at least significantly subsidized, by the government or

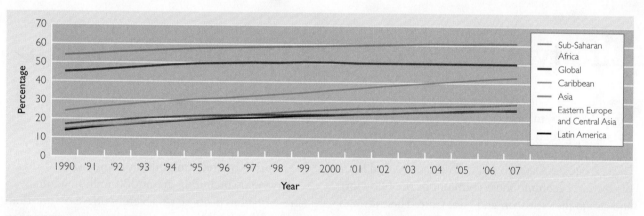

Figure 26–6 Percentage of adults (15+) living with HIV who are females, 1990–2007. In North America we tend to think of HIV/AIDS as a disease that is more common with men than women. Globally, slightly more than half those infected are women; in sub-Saharan Africa, a significant majority are female.

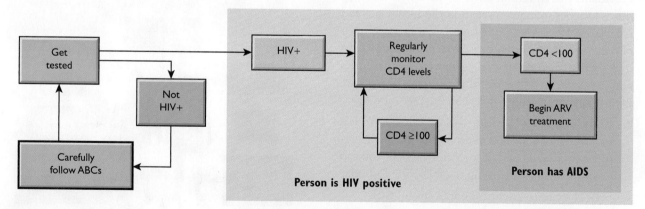

Figure 26–7 The HIV/AIDS cycle. Once a person is found to be HIV positive, it does not mean that he or she needs to begin anti-retroviral (ARV) treatment. A blood test is used to measure the strength of the immune system by counting the number of a certain type of cell (called CD4s) that is a vital part of the immune system. A normal CD4 count is in the range of 600 to 1200 cells/microlitre (µL). ARVs are not started until the count drops below 100. Note that in Old Core countries, treatment may be started at a much higher level—perhaps 300.

private health insurance. In most of Africa, where millions live on less than $1000 a year, such costs are nothing less than a death sentence. The problem is more complex than it might appear at first glance. Pharmaceutical companies have spent hundreds of millions of dollars developing ARVs and need to get a return on their investment. They also fear that anti-AIDS drugs sold cheaply to poor countries might "leak" back into markets in developed countries, further reducing their income and the money they need to develop new medications.

■ Wealthy countries, especially those in the Old Core, must fund the fight against HIV/AIDS. The cost of fighting this worldwide is between US$10 billion and US$15 billion per year. This money can come from a combination of official development assistance and from NGOs. In 2005, the G8 promised to provide US$60 billion in aid to fight HIV/AIDS, tuberculosis, and malaria in Africa.

■ Research on a vaccine for AIDS must be accelerated. Pharmaceutical manufacturers have so far had much greater success creating successive generations of better ARVs, than developing an effective vaccine.

HIV/AIDS—What's Next?

There is growing evidence that the HIV/AIDS pandemic may have peaked in sub-Saharan Africa and is starting to decline. At the same time, problematic rates of infection are just starting to emerge in many other parts of the world. Time will tell if authorities in places as diverse as China and eastern Europe have learned the tragic and valuable lessons—human and financial—that Africa has provided.

Lifestyle Diseases: The Obesity Pandemic

In world issues courses we often tend to focus on diseases like HIV/AIDS, tuberculosis, and malaria in poor countries and ignore the challenges posed by lifestyle diseases in wealthier nations. This is very short-sighted, because diseases like diabetes, various cancers, and heart disease are becoming more common in the Old Core and also in the New Core and Near Core. These diseases limit people's quality of life and reduce life expectancies. The spatial distribution of these diseases can be successfully studied geographically.

Worrying about our weight is common for many Canadians and citizens of other countries. Increasingly this is also becoming a problem in the New Core and Near Core. Researchers have found clear links between **obesity** (and the poor diets that cause it) and many of the diseases that are the major killers in wealthier countries and increasingly in less wealthy countries (see Figure 26–8). First, we need to understand the terminology.

■ **Body-Mass Index (BMI)**—BMI calculation is a frequently used method to determine whether a person is overweight and, if so, by how much. You can determine your BMI using the following formula:

• BMI = Your weight (kg)/Your height (m)^2

• For example, if you weigh 60 kilograms and are 1.6 metres (160 centimetres) tall

$$BMI = 60/1.6^2$$

$$= 23.4$$

■ Underweight = BMI less than 18.5

■ Normal weight = BMI 18.5 to 24.9

■ Overweight = BMI 25.0 to 29.9

■ Obese = BMI 30.0 to 39.9

■ Severely (or morbidly) obese = BMI over 40

Approximately one billion adults worldwide are overweight, including about 300 million adults who are considered obese or severely obese. More than 150 million children are obese, including more than 20 million under the age of five. Why do so many suffer from this potentially serious health problem? What can be done about it? Read on to find out.

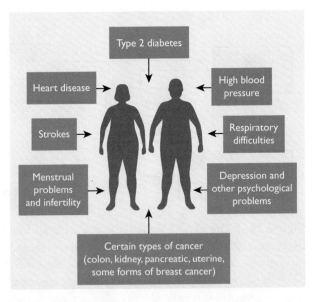

Figure 26–8 Obesity is linked to many of the diseases that kill millions.

NUTRITION TRANSITION IN THE WORLD

Earlier you learned about the importance of demographic transition. From a health perspective, **nutrition transition** is also tremendously important. Examine Figure 26–9 and answer these questions.

1. What trend do you see in the average consumption of food energy in the world? Give specific values for each time period.

2. The obvious next question to ask is how much food energy does a person need to function. This is a more complex question than it might seem at first glance. Suggest at least four factors that influence this amount. Try to give both personal and environmental factors.

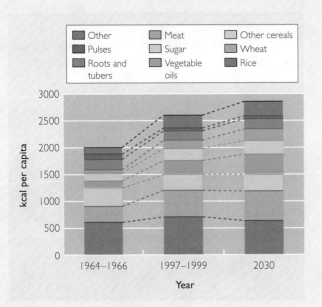

Figure 26–9 Global food-consumption patterns have changed and are continuing to change, both in terms of absolute amounts of food consumed and the sources of food energy that people rely on. Note that "roots and tubers" includes potatoes, yams, carrots, and similar foods, while "pulses" are various kinds of beans, peas, and lentils.

3. With a weight-loss/energy-needs calculator, you can estimate the number of calories needed for people with various personal and lifestyle characteristics. Calculate and record the amounts needed for at least six people with very different characteristics.

4. Compare the range of values you obtained in question 3 to the trend you found in question 1. What conclusions can you draw about the adequacy of food-energy supply in each time period?

5. What source(s) of calories would be included in the "Other" category?

6. Divide the nine categories of food into two groups: i) those that are becoming a more important part of global diets and ii) those that are becoming a less important part of diets or staying relatively the same.

7. a) Now divide the nine categories into two other groups:
   i) those that are generally considered to be healthy and
   ii) those that are generally considered to be less healthy, particularly when consumed in larger quantities.

   b) What relationships do you see between the members of the two groups?

8. Describe, in your own words, the nutrition transition that has occurred and is occurring in the world. In what ways is this transition positive and in what ways is it negative?

 Go to the link on our Web site to find a weight-loss/energy-needs calculator.

Nutrition Transition

Nutrition transition can be summed up by the following stages:

■ **Stage 1.** Most people are undernourished, and fear of famine is a fact of life.

■ **Stage 2.** Fear of famine recedes as agricultural-productivity increases. Most people are in the ideal weight range.

■ **Stage 3.** Diets continue to change both *quantitatively* (amount) and *qualitatively* (makeup). Many people are overweight or obese. Nutrition-related, lifestyle diseases come to predominate.

- **Stage 4.** Focus is on reducing the impact of lifestyle diseases. There are three aspects to this focus: medical intervention, government action, and individual behavioural change.

Historically, most people had active lifestyles, originally as hunter/gatherers and later as farmers without the aid of labour-saving machinery. Now, most people in the Old Core and, increasingly, elsewhere have *sedentary* (characterized by much sitting) lifestyles. Lack of physical activity leads to an increase in obesity.

Similar to demographic transition, nutrition transition happened first and is most advanced in the Old Core. Some historical statistics from the United States illustrate this point well (see Figure 26–10). Countries like the US and Canada are trying to make the difficult transition from Stage 3 to Stage 4. Evidence to support this transition includes:

- Healthcare systems focus on preventing and treating problems like heart disease, diabetes, and cancer rather than infectious diseases.

- Governments are changing laws to encourage people to live in a more healthy way, for example, by requiring nutritional information to be placed on all food packaging, or by eliminating unhealthy trans fats from processed foods.

- Many individuals strive to watch their diets and get more exercise.

Not all countries in the Old Core have been affected equally by nutrition transition (see Figure 26–11). In some countries, such as Japan, traditional diets that are healthier than modern Western diets have remained popular with most people. In these countries, the prevalence of lifestyle diseases is significantly lower.

Growing prosperity is reflected by growing rates of obesity and lifestyle diseases. In Brazil, China, and India, national statistics can be misleading since each of these countries contains large populations that are at different stages of nutrition transition. Rural populations typically are in Stage 2, while urban ones are in Stage 3. Figure 26–12 shows the increase in overweight people in just eight years as China's wealth and agricultural productivity increased. The problem is even more acute if we consider regional data. In rural (and poor) Gansu province, people obtain only 14 percent of their calories from unhealthy animal fats. Most people work very hard on farms or doing other physical labour. In contrast, people in Beijing get 32 percent of their calories from animal fat and most have sedentary jobs; almost half of the adults in Beijing are overweight.

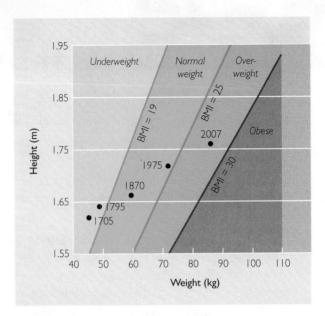

Figure 26–10 The impact of nutrition transition on the size of the average adult male in the US in the last 300 years has been striking. Similar changes have occurred in other countries in the Old Core and are happening, much more rapidly today, in many other parts of the world.

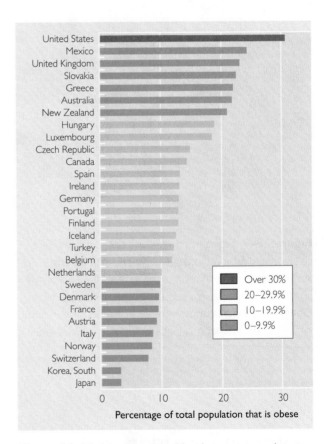

Figure 26–11 Nutrition transition has progressed furthest in the wealthiest countries. In many countries this has resulted in the high obesity rates shown here for many wealthy countries. Note that most of these countries are in the Old Core, with a few in the New Core.

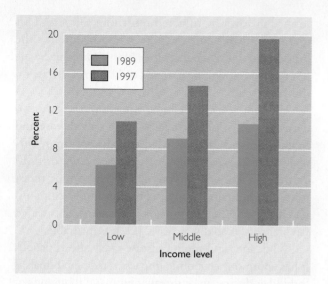

Figure 26–12 As China became wealthier in the 1990s, nutrition transition occurred extremely rapidly. This graph shows the percentage of the population, in different groups, who are overweight (BMI > 25). The numbers of obese and overweight people have continued to increase since 1997. As one might expect, lifestyle diseases in China have become more common. For example, more than 50 million Chinese now suffer from Type 2 diabetes.

What Can We Do About Obesity?

What does this all mean? The pattern of disease in the developing world is rapidly becoming like that of the developed world (see Figure 26–13). The solutions to the problems of lifestyle diseases are proving to be enormously challenging even to Old Core countries that have both the wealth to tackle them and more experience in dealing with them. The challenge for countries just moving into Stage 3—that do not have these advantages—will be that much tougher. What must be done in all countries is to promote healthy lifestyles that include

- regular exercise
- diets with lower amounts of saturated fats and sugar
- diets that contain more fruits, vegetables, whole grains, and vegetable oils

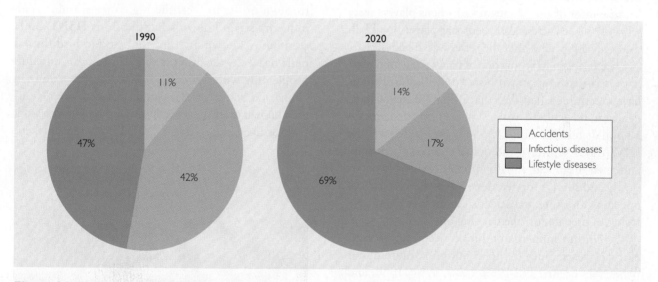

Figure 26–13 These graphs illustrate the dramatic changes in disease patterns that are occurring in the developing world as nutrition transition occurs. Percentages here represent the cause of deaths in each year.

The Next Pandemic

It was called the "Spanish flu," even though it is now thought to have originated in the US and then taken to France by soldiers who were going there to fight in World War I. Millions of soldiers from various parts of the world were crowded onto the battlefields of France and Belgium in extremely unsanitary conditions that were ideal for the spread of a deadly infectious disease. When the war ended in 1918, the soldiers took home the deadly virus responsible for the most serious pandemic that the world had faced in five centuries.

GLOBALIZATION

During World War I (1914–1918) there were approximately 40 million casualties worldwide. The influenza pandemic that followed the war killed almost twice as many people in much less time. Some estimates give a death toll as high as 100 million worldwide.

Why do you think that the influenza pandemic gets so much less attention than World War I?

During World War I (1914–1918) there were approximately 40 million casualties worldwide. The **influenza** pandemic that followed the war killed almost twice as many people in much less time. Some estimates give a death toll as high as 100 million worldwide. In Canada, one in six people got sick and 60 000 died (an equivalent death toll of over 200 000 today). The number of fatalities would have been even higher had it not been for the extraordinary steps that were taken to prevent people from passing the highly infectious virus on to others. Schools were closed and public meetings were outlawed. The outbreak was so severe that the 1919 Stanley Cup hockey playoffs were never finished. They were called off after five games because most of the Montreal Canadiens players were seriously ill. In fact, a Canadiens star player, Joe Hall, died only a few days after the series was abandoned.

The Spanish flu is only one of many pandemics that have occurred in recorded history. Medical historians have determined that there have been 32 major pandemics in the past 400 years. Will the next pandemic be a familiar foe like influenza, or a newer disease like HIV/AIDS? Will it spread quickly, kill many people, and then disappear equally quickly, or will it occur slowly and survive for decades? When will it start? No one knows for sure, but scientists and governments are trying to prepare for "the next big one."

Significant influenza outbreaks occur, on average, every 11 years. Since the 1918 outbreak, more minor pandemics occurred in 1933, 1946, 1957, 1968, and 1977. Health Canada has predicted that the next major influenza outbreak will come by 2010 and will kill between 9000 and 51 000 Canadians—hence the calls each fall for people to get the "flu shot."

Disease Transmission

Evidence has emerged that the 1918 influenza pandemic may have been transmitted to humans from pigs, and that the virus may have been passed, in turn, back to pigs in Iowa by infected returning soldiers. This disease transmission was likely responsible for the introduction of swine fever into North America. Swine fever remains a significant and costly animal disease on this continent.

In recent years, the United Kingdom has faced two devastating disease outbreaks—mad cow disease and foot-and-mouth disease. Mad cow disease (more formally called *bovine spongiform encephalopathy*, or BSE) destroys an animal's nervous system and can be transmitted to humans through consumption of contaminated meat. When it appears in humans, it is called Creutzfeldt-Jakob disease, or CJD. It is incurable.

While foot-and-mouth disease rarely affects people, it has enormous economic impacts. Trade in animals is forbidden during an outbreak, and many thousands of animals must be destroyed to prevent the disease from spreading (see Figure 26–14). Foot-and-mouth disease has also had a dramatic impact on Canada's international trade in beef cattle in recent years, even though only a tiny number of sick animals have been found. It is thought that foot-and-mouth outbreaks in Canada were linked to animals imported from Britain.

For many years, influenza has been known to spread through birds. In fact, the big concern today is an influenza strain known scientifically as **H5N1**, more commonly known as "bird flu." So far, bird flu has remained a disease of birds that can be transmitted to people only with difficulty. It has occurred mainly in China and Southeast Asia and has caused several hundred human deaths—generally among people who work with or live close to domesticated birds like chickens

Figure 26–14 Government workers in England in 2001 inspect piles of sheep and cattle carcasses. Hundreds of thousands of animals were slaughtered and burned to prevent the spread of foot-and-mouth disease.

and ducks. About 60 percent of people who catch bird flu die. Scientists worry about H5N1 because it is extremely infectious and has a high mortality rate. The conditions that make this disease well-suited for a genetic modification that would make it directly transmittable from person to person are hot, humid weather and close contact with animals and fowl.

To date, the most commonly used approach when an outbreak of bird flu occurs is to isolate the infected area and kill and burn any birds in the area. A particular concern is that wild migratory birds can catch H5N1 influenza when they intermingle with domesticated birds and then spread the disease to other wild and domestic populations as they migrate.

An influenza epidemic today would be different from the Spanish flu epidemic of 1918. We have a much better understanding of the disease mechanisms involved and have a wide range of medical interventions to use. For example, an effective vaccine could be created in a matter of weeks or months. Also, we have a variety of medicines that can be used; a number of Old Core nations have stockpiled medications to fight these diseases. The problem with this strategy is that the cost of buying enough medicine for the entire population is prohibitive, and there is also the very real fear that these medicines might not be effective against a new disease. Even if a vaccine could be created, it would be time-consuming to produce the hundreds of millions of doses needed quickly. Another concern is the mobility

of the human population today. Just as the unprecedented human movement at the end of World War I contributed to the 1918 influenza outbreak, a future pandemic is likely to be made worse by the mobility of people today. The SARS outbreak in 2003, which some feared could become a pandemic, illustrates the effectiveness of air travel as a method of spreading disease. The disease was focused in China and Hong Kong, but localized outbreaks occurred in areas to which many people travel from China—including Toronto, Vancouver, San Francisco, and Singapore.

What Will Happen Next?

The decades to come are likely to bring a sequence of news stories about outbreaks of known and unknown diseases. In many cases, these will end up being false alarms, while in others the death toll (and economic damage) could be significant. The great fear is that the next pandemic, whenever it may occur, could be the "big one," a disease that will kill tens of millions of people worldwide.

 Go to the link on our Web site to find out more about the Spanish flu.

Chapter Questions

Knowledge and Understanding

1. **a)** Describe the differences that exist between the diseases that affect the developing world and those that are most common in the developed world.

   b) What is happening to the relative prevalence of these two disease groups? Why is this happening?

2. **a)** Explain how "silence, stigma, discrimination, and denial" have contributed to the spread of HIV/AIDS in Africa.

   b) Can a similar argument be made about the spread of this virus in Canada?

   c) How can these four attitudes be overcome?

3. What is obesity and why is it considered to be a pandemic?

4. **a)** What is nutrition transition?

   b) What aspects of nutrition transition have been helpful to human beings?

   c) What aspects of nutrition transition have been harmful to human beings?

   d) In what ways can nutrition transition be tied to globalization?

Thinking

5. **a)** Malaria and tuberculosis have been called the forgotten diseases of the Near Core and Far Periphery. Who has forgotten them, and why does this matter to sufferers of these diseases in poor countries?

   b) Why have these diseases been forgotten outside the Near Core and Far Periphery? Why is this, perhaps, not a surprise?

6. In many countries of southern Africa, it is common for men to become migrant workers, leaving home for months at a time to work in mines or at other jobs in distant cities and towns. How has the common use of migrant labour contributed to the spread of HIV/AIDS? How might this impact be reduced?

7. **a)** Give two historical examples of a pandemic and two modern ones.

   b) Is the world more able to deal with a pandemic today than a century ago? Explain your answer.

   c) Suggest at least four things that Canada should do to be as prepared as possible for a future pandemic.

8. Why are scientists particularly worried about the pandemic potential of the H5N1 strain of influenza?

Communication

9. Summarize, in a visual fashion of your choice, the various initiatives needed to fight one of the following:

   a) HIV/AIDS in Africa

   b) the rise of obesity among teenagers

   c) the rise of obesity in New Core countries

10. **a)** A non-profit agency is to be created that would finance and coordinate research into vaccines and other pharmaceuticals needed to fight infectious diseases in the developing world. Your class is to simulate hearings that might be held at the UN. The purpose of the hearings is to establish the guidelines for this agency. The groups listed below will present their suggestions for how the agency should operate and what contribution their group can make. Your teacher will divide the class into groups that will take each of these roles, and give you specific instructions about the kind of presentations you will do.

   i) the governments of developing countries suffering from infectious diseases

   ii) the governments of developed countries

   iii) UN agencies including the World Bank and World Health Organization (WHO)

   iv) major transnational pharmaceutical manufacturers that develop new vaccines and drugs

   v) smaller pharmaceutical manufacturers that make copies of pharmaceuticals after patent protections run out

   vi) NGOs that operate in Africa and elsewhere in the developing world

   b) After each group has made its presentation, discussions among representatives of each interest group should occur, during which compromises between groups should be considered.

   c) After all the presentations have been made, each student is to create a written proposal suggesting the most appropriate organizational and operational structure for this agency. Note that in doing this you will have to reconcile the differing views put forward by the six parties. **G**

Application

11. The world has given a great deal of attention to HIV/AIDS in Africa, but potential crises exist for this disease in many other parts of the world. Put yourself in the role of health minister of a country that has yet to experience a major HIV/AIDS outbreak, but where infection rates are on the rise. Outline the policies you would implement in this country to minimize the risk of a major epidemic.

12. Prepare a report on one of the infectious diseases that affects the developing world. Your teacher will give you a list of diseases. For the disease you choose, include the following information:

    a) cause of the disease

    b) impact on a person's health

    c) map of the distribution of the disease

    d) number of cases in the world

    e) what is being done to provide a cure for and/or protection against the disease

    f) impact the disease has (or might have) on Canada and other developed nations

13. a) In Figure 26–11 you learned that there are enormous differences in obesity rates in wealthy countries and that this might be related to the nature of national diets. Investigate the characteristics of typical diets in Japan and France on one hand and the US and UK on the other.

    b) Is your school cafeteria part of the solution or part of the problem when it comes to you and your schoolmates eating a healthy diet? How could it do better? What role(s) could you play in this?

14. In general, you live in the time with the most advanced health systems and longest life expectancies in history, but you still face threats from various diseases. Describe what you can do to limit the risks you face from the diseases listed below a) while you are in Canada and b) if you travel to other countries, including very poor countries.

    i) HIV/AIDS

    ii) tuberculosis

    iii) malaria

    iv) obesity

    v) heart disease

    vi) bird flu

15. Many individuals and NGOs have made enormous contributions in the battle against HIV/AIDS. Research, and briefly report on the contributions of

    a) Stephen Lewis

    b) Bill and Melinda Gates Foundation

    c) William J. Clinton Foundation

CHAPTER 27

Human Rights Issues

Key Terms

human rights

Universal Declaration
of Human Rights

ethnic cleansing

Convention on the Rights
of the Child

caste

forced labour

bonded labour

cultural exceptionalism

A protestor at the Summit of the
Americas Conference in Quebec
City, 2001; a mural in South Africa.
How would you turn human
wrongs into human rights?

Key Questions

By the end of this chapter you will be able to answer
the following questions.

■ What are universal human rights and how do they affect your life?

■ What obstacles hinder the political participation of women around
the world?

■ How does war affect the human rights of women and children?

■ How can slavery exist in the 21st century?

■ How does cultural exceptionalism hinder a universal view of
human rights?

What Are Human Rights Issues?

The "greater good" for human society means different things to different people. To some, it is the growth of wealth. To others, it is the advancement of science or the creation of a great work of art. But to many, it means that a growing proportion of the world's population should live in freedom, peace, and dignity—in other words, that there should be a growth in respect for universal **human rights** (see Figures 27–1 and 27–2).

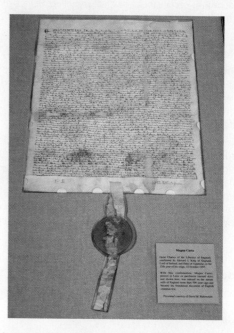

The Cyrus Cylinder, often described as the world's first charter of human rights, was written in 539 BCE by King Cyrus The Great of Persia. It abolished slavery and declared that citizens of the empire could freely practise their religious beliefs.

The Magna Carta, writtten in England in 1215 CE, protected citizens from unlawful imprisonment (the writ of habeas corpus) by the state.

The Declaration of the Rights of Man and of the Citizen was one of the fundamental documents of the French Revolution. Written in 1789, it provided for freedom of speech and of the press, but did not address slavery or the rights of women.

The Universal Declaration of Human Rights was adopted by members of the United Nations in 1948. It promotes human, civil, economic, and social rights. Shown here from left to right are: Mrs. Eleanor Roosevelt, Chairman; Mr. A.H. Feller, General Counsel and Director of the UN Legal Department; and Mr. John Peters Humphrey, Director of the Human Rights Division of the UN.

Figure 27–1 Human rights have been advanced, to varying degrees, throughout history.

The Universal Declaration of Human Rights of the United Nations

PREAMBLE

...THE GENERAL ASSEMBLY proclaims THIS UNIVERSAL DECLARATION OF HUMAN RIGHTS as a common standard of achievement for all peoples and all nations, to the end that every individual and every organ of society, keeping this Declaration constantly in mind, shall strive by teaching and education to promote respect for these rights and freedoms and by progressive measures, national and international, to secure their universal and effective recognition and observance, both among the peoples of Member States themselves and among the peoples of territories under their jurisdiction.

Article 1.

All human beings are born free and equal in dignity and rights. They are endowed with reason and conscience and should act towards one another in a spirit of brotherhood.

Article 2.

Everyone is entitled to all the rights and freedoms set forth in this Declaration, without distinction of any kind, such as race, colour, sex, language, religion, political or other opinion, national or social origin, property, birth or other status. Furthermore, no distinction shall be made on the basis of the political, jurisdictional or international status of the country or territory to which a person belongs, whether it be independent, trust, non-self-governing or under any other limitation of sovereignty.

Article 3.

Everyone has the right to life, liberty and security of person.

Article 4.

No one shall be held in slavery or servitude; slavery and the slave trade shall be prohibited in all their forms.

Article 5.

No one shall be subjected to torture or to cruel, inhuman or degrading treatment or punishment.

Article 6.

Everyone has the right to recognition everywhere as a person before the law.

Article 7.

All are equal before the law and are entitled without any discrimination to equal protection of the law. All are entitled to equal protection against any discrimination in violation of this Declaration and against any incitement to such discrimination.

Article 8.

Everyone has the right to an effective remedy by the competent national tribunals for acts violating the fundamental rights granted him by the constitution or by law.

Article 9.

No one shall be subjected to arbitrary arrest, detention or exile.

Article 10.

Everyone is entitled in full equality to a fair and public hearing by an independent and impartial tribunal, in the determination of his rights and obligations and of any criminal charge against him.

Article 11.

(1) Everyone charged with a penal offence has the right to be presumed innocent until proved guilty according to law in a public trial at which he has had all the guarantees necessary for his defence.

(2) No one shall be held guilty of any penal offence on account of any act or omission which did not constitute a penal offence, under national or international law, at the time when it was committed. Nor shall a heavier penalty be imposed than the one that was applicable at the time the penal offence was committed.

Article 12.

No one shall be subjected to arbitrary interference with his privacy, family, home or correspondence, nor to attacks upon his honour and reputation. Everyone has the right to the protection of the law against such interference or attacks.

Article 13.

(1) Everyone has the right to freedom of movement and residence within the borders of each state.

(2) Everyone has the right to leave any country, including his own, and to return to his country.

Article 14.

(1) Everyone has the right to seek and to enjoy in other countries asylum from persecution.

(2) This right may not be invoked in the case of prosecutions genuinely arising from non-political crimes or from acts contrary to the purposes and principles of the United Nations.

Article 15.

(1) Everyone has the right to a nationality.

(2) No one shall be arbitrarily deprived of his nationality nor denied the right to change his nationality.

Article 16.

(1) Men and women of full age, without any limitation due to race, nationality or religion, have the right to marry and to found a family. They are entitled to equal rights as to marriage, during marriage and at its dissolution.

(2) Marriage shall be entered into only with the free and full consent of the intending spouses.

(3) The family is the natural and fundamental group unit of society and is entitled to protection by society and the State.

Figure 27–2 The Universal Declaration of Human Rights of the United Nations

Article 17.

(1) Everyone has the right to own property alone as well as in association with others.

(2) No one shall be arbitrarily deprived of his property.

Article 18.

Everyone has the right to freedom of thought, conscience and religion; this right includes freedom to change his religion or belief, and freedom, either alone or in community with others and in public or private, to manifest his religion or belief in teaching, practice, worship and observance.

Article 19.

Everyone has the right to freedom of opinion and expression; this right includes freedom to hold opinions without interference and to seek, receive and impart information and ideas through any media and regardless of frontiers.

Article 20.

(1) Everyone has the right to freedom of peaceful assembly and association.

(2) No one may be compelled to belong to an association.

Article 21.

(1) Everyone has the right to take part in the government of his country, directly or through freely chosen representatives.

(2) Everyone has the right to equal access to public service in his country.

(3) The will of the people shall be the basis of the authority of government; this shall be expressed in periodic and genuine elections which shall be by universal and equal suffrage and shall be held by secret vote or by equivalent free voting procedures.

Article 22.

Everyone, as a member of society, has the right to social security and is entitled to realization, through national effort and international co-operation and in accordance with the organization and resources of each State, of the economic, social and cultural rights indispensable for his dignity and the free development of his personality.

Article 23.

(1) Everyone has the right to work, to free choice of employment, to just and favourable conditions of work and to protection against unemployment.

(2) Everyone, without any discrimination, has the right to equal pay for equal work.

(3) Everyone who works has the right to just and favourable remuneration ensuring for himself and his family an existence worthy of human dignity, and supplemented, if necessary, by other means of social protection.

(4) Everyone has the right to form and to join trade unions for the protection of his interests.

Article 24.

Everyone has the right to rest and leisure, including reasonable limitation of working hours and periodic holidays with pay.

Article 25.

(1) Everyone has the right to a standard of living adequate for the health and well-being of himself and of his family, including food, clothing, housing and medical care and necessary social services, and the right to security in the event of unemployment, sickness, disability, widowhood, old age or other lack of livelihood in circumstances beyond his control.

(2) Motherhood and childhood are entitled to special care and assistance. All children, whether born in or out of wedlock, shall enjoy the same social protection.

Article 26.

(1) Everyone has the right to education. Education shall be free, at least in the elementary and fundamental stages. Elementary education shall be compulsory. Technical and professional education shall be made generally available and higher education shall be equally accessible to all on the basis of merit.

(2) Education shall be directed to the full development of the human personality and to the strengthening of respect for human rights and fundamental freedoms. It shall promote understanding, tolerance and friendship among all nations, racial or religious groups, and shall further the activities of the United Nations for the maintenance of peace.

(3) Parents have a prior right to choose the kind of education that shall be given to their children.

Article 27.

(1) Everyone has the right freely to participate in the cultural life of the community, to enjoy the arts and to share in scientific advancement and its benefits.

(2) Everyone has the right to the protection of the moral and material interests resulting from any scientific, literary or artistic production of which he is the author.

Article 28.

Everyone is entitled to a social and international order in which the rights and freedoms set forth in this Declaration can be fully realized.

Article 29.

(1) Everyone has duties to the community in which alone the free and full development of his personality is possible.

(2) In the exercise of his rights and freedoms, everyone shall be subject only to such limitations as are determined by law solely for the purpose of securing due recognition and respect for the rights and freedoms of others and of meeting the just requirements of morality, public order and the general welfare in a democratic society.

(3) These rights and freedoms may in no case be exercised contrary to the purposes and principles of the United Nations.

Article 30.

Nothing in this Declaration may be interpreted as implying for any State, group or person any right to engage in any activity or to perform any act aimed at the destruction of any of the rights and freedoms set forth herein.

Read the following scenarios. Each describes a situation that might be regarded as a violation of human rights.

- In downtown Toronto, a man who was living under a bridge is found dead on a cold winter night.
- Refugees fleeing the fighting in the Darfur region of Sudan are denied entry into neighbouring Chad.
- In North America, young black men driving expensive cars are more likely to be stopped and questioned by police than are other motorists.
- In Quebec City, police use copious amounts of tear gas to break up anti-globalization protests.
- A gay man is attacked and beaten to death in Wyoming, USA.
- In Saudi Arabia, a convicted thief is punished by having his hand amputated in a public ceremony.
- In India, a young woman is expected to marry a much older man selected by her parents.
- In China, thousands of illegal copies of a CD featuring a famous Canadian singer are produced.

Questions

1. For each of the situations given, identify the specific human right that has been abused. (If you are having difficulty, check the United Nations Universal Declaration of Human Rights on the previous two pages.)

2. Like most people, you likely have a working knowledge of what human rights are. But can you give a clear and comprehensive definition of the term? Try to do this in your notebook.

3. Are there any rights that should be added to the Declaration of Human Rights? Explain.

What Are Universal Human Rights?

The political and legal rights that Canadians are familiar with evolved over centuries as democracy developed in Western nations. The idea that social and economic factors may also be human rights issues is relatively modern. Spurred by the events of World War II and the desire for world peace, the newly formed UN decided in 1946 that there should be a code of human rights for the entire world. The UN stated that such a code would be a "blueprint for the future of humanity."

A Canadian diplomat was asked to write the code. John Peters Humphrey was the director of the Human Rights Division of the UN. He completed a 400-page working paper on human rights in 1947. From this working paper came the document called the **Universal Declaration of Human Rights** (Figure 27–2) that was approved by the UN in December 1948. This declaration—the most detailed analysis of human rights ever produced—embodies concepts that go back to the Cyrus Cylinder of the sixth century BCE.

Although the Universal Declaration of Human Rights does not have the force of international law, most countries have signed it. However, not all of these countries have put the principles of human rights into practice. The UN has little power to force a country to follow the conditions of the Declaration; it relies on persuasion and public opinion to achieve compliance.

Women and Political Power

A fundamental aspect of gender equity is access to political power (see Figure 27–3). When women lack political power, they are not able to assume leadership positions and reach their full potential. Societies that do not have women in leadership positions are deprived of their experiences, perspectives, and approaches.

Figure 27–3 Women around the world have held leadership positions. Pictured here are Angela Merkel, Cristina Fernandez de Kirchner, Ellen Johnson-Sirleaf, and Benazir Bhutto.

In Beijing in 1995, at the UN's Fourth World Conference on Women, the governments of 189 countries promised to provide women with "equal access to" and "full participation in" political decision making and the power structures of government. They also pledged to ensure "measures to increase substantially the number of women ... in all governmental and public administration positions." Women are still under-represented in governments all over the world, even though they have gained the right to vote and to stand for elections in almost all countries. Why did so many countries make such promises and then not follow up?

In both Core and Periphery countries, there are obstacles that prevent women from seeking public office. Some governments have a selection and nomination process within political parties that traditionally excludes women. In some countries, there are no grassroots political networks to recruit and support women candidates. In countries where they lack access to political networks that raise money from private organizations and individuals, women find it difficult to finance a campaign. Even when nominated, women are less likely to be elected in a "winner take all" electoral system such as Canada's. Since it is not necessary to win a majority of votes to win a seat or even form a government, this electoral system also works against the election of minority candidates. In proportional representation systems, which are designed to elect candidates in proportion to the number of votes they receive, women and minorities stand a better chance of being elected.

Some suggestions have been made to increase the number of women in government.

■ In 1995, the Sixth UN Human Development Report recommended that a "critical mass" of at least 30 percent of government representatives should be women. It states that anything less than this critical mass is mere *tokenism* (a symbolic effort as opposed to a genuine one).

■ Laws should be implemented to limit the amount of money spent on political campaigns because financing a campaign is often a major barrier to women. A limit would put both men and women on a more equal footing.

■ Since financing a campaign is frequently difficult for women, public funds should be allocated for financing the campaigns of both women and men.

■ Quotas should be established for women within elected bodies. About 80 countries have established or debated the use of quotas for women candidates in local and national elections. Some countries, such as Afghanistan, Burkina Faso, and the Philippines, have incorporated minimum quotas for women in government into their constitutions. Others, such as Austria, Botswana, Denmark, Finland, Germany, the Netherlands, Norway, Sweden, Venezuela, and Israel have established minimum quotas for women in their governing bodies. Still other countries, including Argentina and Tanzania, have implemented quotas that reserve a minimum number of seats in their legislatures for women (see Figure 27–4). In the Nordic countries, quotas of 40 to 60 percent for each gender are applied to all public boards and committees.

Despite international recognition of the difficulties they encounter, and despite the progress they have made, women continue to face challenges as they try to participate in the political process.

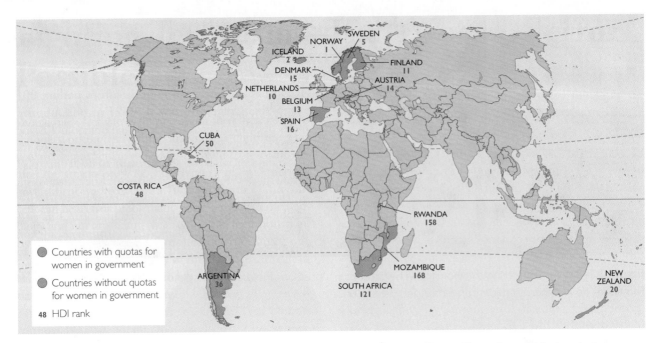

Figure 27–4 The 16 countries with the highest percentage of women in government. The colours indicate whether or not a country has a quota set for women and the number shows the country's HDI rank for 2006.

WORKING IT OUT · WOMEN IN GOVERNMENT

Examine Figure 27–5.

1. Which of the country groupings (Old Core, New Core, Near Core, and Far Periphery) has the greatest percentage of seats in government held by women? Why do you think this?

2. Work in groups of six. What do you think will be the relationship between the percentage of legislative seats held by women and each of the following variables:

    • Human Development Index (HDI) ranking

    • per-capita GDP PPP

    • literacy rate

    • political rights (Freedom House ranks the level of freedom from 1 as the highest to 7 as the lowest.)

    • health expenditures

    • total fertility rate

3. Each person in the group, working individually, should construct one scattergraph to show the relationship between the percentage of seats held by women in government and one of the variables for each of the 20 countries listed in Figure 27–5. For example, you might graph percentage of seats held by women (on the y-axis) and the HDI (on the x-axis), while another

member of your group might graph percentage of seats held by women and per-capita GDP PPP, and so on.

Note: You should graph the dots for each country grouping in a different colour. All members in the group should use the same colour scheme.

4. a) How strong is the *correlation* (relationship) between the percentage of seats held by women in government and your variable?

    b) Were you surprised by the degree of correlation that you found? Explain.

5. a) Examine all of the graphs to see what patterns, if any, there are.

    b) What variables, if any, seem to be better predictors of female participation in government?

    c) How do the results of your analysis compare to the predictions you made in question 2?

6. Is there a relationship between the level of development in the four country groupings and the participation of women in government?

	Seats in Government Held by Women (%) 2006	HDI Rank 2006	GDP PPP per capita 2006 in US$	Literacy Rate (%) 2007	Freedom House Political Rights Ranking (1 highest, 7 lowest level of freedom) 2007	Health Expenditures per capita in US$ (rounded off) 2004	Total Fertility Rate (children per woman) 2007
OLD CORE							
Canada	20.8	6	35 514	99.0	1	3000	1.61
US	15.2	8	43 223	99.0	1	6100	2.09
Germany	31.8	21	31 390	99.0	1	3521	1.40
Australia	24.7	3	33 037	99.0	1	3100	1.76
Japan	9.4	7	32 530	99.0	1	2800	1.23
NEW CORE							
Argentina	35.0	36	16 080	97.5	2	383	2.13
Poland	20.4	37	14 400	99.7	1	411	1.26
India	8.3	126	3 802	61.0	2	31	2.81
China	20.3	81	7 722	90.0	7	71	1.75
Malaysia	9.1	61	11 957	88.7	4	180	3.01
NEAR CORE							
Costa Rica	38.6	48	11 862	95.8	1	290	2.21
Philippines	15.7	84	5 365	92.6	3	36	3.05
Iran	4.1	96	8 535	80.0	6	158	1.71
Tunisia	22.8	87	8 975	74.3	6	126	1.73
Cuba	36.0	50	4 100	99.8	7	230	1.60
FAR PERIPHERY							
Bolivia	16.9	115	2 931	86.5	3	66	2.76
Bangladesh	15.1	137	2 300	41.1	4	14	3.09
Yemen	0.3	150	984	49.0	5	34	6.49
Zambia	14.6	165	1 088	67.9	4	30	5.31
Uzbekistan	17.5	113	2 304	99.3	7	23	2.88

Figure 27–5 The percentage of government seats held by women and the six variables for comparison

Human Rights and War

Soldiers are not the only victims of war. Civilians in war zones, especially children, also suffer death and injury. UNICEF estimates that since the late 1990s at least six million children have been permanently disabled or seriously injured by war (see Figure 27–6), more than one million children have been orphaned or separated from their families, and 8000 to 10 000 children are killed or maimed by land mines every year.

Women and children become victims of serious human rights abuses that occur as a result of war. They face severe difficulties when food production and distribution are disrupted, when law and order break down, and when basic needs for *potable* water (fit to drink), medical care, shelter, and clothing cannot be met. They are often the innocent victims of land mines and bombing "mistakes." Even wartime sanctions imposed by external nations tend to affect women and children most severely because any available medical and food supplies are directed to military and government officials.

In 2007, UNICEF estimated that 300 000 child soldiers—boys and girls under 18 and some as young as eight—were fighting in 30 conflicts around the world in countries such as Colombia, Ethiopia, Sri Lanka, Sudan, Afghanistan, Uganda, and the Democratic Republic of Congo. The use of child soldiers is escalating as governments, opposition movements, and guerrilla factions recruit or kidnap children from streets, schools, and orphanages. Child soldiers are valued because they are obedient, are seen as expendable, and do not ask to be paid. They are easily *indoctrinated* (brainwashed), sometimes through the use of drugs, and sometimes

To learn more about child soldiers go to the link on our Web site.

through exposure to brutalizing acts of violence. They are given a range of military duties, but are especially effective as messengers and spies because they are small and inconspicuous. Moreover, the proliferation of light, relatively inexpensive, and easy-to-operate weapons has made the use of children as soldiers more feasible (see Figure 27–7).

GLOBALIZATION

Child soldiers are valued because they are obedient, seen as expendable...

How would you like to be thought of in this way?

Some armed groups work through the school system to indoctrinate children who then volunteer to become soldiers. Some children volunteer in an effort to survive the chaos of war, particularly if they have been orphaned or separated from their families. Others fight because they have grown up knowing no alternative to warfare.

The international community has taken action to curb the use of child soldiers. The UN Optional Protocol to the Convention on the Rights of the Child came into effect in 2002. It stipulates that no child under the age of 18 can be recruited or required to engage in conflicts of any kind. Whether this protocol will reduce the number of child soldiers remains to be seen.

Figure 27–6 Over one million children and adults have been killed or maimed by landmines since 1975.

Figure 27–7 A child or adolescent could end up as either a victim (see Figure 27–6) or a combatant (above).

During times of conflict, the breakdown of law and order in war zones takes a terrible toll on women and girls. In societies where they have less status, women often suffer higher incidences of neglect and violence during times of war. Rape is considered a weapon because it humiliates and demoralizes both civilian and military populations. Women who become pregnant through rape are often ostracized by their society or considered unmarriageable. Many abandon their babies at birth. Sexual abuse is especially widespread in conflicts where ethnic cleansing is a primary objective, because causing women to bear the enemy's children destroys family relationships and weakens cultural stability. **Ethnic cleansing** refers to various practices used to displace an ethnic or religious group from an area to create an ethnically "pure" society. It can also be a code word for genocide in which a group is removed from an area by systematic killing.

The Geneva Convention of 1949, which codifies the laws regarding armed conflict, did not specify sexual violence against women as a war crime, although it did prohibit "outrages upon personal dignity, in particular, humiliating and degrading treatment." It was not until the 1993 UN World Conference on Human Rights in Vienna that sexual atrocities against women were condemned as human rights violations. In 1995, the Fourth World Conference on Women in Beijing recognized that as a result of armed conflict, women suffer not only sexual violence, but also many social and economic traumas.

Human Rights and Children

Children are the most vulnerable of the world's citizens. In addition to being victims of war, they suffer some of the most abusive conditions. Because they cannot speak for themselves, they must rely on others to speak for them.

Child Labour

The exact number of children worldwide who work is unknown. In 2006, UNICEF estimated that 246 million children, aged 5 to 17, were engaged in child labour and that 171 million of them were engaged in hazardous industries such as mining, fireworks manufacturing, stone quarrying, and the sex trade, or were working with chemicals and pesticides in agriculture. Children are considered desirable workers for a variety of reasons, depending on the industry. For example, their sharp eyes and small fingers are ideal for weaving carpets or doing fine needlework. More generally, children can be paid less than adults and are less likely to stand up for their rights (see Figure 27–8).

Some authorities suggest that child labour is a necessary evil in the face of widespread poverty, and that child labour will continue until the problems of poverty are overcome. Children must work to supplement their family's income. Many governments in developing nations feel that child labour is needed to sustain and increase economic growth. This does not necessarily mean that they support dangerous or exploitative forms of child labour. They also point out that child labour was a common feature of industrialization in western Europe and North America.

Experts suggest that several factors must be considered in determining the appropriateness of child labour.

- The age of the child. There is a big difference between a 7-year-old and a 16-year-old in the labour force.

- The work conditions to which the child is exposed. Compare the situation of a child working in a fireworks factory to that of a child weaving in the family home.

- Whether the work hinders (or enhances) the child's ability to get an education

The fight against child labour occurs at many levels. The most obvious is the legal one. Child labour is illegal under the provisions of the UN and the laws in most countries. However, governments do not always have the will or resources to enforce these laws.

Figure 27–8 This little girl works to help feed her family.

Child labour can also be fought in the world's marketplaces. Some products made by child workers—clothing, for example—are sold in developed countries. Some NGOs make consumers aware of the role of child labour in producing these items, but it is difficult for consumers to monitor the use of child labour in other countries. Boycotts are marginally successful, since only a small percentage of the products may be exported to developed countries. Campaigns can also fail to help children. A successful campaign against one business may force children into another line of work.

In many countries that practise child labour, projects have been created that recognize the economic necessity of child labour and yet provide children with a practical education. One example is a project for homeless children in Brazil. These children are given a chance to live, work, and learn in a "children's village." They receive lessons in woodworking and other crafts, along with basic academic training. The items they make are sold to help pay for the program.

Child Poverty

UNICEF reports that of the world's 2.2 billion children, one billion live in poverty (see Figure 27–9). For children under the age of 18, poverty is the result of many causes, including disease, lack of education, natural disasters, and government corruption. According to UNICEF, "poverty in childhood is a root cause of poverty in adulthood. Impoverished children often grow up to be impoverished parents, who in turn bring up their own children in poverty. In order to break the generational cycle, poverty reduction must begin with children."

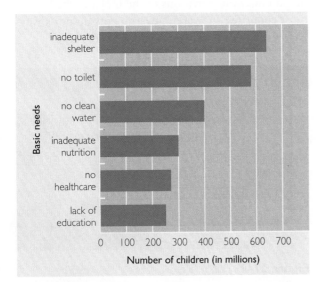

Figure 27–9 Millions of children live without the basics that you take for granted.

In 2005, UNICEF estimated that in Old Core countries, up to 50 million children lived in poverty. Further, it stated that the figure was rising. Children in Nordic countries were best off because of higher social spending. In the United States, about 22 percent of people under the age of 18 lived in poverty. In Canada, the figure was about 18 percent. This means that more than one million Canadian children—almost one child out of every six—lived below the poverty line.

Child poverty in Canada is not a new problem. The rate has not been below 15 percent since 1989, the year the House of Commons voted unanimously to eliminate child poverty in Canada by 2000. Not all estimates of child poverty in Canada agree. In 2006, Statistics Canada estimated child poverty at 17 percent, while a report published by the Fraser Institute put the figure at 6 percent. Why do you think there is such a discrepancy between these two figures?

Protecting the Rights of the Child

Although the provisions of the Universal Declaration of Human Rights generally covered the rights of children, the international community agreed that more specific protection was needed. The result was the **Convention on the Rights of the Child**, adopted by the UN in 1989. By 2001, the Convention had been ratified by every country in the world except Somalia and the US. The purpose of the convention is to protect the rights listed below:

- right to life
- right to be free from discrimination
- right to be protected in armed conflicts
- right to be protected from torture or cruel, inhumane, or degrading treatment or punishment
- right to be free from arbitrary deprivation of liberty
- right to special treatment within the justice system
- right to education, healthcare, and an adequate standard of living
- right to be free from economic exploitation and other abuse

Since the adoption of the Convention, considerable progress has been made. Many countries have ensured that their own child-protection laws meet the Convention's requirements. In some countries, senior government officials have been appointed as children's advocates. However, much remains to be done before all children worldwide can feel safe.

Slavery in the 21st Century

Slavery in some form still exists in countries such as Mauritania, Niger, and Sudan; the first two countries have a **caste** system. Castes are hereditary social classes. Members of a "higher" caste can own people in a "lower" caste. Slaves who attain their freedom may still have to pay tribute to their former owners.

Northern and southern Sudan are ethnically and religiously distinct. Militia from the north abduct women and children in the south and sell them in the north.

Forced and Bonded Labour

Forced labour denies individuals their freedom and is usually imposed by a government or paramilitary group. In this form of slavery, the threat of violence or other intimidation coerces people into working against their will. One example is the Laogai system in China. Political prisoners are sent to Laogai camps until they are no longer considered a threat to the state. While there, they work on farms and in factories. More than 200 products from these camps are sold on the international market. Observers suggest that as many as 1000 Laogai camps holding four to six million people existed in 2007.

Because of the illegal nature of **bonded labour**, there are no reliable estimates of the scale of the problem. Bonded labour, also known as debt bondage, is a means of paying off debts with labour instead of money. Bonded labourers are frequently farm workers, domestic workers, carpet weavers, or sex-trade workers. The UN estimated that in 2002 there were about 27 million people bought, sold, or forced into bonded labour. The International Labour Organization (ILO) estimated that of those in bonded labour, about 5.7 million were children.

Trafficking in people frequently leads to a form of bonded labour. People who want to migrate to another country borrow the money for their trip from smugglers who agree to transport them to their country of choice (see Chapter 8). They are told that they can earn enough in the new country to pay for their passage. When they arrive, they find they can never earn enough money to pay off their debt. The UN estimates that people-trafficking generates about $10 billion annually, making it a core business for transnational criminal networks.

The Issue of Cultural Exceptionalism

Cultural exceptionalism is the idea that the political, social, economic, religious, and cultural traditions of a country are more important than a universal concept of human rights. This is one reason why the fight for human rights is so difficult. In 2000, during the Taliban rule in Afghanistan, a woman could be stoned to death for adultery. In the Declaration, this is a violation of human rights. But by the prevailing morality and laws of the Taliban, it was an acceptable punishment. The outrage of the international community and of many Afghanis was considered irrelevant by the Taliban.

Attitudes about capital punishment in some of the Old Core illustrate cultural exceptionalism. In almost the entire developed world, capital punishment is regarded as inappropriate and unacceptable. The exceptions to this are the US and Japan. When criticized for their use of capital punishment, lawmakers in the US often reply that this is the business of citizens of the US. The US and Japan both believe that their use of capital punishment does not constitute a human rights abuse because many people consider it an acceptable penalty for certain crimes.

Canada may also be charged with cultural exceptionalism for its treatment of Aboriginal peoples. A highly disproportionate number of Aboriginal people suffer serious social ills such as poverty. The response to international criticism by the Canadian government and many Canadian citizens is that how we treat our citizens is our business. Similar situations can be found in virtually every country in the world.

The essential question of human rights in the world today is how to reconcile the sovereignty of individual nations and cultures with a cultural globalization that favours a universal view of human rights.

Chapter Questions

Knowledge and Understanding

1. The Universal Declaration of Human Rights has been described as a "blueprint for the future of humanity." Is it a blueprint for the future? Explain.

2. Imagine that your mother or a female relative or family friend wants to run for Parliament, the Legislature, or local council. What socio-economic and political obstacles would she face that a male relative would not?

3. Examine Figure 27–4. Does the presence of a quota appear to influence the number of women in government? Explain.

4. a) What is meant by "critical mass" in the political process?

   b) Why is it important for a critical mass to be achieved if women are to gain political equity?

5. In what ways do forced labour and bonded labour deny people their human rights?

Thinking

6. Since the Universal Declaration of Human Rights came into effect in 1948, many NGOs have formed based on the demand for recognition of the rights enumerated in the Declaration. For example, Article 26: "Everyone has the right to education...". The Canadian NGO, Education Without Borders, was created in 2002 to "provide improved educational opportunities and facilities in disadvantaged regions of the world." Its first project was to expand the only black high school in South Africa that offers classes in the Xhosa, Sotho, and Tswana languages.

   a) Select an Article from the Declaration.

   b) Find an NGO working to promote the right(s) stated in the Article (for example, education, protection of cultures, political rights).

   c) What is the mission statement of the NGO?

   d) Explain how its programs or activities address the right(s) expressed in the Article it deals with.

   e) Follow the same procedure for two additional Articles from the Declaration.

7. a) Some of the rights described in the Universal Declaration are denied to a relatively small number of people in the world. Identify at least two such rights, and the people who are denied them.

   b) Other rights are not available to large numbers of people in many countries. Identify at least two of these.

   c) Some of these rights are not available to all Canadians. Identify at least two of these, and explain why this happens. **G**

Communication

8. Prepare for a class debate on the pros and cons of establishing a quota system to ensure that women have access to a certain number of seats in the Canadian government. In the debate you will support the side that you *do not* agree with.

9. In 1987, a rebel guerrilla group called the Lord's Resistance Army (LRA) formed in northern Uganda to fight against the government. Since its formation the LRA has committed widespread human rights violations: massacres, mutilations, rapes, and the abduction of thousands of children for use as soldiers and sex slaves. Fearing abduction, as many as 40 000 children, known as "night commuters," walk each night from their rural villages to larger towns such as Gulu to sleep in relative safety. To raise awareness of the plight of these children, two Canadians, Adrian Bradbury and Kieran Hayward, mimicked their daily routine. For 31 days in 2005, they walked from their homes in the evening to sleep in front of Toronto City Hall, returning to their homes in the morning. To raise money for the children of northern Uganda, the two established a charity called GuluWalk. It has become a worldwide movement.

   Do some more research on GuluWalk, and answer the following questions.

   a) Describe the history of GuluWalk.

   b) What groups/organizations are partnered with GuluWalk?

   c) What programs does GuluWalk support in northern Uganda?

   d) What is the current status of the conflict in Uganda?

   e) How can individuals like you become involved?

   f) In groups of four or five, create one public-service announcement/poster dealing with the plight of children in northern Uganda, and another that outlines how students in your school can help by participating in a GuluWalk in your community.

Application

10. Assume that you have decided to continue the work of John Peters Humphrey. How would you modify the Universal Declaration of Human Rights to meet the needs of the 21st century? Explain your reasons for the modifications. **G**

11. Government is not the only place where the representation of women in decision-making positions needs to be increased. A report in 2005 of the Fortune 500 companies indicated that only 16.4 percent of corporate officers were women and that women held only 6.4 percent of the highest positions.

    a) What barriers are there to the advancement of women in corporations?

    b) What is being done to remove these barriers to advancement?

12. **a)** Introduction: In this chapter you have learned that there are an estimated 246 million child labourers. What can be done about child labour in countries such as India, Pakistan, Bangladesh, or Cambodia where this practice is common? In this Webquest, you will examine different points of view regarding child labour in developing countries.

    b) Task: Your teacher will divide the class into groups to examine the issue of child labour. Each group will consist of the following characters:

    • Company director: wants to produce products at the cheapest price possible

    • Parents of the child: need their oldest child to work in the factory to help support the younger children

    • Eldest child: would like to attend school, but knows the family needs more money to buy the basic necessities of life

    • Local school teacher: wants to teach the children of poor families so they will have more opportunities in their lives

    • NGO representative: wants to have children attend school so they are not exploited

    c) Process: "Jigsaw activity"

    i) In your "home" group, determine who will play each of the five roles.

    ii) Students from different groups who have similar roles work together in a "research" group.

    iii) Using resources found on the Internet, determine your arguments based on your character's point of view.

    iv) Prepare your arguments to defend your point of view.

    v) Rejoin your "home" group. One member of the group should be appointed as a facilitator to organize and manage the discussion. Each character presents their point of view and supporting arguments to the other members of the home group.

    vi) Discuss the issues and identify
    • what points of view you can agree on
    • what the real points of disagreement are

    vii) Develop a presentation in your "home" group that describes your deliberations and the outcome you have reached.

    viii) Make your presentation to the class.

    d) Evaluation: Your teacher will decide if this activity will be evaluated and what form the evaluation may take.

    e) Conclusion: When the "home" groups have completed their presentations, the class as a whole should reach a consensus about how child labour should be dealt with. **G**

CHAPTER 28

Empowerment in a Globalized World

Key Terms

empowerment

community initiative

socially responsible investing (SRI)

microcredit

comparative advantage

fair trade

PIR (Planning, Implementation, Review)

Microcredit lending organizations such as the Grameen Bank provide start-up loans to poor entrepreneurs because large banks do not usually lend money to the poor. More than 97 percent of borrowers are women.

Key Questions

By the end of this chapter you will be able to answer the following questions.

■ How can you be empowered in a globalized world?

■ Is socially responsible investing (SRI) for you?

■ How is microcredit helping the world's poor?

■ How does fair trade promote a reasonable price for goods produced by poor farmers and workers in developing countries?

Powerlessness Versus Empowerment

The problem with globalization is that it is so *global*. In other words, the world is so large and its population so great that individuals often feel insignificant and unable to control important aspects of their lives. Today, this is especially true when people make decisions that affect strangers halfway around the world. These decisions are frequently made without regard to the impact they will have on other people or the environment. As a result, many individuals feel they are powerless to manage their own lives.

GLOBALIZATION

The problem with globalization is that it is so *global*.

Do you think this is a problem?

People react to feelings of powerlessness in a variety of ways. Some may do nothing, believing that the global forces they face are just too powerful to overcome. Others may take to the streets to protest the movement toward globalization at meetings of the World Trade Organization or the G8. Still others may respond by finding ways to empower themselves to solve environmental, economic, political, or social problems. **Empowerment** is the act of taking authority or control over some aspect of your life.

In this chapter, you will study some examples of people who have empowered themselves by undertaking a **community initiative**. Although these people may be from different places, they nevertheless form a "community" because they work together to find a solution to a problem.

Socially Responsible Investing

Is it possible to invest money while being socially responsible? Some companies, although they make profits that are passed on to their shareholders, do not actually improve the living conditions or protect the environment in the places where they carry on their business. As a consequence, many investors who wish to be socially responsible have adopted an ethical investment strategy called **socially responsible investing (SRI)**. When people who believe in SRI make decisions about how to invest their money, they take their moral values into consideration (see Figure 28–1). They avoid investing in companies that damage the environment or cause illness—those that produce or sell tobacco, alcohol, toxic chemicals, or weapons.

SRI is growing rapidly in Canada. For example, assets invested according to socially responsible guidelines increased from approximately $65 billion in 2004 to approximately $504 billion in 2006. Discover more about socially responsible investing in the following activity.

Figure 28–1 People who adopt a socially responsible investing strategy would invest in ecologically friendly activities such as organic agriculture (left) and avoid ecologically damaging activities such as strip mining (right).

WORKING IT OUT

SOCIALLY RESPONSIBLE INVESTING

Use the Internet to answer the following questions.

1. Socially responsible investing (SRI) is not a new phenomenon. It has existed since the 1700s. Provide at least three historical examples of SRI.

2. How is SRI an example of a community initiative?

3. SRI uses four basic strategies:
   - screening
   - divesting
   - shareholder activism
   - positive investing

   Explain, with the help of examples, how each of these strategies contributes to maximizing financial return as well as social improvement.

4. Demonstrate, with an example, the concept of community investing.

5. a) If you were to invest your money in socially responsible companies, which types of companies would you include and which types would you exclude from your *investment portfolio* (all the investments held by a person or organization)? Explain.

   b) Some SRI critics claim that because many companies are extremely large and diversified, it is difficult to discern if they are truly engaged in sustainable activities. Based on your answer to part a), select two companies that would be good, socially responsible investments. Explain how these companies meet your SRI criteria.

6. Investment in alternative energy sources is an example of SRI. The Toronto Renewable Energy Cooperative (TREC) and the Windshare Cooperative it created with Toronto Hydro are two organizations involved in developing electricity from wind power. How do these organizations demonstrate empowerment and community initiatives?

Microcredit and Bangladesh's Grameen Bank

Microcredit is the provision of small sums of money to people to help them develop a better livelihood and break out of the cycle of poverty. The United Nations designated 2005 as the International Year of Microcredit. Microcredit was pioneered by Dr. Muhammad Yunus, a Bangladeshi academic who returned to his homeland in 1972 after completing a doctoral degree in economics in the United States. The idea of microcredit began with a chance meeting between Yunus and a young woman who made bamboo stools. Yunus was appalled to learn that the stool-maker lived in grinding poverty because she earned only three cents a day for her work. The reason for her poverty was distressingly simple: her only source of raw materials was the person who bought the finished stools. Because the same person set the price of both the raw materials and the finished product, he had complete control of the transaction. Furthermore, the man would supply materials only for stools that the woman would sell to him. Had the stool-maker been able to accumulate 30 to 40 cents, she could

In the News

Create a profile of **Dr. Muhammad Yunus**, focusing on his work with the Grameen Bank. Use the profile on page 14 to help you.

have bought bamboo from other suppliers and made more stools to sell to other buyers.

Yunus was shocked to realize that for the sake of little more than 25 cents, this woman was doomed to a life of abject poverty. He wondered if her situation was common and if he could do anything to help alleviate her poverty. After a few days of research in the village where the stool-maker lived, Yunus identified 42 such people who needed a total of only about

US$40 to dramatically improve their ability to earn a living. Yunus gave these 42 people the money they needed in the form of loans that they used to invest in making stools, pots, and other products. He told them to pay him back when they could. The villagers were able to improve their standard of living and repay the loans. With this simple experiment, Yunus identified the potential of microcredit. But this was only the beginning of the story.

Yunus' next move was to approach the banks of Bangladesh. He demonstrated the desperate need of Bangladesh's poorest people for small amounts of credit and described the success of his experiment—but the bankers dismissed him. They said the poor could offer no *collateral* to guarantee their loans. (Collateral is a key feature of most bank loans. For example, when you get a car loan, the car is the collateral. If you do not make your loan payments, the bank can seize the car to cover its loss.) The bankers also told Yunus that the poor would not be able to repay their loans. Finally, they said that the loans involved were so tiny that they were not worth the bother to process and administer. The only thing that Yunus could do was borrow money in his own name, and use it to provide loans to the poor.

In spite of warnings from bankers that poor people were a bad credit risk, the rate of repayment from Yunus' borrowers turned out to be remarkably high—far higher than the rate the banks received from their wealthier, more "credit-worthy" clientele. Yunus' scheme continued to expand until he was providing microcredit loans in more than 100 villages. But he was still unable to interest the banks in microcredit (see Figure 28–2).

Yunus realized that while his small efforts had been successful beyond all expectation, a more formal organization was necessary if the scheme were to expand. He concluded that if existing banks would not provide credit to the poor, a new kind of bank should be set up. In 1983, he established the Grameen Bank to provide small loans to people (see Figure 28–3). By 2007, the Grameen Bank had grown to the point that it operated in more than 81 000 villages and had more than seven million borrowers.

Microcredit loans from the Grameen Bank had expanded from Yunus' initial US$40 to more than $6.5 billion by 2007. More than 97 percent of borrowers were women. More importantly, the Grameen Bank had become the model for similar schemes in almost 60 other countries. In 2006, the Grameen Bank and Muhammad Yunus won the $1.4 million Nobel Peace Prize.

According to Dr. Yunus, poverty exists to a great extent because society has created institutions, including

The Grameen Bank of Bangladesh operates under the following principles:

- Loans are made at market rates and must be paid back within one year.

- A borrower who repays a small loan becomes eligible for a larger loan.

- Most loans are less than $50.

- Women are given priority in obtaining loans because their economic potential has generally not been recognized and because the money they earn is more likely to be spent on their children than money earned by men.

- Borrowers are set up in groups of five. The women in the group provide moral support for one another and critique one another's business plan.

- If one member of the group defaults on a loan, all members are cut off from future loans. This tactic emphasizes each member's responsibility to succeed and not let others down.

- Borrowers must agree to certain conditions because the ultimate goal of the Grameen Bank is social development. For example, they agree to limit the size of their family and to boil their drinking water. It has been found that people who adopt family-planning practices are twice as likely to be involved in microcredit than those who don't adopt family-planning practices.

Figure 28–2 A volunteer worker meets with a group of women seeking loans to start small businesses in the Manikgoj district of Bangladesh, north of the capital city of Dhaka.

Figure 28–3 The seven principles of the Grameen Bank of Bangladesh

Figure 28–4 This man was able to establish his small business in a developing country with a microcredit loan.

banks and governments, that discriminate against a wide variety of people, such as the poor. The discrimination is not necessarily deliberate; more often, it reflects a lack of understanding about people's practical situations. The ultimate solution lies in recognizing that institutions have a responsibility to ensure that all people are treated with respect and human dignity (see Figure 28–4). To achieve this, we must redesign society's institutions. To date, there has been considerable discussion in organizations including the UN and the World Bank about what should be done. But few *substantive* (significant and important) changes have been made. This particular community initiative, begun by one person and then taken up by a community of people who understood the value of microcredit to the poor, has succeeded where many large institutions, although dedicated to helping the disadvantaged, have failed.

SUSTAINABILITY

[Microcredit for the poor] has succeeded where many large institutions, although dedicated to helping the disadvantaged, have failed.

Why do you think microcredit has succeeded where other types of lending have failed?

Global Microcredit Summit

In 2006, more than 2000 delegates from over 110 countries attended the Global Microcredit Summit in Halifax, Nova Scotia. These delegates came from more than 3000 microcredit institutions that have helped almost 100 million of the world's poorest people. At the Summit, delegates set two new goals.

- They agreed that they would work to ensure that 175 million of the world's poorest families, especially the women of these families, were receiving credit for self-employment and other financial and business services, by the end of 2015.

- They also agreed that they would work to ensure that the income of 100 million families would rise above the US$1 a day threshold by 2015.

WORKING IT OUT MICROFINANCE ON THE WEB

You can support a small business in a developing country online. Find out how easy it is in the following activity.

Kiva was the first person-to-person micro-lending Web site. Begun in 2004, Kiva enables individuals to lend money to a micro-entrepreneur in a developing country. In 2007, MicroPlace, a subsidiary of eBay, was launched to provide loans to micro-borrowers. Research the answers to the following questions:

1. Describe the investment process for Kiva and MicroPlace.

2. How do Kiva and MicroPlace differ?

3. If you had money to invest, would this type of investing appeal to you? Explain.

Free Trade and Fair Trade

When people discuss globalization, free trade receives a great deal of attention. It is a fundamental part of the economic globalization that has been such an important trend since the late 1980s. Free trade allows commodities that are produced in one country to be sold as cheaply as possible in another. As a result, consumers have greater access to goods they may not otherwise be able to afford, and economic growth is promoted.

Where there is free trade, nations or regions focus on producing commodities for which they have the greatest **comparative advantage**, which is the advantage of producing goods better and more cheaply than other nations (see Figure 28–5). With the elimination of trade barriers under free trade, Canada has experienced economic growth based primarily on the comparative advantage of its rich natural resource base and advanced manufacturing. In comparison, China has experienced economic growth based on the comparative advantage of its immense, cheap labour force.

GLOBALIZATION

... many people do not benefit from free trade even if it is efficient and promotes economic growth ...

What can you do to help more people benefit from free trade?

Critics contend that many people do not benefit from free trade even if it is efficient and promotes

	Country A	Country B
Corn	10% advantage results in a...	10% disadvantage
Soybeans	30% advantage results in a...	30% disadvantage

Figure 28–5 Country A has a comparative advantage of 10 percent for corn and 30 percent for soybean production over Country B. Since Country A has a greater comparative advantage in the production of soybeans, it will focus on producing this crop. Country B has a comparative disadvantage in both crops. However, it will focus on producing corn because its comparative disadvantage is less for corn than for soybeans.

economic growth in general. For example, factory workers in Near Core and Far Periphery countries are often adversely affected by the competition that results from free trade. To keep the price of their products as low as possible, manufacturers in developing countries lower their production costs. A common method for lowering production costs is to keep labour costs low. Workers must accept low wages because they realize that their factory will close and they will lose their jobs if consumers can buy a cheaper product from another manufacturer. **Fair trade**, a trading partnership that aims to achieve more equity in international trade, is one way of addressing this problem. Although fair trade does not receive a great deal of attention, it plays an important role in the globalization process.

The terms "free trade" and "fair trade" sound alike, but they have very different meanings and implications for the poor. Free trade supporters believe that a free market economy works best for everybody. Fair trade supporters, however, believe that poor producers of many products in developing countries can benefit only if the free market system is regulated to some degree.

The fair trade movement is growing. In 2001, there were 224 certified organizations that produced fair trade products. By 2006, that number had increased to 569 (see Figure 28–6). Fair trade standards exist for a wide variety of agricultural products that include tea, coffee, cocoa, honey, sugar, juices, dried fruits, nuts, spices, flowers, and seed cotton. Some other certified products are soccer balls and traditional handicrafts.

All these commodities have one thing in common: they require relatively little processing in order to travel from developing countries to developed countries.

Consider the case study on page 444 that illustrates how coffee producers in developing countries benefit from fair trade.

Did You Know?

In Old Core countries, the number of licenced sellers of fair trade products grew from 1164 in 2004 to almost 2000 in 2006. In the same period, Canadian licencees increased from 124 to 185.

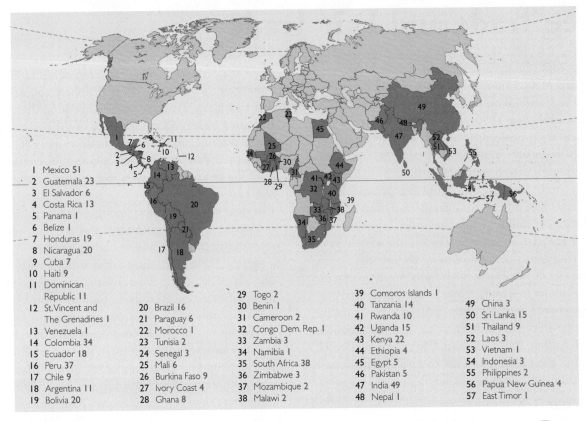

1 Mexico 51			
2 Guatemala 23			
3 El Salvador 6			
4 Costa Rica 13			
5 Panama 1			
6 Belize 1			
7 Honduras 19			
8 Nicaragua 20			
9 Cuba 7			
10 Haiti 9			
11 Dominican Republic 11			
12 St. Vincent and The Grenadines 1	20 Brazil 16	29 Togo 2	39 Comoros Islands 1	49 China 3
13 Venezuela 1	21 Paraguay 6	30 Benin 1	40 Tanzania 14	50 Sri Lanka 15
14 Colombia 34	22 Morocco 1	31 Cameroon 2	41 Rwanda 10	51 Thailand 9
15 Ecuador 18	23 Tunisia 2	32 Congo Dem. Rep. 1	42 Uganda 15	52 Laos 3
16 Peru 37	24 Senegal 3	33 Zambia 3	43 Kenya 22	53 Vietnam 1
17 Chile 9	25 Mali 6	34 Namibia 2	44 Ethiopia 4	54 Indonesia 3
18 Argentina 11	26 Burkina Faso 9	35 South Africa 38	45 Egypt 5	55 Philippines 2
19 Bolivia 20	27 Ivory Coast 4	36 Zimbabwe 3	46 Pakistan 5	56 Papua New Guinea 4
	28 Ghana 8	37 Mozambique 2	47 India 49	57 East Timor 1
		38 Malawi 2	48 Nepal 1	

Figure 28–6 In 2006, there were 569 certified, fair trade producer organizations in 57 developing countries. The number of organizations in each country is shown in red.

CASE STUDY Fair Trade Coffee

People around the world drink about 1.6 billion cups of coffee every day. The greatest part of the price that consumers pay for coffee does not go to the farmer (see Figure 28–7) who grew and dried the coffee "cherries" (the ripe beans). Each cup of coffee consumed is at the end of a long supply chain that began in the tropical upland areas of Brazil, Vietnam, Côte d'Ivoire, or one of a number of other countries (see Figure 28–8).

In developed countries, fair trade focuses on replacing commercial shippers/roasters with non-profit ones, and finding retailers to sell the more expensive fair market product. In most developed countries, non-profit groups have emerged to roast and distribute fair trade coffee.

Fair trade products are marked with a distinctive logo that indicates that they were produced and marketed according to fair trade principles. In Canada, this is the TransFair certification label. Other countries have similar

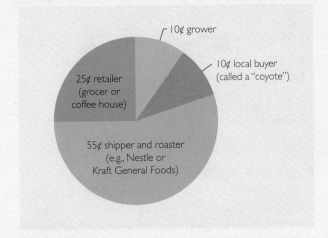

Figure 28–7 Without fair trade, the coffee grower receives only a very small portion of the dollar spent by the coffee consumer.

 For your research on fair trade coffee, you may want to start at the links on our Web site.

logos. Fair trade coffee is generally more expensive than free market brands and is most readily available in small specialty food stores or over the Internet. Fair trade coffee has made progress, however, in finding its way into supermarkets and large coffee chains. In 2005, for example, Starbucks purchased about 10 percent of global fair trade certified coffee imports (about 5 million kilograms).

Questions

Research the answers to the following questions.

1. How is fair trade an example of a community initiative?

2. How many coffee farmers are there in the world?

3. a) When did the coffee crisis occur?
   b) What caused the crisis?
   c) What happened to producers during the crisis?

d) How does the producers' average price for coffee beans during the crisis compare to today's average price? Does the price give producers a good return for their product? (In the coffee industry, this price is called the "ICO composite indicator price.")

4. Explain how the principle of fair trade is applied to coffee production.

5. Why is fair trade coffee generally more expensive than free market brands?

6. a) What major supermarkets and coffee and donut shops in your community sell fair trade coffee?
   b) Do you think it is important for fair trade coffee to be sold in major supermarkets and coffee and donut shops? Explain.

7. Would you be willing to pay a little extra for fair trade products? Explain.

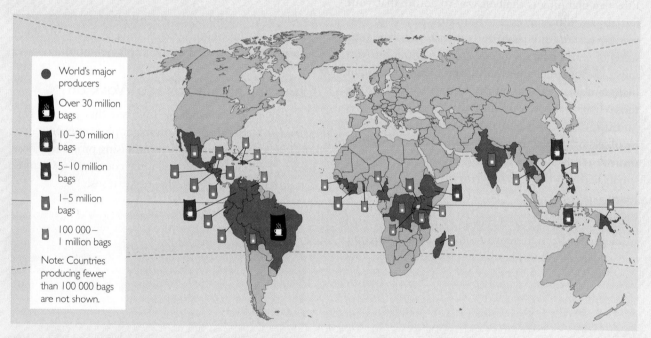

Figure 28–8 Total world coffee production in 2006 was 122 780 000 bags. World consumption in 2005/2006 was estimated at 116.2 million bags. What problem is revealed by these numbers?

Taking the Initiative in Your Community

A community initiative begins with an individual or a group of people identifying a problem, or several related problems, that threaten their well-being or the well-being of others. The problem may be environmental, social, ethical, or political. Then, someone or a group must determine how to solve the problem. The individual or the group must also have the courage to act.

The PIR Approach

To organize an initiative or address an issue, try the **PIR (Planning, Implementation, Review)** approach.

Planning

Effective planning is the best way to ensure that your initiative will be successful. You must be certain that you understand the problem you wish to solve. Your study of world issues is a good starting point, but you must investigate all aspects of the problem. This might include doing research on the Internet or contacting those directly involved in the situation to get answers. You might also wish to survey your classmates or members of your community, so that you are aware of the attitudes you will be dealing with.

Implementation

Identify the resources available in your class and school to help you. Beyond your school, a variety of people and organizations may be able to provide expertise and, possibly, financial aid. Local, national, and international non-governmental organizations (NGOs) in your field of interest; local service groups, such as Kiwanis clubs; and religious organizations may be able to help.

Plan a campaign that is realistic for the time available. Your goal should be achievable so that you can experience some measure of success. Establish a series of staged targets. When one is achieved, work toward the next one. You should determine whether your initiative will be active for a fixed period of time or will continue indefinitely. If the latter, build in a way for new people to take over when those who started the initiative leave the school or end their involvement with the project.

Review

Build a mechanism into your initiative to review your progress, on an ongoing basis, and to make whatever adjustments are needed in the implementation.

Choosing an Initiative to Work on

You may choose to work on any issue that you feel particularly concerned about: you might plant trees on school property or support specific fundraising projects to raise money for children in a developing country. See Chapter Question 12 on page 447 for suggestions.

Chapter Questions

Knowledge and Understanding

1. What is socially responsible investing? Provide examples.

2. **a)** Explain, in general, how microcredit works.

   b) How do the specific requirements of Grameen Bank loans contribute to the success of microcredit?

3. **a)** Why do commercial banks have little interest in helping the poor to build successful businesses in both developing and developed countries?

   b) Explain how a microcredit system addresses this problem.

4. Briefly describe the comparative advantage that each of the following areas has in a globalized economy:

   a) United States

   b) Southeast Asia (including Vietnam, Cambodia, and Thailand)

   c) Japan

5. How has free trade contributed to the economic marginalization of many workers in the developing world?

Thinking

6. Explain why the following statement is true: "While microcredit may help many poor people, it may be of most help to the poorest of the poor."

Communication

7. Create a one-page handout to encourage people in your community to buy fair trade products. Begin by researching the availability of fair trade products, like coffee, in your community. Include an explanation of the benefits of fair trade, along with information about where people can purchase fair trade products.

8. Use the Internet to investigate the efforts of Habitat for Humanity to construct homes in Canada and abroad. Prepare a visual presentation to explain this group's principles. If there is a Habitat for Humanity chapter in your community or region, perhaps you can arrange for a guest speaker to visit your school.

Application

9. Fair trade has expanded beyond products to include towns.

   a) What is a "Fair Trade Town"?

   b) When and where did this program begin?

   c) How does a town or city achieve this designation?

   d) What Canadian towns and cities have earned this distinction?

10. Research efforts that are being made to deal with poverty by one of the following agencies:

    a) Sleeping Children Around the World

    b) Doctors Without Borders

    c) Mennonite Central Relief Committee

    d) Grameen Bank

    e) Calmeadow

    f) another agency

11. Investigate the supply chain, from the grower to your table, of one of the following commodities: sugar, tea, chocolate, spices (such as cinnamon), or bananas. Try to determine prices at each step, and find out how fair trade either could be or has been applied to the commodity. **ⓖ**

12. Can one person bring about world peace? Reverse global warming? Eliminate poverty? Probably not. At least, not all at once. But there is evidence that one person can make a difference. In 1994, a young Canadian named Craig Kielburger was only 12 years old when he began a campaign against child labour in the developing world. He had been horrified to learn of the murder of a 12-year-old child-labour activist in Pakistan, and wanted to do something about it. He created an organization called Free The Children that works to eliminate child labour in the developing world. Kielburger's efforts have done much to bring the plight of these young workers to the world's attention. As of 2005, Free The Children had built more than 450 schools around the world and reached more than one million young people.

    Working in small groups, devise a plan to start your own local initiative using the PIR approach and the following suggestions as a starting point. (Feel free to tackle any other issue that interests you.) Identify appropriate targets for each of the Planning, Implementation, and Review stages. **S**

- Create a chapter of Free the Children at your school to help fight child labour.

- Organize a cleanup of a local ravine.

- Make your schoolmates more aware of the plight of refugees living in camps in war zones.

- Found an environmental club in your school.

- Organize a fundraising campaign to support the efforts of an international charity like Sleeping Children Around the World or World Vision.

- Plant trees on your school's land, or other vacant land, to provide improved habitats for animals and birds, and to create carbon sinks to fight global warming.

- Publicize and coordinate a campaign in your school to reduce the production of greenhouse gases caused by travel to and from school.

- Become involved in the work of Amnesty International or another group that fights to protect human rights.

- Become involved with a local food bank.

UNIT 7 RESPONSIBILITY AND HOPE FOR THE FUTURE

These seedlings can be seen either literally or metaphorically as a symbol of hope in a complex world. Literally, they represent an increase in food supply for the very poor. Metaphorically, they represent the new beginning that is possible for all of us.

CHAPTER 29

Achieving a Sustainable Future in a Globalized World

Key Terms

Bellagio Principles

specific indicator

comprehensive indicator

Living Planet Index

ecological footprint (EF)

Index of Sustainable Economic Welfare (ISEW)

fair Earthshare

Genuine Progress Indicator (GPI)

extended producer responsibility (EPR)

green taxation

Slow Cities

smart growth

How do these images illustrate the title and content of this chapter?

Key Questions

By the end of this chapter you will be able to answer the following questions.

■ What advantages are there for you in a more sustainable world?

■ How can sustainable development be measured?

■ What is your ecological footprint?

■ What initiatives are associated with smart growth?

■ What is the Brundtland Report and what does it suggest we do to achieve sustainable development?

Economic Growth and Sustainability

Economic globalization is closely tied to the idea that maximum economic growth is desirable and necessary. Unfortunately, economic growth too often leads to reduced sustainability. Today, many people are challenging business and government leaders around the world to find a balance between economic growth and sustainability.

GLOBALIZATION

Today, many people are challenging business and government leaders around the world to find a balance between economic growth and sustainability.

Why are people more inclined to demand such a balance now than they were in the past?

Sustainability and globalization dominate world issues today. The goals of the former, however, often seem to conflict with the demands of the latter. We must develop lifestyles that enhance living standards at the same time as they protect the environment. Before we can do this, we need to formulate a way to measure our economic success and our progress toward sustainability. Then, when we know how much or how little progress we are making, we can modify our lifestyle accordingly.

Gross Domestic Product (GDP) is the total value of all the country's good and services produced over a period of time. A recession is defined as at least two consecutive quarters of negative economic (GDP) growth. The world "recession" evokes fear in government and business leaders, the media, and the public. During a recession, the size of the economy shrinks. Corporations lose sales, governments lose tax revenues, and workers lose jobs. But something else happens as well.

The use of fossil fuels declines as factories cut output and people travel less. Other resource use decreases as the demand falls for metals, forest products, and agricultural goods. Air pollution, global warming, and other environmental degradation lessen. Although a recession is bad for the economy, it is good for the environment. As Chris Turner mentions in his book *The Geography of Hope*, discussed in Chapter 30, the environment must be given the same priority as the economy.

What Does the GDP Really Measure?

Although it may be an indicator of the state of the environment, many observers question the GDP's worth as an indicator of economic and social progress. As an example of how the GDP can be misleading, critics point to the terrorist attacks on the US in September 2001. The airplane hijackers had all lived for some time in the US, spending money on housing, food, transportation, and other necessities. After the attacks, billions of dollars were spent on repairing the damage, increasing border and airline security, and waging a war on terrorism. These expenditures were added to the GDP of the US and other countries, and so, according to conventional thinking, could be seen as contributing to economic progress. This spending, however, did not enhance the general quality of life. There are other indicators, discussed later in this chapter, that measure economic success and progress toward sustainability in a more comprehensive manner.

Measuring Sustainable Development

One of the initiatives at the 1992 Earth Summit in Rio de Janeiro, Brazil, was a call for ways to measure sustainable development. We need to measure sustainable development because we have to know if we can continue to take what we need from the environment.

In response to this call, a group of measurement experts and researchers met in Bellagio, Italy, in 1996. They developed the **Bellagio Principles** to help assess progress toward sustainable development at community and world levels.

ASSESSING SUSTAINABLE DEVELOPMENT

The Bellagio Principles (see Figure 29–1) encompass a remarkable range of ideas that are central to assessing progress toward sustainability. You can use them to assess the effectiveness of sustainable development indicators.

1. The Bellagio Principles deal with four general questions that we ask when assessing our progress toward sustainable development. The four questions appear in Figure 29–2. Which Bellagio Principles answer the questions listed in Figure 29–2?

2. Briefly comment on the significance of any four of the Bellagio Principles in assessing progress toward sustainable development.

3. Why is it difficult to measure progress toward sustainable development?

1. Guiding Vision

Assessing progress towards sustainable development is guided by the goal to deliver well-being within the capacity of the biosphere to sustain it for future generations.

2. Essential Considerations

Sustainability Assessments consider

- the underlying social, economic, and environmental system as a whole and the interactions among its components
- dynamics of current trends and drivers of change and their interactions
- risks, uncertainties, and activities that can have an impact across boundaries
- implications for decision making, including trade-offs and synergies

3. Adequate Scope

Sustainability Assessments adopt

- appropriate time horizon to capture both short and long-term effects of current policy decisions and human activities
- appropriate geographical scope ranging from local to global

4. Framework Indicators

Sustainability Assessments are based on

- a conceptual framework that identifies the domains that core indicators have to cover
- the most recent and reliable data, projections, and models to infer trends and build scenarios
- standardized measurement methods, wherever possible, in the interest of comparability
- comparison of indicator values with targets and benchmarks, where possible

5. Transparency

The assessment of progress towards sustainable development

- ensures the data, indicators and results of the assessment are accessible to the public
- explains the choices, assumptions, and uncertainties determining the results of the assessment
- discloses data sources and methods
- discloses all sources of funding and potential conflicts of interest

6. Effective Communication

In the interest of effective communication to attract the broadest possible audience and to minimize the risk of misuse, Sustainability Assessments

- use clear and plain language
- present information in a fair and objective way, that helps to build trust
- use innovative visual tools and graphics to aid interpretation and tell a story
- make data available in as much detail as reliable and practical

7. Broad Participation

To strengthen their legitimacy and relevance, sustainability assessments should

- Find appropriate ways to reflect the views of the public, while providing active leadership
- Engage early on with users of the assessment so that it best fits their needs

8. Continuity and Capacity

Assessments of progress towards sustainable development require

- repeated measurement
- responsiveness to change
- investment to develop and maintain adequate capacity
- continuous learning and improvement

9. Ongoing Assessment

Assessment of progress should

- develop a capacity for repeated measurement to determine trends
- adjust goals, frameworks, and indicators as new insights are gained
- promote development of collective learning and feedback to decision making

10. Institutional Capacity

Continuity of assessing progress toward sustainable development should be assured by

- clearly assigning responsibility and providing ongoing support in the decision-making process
- supporting development of local assessment capacity

Figure 29–1 Key points of the Bellagio Principles. These principles act as guidelines when you assess progress toward sustainability. You may use these principles to evaluate the indicators and the methods of interpreting and communicating information that has been gathered.

Four questions for assessing progress toward sustainable development	Bellagio Principle(s) that answer each question
We're ready to assess our progress toward sustainable development, but where do we start?	■
Do our sustainability practices meet the requirements that make them valid indicators of progress?	■
Is our assessment of our progress toward sustainability clearly laid out so that people at all levels of society can understand it and participate if they wish?	■
Are we flexible, and do we have the capacity to keep on measuring our progress? If so, who is going to give us the ongoing support we need to do so?	■

Figure 29–2 Complete a table like this one by filling in the Bellagio Principle(s) that answers each question we ask when assessing progress toward sustainable development.

Indicators of Sustainable Development

Indicators of sustainable development fall into two broad categories. A **specific indicator** is a single measure that shows progress toward sustainable development in one specific area. A **comprehensive indicator** is a collection of measures that, taken together, shows overall progress toward sustainability.

Specific Indicators

A statistic that has been used to measure something other than sustainability can work as a specific indicator of sustainable development. For example, the number of sidewalks in Richmond, BC, was used as a specific indicator of sustainability. The number of sidewalks indicates the number of people that could be walking in comparison to those driving. Walking saves fossil fuels and reduces air pollution.

Living Planet Index. In addition to using an already existing statistic as a specific indicator of sustainable development, we can use *purpose-built indicators* (statistics gathered specifically to measure one thing). One purpose-built indicator is the **Living Planet Index** created by the World Wildlife Fund (see Figure 29–3). It measures the state of the world's biodiversity in terrestrial, freshwater, and marine ecosystems. Although this is a useful measure, and one that will indicate that there may be a problem, it measures only one aspect of sustainability.

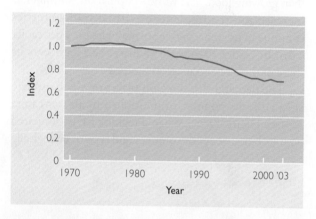

Figure 29–3 The Living Planet Index is an example of a specific indicator of sustainability. It measures the level of species diversity of more than 1300 vertebrate species around the world. The Index shows an overall decline of approximately 30 percent between 1970 and 2003.

Comprehensive Indicators

Like the GDP, a comprehensive indicator is easily understood; it is the sort of measurement that is often featured in news headlines. Since the Rio Summit, a number of comprehensive indicators have been proposed, but none has successfully seized the interest of governments or the public, or satisfied a broad range of the Bellagio Principles.

Ecological Footprint. You have probably heard about one of the most commonly used comprehensive measures of sustainability, the **ecological footprint (EF)**.

The EF uses a physical metaphor, a measure of land area, to suggest the ecological pressure created by the residents of a country. Human activities are related directly to the amount of land needed to support them. For example

- The food we eat depends on wheat land in Western Canada, market gardens in Mexico, coffee plantations in Brazil, and so on.

- The clothing we wear is related to cotton fields in China, pastureland for sheep in Australia, grazing areas in Alberta used to raise cattle that produce leather for shoes, and oil-producing and processing areas for synthetic material.

- Homes, buildings, and roadways degrade land that could be used for agriculture or other purposes.

The American humorist Mark Twain summed it up when he said, "Buy land; they're not making it anymore." The demand for productive land, in particular, is increasing as this limited resource is used for activities other than growing food. The world's population continues to increase and the residents of virtually all countries continue to use more and more resources on a per-capita basis. In Figure 29–4, each country's size represents its share of the global ecological footprint.

The demand that a region places on the biosphere is equal to its population multiplied by its per-capita EF (see Figure 29–5). When a region's EF is compared with its biocapacity (the number and type of biologically productive hectares within its borders and their average yields), the region's ecological reserve or deficit is visible.

What will happen to Earth's ecological balance as the EF for the Asia-Pacific region, in particular, gets much larger? In China and India alone, there are more than 2.3 billion people working to improve their living standards; this will, of course, increase their EFs.

Index of Sustainable Economic Welfare (ISEW). Although the EF is helpful, it is unlikely to replace the GDP as a measure of economic and social progress. EF values measure pressures put on Earth; they say nothing about economic measures that make the GDP such a widely used economic indicator. What is needed is a dollar-based measure that addresses the shortcomings of the GDP. One such measure is the **Index of Sustainable Economic Welfare (ISEW).** In measuring economic and social progress, it takes into account the positive value of a beneficial activity, but also the negative value of an activity that is ultimately unsustainable. For example, child-care costs are added to the index, but the economic costs of air pollution are subtracted.

 To calculate the EFs of your family, go to the link on our Web site. Follow the instructions.

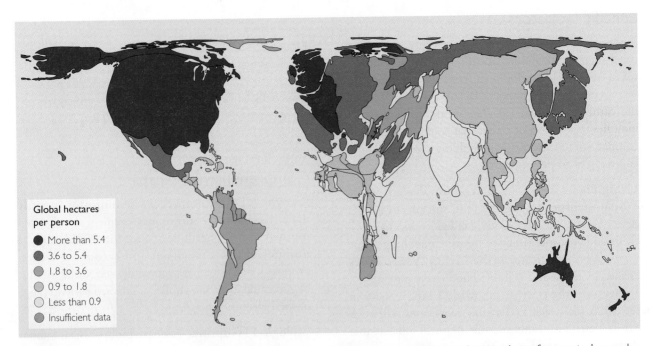

Global hectares per person

- More than 5.4
- 3.6 to 5.4
- 1.8 to 3.6
- 0.9 to 1.8
- Less than 0.9
- Insufficient data

Figure 29–4 National ecological footprints, 2003. The size of each country on this map is a product of a country's population and the average EF of each person in the country. Does the pattern match your expectations?

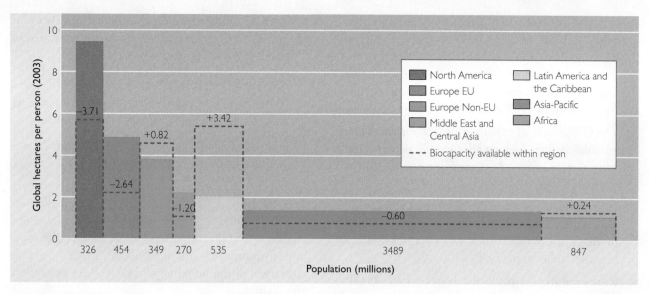

Figure 29–5 In this graph, regional ecological footprints are shown by coloured rectangles and biocapacities by blue dotted rectangles. Plus/minus numbers show ecological reserves (+) or deficits (−). Data are for 2003.

WORKING IT OUT
YOUR ECOLOGICAL FOOTPRINT

1. Calculate the ecological footprint for each member of your family. After you have determined each person's EF, calculate the average EF for your family. Why does it make sense to use an average to represent your EF, rather than the amount you calculated as your own EF?

2. How does your family's average EF compare to the North American average of 9.4 hectares? If your own EF value is significantly different from the average, explain why this might be.

3. a) There are about 11.2 billion hectares of productive land in the world. How many people with your EF could be supported by the world's productive land? What implications does this figure have for Earth's future, especially if we remember that people in developing countries are working to improve their own standards of living?

b) Assume that the world's population is 6.7 billion. How many planets with Earth's productive capacity would be needed to support all of Earth's people at your standard of living?

4. The **fair Earthshare** is the amount of land each person would get if all the productive land on Earth were divided evenly among all people of the world.

a) Based on the information given in question 3, calculate the fair Earthshare.

b) What options exist if the EF of some people is much higher than the fair Earthshare, while that of others is much lower?

5. Complete a mapping activity on the ecological footprint. Your teacher will tell you whether you will do this on paper or using GIS.

Genuine Progress Indicator. The developers of the ISEW added several other "economic costs" to their index to create a new measure called the **Genuine Progress Indicator (GPI)**. The GPI uses economic, social, and environmental indicators, and, like the ISEW, attempts to measure genuine progress by adjusting its measurement positively or negatively according to how an activity affects people's well-being. The following is a summary of how the GPI attempts to address the concerns that have been expressed about GDP measures.

- The GDP assumes that if an activity lacks a dollar value, it is not valuable. For example, the costs of fighting crime, such as police forces and prisons, are included in the GDP, while the value of stable family environments that prevent young people from becoming criminals is not.

- The GPI assigns an economic value to such activities as child-rearing, looking after elderly parents, and volunteering, since these contribute to a society's quality of life.

- Increases in the uneven distribution of income are recognized in the GPI, but ignored in the GDP. An increase in the Gini index (see Chapter 13) is a negative factor in the GPI.

- Resource depletion contributes to the GDP. For instance, as an oil company mines its non-renewable oil reserves and then sells the oil, the profit is figured into the calculation of the GDP. With the GPI, resource depletion is treated as a liability.

- Habitat degradation and restoration contribute equally to the GDP. In the GPI, degradation is a liability, while restoration costs are neutral activities.

- When people are forced to work longer hours or need multiple jobs to survive, the GDP considers it a gain but the GPI sees it as a loss.

- The building of public infrastructure and the manufacture of consumer products are handled differently by each measure. With GDP accounting, it is better to make cars, electronics, and household goods that will be obsolete or unreliable in a few years and will need to be replaced. With GPI accounting, a desirable product is a high-quality one that will depreciate slowly and provide benefits for many years.

- In 2003, the Pembina Institute, an environmental organization in Alberta, applied the GPI to Alberta. It used a total of 51 economic, social, and environmental indicators to compile information about the economic and social progress of the province.

The GPI indicated a much different quality of life for Alberta's citizens compared to that indicated by the GDP (see Figure 29–6).

GLOBALIZATION

When the GDP rises, some people may feel that, in fact, they are not better off.

Ask your parents whether they feel that their lifestyle is improving as Canada's GDP increases.

When the GDP rises, some people may feel that, in fact, they are not better off. They say that they are working harder, yet experiencing a lower quality of life. According to GPI supporters, people feel that the social and environmental costs of economic growth have come to outweigh the benefits; the GDP does not reflect this feeling.

Not everyone agrees that the GPI and ISEW are valid measures. These indicators may be viewed as too subjective since they arbitrarily assign economic values to non-economic activities.

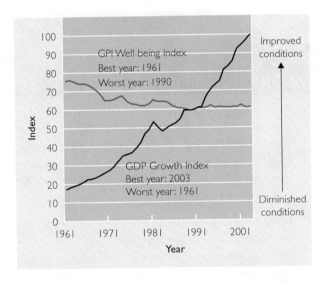

Figure 29–6 What does this graph tell you about the economic growth of Alberta's economy compared to the well-being of its citizens? Alberta's GPI declined from its highest rating of 76 in 1961 to its lowest rating of 60 in 1990. It stood at 61 in 2003.

Achieving a More Sustainable Future

So far, we have looked at how we might measure our progress toward sustainability. The next step is to consider changes that could be made in our lifestyle, economy, and government that would help us achieve sustainability.

ISO 14001

The International Organization for Standardization (ISO) is an old and very important agency that, for the most part, works quietly behind the scenes. (Founded in 1947, the ISO has its headquarters in Geneva, Switzerland.) It has created more than 16 500 international standards to ensure that companies in different countries have corresponding measurements and meet agreed-upon levels of quality in manufacturing. For example, a standard set by the ISO ensures that a bolt made in South Korea will fit a nut made in Spain. It has also established standardized criteria for the management and disposal of waste water.

As a result of discussions at the 1992 Earth Summit on the Environment in Rio, a technical committee of the ISO published a set of environmental standards that were updated in 2004. Several thousand companies and government agencies around the world have now been certified for ISO 14001. They have an environmental management system that establishes procedures that minimize the harmful effects of their activities on the environment. ISO 14001 certification also denotes that companies and agencies are continually improving their environmental performance. When you see an ISO 14001 sign on the side of a building, it means that the company is following ISO environmental standards.

Extended Producer Responsibility

The last time your family bought a new computer, you probably had to dispose of a big cardboard box and lots of Styrofoam packaging. Plus, you probably put your old computer into your household garbage to be taken away by your city's garbage removal service. The "environmental cost" of disposing of this waste material is borne by members of society when they pay their taxes. Naturally, this cost is shared by those who cannot, or choose not to, buy consumer goods. The principle of **extended producer responsibility** (**EPR**) changes this situation.

The logic behind EPR is that the company that produces the product and the person who buys it should be responsible for its environmental cost. Just as the company is held responsible for any waste or pollution produced by its manufacturing process, with EPR, the company is also held responsible for the product over its lifespan. This responsibility might take several forms. For example, a manufacturer might choose environmentally sound packaging, or ensure that the product is easily recycled at the end of its useful life. The cost of disposing of the more easily recycled packaging and product is now lower for the taxpayer. Furthermore, the cost of the environmentally improved product has been built into its price, and the consumer pays a large part of the environmental cost.

The city of Ottawa has created a "Take It Back!" program for a range of consumer goods such as burned-out fluorescent tubes and old car parts. City residents can return these materials to participating businesses that sell them, and these companies will dispose of them appropriately. Elsewhere, some communities have free disposal for computers and other electronic equipment. These disposal programs are usually run by local companies that recycle the components and recoup their costs by reusing or selling them.

Green Taxation

Many years ago, Canadians used reusable shopping bags to take home their groceries. Later, brown paper bags were used. More recently, the *ubiquitous* (present everywhere) plastic shopping bag has replaced the paper bag. At each stage there has been an increase in convenience, but a decrease in sustainability. Plastic shopping bags have become an environmental problem.

In 2002, politicians in Ireland decided to do something about this. They imposed a tax of about Can15¢ on each plastic bag used at the supermarket checkout. In the first two years of this tax, over Can$45 million was raised for recycling programs. The tax also resulted in a 90-percent decrease in plastic bag use. Other countries or cities with bans, taxes, or other campaigns in place to eliminate plastic bags include Australia, Italy, South Africa, Paris, and San Francisco. (In South Africa, plastic bags have been dubbed the "national flower" because so many can be seen flapping from fences and caught in bushes.)

In 2007, the Quebec government was exploring a new tax to target the use of plastic shopping bags. Companies across Canada now sell reusable cloth/composite bags labelled with their logos and advertising their "green" commitment while at the same time reducing their environmental impact on Earth.

The use of taxation to encourage environmentally responsible behaviour is called **green taxation**. To be effective, green taxes must be high enough to encourage people to change their behaviour. For example, Ontario has imposed a Tax for Fuel Conservation (TFFC) on new vehicles. This tax is a significant penalty, sometimes as much as $7000, for those who choose a vehicle with high fuel consumption (see Figure 29–7).

Most vehicles, however, fall in the category of a maximum tax of $75. A Tax Credit for Fuel Conservation (TCFFC) of up to $100 is available to purchasers of new passenger vehicles that use less than six litres of fuel per 100 kilometres of highway driving. These tax credits, however, are not large enough to influence consumer behaviour.

Highway Fuel-Use Ratings (L/100 km)	Tax on New Passenger Vehicles ($)	Tax on New Sport Utility Vehicles ($)
Under 6.0	0	0
6.0 to 7.9	75	0
8.0 to 8.9	75	75
9.0 to 9.4	250	200
9.5 to 12.0	1200	400
12.1 to 15.0	2400	800
15.1 to 18.0	4400	1600
Over 18.0	7000	3200

Figure 29–7 The Ontario Tax for Fuel Conservation is calculated using Transport Canada's highway fuel-economy ratings.

Figure 29–8 The hillside town of Positano, on the west coast of southern Italy, is a member of the Slow Cities movement.

Critics of the program argue that the TCFFC has lost its original purpose and has become primarily a source of income for the government, rather than a measure to encourage more sustainable consumer practices. Another problem with the TCFFC is that most people hear about it only when it comes time to sign the contract for the new car.

In the 2007 budget, the federal government proposed a green tax on fuel-inefficient vehicles. A vehicle that used 16 or more litres per 100 kilometres, for example, would have a green tax of $4000 placed on it. While it appears that the scheme punishes "gas-guzzlers" severely, in reality most vehicles do not reach this tax level. For example, since the very large 2007 Cadillac Escalade uses about 14 litres of fuel per 100 kilometres the green tax would be $800. (See Chapter 20 for a related discussion on the carbon tax.)

Città Lente

In many parts of the developed world, people are questioning the assumptions that underlie both economic and cultural globalization. In most situations, this involves the decision by an individual to buy less, to live in a more ecologically responsible way, or to value local culture more. Increasingly, though, people are taking these actions collectively.

A particularly good example of a collective action is the Città Lente, or **Slow Cities**, movement. A group of about 50 Italian towns and small cities has decided not to become part of the globalized world of the 21st century (see Figure 29–8). Instead, people are setting out to protect the qualities that make their communities and the regions around them special. They are doing this, not by one large action, but by many small ones. For example, they do not allow the construction of fast-food restaurants or cellphone antennas, and they ban the use of car alarms and garish neon signs. Local cultural traditions are protected and encouraged, and restaurants serve local foods and wines. In some places, people are passing laws that protect farmland to ensure that consumers can buy directly from local farmers.

Most Slow Cities rely on tourism for much of their income. The residents realize that the main reason people want to visit their region is because it is different; it has

Did You Know?

Green accounting is a system of bookkeeping that considers the impact of production and consumption on the environment. In 1995, the Danish Parliament passed the Green Accounts Act (revised in 2002), which requires corporations and government agencies to submit annual green accounting reports to the government. Consumers who are concerned about sustainability can use these reports to decide with whom they want to do business. Over 1200 companies in nine specific sectors, including iron and steel, oil and gas, chemicals, and animal processing, are obliged to publish green accounts annually.

not become a homogenized, globalized kind of place. Something similar to the Slow Cities movement has emerged in a number of smaller communities in Canada. Places such as Niagara-on-the-Lake (Ontario), Lunenburg (Nova Scotia), and Grand Bruit (Newfoundland) have built an economy based on the unique nature of their communities.

Smart Growth

Smart growth refers to a new approach in urban planning. It is the idea that communities must be developed and managed in ways that promote environmental and economic sustainability, through the use of long-term urban planning policies that focus on preventing urban sprawl.

The goal of smart growth is to build high-density communities, with vibrant downtown cores that are pedestrian and bicycle friendly and have both commercial and residential land uses. Commercial land uses provide employment for residents who live in or near the downtown core; residential land uses are characterized by a wide variety of affordable housing. Public transit is promoted. All factors lead to the growth of closely knit communities with neighbourhood schools and nearly all the services residents require.

The compact, urban development of smart-growth communities provides several environmental benefits:

- reduced greenhouse gas emissions
- improved air quality
- protection of ecologically important areas, drinking-water sources, and prime agricultural land
- reduced infrastructure development and maintenance costs

The Ontario Smart Growth Network believes that there are three basic requirements for achieving smart growth throughout the province: stop urban sprawl, foster healthy communities, and support community involvement in planning.

Changing Our Behaviour

As Earth's population continues to grow, demands on the environment escalate. How do we deal with the expansion of human development into natural environments, especially when some areas, such as rainforests, are necessary for the protection of Earth itself? The simple solution is to manage development—prohibiting it in sensitive areas, and allowing it in less critical areas. This solution, however, is not as easy as it seems. Prohibiting development may not meet the economic needs of society, especially in the developing world. But in the long term, perhaps it may.

Humans seem to value things only when monetary worth is attached to them. How much money do you think clean air and fresh water are worth? If you're having trouble trying to determine a value for these resources, think about how much it would cost to do what nature does for free. For example, if pollinators, such as bees, could not do their job, how much would it cost for humans to do the pollinating? What nature does for us is worth far more than we could ever afford to do ourselves. In fact, our entire agricultural system is "subsidized" by nature. As well, many of our natural areas have far more monetary value to us when they are kept healthy.

Costa Rica provides an example of people placing a monetary value on a natural resource that they are willing to protect through their taxes. They do so because they realize that the long-term monetary value of the resource is far greater than the short-term economic gain from its exploitation.

Costa Rican cities needed the fresh, clean water that comes from watersheds in nearby farming areas. This water is also needed by the farmers. In the agricultural process, however, the water was subjected to pollution and degradation. The government decided that to protect the water resource, it would pay farmers to return their agricultural land to forest. As a result, farmers maintained their income from the land, while the cities received clean water. In other words, the water in the watershed was worth far more to society than the agricultural products grown on the land.

So, where do the agricultural products that were formerly raised by the farmers—whose land has been returned to forest—come from? They come from areas where the supply of water necessary for agriculture is not as essential for other purposes.

Some conservationists say that if we put a monetary value on nature, we are recognizing its worth in a concrete way, and therefore, we will think twice about how we use it. What do you think?

Our Common Future

SUSTAINABILITY

The concept of sustainable development implies that there are limits—not absolute limits, but limitations—on our use of environmental resources.

What impacts will these limitations have on how we live? Are we willing to accept them?

Ultimately, the fight to achieve sustainability comes down to the question of whether people, particularly in developed countries, are prepared to change their behaviour. In 1983, the UN established a commission to examine long-term environmental strategies for achieving sustainable development. The commission became known as the Brundtland Commission, named after the chairperson Dr. Gro Harlem Brundtland. The Brundtland Report, published in 1987 and called "Our Common Future," suggests what must be done to achieve sustainable development:

- The concept of sustainable development implies that there are limits—not absolute limits, but limitations—on our use of environmental resources. These limits are imposed by the present state of technology and social organization, and also by the ability of the biosphere to absorb the effects of human activities.

- Sustainable development requires meeting the basic needs of all and extending to all the opportunity to fulfill aspirations for a better life.

- Meeting basic needs requires a new era of economic growth for nations in which the majority of people are poor. Economic growth must be accompanied by an assurance that the poor get their fair share of the resources that lead to economic growth.

- Sustainable global development requires that those who are more affluent adopt lifestyles within the planet's ecological means, for example, in their use of energy.

Consider what each of these points suggests about how *your* behaviour and your expectations for the future may have to change.

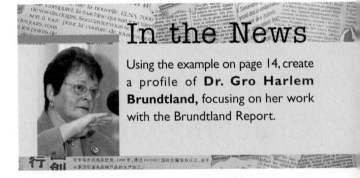

In the News

Using the example on page 14, create a profile of **Dr. Gro Harlem Brundtland,** focusing on her work with the Brundtland Report.

Chapter Questions

Knowledge and Understanding

1. Explain the relationship between economic cycles and environmental degradation.

2. a) Explain, using a specific example not given in this chapter, why the GDP is a flawed measure of economic and social progress.

   b) Identify at least three ways that the Bellagio Principles demonstrate the limitations of the GDP.

3. Make a chart to compare, in a general way, the a) characteristics, b) strengths, and c) limitations of specific indicators and comprehensive indicators of progress toward sustainability.

Thinking

4. How do the goals for sustainable development conflict with the goals for globalization? Is this conflict inevitable or can the two concepts be reconciled so that both can be achieved? If so, how? If not, why not?

5. a) Choose one of the sample indicators of sustainable development and explain why it is a suitable indicator of sustainable development.

   b) Choose a different statistical measure that you think could be used to measure sustainable development. Provide evidence to prove that it is an appropriate indicator.

6. Refer to the principles cited by the Brundtland Report (page 460). Describe how your behaviour might have to change if sustainability is to be achieved.

7. Through research, expand on the concept of "smart growth."

8. What are your views on placing a monetary value on nature?

Communication

9. Write a short essay (or create a graphic organizer) outlining the greatest advantages and limitations of working with ecological footprints.

10. Work in a group of three or four students. A global business report, *An Abrupt Climate Change Scenario and its Implications for United States National Security* by Peter Schwartz and Doug Randall, 2003, warns: "As global and local carrying capacities are reduced, tensions could mount around the world… Nations with the resources to do so may build virtual fortresses around their countries, preserving resources for themselves. Less fortunate nations… may initiate struggles for access to food, clean water, or energy. Unlikely alliances could be formed as defense priorities shift and the goal is resources for survival rather than religion, ideology, or national honour…"

    a) What nations might "build virtual fortresses around their countries, preserving resources for themselves"?

    b) If countries decided to keep resources for themselves, what could happen?

    c) Do you think this scenario is plausible? Explain.

Application

11. In a group of three or four students, create a working, comprehensive indicator of sustainability. Consider what the Bellagio Principles suggest as requirements for an effective indicator. Your indicator must include at least six statistical measures for a minimum of 30 countries from all four country groupings. Your work should include an explanation of why you chose the measures that you did, and why your indicator is a useful measure of sustainability. **S**

12. a) Describe how each of the following contributes to the achievement of a more sustainable future:
    i) ISO 14001
    ii) extended producer responsibility
    iii) green taxation
    iv) Città Lente

    b) Discuss the usefulness of each of these in Canada.

    c) Explain if these can be implemented in China and India. Would they be just as effective? **S**

13. Apply the Bellagio Principles to a) the ecological footprint and b) the Genuine Progress Indicator. To what degree does each of these indicators satisfy the Bellagio Principles? Where do they seem to fall short?

CHAPTER 30

The Geography of Hope

Key Terms

International Year of Planet Earth (IYPE)

With ideas, investments, determination, perseverance, and hope, the world can be a better place. In whose hands do you want the future of Earth to rest?

Key Questions

By the end of this chapter you will be able to answer the following questions.

■ What does the International Year of Planet Earth seek to accomplish?

■ Why do people in developing countries, in general, have a more positive attitude toward globalization than people in developed countries?

■ Do we have the means to achieve a sustainable future?

■ How can you contribute to a sustainable future?

Time for Some Good News?

At times, you may have found your study of world issues quite depressing. The issues we examine are not only very complex, but the solutions seem so very difficult to achieve. If you have felt this way, take heart; there are ways to work toward solutions, and millions of people are working on them every day.

Chris Turner, a journalist living in Calgary, also felt depressed by the environmental and social problems that constantly confronted him in the media. Rather than accept the idea that the future was bleak, he set out on a global journey to look for anything that promised a positive future. In 2007, he published a book that provided many examples of people and organizations using their creative energies to achieve a sustainable future. The title of the book? *The Geography of Hope*.

In this chapter with the same title, we will look at some successful efforts that counter the climate of fear and negativity so often associated with the globalization and sustainability issues facing humankind.

The International Year of Planet Earth

The United Nations declared 2008 the **International Year of Planet Earth (IYPE)** (see Figure 30–1). They began in 2007, raising awareness about IYPE activities. During 2008—the middle of a triennium (a period of three years)—research based on ten broad themes in earth science was undertaken (see Figure 30–2). Results of the research will be presented in 2009.

A key component of the IYPE was an outreach program. Exhibitions, education programs, and radio and TV broadcasts presenting the benefits of earth sciences to human society were aimed at developing interest and awareness among the general public, politicians, and business leaders. What does the International Year of Planet Earth try to accomplish? Just this: By learning all we can about Earth, you and all people around the world will never take for granted the state of our climate and our supply of good food, water, soil, air, and natural resources. By learning all we can about Earth, we will be inspired to work toward a sustainable future.

Figure 30–1 The logo of the International Year of Planet Earth (2007–2009) came from a 2002 German Ministry of Education and Research activity. The logo represents all the constituents of the Earth System: a red inner circle representing the solid earth, a green layer for the biosphere, a dark-blue layer for the hydrosphere, and a pale-blue layer for the atmosphere.

Positive Aspects of Globalization

A worldwide poll conducted in 2003 by the Pew Global Attitude Survey interviewed 38 000 people in 44 countries to determine their opinions on globalization. This poll also found that an anti-globalization sentiment was common in Old Core countries, but was not prevalent in New Core, Near Core, and Far Periphery countries. In these countries, there were more positive views of globalization and more enthusiasm for foreign trade and investment than in the Old Core.

GLOBALIZATION

A worldwide poll... found that an anti-globalization sentiment was common in Old Core countries, but was not prevalent in New Core, Near Core, and Far Periphery countries.

Do you find this surprising? Why or why not?

Respondents in New Core, Near Core, and Far Periphery countries also viewed the institutions of globalizatio in a more positive light. For example, in sub-Saharan Africa, 75 percent of households thought that multinational corporations had a positive influence on their country, compared to only 54 percent in rich countries. In Africa as a whole, 72 percent had positive views of the effects of the WTO, the World Bank, and the IMF. It is interesting to note that only 28 percent of respondents in Africa thought that anti-globalization protests were helping their country.

Do you find it surprising that support for globalization and international trade was higher in New Core, Near Core, and Far Periphery countries than in Old Core countries? Perhaps the new jobs created by foreign investment, the opportunities for local manufacturers to sell to larger markets, and the higher standard of living from economic growth outweigh the negative impacts. In Old Core countries, concern about the negative impact on the environment, the loss of jobs to countries where labour is cheap, and the extensive control of multinational corporations in developing countries have raised concerns about globalization.

In some countries, where the gap between rich and poor is widening—for example, China and the United States—there are widespread concerns about the availability of good jobs, old-age support, and other quality-of-life issues. The survey found, however, that people tended not to blame globalization for lack of progress in these areas, but rather poor governance in their own countries.

New Resources
Discover and use new natural resources in a sustainable manner

Hazards
Reduce health problems caused by natural and human-induced hazards

Earth and Health
Build a safer environment to reduce health problems

Climate
Examine the non-human factors in climate change

Groundwater
Improve our knowledge of the location and extent of groundwater

Megacities
Build safer urban structures

Deep Earth
Gain more knowledge of the earth from the core to the crust

Ocean Floor
Improve our knowledge of the ocean floors

Soil
Enhance our knowledge of soils

Earth and Life
Improve our understanding of the evolution of life

Figure 30–2 The IYPE's research program focused on ten themes in earth science and each theme's importance to the welfare of all humanity.

Globalization and the Economy

In 2006, the Chicago Council on Global Affairs and the Web site for *WorldPublicOpinion*, an online journal, conducted a survey in 17 countries and the Palestinian territories, which represented 56 percent of the world's population. You can analyze the results in the following activity.

Examine Figure 30–3 and answer the questions that follow.

Questions

1. a) Which three countries show the greatest support for globalization?

b) Why do you think the citizens of these countries generally support economic globalization?

2. a) Which three countries show the least support for their own economic globalization?

b) Why do you think citizens of these countries generally do not support economic globalization?

3. Did the level of support for economic globalization within countries surprise you? Explain.

The Effects of International Trade

Examine Figure 30–4. The data are based on responses from 14 countries: Argentina, Armenia, China, France, India, Israel, Mexico, Palestinian territories, Poland, Russia, South Korea, Thailand, Ukraine, and the US.

Questions

1. The four countries with the highest approval rating for international trade were China (88 percent), Israel (88 percent), South Korea (79 percent), and Thailand (79 percent). Why do you think the approval rating was so high in these countries?

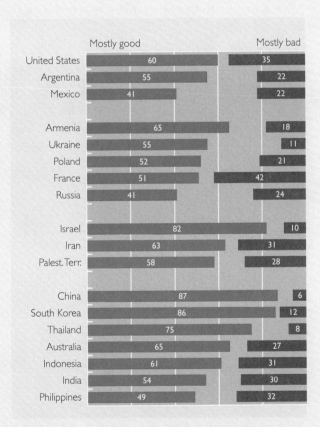

Figure 30–3 Views of globalization. The percentages reflect the answers to the question, "Do you believe that globalization, especially the increasing connections of your economy with others around the world, is mostly good or mostly bad for your country?"

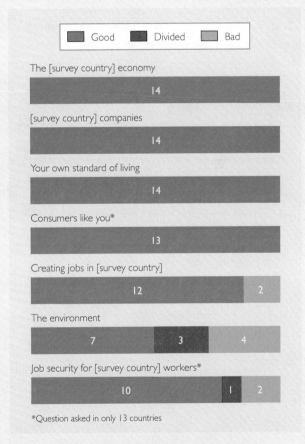

Figure 30–4 Attitudes toward international trade. Questions were of the form, "Overall, do you think international trade is good or bad for your country?"

2. The four countries with the lowest approval rating for international trade were the United States (42 percent), France (34 percent), Mexico (27 percent), and India (27 percent). Why do you think the approval rating was so low in these countries?

3. In exactly half of the countries, respondents expressed a low approval rating for one category in particular. What was the category, and what impact does international trade have on this category?

International Trade and the Environment

Another question in the same poll asked respondents about the effects of international trade on the environment (see Figure 30–5).

Questions

1. a) In which four countries do a majority of the respondents feel that international trade is good for the environment?

b) Speculate as to why respondents in these countries feel that international trade does not negatively affect the environment.

2. a) In which country do two-thirds of respondents think trade is bad for the environment?

b) Speculate as to why this is the only country in which more than half the population thinks this way.

3. One way to lessen the negative impact of international trade on the environment is to require minimum environmental standards as part of trade agreements. In ten countries polled, large majorities supported the inclusion of minimum standards for the protection of the environment. Even respondents in countries that rely on exports and have poor environmental standards support environmental protections. Despite this support, why do you think most trade agreements do not include environmental protection?

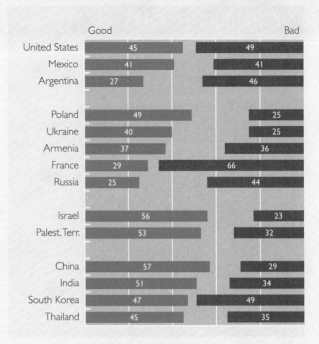

Figure 30–5 International trade and the environment. The percentages reflect the answers to the question, "Overall, do you think international trade is good or bad for…the environment?"

 Learn more about globalization, sustainability, and *The Geography of Hope* at the link on our Web site.

Achieving Sustainability

Chris Turner's global search for people and organizations that promote sustainable development resulted in the discovery of a number of groundbreaking initiatives. Figures 30–6 to 30–9 present four examples.

Toronto's Deep Lake Water Cooling System

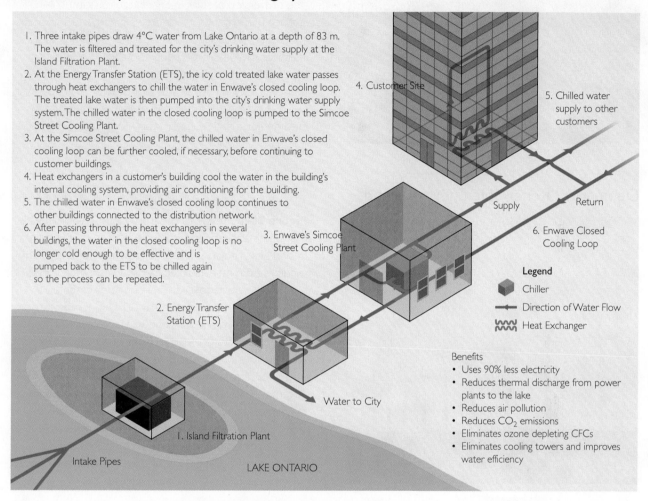

1. Three intake pipes draw 4°C water from Lake Ontario at a depth of 83 m. The water is filtered and treated for the city's drinking water supply at the Island Filtration Plant.
2. At the Energy Transfer Station (ETS), the icy cold treated lake water passes through heat exchangers to chill the water in Enwave's closed cooling loop. The treated lake water is then pumped into the city's drinking water supply system. The chilled water in the closed cooling loop is pumped to the Simcoe Street Cooling Plant.
3. At the Simcoe Street Cooling Plant, the chilled water in Enwave's closed cooling loop can be further cooled, if necessary, before continuing to customer buildings.
4. Heat exchangers in a customer's building cool the water in the building's internal cooling system, providing air conditioning for the building.
5. The chilled water in Enwave's closed cooling loop continues to other buildings connected to the distribution network.
6. After passing through the heat exchangers in several buildings, the water in the closed cooling loop is no longer cold enough to be effective and is pumped back to the ETS to be chilled again so the process can be repeated.

4. Customer Site

5. Chilled water supply to other customers

Supply   Return

6. Enwave Closed Cooling Loop

3. Enwave's Simcoe Street Cooling Plant

Legend

◆ Chiller
→ Direction of Water Flow
〰 Heat Exchanger

2. Energy Transfer Station (ETS)

Benefits
• Uses 90% less electricity
• Reduces thermal discharge from power plants to the lake
• Reduces air pollution
• Reduces CO_2 emissions
• Eliminates ozone depleting CFCs
• Eliminates cooling towers and improves water efficiency

Water to City

1. Island Filtration Plant

Intake Pipes   LAKE ONTARIO

Figure 30–6 Since 2004, cold water from Lake Ontario has been used by the Enwave Energy Corporation (partially financed by the City of Toronto) to air condition office buildings in Toronto's financial district. Deep Lake Water Cooling is cheaper and more efficient than having a separate air-conditioning unit in every building. Lake water drawn from a depth of 83 metres, at a temperature of 4°C, chills water in a separate, or "closed," network of pipes that runs under the financial district. The chilled water cools the air pumped throughout the buildings. **Impact:** Deep Lake Water Cooling uses 90 percent less electricity than conventional air conditioners, significantly reduces carbon dioxide emissions from coal-fired power plants, and is sustainable, clean, and renewable.

NGOs and Resourced-based Programs

Figure 30–7 In Ladakh, a desert area in northwest India, NGOs have helped institute traditional, sustainable, resource-based programs. Working with partner organizations, the NGOs encourage the use of renewable natural resources in ways that harmonize with Ladakh's traditional culture. Programs include seed production, photovoltaics (the conversion of solar energy into electricity), solar architecture, irrigation canals, tree planting, and improved production of food for livestock. Since the 1980s, these initiatives have improved people's standard of living in a sustainable manner. **Impact:** Higher agricultural production; electricity in remote areas for heating and cooking (in solar ovens such as the one shown here); solar-powered homes; a secure water supply for growing crops.

Denmark's "Renewable Energy" Island

Figure 30–8 Residents of Samsø Island, Denmark, have completely abandoned fossil fuels as a source of electricity and heat. They now obtain 100 percent of these commodities from renewable energy sources. When OPEC limited oil exports to Old Core countries in the early 1970s, Denmark was particularly hard hit because it imported 94 percent of its energy. Starting in 1997, Samsø built over 100 wind turbines on land, ten larger wind turbines offshore, and heating plants that use solar energy or furnaces that burn straw or wood-chips. Local government also instituted emission and consumption taxes, gave grants to wind-power companies, and provided tax breaks to individuals to invest in renewable energy projects. **Impact:** Samsø is completely self-sufficient in electricity and earns income from extra electricity produced by the offshore wind turbines.

Clean Energy for the World's Poor

Figure 30–9 Since 1994, non-profit US corporation E+Co has financed businesses in developing countries that provide clean energy from solar, hydro, biomass, biogas, wind, and geothermal enterprises. More than two billion people live without access to clean energy, and many more live with pollution produced from the burning of fossil fuels. E+Co "grows" local clean-energy businesses by giving them loans they eventually repay and by providing advice on how to run a business. **Impact:** By 2005, E+Co's businesses had provided almost 40 000 households with clean water, saved 76 million kilograms of firewood, and reduced CO_2 emissions by 60 million tonnes in developing countries. By 2007, over three million people had access to clean energy.

A Call to Action

... humanity already possesses the fundamental scientific, technical, and industrial know-how to solve the carbon and climate problem for the next 50 years.

If this is the case, why aren't we solving the problem now?

Stephen Pacala and Robert Socolow, the co-directors of Princeton University's Carbon Mitigation Initiative, stated in 2004 that humanity already possesses the fundamental scientific, technical, and industrial know-how to solve the carbon and climate problem over the next 50 years. Our choice is between action and delay. Which will it be?

In his acceptance speech for the Nobel Peace Prize in 2007, Al Gore said

The future is knocking at our door right now. Make no mistake, the next generation will *ask us one of two questions. Either they will ask: "What were you thinking; why didn't you act?"*

Or they will ask instead: "How did you find the moral courage to rise and successfully resolve a crisis that so many said was impossible to solve?"

We have everything we need to get started, save perhaps political will, but political will is a renewable resource.

So let us renew it, and say together: "We have a purpose. We are many. For this purpose we will rise, and we will act."

What actions can *you* take? Here are two of the most important things you can do:

1. Learn about what is going on and make it a life-long habit to keep learning. Taking this course is a good first step. How do you keep informed? Reading books such as the following recent publications will help. As you read them, keep in mind that some of the authors are promoting a specific point of view. Therefore, the sources may not always present a balanced examination of the topic or issue.

2. Consider the impact of your lifestyle choices on both sustainability and globalization. Think about your housing choices, transportation choices, recreational/travel choices, and your food and clothing choices. Consider the relationship between the values you have and the behaviours you exhibit. Consider the roles you play now and will play in the future

   a) as a consumer

   b) as a spouse and parent

   c) as an employee, possibly as an employer

   d) as a global citizen

Globalization and sustainability are the key trends of this new century. It is the role of the world's people, governments, and corporations—by their choices and actions—to make sure that they are positive forces.

The Sacred Balance: Rediscovering Our Place in Nature (3rd Edition) by David Suzuki and Amanda McConnell

Fences and Windows: Dispatches from the Front Lines of the Globalization Debate by Naomi Klein

An Inconvenient Truth: The Planetary Emergency of Global Warming and What We Can Do About It by Al Gore

The Geography of Hope: A Tour of the World We Need by Chris Turner

The Pentagon's New Map: War and Peace in the Twenty-first Century by Thomas P.M. Barnett

The Collapse of Globalism: And the Reinvention of the World by John Ralston Saul

Soft Power: The Means to Success in World Politics by Joseph S. Nye

The J Curve: A New Way to Understand Why Nations Rise and Fall by Ian Bremmer

ZOOM: The Global Race to Fuel the Car of the Future by Iain Carson and Vijay Vaitheeswaran

The Ingenuity Gap by Thomas Homer-Dixon

The Corporation: The Pathological Pursuit of Profit and Power by Joel Bakan (the book and the DVD)

Chapter Questions

Knowledge and Understanding

1. **a)** What activities were conducted around the world during the International Year of Planet Earth?

   b) What activities were conducted in Canada and your local community during the IYPE?

Thinking

2. Some people say that having the words "sustainable" and "development" together is a contradiction of terms. What do you think? Explain.

3. Many people participate in non-violent movements to raise awareness of environmental issues or to protect resources and environments. Evaluate the effectiveness of a movement that is focused on globalization and a movement that is focused on sustainability.

4. Our economic growth seems to be based on increasing consumption. How can we achieve sustainable development if our economy functions in this way?

5. In Chapter 1, you were given the opportunity to determine where you would spend $50 billion to make the world a better place. Re-examine your list of ten most desirable solutions. Now that you have examined many of the issues during your course of study, you can answer the following questions.

   a) Would you change the ranking of your original list? Explain.

   b) Are there other solutions to issues that you would add to your list? Explain.

   c) Now consider how the $50 billion should be allocated. Are there any differences? Explain.

Communication

6. Using the Internet and other sources, research and write a report about one organization, such as an NGO, or a technology, such as the play pump, that is promoting sustainable development.

Application

7. **a)** What role can or should you play in searching for solutions to the issues covered in *Global Connections*? Consider what you can do

   i) while you are in school (high school and post-secondary institutions)

   ii) when you are working

   b) Compare the results among all the groups.

8. Working in small groups, complete the following three statements using the sequence outlined in parts a) through g):

   i) "Globalization is positive if..."

   ii) "A sustainable future environment is one that..."

   iii) "To make my community a more sustainable place, I should..."

   a) Each student completes statement i), puts his or her answer on a piece of paper, and places the paper upside-down on the table.

   b) When everyone has completed their statement, everyone turns over the paper and shows the other members of the group what they have written.

   c) If the other students accept that a statement is valid, the person who wrote it gets one point.

   d) Next, complete the same process for statement ii) and then for statement iii).

   e) Now, go back to statement i) and write a different point to complete the statement. Continue with statements ii) and iii).

   f) Keep going until the designated time is reached.

   g) Tally up the points to see who has received the greatest number. **G S**

9. Philanthropy is the desire on the part of individuals or groups to promote good in the world and improve the quality of life of people through good deeds and charitable activities. Philanthropy has become a major topic in the media because wealthy, high profile people such as Bono, Angelina Jolie, and J.K. Rowling, among others, have adopted important causes around the world. Use the Internet and the following questions to examine different aspects of philanthropy.

   a) Some of the wealthiest 19th-century capitalists became major philanthropists. Select one and write a summary of his/her actions.

   b) In 2006, *The Economist* magazine published an article called "Billanthropy."

   i) Who does this term refer to?

   ii) What does the term mean?

   iii) Use the Internet to write about some of the activities of this person/foundation.

c) Former US President Bill Clinton formed a foundation to address, among other things, the growing inequality among people, the unsustainable way we are living, and the need to have a shared vision for humankind that brings people together.

i) What is the mission of the William J. Clinton Foundation?

ii) What initiatives has the Foundation taken to meet its mission?

iii) Describe the Clinton Global Initiative Project.

10. a) Futurists make projections based on trends they discern in fields as varied as economics, demographics, technology, and the environment. Canadian Richard Worzel, a member of the World Future Society, is one of North America's leading futurists. When making projections, Worzel considers

i) Trends: How likely is it that a trend in any particular field will persist or change? For example, since demographics change slowly, projections based on demographic trends are highly reliable. On the other hand, since clothing fashions change quickly, projections based on fashion trends are much less reliable.

ii) Factors: A small number of factors will drive most of the change in any particular field. What are the relevant factors, and how might they interact to produce an unexpected consequence?

iii) Assumptions: Every projection assumes certain things. What assumptions are you making? If you made different assumptions, would your projection be different?

iv) Alternative Futures: Once you have made the most likely projection for the future, consider the possibility that you're wrong. What would be the next most likely projection? The one after that?

v) Bias: People tend to project the future that they want to happen. How might your own biases have interfered with your consideration of the future?

b) Using Richard Worzel's considerations as a guide, try your hand at being a futurist.

• determine one trend related to globalization and one related to sustainbility

• make a projection for the future based on each trend

• describe the impact of each trend

c) Present your projections for the future to your class. Make sure you are able to explain the current trends on which you have based your projections.

d) Make a list of your class' projections for the future.

e) Richard Worzel has written about many of the issues covered in *Global Connections*. Examine his thoughts on one of the issues covered in this course. Use the following questions as a guide:

i) What major projection does Worzel make on this issue?

ii) Why does he make this projection?

iii) Do you agree with his projection for this issue? Explain.

 Visit Richard Worzel's Web site at the link on our Web site.

Introduction

You will now have the opportunity to examine a world issue from a geographic perspective and to determine and comment upon the issue's effects on Canada, the world, or both. During this process, you will

- explore a topic
- locate, select, and evaluate resources
- manage information
- organize information
- process information
- communicate information

Writing a research paper involves searching out and examining many relevant facts and ideas, and then piecing them together in a well-organized and compelling way. You may present and support a point of view, explain the origins of an idea, discuss the pros and cons of an issue, disagree with other people's theories, or present original research. The steps outlined below can help you develop your independent inquiry as well as guide you through the research process. There are four steps in the research process:

- preparing for research
- accessing resources
- processing information
- transferring learning

Preparing for Research—Select an Issue and Get Started

Select an issue that interests you. Your teacher may give you a list of issues or topics to choose from, or you may select your own.

First, brainstorm the issue with someone to obtain ideas about it. Then begin your preliminary research by consulting a variety of resources, including books, newspapers, magazines, pictures, and the Internet to learn as much as you can about the issue. Internet searches may be more productive with the use of key words and topics and/or using Boolean searches (using operators such as AND, OR, NOT and NEAR). Next, choose one particular aspect of the issue that interests you. Make sure that the scope of this component is manageable.

Accessing Resources—Develop a Thesis and Conduct Research

After you have selected your issue and have completed preliminary research on the aspect that interests you, you can begin to develop a tentative thesis. You can state your opinion on the issue or ask a related question that could be answered through further research. Remember that your beginning thesis could change; after your research, you may wish to adjust your thesis and adopt a slightly different final version.

During the research phase, you will examine a wide range of published materials. Skim through your selections to find the best and most reliable resources. Locate the information that is pertinent to your issue by using content, index, and summary pages. Keep point-form notes of any relevant information you find, as well as your own observations and insights. Information can appear as maps, charts, graphs, illustrations, and analyses, as well as in the form of straight facts. Keep a list of sources, record page numbers, and bookmark any useful Web sites so that you can find them again later.

It is also important to keep a record of sources in order to avoid plagiarising other people's words or ideas. Plagiarism is when you represent someone else's words, ideas, or research as your own. Keeping a careful record of where information came from will help you properly acknowledge the work of others. When you write your paper, you will credit your sources by using citations within your writing, and create a Works Cited list.

Processing Information—Evaluate Sources and Prepare an Outline

An important part of the research process is to evaluate your information sources. First, ensure that all relevant perspectives are represented. Then, critically examine your sources for relevance, bias, accuracy, currency, point of view, and authority. Based on these criteria, select the most suitable resources for your final thesis.

Now is the time to decide whether to keep or change your tentative thesis. Remember that your thesis should be a clear, precise statement of the purpose of your paper. It should reflect your personal opinion and be a good starting point from which to examine all sides of the issue.

Your next step is to prepare an outline. Organize your materials in the way that you intend to present them. This will enable you to see if there is any conflicting or missing information. Are you able to support your thesis with the evidence you provide? At this point, you may wish to confer with your teacher to make sure you are on the right track.

Transferring Learning—Develop a First Draft, Edit, and Prepare Your Final Version

Now begin the writing process. Writing can be time consuming, so budget plenty of time to complete it. Since getting started can be the most difficult part, you can try starting with a section in the middle or end if you feel more confident. Remember, this is your first draft; it doesn't have to be perfect on the first try.

In the introduction to your paper, try to create curiosity about your issue. This can be done with an anecdote or short description that sets the scene for your thesis. At some point in the introduction, you need to state your thesis. Then outline the steps that you will take to support your thesis.

In addition to developing a point of view and supplying evidence that supports your thesis, you will present arguments that refute the most obvious positions on the other side. Use your own words to state each point of view, and support each argument with cited (referenced) materials. Your evidence may be in the form of quoted information, statistics, graphs, figures, maps, etc. You do not have to cite an item if it is *common knowledge* (information that is generally known by a great many people).

Your conclusion should summarize your arguments and demonstrate the validity of your thesis. In some cases, there may be no clear solutions to your issue. In this situation, you may indicate that the issue or dispute is beyond easy resolution.

Once you have finished your first draft set it aside for a day or two before you decide what changes you want to make. If possible, have someone else read it. Ask this person to look for inconsistencies and sections that require further explanation. Your final draft should include a Works Cited list of all the research materials you have used.

The final version of your paper should look professional. Use double- or one-and-a-half line spacing and an 11-point or 12-point font. Include a title page and place your Works Cited list at the end.

Keep your research notes in case you have to support some of your claims. Also, keep a copy of your independent inquiry for your files so that you know exactly what you handed in for evaluation. If you are to prepare a presentation of your independent inquiry, confirm the format with your teacher.

Evaluation

Your teacher may have given you a marking scheme, or rubric, at the beginning of your independent inquiry to let you know how you will be evaluated. During the writing of your final version, make sure you have covered the items in the categories of achievement shown in the rubric. Evaluate yourself to determine how your paper meets the basic criteria of the independent inquiry.

Selected Issues

The issues and topics in the following list are divided by Unit to provide you with a starting point. You will find that your study of Canadian and world issues will lead you beyond the narrow themes of any particular chapter to a broader understanding of your issue and to the discovery of connections among the themes of different chapters.

Selected Issues and Topics

UNIT 1 Looking at the World

- Exploring World Issues in Stories, Music, Movies, and Cartoons
- Bias in Everyday Life
- Solving the World's Major Issues
- Can Dubai Survive Its Unsustainable Growth?
- Evaluating the Positive and Negative Aspects of Globalization
- Evaluating the Expansionist and Ecological World Views
- How Countries Are Grouped
- Examining Measures of Global Involvement
- How and Why Mental Maps Differ Around the World

UNIT 2 Human Population

- Population Trends
- Technological Change and Population
- The Pros and Cons of a Declining Population
- The Impact of Demographic Transition
- Optimistic and Pessimistic Views about Population Growth
- Population Projections for the 21st Century
- The Demographic Trap
- Comparison of India's and China's Approaches to Population Control
- Can the Kerala Model Be Applied to Other Countries?

- Population Futures in the Old Core
- The Birth Dearth
- Immigration as a Population Replacement Strategy
- The Pros and Cons of Migration
- Illegal Migration
- Canada's Refugee Policy: Too Harsh or Too Lenient?
- Global Patterns of Urbanization
- Life in Squatter Settlements
- The Elderly in Urban Communities

UNIT 3 Economic Issues

- The Geography of Hunger
- Food Production Issues
- The Search for Sustainable Agriculture
- Changing Economies
- Impact of Colonialism and Neo-Colonialism
- Economic Systems
- Transnational Corporations
- New Centres of Global Economic Power
- Free Trade Agreements
- Economic Disparity
- NGOs and Development Assistance
- Income Disparity within Countries
- The Burden of International Debt
- Debt Relief/Forgiveness
- The World Bank/IMF

UNIT 4 The Earth in Balance

- Land Degradation
- Desertification

- Solid Waste Management
- The Spectrum of Viewpoints of NGOs on Forest Resources
- Rainforests and Old-Growth Forests
- Ecoterrorism
- Pollution of Freshwater Resources
- Fossil Water
- Water Transfers
- Poisons In The air
- Trans-boundary Air Issues
- Ozone Depletion
- Alternative Energy Sources
- Hydricity
- Personal Lifestyles and Energy Use
- Causes and Consequences of Climate Change
- Scientific Disagreements over Climate Change
- International Agreements on Climate Change

UNIT 5 Conflict and Cooperation

- Sovereignty of Nations
- Superpower Rivalry During the Cold War
- Sports as Political Statements
- Border Conflicts
- The Role of Hard and Soft Power
- A Clash of Civilizations or a Clash of Globalizations?
- Causes of Terrorism
- Freedom Fighter or Terrorist?
- Dealing with Terrorism
- Changing Global Power Structures
- Is this China's Century?

- Political Islam
- Peacekeeping and Peacemaking
- The Role of NATO
- International Treaties to Deal with Conflict

UNIT 6 Quality of Life
- Dealing with HIV/AIDS
- The Spread of Lifestyle Diseases
- The Next Pandemic

- Women and Political Power
- Child Soldiers
- Cultural Exceptionalism
- Microcredit
- Fair Trade
- Developing a Local Initiative

UNIT 7 Responsibility and Hope for the Future
- Measuring Sustainable Development
- Ecological Footprints

- Changing Our Behaviour
- The International Year of the Planet
- Evaluating Globalization
- Achieving Sustainability

Glossary

3Rs Short-form used to describe the three ways in which the amount of garbage we produce can be reduced: "Reduce, Reuse, Recycle."

age-dependency ratio The ratio between the number of dependent people in a population (i.e., less than 15 and more than 64) and the number of working-age people.

acidic deposition Addition to the environment of acidic materials in liquid (acid rain), gaseous, and solid forms.

Agricultural Revolution The cultivation of plants and domestication of animals that likely started in the Middle East about 10 000 years ago.

agricultural support policies A variety of government programs, including subsidies, tariffs, and supply management programs, designed to support and protect the agricultural industry within a country.

aid fatigue Reluctance on the part of donor countries and private donors to continue giving development assistance when it does not seem to improve conditions in the countries receiving it.

alternative energy Sources of energy other than fossil fuels, nuclear energy, and hydro-electric power. These include wind and solar power, tidal power, geothermal power, ocean thermal energy conversion, and biomass conversion.

anti-retroviral drugs Drugs that treat retroviruses, especially HIV/AIDS.

aquifer Porous rock and sediments deep underground that hold water and let it pass through.

armed conflict The use of military force by a country to try to enforce its will on another.

Asia-Pacific Economic Cooperation (APEC) Refers to an organization of 21 nations around the Pacific Rim. A massive free trade agreement among these nations has been proposed.

asymmetric warfare The type of warfare fought by opponents with dramatically different conventional military capabilities. Actions by the weaker power (e.g., bombs and kidnapping) are often equated to terrorism by the stronger opponent.

authoritarian A form of government that limits the freedoms of its citizens, demands strict obedience to government authority, and generally does not allow criticism of its policies.

Bellagio Principles A set of guidelines established in 1996 to assess the accuracy of measures of sustainable development.

bias A prejudice or preference for or against a particular point of view.

bilateral aid Aid provided directly from one country to another.

bioaccumulation The buildup of chemicals such as POPs in the fatty tissues of organisms. These substances become increasingly concentrated as they move upward in the food chain.

biodegradable The ability of organic materials and some industrial pollutants to break down as a result of natural processes in the environment.

biodiesel A biofuel that combines organic materials and conventional diesel fuel.

biodiversity The variation of life forms that exist with a particular ecosystem.

bioethanol Ethyl alcohol produced from plant materials that can be used as a motor fuel when mixed at various concentrations with gasoline. Many gasolines today contain up to 10 percent ethanol.

biofuel A fuel, like ethanol or biodiesel, that is produced from plant materials.

biotechnology The field of study that uses genetic engineering for agricultural and industrial purposes.

bioterrorism The use of biological agents, e.g., viruses, in terrorist acts.

birth control Technological means used to prevent conception (e.g., oral contraceptives). The term also applies to the desire of couples to limit the number of children they have.

birth dearth The situation in a country where a low total fertility rate is causing the population to decline.

birth rate Number of births per 1000 people in a country or region in a given year.

Body-Mass Index (BMI) A simple measure used to relate a person's height and weight. It is frequently used to determine whether a person is overweight or underweight.

bonded labour A form of slavery affecting some 20 million people worldwide. It happens when people borrow money and cannot repay the loan because of high interest rates. They must work for the company or individual until the loan is repaid.

brain drain The loss of highly educated people from a country because of emigration.

brain gain The increase of highly educated people in a country because of immigration.

BRIC Acronym for the four major New Core countries—**B**razil, **R**ussia, **I**ndia, and **C**hina.

busways Dedicated rights-of-way (roads) that are reserved only by buses.

caliphate A potential, transnational state based on Islamic belief and traditions. This has been visualized by some as similar to the European Union in many respects, except for the fundamental reason for its creation.

Canadian International Development Agency (CIDA) The branch of the Canadian government responsible for providing development assistance—both directly and through NGOs.

capitalization The total value of a country's stock (i.e., number of shares × the share price)

cap and trade system A proposed method for reducing GhG emissions. Companies, utilities, and other GhG producers would be assigned an emissions limit. If they reduced emissions below this limit they could sell their surplus quota in a free market system. If they exceeded their limit they would have to buy additional quota in the free market.

carbon cycle The natural cycle through which carbon moves in the environment. It includes the hydrosphere, atmosphere, biosphere, and lithosphere.

carbon sink   Natural features (such as forests) that remove carbon from the atmosphere for a period ranging from a few minutes to a few centuries.

carbon source   Any activity, natural or human, that adds carbon to the atmosphere (principally as carbon dioxide and methane).

carbon tax   A proposed method for reducing GhG emissions. All products and services that are sold would have a tax added based on the emissions that were generated to provide that product or service.

carrying capacity   The maximum number of people that can be sustained by an environment (e.g., the Earth's resources).

cash crop   A crop grown for sale rather than for personal use.

caste   Highly influential, hereditary social class system in the Hindu society of India and in the traditional societies of Mauritania, Niger, and Sudan in Africa.

chain of custody   The tracking of logs harvested from certified forests through transportation and processing to the final product. The chain of custody ensures that the end product is made of wood from a certified forest.

change by diffusion model   Change that is accomplished gradually as people recognize the benefits of that change—e.g., in Kerala, India, population growth declined as people came to recognize the benefits of smaller families.

chemical deterioration   This refers to damage to soil as a result of leaching, salinization, acidification, or pollution.

chemical terrorism   The use of chemical agents, e.g., poison gas, in terrorist acts.

chlorofluorocarbons (CFCs)   Chemicals created for use as fire retardants, propellants in spray cans, and coolants in refrigerators and air conditioners. They are inert at ground level but when exposed to UV radiation in the upper atmosphere, they release chlorine atoms that break down ozone.

chronic hunger   Lack of a balanced diet over an extended period of time, leading to malnutrition that weakens people and makes them susceptible to infectious diseases.

civil liberties   The rights of citizens to certain freedoms established in law, such as freedom of speech, political association, and religion.

civil society   A largely unorganized group of NGOs and independent citizens concerned about labour rights, the environment, human rights, and social development. Members have participated in street demonstrations because they believe that people in developing countries do not benefit from free trade and globalization.

climate change   The scientific theory that Earth's climate is being altered by human activities. More generally, any change in global climates, whether caused by natural fluctuations or human activities.

Cold War   A state of hostility, without actual large-scale warfare, that existed between the power blocs led by the US and the USSR from the mid-1940s to the end of the 1980s.

colonialism   Acquisition and settlement of a territory or country by another nation.

command economy   An economic system in which the supply and pricing of goods and services are determined entirely by government as part of a total plan.

communism   A form of government in which ownership of most goods is held by the state, which generally has some form of authoritarian government.

community initiative   Projects carried out by individuals within a community working together to find solutions to mutual problems.

comparative advantage   Economic advantage that one country has over another because of an ability to produce goods more cheaply as a result of abundant raw materials, cheap labour, better marketing, cheaper transportation costs, or better quality control.

comprehensive indicator   A measure that shows overall progress toward sustainability; e.g., the ecological footprint relates to the amount of land needed to support various human activities.

conceptual model   A simplified representation of a complex reality often expressed in metaphorical terms.

concession company   A company created by an imperialist country to develop trade in its colonies; e.g., the British created the Hudson's Bay Company in Canada. Concession companies traded in particular products and often acted as the government in remote parts of empires.

containment   The policy of Western democracies after World War II to stop the expansion of the influence of the Soviet Union beyond its sphere of influence through defence agreements (e.g., NATO) and to prevent the spread of communism through the use of aid programs (e.g., the Marshall Plan).

Convention on the Rights of the Child   A 1989 UN agreement that established the particular rights that children in the world should have.

Copenhagen Consensus   A conference held in 2004 in Copenhagen at which a group of leading economists tried to agree on how to solve the world's major problems.

cornucopian thesis   The belief that as science and technology advance, new resources will be developed to replace depleted ones.

corporate farming   In contrast to family farms (which technically are corporations too), farming done on a large scale by large companies.

counterterrorism   Efforts made by governments and international groups to interfere with the planning, organization, and carrying out of terrorist acts.

critical load   The amount of pollution (e.g., acidic deposition) that an ecosystem can tolerate before that pollution harms the environment.

cultural exceptionalism   The rejection of certain rights or values by a country because its political, social, economic, and cultural traditions differ from those embodied in the Universal Declaration of Human Rights.

death rate   Number of deaths per 1000 people in a country or region in a given year.

debt/export ratio   Beyond its literal meaning, this is used as a measure of a country's ability to pay for its international debts.

decentralization   The movement of people from central city areas to suburban locations.

deep ecology   An approach to protecting the environment that uses confrontational, direct action and that does not accept compromise solutions.

deforestation   The conversion of forested land into a non-forest use, for example, to allow for agriculture.

democracy   The form of government in which citizens choose their leaders in open and fair elections.

demographic transition A theory that states that birth rates and death rates will decline over time as a result of economic and social development. It is the most widely accepted theory explaining population change over time.

demographic trap A situation in which a developing country continues to have a high birth rate instead of experiencing the declining birth rate of the late transition stage. Combined with declining death rates, this situation causes a large population increase that threatens the country's economic and social development.

demography This is the study of population and implications of changes in population size and composition.

dependency load The percentage of a population that is younger than 15 or older than 64 years.

dependency measures Used to measure the proportion of people not of "working age" (i.e., those younger than 15 and older than 64 years of age) in a population.

debt relief Various programs being used and suggested to help highly indebted countries deal with their international debt responsibilities.

debt service charges The interest which falls due on a loan.

desertification The process by which an arid or semi-arid area loses its productivity to the point that it resembles a desert. Desertification results mainly from human activities (e.g., deforestation, overgrazing).

development assistance Foreign aid from wealthier to poorer countries. Includes both aid from governments and from NGOs.

DINK A family structure common in countries with very low birth rates. It stands for Double Income No Kids.

Doha Round A series of trade meetings of the WTO that began in 2001.

drip irrigation An irrigation system that uses pipes with tiny holes that continuously drip small amounts of water directly to plants, thereby reducing evaporation. It was developed in Israel to increase crop yields while using less water.

earth energy Low-grade energy that is extracted, generally using heat pumps, from the earth.

early transition Stage in demographic transition in which a high birth rate and a falling death rate result in a high population growth rate (population explosion).

ecological footprint (EF) A measure of sustainability in which a unit of land area is used to demonstrate the ecological pressure created by the residents of a country. The EF is based on the principle that human activities are related to an amount of land needed to support them.

ecological world view Looking at the world with an emphasis on the emotional and spiritual relationships that bind humans and the environment together.

Economic and Social Council This is the body within the United Nations that coordinates the operation of the UN's many commissions and specialized agencies.

economic development The level of a community's material wealth and trade; illustrated by such measures as per capita GDP, ratio of cars to people, and per capita electrical power capacity.

economic disparity An inequality in which some people or countries are much better off economically than other people or countries.

economic globalization The trend toward a worldwide economic system that permits easy movement of goods, production, capital, labour, and resources. Economic globalization occurs as trade restrictions, such as tariffs and quota systems, are removed in favour of freer trade.

economic liberalism An economic system that functions without the intervention of government. The concept was developed by Adam Smith in 1776 as an alternative to mercantilism.

economies of scale The lower costs that exist in a large-scale industrial, agricultural, or other business.

Ecosystem-Based Management (EBM) A method of logging that has the least possible impact on the environment.

emigration rate Number of people leaving an area in a given year per 1000 population.

empowerment The act of taking authority or control over some aspect of one's life.

energy intensity The basis of a proposal by APEC nations to have emissions targets related to the amount of energy being used (i.e., reductions per tonne of oil equivalent used), rather than to have absolute emission reduction targets (i.e., tonnes of carbon emitted).

environmental dredging The removal of solid toxic wastes from the bottoms of water bodies and disposal in a safe location.

environmental migration Migration in response to changing environmental conditions (e.g., desertification)

erosion The breakdown of a land surface (weathering) and the carrying away of weathered materials (transportation) by various agents.

ethnic cleansing The removal of an unwanted ethnic group from a society or an area, typically by genocide or forced emigration.

eutrophication The depletion of oxygen in water caused by the excess growth of vegetation and decomposition. It occurs as a result of the washing into lakes of detergents, sewage, and agricultural fertilizers. As a result, organisms not suited to low oxygen levels die.

Exclusive Economic Zones (EEZs) Also called the 200 [nautical] mile limit; recognizes the sovereignty of nations over adjacent parts of the ocean.

extended producer responsibility (EPR) A corporate and public policy in which the manufacturer is deemed responsible for the environmental impact of its product's packaging and the product itself during its entire lifespan.

extreme poverty Defined by the UN as the condition of a person living on less than US$1 per day (in non-PPP terms).

fact Knowledge that is considered to be true because it can be verified by experience or observation.

factory farms Large-scale farming operations that have been created to allow production at the lowest possible cost.

fair Earthshare Within the idea of ecological footprints, this is the amount of land available to support each person if all the productive land on Earth were divided evenly among all people of the world.

fair trade A market system that is to some degree regulated, to ensure that producers benefit from trade; e.g., producers are guaranteed a minimum price when they sell their product. Fair trade is based on the belief that marginalized producers in developing countries do not benefit sufficiently from free trade.

famine   A severe, short-term shortage of food caused by a temporary failure of food production or food distribution systems.

Far Periphery   Those countries of the Periphery that are least globalized and farthest from joining the Core.

feedback loop   A situation in a cycle in which the outcome has an impact on the initial condition. If the impact increases the initial condition, it is positive feedback; if it reduces the condition, it is a negative impact.

fiscal squeeze   The economic constraint that results when money raised through taxes is insufficient to pay for all the services that a city needs to function efficiently.

fixed carbon   Carbon that has been removed from the atmosphere for a very long time; e.g., carbon in limestone or coal has been out of the atmosphere for millions of years.

food miles   The distance that food travels between where it is produced and where it is consumed.

forced labour   A form of slavery, usually imposed by a government or paramilitary group, in which the threat of violence is used to force people into working against their will.

Forest Stewardship Council (FSC)   A worldwide organization, formed in Toronto in 1993, to fight deforestation by encouraging the wise use of forests.

fossil water   Water that went into storage (as groundwater or in large lakes) thousands or even millions of years ago.

free market economy   An economic system in which the prices of all goods and services are determined by supply and demand in the absence of other factors like government action or monopolies.

free trade   Trade that occurs without the restrictions caused by tariffs and non-tariff barriers.

Free Trade Agreement of the Americas (FTAA)   A proposed trade agreement involving all of the nations of the Americas other than Cuba.

Gaia hypothesis   James Lovelock's theory that views Earth as a self-regulating, living entity made up of organisms that modify the environment for their survival.

General Assembly   The body within the United Nations in which all countries are represented and have equal voting power.

genetically modified organisms (GMOs)   Organisms whose genetic structure has been changed to give them characteristics that are seen as desirable. E.g., a plant might be made tolerant of herbicides or resistant to insects or frost.

gentrification   The renewal of older, run-down housing in a city by people who move into such areas looking for bargains.

Genuine Progress Indicator (GPI)   A measurement that addresses the shortcomings of the GDP by assigning a positive dollar value to all activities that positively contribute to society's quality of life, and a negative dollar value to all activities that have a negative impact of the quality of life.

geo-engineering   A range of proposals that have been made to reduce GhG emissions into the atmosphere by using various technological methods to capture or eliminate the gases before their release into the atmosphere. E.g., carbon sequestration would pump carbon dioxide into sealed rock layers in the earth.

geopolitics   The interplay of political, economic, and geographical factors (such as location and physical environment) at a national or an international level. This interplay affects governmental decision making and relationships among countries.

geothermal energy   Energy that comes from naturally occurring heat inside the earth. The energy is extracted in the form of heated water or steam.

germ theory   The theory that some diseases are caused by organisms too small to be seen (except under a microscope).

Gini index   A measurement of how evenly wealth is distributed among classes in a society. The lower the Gini index, the more evenly spread the income.

Global 500   A list of the 500 largest companies in the world that is published annually by *Forbes* magazine.

globalization   The trend toward greater interconnectedness of the world's financial, economic, technological, political, cultural, sociological, ecological, and geographical systems. Some argue that globalization improves living standards throughout the world, while others say that its effects are more harmful than beneficial.

grasshopper effect   A global phenomenon in which Persistent Organic Pollutants (POPs) move from warmer to colder regions. The pollutants evaporate, travel through the atmosphere on air currents, and then condense over a new location. They tend to concentrate most in cold regions because condensation is highest here.

Great Leap Forward   An economic and social plan to transform China's agriculture from small individually run farms to large collective farms and to develop heavy industry to create a modern industrialized communist society.

Green Revolution   This was a reform program in China, between 1958 and 1960, designed to dramatically modernize the country's economy, but it was an economic disaster that had major impacts on the country's demography as well.

greenhouse effect   The warming of the atmosphere as some of its gases absorb heat given off by Earth's surface. This is a natural phenomenon that maintains Earth's temperature at a level that supports life (e.g., about 14°C).

greenhouse gases   Atmospheric gases that create the greenhouse effect by absorbing and holding heat in Earth's atmosphere. They include naturally occurring gases such as water vapour, carbon dioxide, and methane, and human-made gases such as chlorofluorocarbons (CFCs).

green power   Electricity produced in the least environmentally damaging ways possible (e.g., from wind farms).

green taxation.   Taxation imposed to encourage environmentally responsible behaviour. A carbon tax would be one example.

groundwater   Water existing in permeable rock layers and loose materials underground. Supplies wells and creates natural springs.

guest workers   Temporary, legal migrants who move to a country to help it overcome a labour shortage.

H5N1   The particular strain of influenza that scientists are most concerned about with respect to a future pandemic. H5N1 is more commonly known as "bird flu."

hard currency   Currencies (such as the US dollar, euro, and Japanese yen) that are considered sufficiently sound and widely used to be accepted internationally. Payments associated with international trade or loans are made using hard currencies.

hard power   One category of means by which a country tries to impose its will on another. Includes both economic power (aid, bribes, and economic sanctions) and military power (military sanctions and force of arms).

hedonics   The idea that planning should be done to maximize human happiness. Can be seen as a short form for "happiness economics."

high variant   Numerical population models frequently produce a range of projections rather than only one. The high variant is the highest projection likely to occur.

high-yield variety (HYV)   A crop type that has been developed, in some cases during China's Green Revolution, to be very productive.

highly indebted poor countries (HIPC)   A group of 41 countries that have been identified as having debts beyond their ability to pay.

Highly Indebted Poor Countries (HIPC) initiative   A program by the World Bank and International Monetary Fund to reduce the debt of the HIPC nations.

HIV/AIDS   A global pandemic disease, spread mostly by sexual contact, that is most common in sub-Saharan Africa, but increasing in importance in many other parts of the world.

Human Development Index   A measure of quality of life developed by the UN using three criteria: life expectancy at birth, adult literacy rate, and per capita GDP.

human rights   The basic rights to which all people are entitled, such as freedom, peace, and dignity.

hydricity   An energy system in which all forms of energy would be converted to either hydrogen or electricity for storage and use.

hydrochlorofluorocarbons (HCFCs)   The group of chemicals that were introduced to replace ozone-depleting CFCs. HCFCs are now being eliminated because of their role in causing global warming.

ideology   A set of ideas and beliefs that form the basis of a nation's political and economic systems and its social goals.

illegal migration   The movement of people into a country without following its immigration laws and procedures.

immigration rate   The number of people (immigrants) arriving in a country in a given year, for every 1000 people living at that location.

imperialism   The control (political and/or economic) of one or more countries by a dominant nation.

income redistribution   The belief, held by some people, that one of the roles of government is to shift wealth to poorer citizens.

independent media source   Organizations that are generally small, not affiliated with large corporations, and offer alternative views to those found in mainstream sources.

Index of Sustainable Economic Welfare (ISEW)   An alternative measure to the GDP that adjusts conventional measures of economic progress in two ways: positively for factors that improve societal well-being, and negatively for consumption patterns that are non-sustainable.

Industrial Revolution   The development of uses of non-muscular sources of power in industry, that began in late 18th-century Britain and spread to other parts of the world. It was a technological revolution that was accompanied by profound social and political changes.

infant mortality rate   The number of infants under one year of age who die for every 1000 live births in the country in a year.

infectious diseases   Illnesses caused by microorganisms, such as bacteria, viruses, or protozoa, that may be transmitted from one person to another. Infectious diseases, such as AIDS and tuberculosis, are very prevalent in developing nations.

infrastructure   Facilities (e.g., transportation, power, and communication networks; sanitation systems) and institutions (e.g., education, business, banking, health) that allow a society to function.

intellectual property   Intangible property that exists as a result of creativity. It includes such things as books, movies, and computer software and is protected by patents, copyrights, and similar laws.

internally displaced persons (IDPs)   People who are forced to move from their home area for reasons similar to those that motivate refugees. However, IDPs remain within the borders of their country.

International Conference on Population and Development (ICPD)   A major conference held in Cairo in 1994 at which population control policies for developing countries were to be agreed on. Follow-up conferences are held every five years.

Internal migration   Migration that occurs within a country.

International Monetary Fund (IMF)   A multilateral organization that works to stabilize the world's economy and to supervise the international debt payment system.

International Year of Planet Earth (IYPE)   The IYPE is actually a three-year period (2007 to 2009) during which awareness of the earth is to be heightened and research on ten themes related to the earth is to be carried out and presented.

involuntary migration   Movement of people against their will; often associated with persecution or fear of persecution.

isolationist   Describes a country's foreign policy that is focused on minimizing the country's involvement with the rest of the world.

issue   An important subject open to discussion and debate.

Jubilee 2000 Campaign   An international campaign, spearheaded by the world's major faith communities, to forgive the debts of the world's 50 poorest countries.

Keynesian economics   Economic system conceived by John Maynard Keynes advocating government spending to create jobs in poor economic times. A government-sponsored policy of high employment is viewed as the means to relieve economic depression.

Kyoto Protocol   An international agreement, signed in 1997, intended to begin the fight against climate change by limiting GhG emissions from industrialized countries.

labour shortage   The economic situation during which the demand for workers exceeds the supply. These are likely to become more common as populations age and birth rates decline.

land degradation   Deterioration of the productive capacity of soil for future use.

land reform   The redistribution of land from large estates into smaller farms. It has occurred in some parts of Latin America, Africa, and Asia.

land tenure   The manner in which land is held (e.g., owner-occupied farms, plantations owned by individuals or large companies, and land owned and worked by collectives).

late transition   A stage in demographic transition in which a declining birth rate and a relatively low death rate lead to a slowing population growth rate.

legal migration   Migration that occurs within recognized government programs.

less globalized periphery   That part of the world containing countries that are less involved in and have benefited to a lesser extent from globalization.

libel A legal action based on the fact that one person thinks that their reputation has been seriously harmed by the publication of untruths.

life expectancy The average lifespan that a newborn can expect to live if current mortality trends were to continue.

life experience Participation in events and contact with ideas that affect how one perceives things. Life experience is a result of such factors as age, education, religion, and ethnic background.

lifestyle diseases Diseases whose prevalence is related to the way in which people live. For example, heart conditions, obesity, and diabetes are related to poor diets.

limits-to-growth thesis A theory based on computer models developed by the Club of Rome that predicted pessimistic outcomes for Earth's environment if the growth trends of the 1970s continued.

Living Planet Index A specific indicator, created by the World Wildlife Fund, to measure the state of the world's biodiversity.

loss of genetic diversity A condition that occurs when only a few high-yield varieties of a crop come to replace the hundreds previously grown. This loss tends to make the crop species less resistant to disease and pests.

low variant Numerical population models frequently produce a range of projections rather than only one. The low variant is the lowest projection likely to occur.

malnutrition A condition in which health is damaged by a diet that includes too much or too little of one or more essential nutrients over an extended period of time.

Malthusian Related to the 1798 hypothesis of Thomas Malthus that population grows geometrically while food production increases arithmetically. The result is that population will eventually outstrip food supply and thus fall prey to famine, disease, and warfare. Any person or idea that supports Malthus's pessimistic viewpoint is described as neo-Malthusian.

mainstream media source These include mass communication organizations such as newspapers, television and radio broadcasters, and magazine publishers that are generally owned by large corporations.

media Include various forms of mass communication—e.g., newspapers, television, radio, and the Internet. The word is also used to describe the people involved in their production.

medical geography The branch of geography that applies geographic methods to the distribution of disease and healthcare in the world.

medium variant Numerical population models frequently produce a range of projections rather than only one. The medium variant is the one most likely to occur.

mega-cities Cities with a population of at least 10 million.

mercantile system A system of trade in which the mother country viewed its colonies as sources of raw materials as well as captive markets for its manufactured goods.

microcredit Small loans provided to help poor people develop small businesses so that they can break out of the cycle of poverty.

mixed economy An economic system that combines elements of both free enterprise and government intervention.

monoculture Agriculture that concentrates on growing only one crop in an area.

Montreal Protocol An international agreement, signed in 1987, to control the use of chemicals that harm the ozone layer.

more globalized core (or Core) That part of the world containing countries that are more involved in and have benefited to a greater extent from globalization.

multilateral aid Aid involving more than two donors (e.g., aid that comes from the World Bank or United Nations, institutions that are funded by many governments).

multinational companies Companies that operate in several countries; largely replaced by the term transnational companies because many are not clearly identified with any particular nation.

mutually assured destruction (MAD) A key part of the "rule set" of the Cold War. It meant that if either side were to use nuclear weapons against its rival, it would ensure its own destruction in the massive and inevitable counterstrike that would follow.

nation state An independent nation of people who have adopted a unique common identity and who live together under one government within a defined geographical area. The nation state possesses sovereignty, i.e., the ability to create policies and enforce laws within its borders without interference from other nations.

nationalism The feeling of pride that results from being a citizen of a particular country; a belief in the value of one's own country's sovereignty.

natural increase rate The rate at which a population increases (or decreases) in a given year expressed as a percentage of the total population; calculated by subtracting the death rate from the birth rate.

Near Core Periphery (or Near Core) Those countries in the Periphery that are most globalized and closest to joining the Core.

neo-colonialism A form of colonialism that developed principally after World War II based on economic dominance rather than political dominance.

neo-liberalism A set of economic policies that reduce the role of government because government control and regulation are seen to impede or distort economic growth. Governmental deregulation of industries, privatization of state-owned enterprises, and removal of restrictive trade practices are examples of neo-liberal policies.

net migration rate The combined impact of immigration and emigration on an area's population. The rate can be positive or negative.

New Core Those countries that have joined the Core (i.e., become more globalized) only in recent years. Includes (among many other countries) Brazil, Russia, India, and China.

Nobel Peace Prize A highly prestigious award, given annually to an individual or organization that has made a major contribution to the cause of peace in the world.

nomadic hunters and gatherers Groups of people who survived by moving from place to place looking for foods to collect and animals to hunt.

non-governmental organization (NGO) A private organization that exists for a particular purpose, e.g., to promote international development or to support cultural activities.

non-renewable resource A resource that is finite or limited and cannot be restored or regenerated in nature, e.g., petroleum and natural gas.

non-tariff barriers Barriers to free trade, other than traditional tariff barriers, such as government policies that require domestic purchases.

North In a commonly used two-world model of country groupings, a region with membership similar to the Old Core.

North American Free Trade Agreement (NAFTA) A treaty signed in 1994 by Canada, the United States, and Mexico that phased out most trade restrictions among the three countries.

North Atlantic Treaty Organization (NATO) Originally a military alliance, including the United States, Canada, and many western European nations, designed to confront the Warsaw Pact during the Cold War. Has now expanded both its membership and security role.

nuclear terrorism The use of nuclear weapons or radioactive materials in terrorist acts.

nutrition transition A model used to describe the changes in the quantity and quality of typical diets as a country becomes economically and socially more advanced.

obesity A medical condition in which a person has a Body-Mass Index of 30 or more.

objective Not distorted by personal feelings or bias.

odious debt Debt created by unscrupulous leaders to meet their own needs rather than the interests of the people. E.g., a despotic ruler who borrows money for personal gain or to repress the population creates an odious debt that the state is still responsible for when the ruler leaves power.

official development assistance (ODA) Foreign aid provided by governments.

oil sands Vast deposits of sand in northern Alberta that is coated with "bitumen", a heavy hydrocarbon. Can be processed to create a form of synthetic crude oil.

Old Core The countries of western Europe along with Canada, the United States, Japan, Australia, and New Zealand that have been highly globalized for many years.

old-growth forest Forest that has never been logged.

one-child policy A Chinese government policy, introduced in 1979, designed to reduce the country's population growth rate by restricting most couples to only one child.

opinions Judgments or beliefs that are not necessarily based on certainty or proof.

organic farming Farming in which no herbicides, pesticides, antibiotics, or genetically modified products are used.

overpopulation An excess of people that prevents a country from meeting the needs of its citizens, whether social, economic, or environmental.

overurbanization Condition that results when a city's population grows faster than the number of jobs or housing units available.

pandemic A continent-wide or worldwide outbreak of an infectious disease.

peace dividend The amount of money saved as a result of the cut in military spending that occurred when the Cold War came to an end.

peacekeeping The use of an international military force, under the auspices of the UN or some other organization, to keep a truce already agreed to by the combatants.

peacemaking The use of an international military force, under the auspices of the UN or some other organization, to impose a ceasefire or truce on combatants.

peak oil The point in history at which half of the world's oil reserves have been used. At this point, it is thought that oil will become more and more expensive as production becomes more costly.

pension plans A financial strategy, either private or government, designed to provide income for people during their retirement years.

persistent organic pollutants (POPs) Highly toxic substances used in pesticides and other industrial chemicals. Insoluble in water, they are very stable and last for years in the environment before breaking down.

perspective A point of view or way of looking at things. A perspective is the product of influences such as family, schooling, religion, country, friends, and the media.

phantom carrying capacity Earth's ability to support an immense population at a high standard of living only because it is using up its non-renewable resources to the detriment of future generations.

photochemical smog Smog (dirty air conditions) produced by a photochemical reaction among sunlight and hydrocarbons and nitrogen oxides.

physical deterioration Degradation of land caused by compaction, waterlogging, or subsidence that leads to reduced land productivity.

PIR (Planning, Implementation, Review) An approach that can be used to implement a project or an initiative in a systematic way.

plantations Large farming operations used to grow tropical and subtropical crops, such as bananas, coffee, cocoa, cotton, rubber, sugar, spices, and tea.

political consumerism People making buying decisions based on the values they hold and on how closely these are matched to ways that companies operate.

Political Islam A region that has been posited for some time in the distant future within which the world's Islamic countries develop significant political, social, and economic linkages.

polls An activity, carried out by specialized organizations, in which people are asked questions to determine their beliefs or opinions about a particular issue.

population control Limitation of population growth through such measures as contraception, sterilization, and abortion.

population growth rate Rate at which a population increases or decreases in a given year through natural increase and net migration, expressed as a percentage of the total population.

population implosion The future rapid population decline in Core countries (especially Old Core) as a result of low fertility rates.

population pyramid Special type of graph that shows the distribution of a population by age and gender. Each bar graph indicates an absolute value (number of people) or a percentage of people of each gender in a specific age group.

positive feedback loop A feedback loop that reinforces itself so that the impact of the outcome increases the strength of the causal factor.

post-transition Stage in demographic transition in which a low birth rate and a low death rate lead to a stable population.

Poverty Reduction Strategy Paper (PRSP) An important step in the HIPC program of the World Bank/IMF. The PRSP indicates what plans the country has for economic, structural, and social reforms to promote economic growth and reduce poverty. It also identifies the economic aid that the country would need to achieve its goals.

pre-transition Stage in demographic transition in which a high birth rate and a high death rate result in a more-or-less stable population. No country in the world today is still in the pre-transition stage.

Private development assistance (PDA) Foreign aid that is provided by non-governmental organizations and individuals.

privatize Refers to the process of government activities being transferred to the private sector.

pronatalist strategies Ideas that encourage people to have more children, e.g., tax benefits and inexpensive day care programs.

protected area An area of land or water set aside, e.g., as a national park, to protect its physical features, wildlife, or historical features.

proxy war A war fought during the Cold War between "proxies", i.e., minor allies, of superpowers (US and USSR) or between a superpower and a proxy of the other superpower. Proxy wars helped to avoid direct confrontations between the superpowers.

pull factors Conditions in a place that make it attractive to potential migrants.

push factors Conditions in a place that make it so unattractive to its residents that they may want to migrate to a different place.

R/P ratio A calculation that gives the number of years remaining before a non-renewable resource runs out. It is computed by dividing the size of the recoverable reserves (R) by the amount that is extracted in a given year (P). Note that value calculated assumes that production will continue at a constant rate.

recentralization The movement of population from suburban areas to the central city, after decentralization has occurred.

reduced-impact logging (RIL) Logging that ensures a forest's long-term economic and ecological sustainability. It includes conducting accurate inventories to determine how much timber can be cut, and conducting the harvest as carefully as possible.

refugees People who leave their country under threat of persecution because of their race, religion, nationality, or social or political group. Increasingly, people become refugees because of declining environmental quality.

remittance Refers to money sent to family and friends by a migrant in a different locale.

renewable resource A resource that is not diminished when used carefully, i.e., it is replenishable in nature. Tidal or wind energy, forests, and fish are examples of renewable resources.

replacement migration This is migration that occurs to maintain the overall or working-age population in a country.

replacement rate The fertility rate required for a population to replace itself. Usually, a fertility rate of at least 2.1 is needed, taking into account infant mortality and women who do not have children.

reserves The proportion of a natural resource that can be exploited under prevailing economic conditions and current technology.

resource Anything that meets people's needs; includes natural resources (water, air), human-made items (labour, technology), or items appreciated for their aesthetic qualities (landscapes, ecosystems).

rule of 70 Simple method to estimate how long it will take a population to double. It is calculated by dividing 70 by the population growth rate. E.g., if the population growth rate of a country is 0.5 percent, the population would double in 70/0.5 = 140 years.

rule set More generally, a collection of rules that delineates how an activity should be carried out; more specifically, in international relations it is an implicit understanding of how countries should behave. Rule sets change dramatically in response to major events, e.g., rise of Hitler or the collapse of the Soviet Union. They evolve more slowly at other times.

rural to urban migration The migration that occurs between the countryside and towns and cities.

salinization Refers to buildup of salts at or near the surface of the soil as water evaporates, particularly in dry, hot climates.

sanctions Measures imposed on a state by other countries in an effort to force it to change its policies or behaviour. Sanctions can be either economic or military.

Security Council Generally regarded as the most important body within the United Nations since it has the right to impose sanctions on a member. Five permanent members of the Council (China, France, Russia, United Kingdom, and United States) have veto power over any decision.

silence, stigma, discrimination, and denial A group of factors that contribute significantly to the spread of HIV/AIDS in Africa and elsewhere.

SLAPPs (Strategic Lawsuit Against Public Participation) Action by a corporation against an individual or NGO. The purpose is to stop a protest by forcing the NGO or individual to focus time and money on its legal defence rather than on fighting the company.

Slow Cities Cities that protect and encourage local traditions and develop an economy based on the communities' unique nature.

smart growth Economic growth that occurs while sustainability is maintained. Smart growth occurs as a result of environmentally wise choices made by governments, businesses, and people with regard to their lifestyle.

smart meters Advanced electricity meters that can track not only how much electricity you use but when you use it. This allows different prices to be charged at different times depending on demand.

social development The level of education, healthcare, jurisprudence, life expectancy, and rate of infant mortality in a society.

socially responsible investing An investment strategy that takes the investor's moral values into consideration.

socio-economic status A person's position in society based on factors such as their job, income, and education.

soft power A means by which a country tries to impose its will on another. It includes the use of co-option, public diplomacy, and government diplomacy.

solar energy Energy from the sun that can be used in a variety of ways, e.g., solar heating (passive and active) and photo-voltaics (electricity generation).

solid waste management Garbage disposal, involving primary, secondary, or tertiary treatment of waste.

source control The idea of stopping water (and other forms of) pollution by eliminating the source of the waste.

source reduction Reducing the amount of garbage or other waste products at its source, for example, by using less packaging for products.

South In a commonly used two-world model of country grouping, a region with membership similar to the New Core and Periphery.

sovereign default   A country's inability to pay some or all of its international debts.

sovereignty   A concept in international law recognizing that the authority of the state is not subject to control by other states.

Spaceship Earth concept   The idea that our home, Earth, is a spaceship, and that Earth's resources must be protected because we have nowhere to turn if they run out.

specific indicator   A single measure that shows progress toward sustainability, e.g., changes in greenhouse gas emissions over time.

sphere of influence   Part of the world in which a nation has a special interest and is politically and economically active.

squatter settlements   Areas of illegally built, makeshift housing, usually on the edge of cities in developing countries. Such areas spring up because the demand for cheap housing outstrips the supply.

starvation   Extreme hunger that continues over an extended period of time.

state terrorism   The use of terrorist methods by a government to force obedience from the general population. Sometimes called institutional terrorism.

state-sponsored terrorism   Terrorism by a private group with the direct support of a nation state, e.g., by the provision of funding or safe haven.

structural change model   The use of government policy to effect change in a country, e.g., China's one-child policy.

subjective   Resulting from personal feelings, thoughts, experiences, and prejudices.

sustainability   Development that meets the needs of people today without jeopardizing the ability of future generations to meet their needs.

temperature inversion   A reversal of the normal temperature gradient in the atmosphere. In an inversion, a layer of warm air traps pollutants in cooler air below.

terrain deformation   A change in the physical landscape caused by natural or human forces.

terrorism   The use of violence and intimidation to achieve political or ideological goals.

theory of demographic regulation   A theory developed by D.J. Bogue in the 1960s stating that over an extended period of time, a society limits its population.

thick-layer capping   The isolation of solid toxic wastes from the bottoms of water bodies by covering them with layers of clean materials.

Third World   Originally from a three-world model of country grouping; refers to those countries not in the Old Core.

tipping point   A threshold beyond which a situation dramatically changes, e.g., when support to fight climate change became the dominant belief. More broadly, a point beyond which a situation has changed so profoundly that it is not possible to return to the initial state.

total fertility rate   Average number of children borne over the lifetime of a typical woman in a particular country. This figure answers the question, "How many children are women currently having?"

total stock   All of the material components of the environment (including energy, living organisms, and non-living materials) taken together.

transnational corporations   Corporations that operate in two or more countries (also called multinational corporations). Transnationals are probably the major force affecting global shifts in economic activity, since many have profits greater than the GDPs of some countries.

ultraviolet (UV) radiation   Invisible short-wave radiation from the sun. The ozone layer absorbs much of this radiation, thereby protecting Earth from dangerously high levels.

undernutrition   The result of a diet that has a shortage of one or more essential elements.

unilateralist foreign policy   The approach followed by one country in its dealings with other countries in which it does not consider points of view other than its own. Since the breakup of the USSR in 1991, the United States has tended to follow a unilateralist foreign policy.

United Nations Convention on the Law of the Sea (UNCLOS)   An international agreement designed to promote peaceful uses of the world's oceans, equitable use of the oceans' resources, and protection of marine environments.

Universal Declaration of Human Rights   A profoundly important UN document that was agreed to in 1948. It established the list of human rights that all world citizens should enjoy.

values   Principles and moral values central to a person's behaviour.

vertical integration   A company that operates at all stages of an economic activity, from producing a good to retailing it.

veto   A vote to refuse or stop a course of action. E.g., any permanent member of the Security Council of the UN has the right to veto a resolution if it disagrees with the Council's proposed course of action.

voluntary migration   Migration that occurs because the migrant chooses to move.

War on Terror   Term used by the United States for its anti-terrorist activities after the 2001 attacks on the US.

Warsaw Pact   A military alliance between the Soviet Union and its eastern European allies during the Cold War, to confront NATO. It ceased to exist with the collapse of the Soviet Union at the end of the 1980s.

weapons of mass destruction (WMD)   Biological, chemical, and nuclear weapons that are capable of killing many people at one time and possibly devastating large areas.

wind power   Production of energy from windmills of various sorts.

World Bank   A specialized agency that furthers the economic development of member nations, chiefly through guaranteed loans. The Bank obtains most of its funds through borrowing, and the remainder through government subscription. Since voting power is proportional to the amount of money received from each government, the Bank is essentially controlled by the richer countries.

World Trade Organization (WTO)   The international organization responsible for coordinating and promoting trade in the world.

Index

Aboriginal peoples: and colonialism, 173; and cultural exceptionalism, 435; Friends of the Lubicon, 254; land ownership, 292; Platinex suit, 254; and protected areas, 242, 252–253
abortion, 88–89
absolute measure, 63
acid rain, 280–283
acidic deposition, 280–283
Afghanistan: Afghan-Soviet war, 354–355; NATO, 400; religious nation state, 345; state-sponsored terrorism, 371; terrorism, 368; War on Terror, 374–375
Africa: Green Revolution, 154; HIV/AIDS, 411, 414–415; terrorism, 368
African National Congress, 372
age-dependency ratio, 65
Agricultural Revolution, 61, 62
agricultural support policies, 158
agriculture: and biotechnology, 155–157; and climate change, 163; corporate farming, 159–160; deficiencies, 150; factory farms, 160; fair trade, 163; food miles, 161–162; and global warming, 324–325; and globalization, 162–163; grain production trend, 155; in India, 85–86; and land degradation, 233; land reform, 157; loss of genetic diversity, 157; monoculture, 159; nature of, 150; organic farming, 161; role of women in, 158; and subsidies, 158–159; support policies, 158; sustainability, 161–162; types of, 150; wastes, 264–265
aid fatigue, 207
AIDS. see HIV/AIDS
air travel, 23
albedo, 326, 334
Alberta, 306, 456
Algeria, 368
al-Qaeda, 365, 368, 369, 371, 373
alternative energy: background, 308; biofuel, 309–310; earth energy, 311; geothermal, 310; green power, 313; hydricity, 313; solar, 308–310; wind power, 311–312
alternative media source, 9
Amundsen, Roald, 350
Anglo-Belgian India Rubber Company, 172
Annan, Kofi, 154, 399
anthropogenic greenhouse gases, 319
anti-retroviral drugs, 415–416
apartheid, 356
aquifer, 265
Arafat, Yasser, 372
Aral Sea, 270–271
Arctic, 284, 287, 340, 350–352
Are We Rome?, 378
Argentina, 221, 371
arms, 16, 357–358
Asia–Pacific Economic Cooperation (APEC), 191
Asian Brown Cloud, 284
Asmal, Kader, 272
aspirational goals, 330
Aswan High Dam, 270
asymmetric warfare, 353, 370
atmosphere: acid rain, 280–283; background, 278; cross-section, 278; ozone layer, 286–288; poisons, 278–280; smog, 283–286
Aum Shinrikyo, 373
Aung San Suu Kyi, 405
Australia, 328
authoritarian, 4, 344
authoritarianism, 344, 345
auto industry, 185–186, 190–191
Auto Pact, 190–191

baby bonuses, 109
bald eagles, 13
Bali Conference, 329–331
Ban, Ki-moon, 400
Bangladesh: GDP, 168, 169; global involvement, 44, 45; microcredit, 440–442; sea levels, 323
Barnett, Thomas P.M., 360
Battle in Seattle, 192
beer bottles, 238
Begin, Menachem, 372
Bellagio Principles, 451
Bhopal, 34
Bhutto, Benazir, 429
bias, 15
bilateral aid, 204
Bill and Melinda Gates Foundation, 154, 204
bin Laden, Osama, 361, 372
bioaccumulation, 279
biodegradable, 262
biodiesel, 309
biodiversity, 247
bioethanol, 309
biofuel, 163, 255, 309–310
biotechnology, 155, 156
bioterrorism, 373
bird flu, 420–421
birth control, 73–74, 88
birth dearth, 104–108, 109
birth rate: declining growth rate, 74; defined, 64; and demographic trap, 85; early transition, 71–72; in India, 88–90; late transition, 73–74; post-transition, 74–75; pre-transition, 71
BMW, 186
Body-Mass Index (BMI), 416
bog, 267
Bogotá, 142–143
Bogue, D. J., 79
Bolivia, 158
Bologna, 101
bonded labour, 435
borders, 341
Borlaug, Norman, 151, 153
Bosnia-Herzegovina, 401
Botswana, 414
bovine spongiform encephalopathy (BSE), 420
brain drain, 119–120
brain gain, 119–120
brawn gain, 120
Brazil: biofuels, 309; and colonialism, 171; economic power, 185; progressive thought, 178; slums, 141; and world power structures, 387
bribes, 353
BRIC, 184, 331
British East India Company, 173
British Empire, 378
Brundtland Commission, 460
Brundtland, Gro Harlem, 460
Bush, George W., 123, 375
busways, 142

California, 331–332
caliphate, 361
Canada: and Aboriginal groups, 173; in Afghanistan, 374; agricultural subsidies, 158, 159; agriculture, 85–86, 150; and Arctic sovereignty, 351–352; biofuel, 309; child poverty, 434; and climate change, 328–329, 331; and cultural exceptionalism, 435; and cultural protection, 189; demographics, 64–66; development assistance, 207, 208; economy, 383; energy consumption, 293; equalization payments, 177; and fair trade, 443; fertility rates, 103; forests, 251–252; GDP, 168, 169; global involvement, 43, 44, 45; and global warming, 324; growth rate, 92; healthcare, 201; immigration, 113, 114, 118, 122; internal migration, 119; Kyoto Protocol, 403–404; marriage age, 93; oceans, 273; oil sands, 306; peacekeeping, 398; POPs, 279; population records, 71; poverty, 137; protected areas, 241–242; and refugees, 125; sewage treatment, 261; and socially responsible investing, 439; terrorism, 368; urbanization, 119; and U.S. border, 341–342; and water transfers, 272–273; wetlands, 266, 268; wind power, 312; and world power structures, 382–383
Canadian Foodgrains Bank, 204
Canadian International Development Agency (CIDA), 204
cap and trade system, 332–333
capitalization, 182
carbon cycle, 320–321
carbon dioxide, 32, 320, 328, 334
carbon footprint, 161. see also ecological footprint
Carbon Mitigation Initiative, 469
carbon sink, 320
carbon source, 320
carbon tax, 333
carrying capacity, 35, 61
Carson, Rachel, 14, 34
cash crops, 151, 173
caste, 435
Castro, Fidel, 202
Catton, William, 80
centrist, 4
Chad, 356
chain of custody, 250
change by diffusion model, 94
chemical deterioration, 232
chemical terrorism, 373
chemical waste, 262–264
child labour, 433–434
child tax credits, 109
children: human rights, 433–434; ICPD principles, 96; living conditions, 17; poverty, 434; UN convention, 434; and war, 432–433
Chile, 202
China: authoritarianism, 4; birth and death rates, 91; and climate change, 330; and economic disparity, 199; economic power, 185; forced labour, 435; globalization, 347; illegal migration, 123; nutrition transition, 419; one-child policy, 79, 90, 91, 92, 330; pollution, 390; population, 85, 87, 90–92; Three Gorges Dam, 270; and world power structures, 390–391
cholera, 410
chorofluorocarbons (CFCs), 287
chronic hunger, 148
Churchill, Winston, 189
cities: changes in, 134–135; economic problems, 136–137, 138–139; environmental problems, 138, 141–142; future of, 142–143; livability, 135; problems, 136–143; social problems, 137, 139–141
Città Lente, 458
civil liberties, 375
civil society, 207
civilizations, 361
Clean Air Act, 284
climate change: and agriculture, 163; background, 317–318; carbon dioxide emissions, 328; global warming, 317, 318; greenhouse effect, 319–321; history, 318; impact of, 321–326; loops, 326–327; personal impact, 334; politics of, 327–332; solutions, 332–334; as world issue, 18
Club of Rome, 35
CO_2, 32, 320, 328, 334
coal, 61, 293, 300
Coca-Cola, 187
coffee, 444–445
Cold War, 346, 360, 378–379, 401
Colombia, 356, 368
colonialism: concession companies, 172–173; defined, 171; economic, 174, 203; and economic disparity, 201, 203; history, 171–172; impacts of, 173–174
command economy, 175
command points, 26
commercial forests, 251
commodity prices, 220

communism, 345
community initiative, 439, 446
comparative advantage, 443
comprehensive indicator, 453–456
conceptual models, 35
concession companies, 172–173
conflict: Arctic ocean sovereignty, 350–352; armed, 350; causes of, 353–355; costs of, 357–358, 359; examples of, 355–356; and geopolitics, 345–347, 354; hard power, 352; militaristic countries, 359; nature of, 350–351; soft power, 352–353
Consciously Enraged, 367
containment, 346
contraception. see birth control
Convention on the Rights of the Child, 434
co-option, 352
Copenhagen Consensus, 16–19
Core. see more globalized core
cornucopian thesis, 35
cornucopians, 79, 305
corporate farming, 159
corruption, 16
Corruption-Perception Index (CPI), 42, 43, 44, 45
Costa Rica, 459
counterterrorism, 374
countries, grouping, 41–52, 47–49, 50–52
critical load, 280
crude oil, 295–297
Cuba, 202, 368
cultural exceptionalism, 435
cultural globalization, 27
Cyprus, 356

The Da Vinci Code, 182
Daishowa, 254
Dallaire, Roméo, 174
dams, 268–272
Darfur, 356, 398–399
David Suzuki Foundation, 278
DDT, 12–13
death control, 71
death rate, 71–72, 74–75, 85
debt, 201, 203–204. see also international debt
debt relief, 222–224
debt service charges, 217, 219
debt/export ratio, 216, 218
decentralization, 134
declining growth rate, 60–61
deep ecology, 248
deforestation, 18, 233, 249, 387
democracy, 343, 344
demographic transition, 70–77
demographic trap, 85
demography, 58, 63–66
Denmark, 351–352, 458, 468
dependency load, 65
dependency measures, 65
desalination, 31
desertification, 233
developed worlds, 50, 51
developing worlds, 50, 51
development assistance, 353; Canada, 207; defined, 204; flawed model, 206–207; future of, 207–208; loans, not grants, 219; the Marshall Plan, 205; motives for, 205; NGOs, 204; Organization for Economic Cooperation and Development, 206; Paris Declaration, 207
diffusion, 94
digital divide, 16
DINKs, 105
diplomacy, 352
dirty bomb, 373
dirty dozen, 280
disease: and air pollution, 279, 285; BSE, 420; and economic disparity, 17, 201; foot-and-mouth disease, 420; geography of, 411; and global warming, 325; HIV/AIDS, 17, 96, 203, 411–416; infectious, 411–416, 419–421; influenza, 419–420; lifestyle, 411, 416–419; mad cow disease, 420; obesity, 416–419; pandemic, 411, 419–421; SARS, 421; and sewage waste, 261; transmission, 420–421
Doctors Without Borders, 405
Doha Round, 192–193
Douglas fir, 36
drip irrigation, 272

drugs, illegal, 17
Dubai, 22–25, 31, 32
dump sites, 235–236
Dunant, Jean Henri, 404

E. coli, 265
early transition, 71–73
Earth Day, 34
earth energy, 311
Earth First!, 248
Earth Liberation Front, 249
Earth Summit, 451, 457
Ebola hemorrhagic fever, 413
ecological footprint, 453–455. see also carbon footprint
ecological globalization, 28
ecological world view, 33, 34
Economic and Social Council, 399
economic development, 41, 169–170
economic disparity: among nations, 199–203; assets, 197; causes of, 201–203; within countries, 209–210; development assistance, 204–208; Gini index, 209, 210; nature of, 197; and remittances, 208; solutions, 203–208; wealth distribution, 197
economic globalization, 26, 176
economic liberalism, 175
economic systems, 175–178
economies of scale, 159
Ecosystem-Based management, 253
ecosystems, 323–324
education, 86, 93, 96
Eisenhower, Dwight D., 357
El Salvador, 121
emigration rate, 64
employment, 86
empowerment, 439
The End of History and the Last Man, 360
energy: alternative sources, 308–313, 468; better ways, 307; coal, 61, 293, 300; conventional sources, 304; crisis, 305; crude oil, 295–297; global production and consumption, 294–295; hydro-electric power, 303; natural gas, 298–299; nuclear power, 301–302; oil sands, 306; problems, 292–293; reserves, 304; sources, 61, 269; as world issue, 18
energy intensity, 330
energy recovery, 237
Engels, Friedrich, 345
environment, and urbanization, 138, 141–142
environmental dredging, 264
environmental migration, 116
Environmental Protection Act, 279
environmentalism, 34
erosion, 230
ethanol, 309, 310, 387
ethnic cleansing, 433
European Community, 189
European Union: and climate change, 328, 330; free trade, 189; map, 190; neo-liberalism, 177; and world power structures, 384
eutrophication, 265
evapotranspiration, 232
exchange rates, 220
Exclusive Economic Zones, 273
expansionist world view, 33, 34
expatriate workers, 94
extended producer responsibility, 239, 457
extensive farming, 151
extreme poverty, 199–201

factory farms, 160
facts, 11
fair earthshare, 455
fair trade, 163, 443–444
family size, 70, 73–74
family structure, 104
famine, 147
Far Periphery, 45, 46, 135, 138–142
farming. see agriculture
feedback loop, 86, 326–327
female infanticide, 88
fen, 267
fertility rates, 92, 101, 102, 103
fifth world, 52
finance and business, 23
financial globalization, 26

financial instability, 16
First Nations. see Aboriginal peoples
first world, 50
fiscal squeeze, 136–137
five-world model, 51–52
fixed carbon, 320
flint, 36
Flint, C., 30
flu, 419–420
food, 85, 155–160
food miles, 161
foot-and-mouth disease, 420
force, 353
forced labour, 435
Ford Foundation, 204
foreign aid. see development assistance
Forest Stewardship Council, 249–250
forests: benefits of, 247; and biofuel, 255; commercial, 251; as commodity, 247; competing interests, 247, 251–255; protection, 248; reduced-impact logging, 250–251; state of, 246; use of, 249–251
fossil water, 265, 266
fourth world, 52
France, 368
free market economy, 175
free trade: in the Americas, 191; in Asia, 191; Doha Round, 192–193; and fair trade, 443; growth of, 188–189; in North America, 189–191; Seattle WTO meeting, 192; and the U.S., 193; in western Europe, 189
Free Trade Agreement (FTA), 191
Free Trade Area of the Americas (FTAA), 191
freedom fighter, 372–373
Freedom House, 44, 45
Freedom House rating, 42, 43
Friends of the Lubicon, 254
Frobisher, Martin, 350
frontier forests, 246
fuel tax, 457–458
Fujimori, Alberto, 202
Fukuyama, Francis, 360

G8, 30, 203
Gaia hypothesis, 35
Gandhi, 4
Gapminder, 78, 201
Gates, Bill, 154
gender equality, 96
gender gap, 88–90, 92
General Agreement on Tariffs and Trade (GATT), 188
General Assembly, 397
General Electric, 182, 186
genetic diversity, 152
genetically modified organism (GMO), 155
Geneva Convention, 433
gentrification, 134
Genuine Progress Indicator, 455–456
geo-engineering, 333
geographical globalization, 28
The Geography of Hope, 451, 463
geological sequestration, 333
geopolitical migration, 116
geopolitics, 339, 345–347, 354
geothermal energy, 310
germ theory, 72
Germany: GDP, 169; global involvement, 43, 44, 45; guest workers, 117; immigration, 118; replacement migration, 123
ghettos, 121
Gibbon, Edward, 378
Gini index, 209, 210
girls, 88–90, 92, 96
Gitga'at people, 252–253
Gladwell, Malcolm, 317–318
Global 500, 182
Global Forest Watch, 248
Global Hunger Index, 149
global involvement: Bangladesh, 44, 45; Canada, 43, 44, 45; Germany, 43, 44, 45; Malaysia, 45; measures of, 42; Philippines, 45; Poland, 45; Zambia, 44, 45
global village, 340
global warming, 317, 318, 321–326
globalization: and agriculture, 162–163; and the Arctic, 350; and big business, 182; and cash crops, 173; China, 347; and colonialism, 171;

concerns about, 30; and conflict, 353, 360–361; defined, 22; and disease, 410–423; Dubai example, 22–25; economic, 176, 187; and economic disparity, 199; eight dimensions of, 30; and empowerment, 439; and energy, 292, 307; and fair trade, 443; and food production, 152; and free trade, 190; and GDP, 456; and the Golden Arches, 29; and international debt, 221, 223; nature of, 25–28; New Core growth, 46; positive aspects of, 463–468; and refugees, 125; and remittances, 208; and sovereignty, 340; survey, 465–466; and sustainability, 451; terminology, 50; and terrorism, 366, 372; and traditional values, 28; and transnational companies, 188; and the UN, 399; US superpower, 379; and war, 432; and waste management, 239; and world power structures, 380

The Good, the Bad, and the Ugly, 401

Gore, Al, 469

government diplomacy, 352

Grameen Bank, 440–442

grasshopper effect, 279

Great Barrier Reef, 241

Great Bear Rainforest, 252–253

the Great Depression, 189

Great Lakes, 262–264

Great Leap Forward, 90

Great Ocean Conveyor, 325–326

Great War. *see* World War I

Green Accounts Act, 458

green manure, 161

green power, 313

Green Revolution: in Africa, 154; background, 151–152; concerns about, 152–154; in India, 85; success of, 152

green taxation, 457

greenhouse effect, 319–321

greenhouse gases, 278, 319

Gross Domestic Product (GDP): and economic disparity, 198; and economic progress, 451; and GPI, 455–456; industry percentages, 168, 169; and international debt, 216; as measure of global involvement, 42, 43, 44, 45

groundwater, 259

grouping countries, 41–52

guest workers, 117, 118

guns or butter, 357

Guyana, 207

H5N1 (bird flu), 420–421

hall of shame, 202

halocarbons, 321

Hammarskjöld, Dag, 400

hard currency, 216, 220

hard power, 352, 378

Harper, Stephen, 328, 351

hazardous waste, 18

health, 325

healthcare, 94, 96, 201

heat island effect, 138, 141

hedonics, 143

herbicides, 255–256

high variant, 102

highly indebted poor countries, 220, 223

Highly Indebted Poor Countries initiative, 222

high-yield variety (HYV), 151–152

The History of the Decline and Fall of the Roman Empire, 378

HIV/AIDS: ABC approach, 414; in Africa, 414–415; cycle, 415; and economic disparity, 203; history, 412–413; ICPD goals, 96; impact of, 413–414; pandemic, 411–412; statistics, 412, 415; and women, 415; as world issue, 17

Home Depot, 250

homelessness, 137, 178

Hoover Dam, 269

housing, affordable, 137

Hubbert, M. King, 305

Hudson's Bay Company, 172

Human Development Index, 42, 43, 44, 45, 218

human rights: children, 433–434; history, 425; slavery, 435; Universal Declaration of Human Rights, 426–427, 428; violation of, 428; and war, 432–433; women, 428–431

human settlements, 17

Humphrey, John Peters, 428

hunger: diseases related to, 148; geography of, 149; nutrition availability, 147; terminology, 147–148; as world issue, 17

hunting and gathering, 61

Huntington, Samuel P., 360–361

Hurricane Katrina, 316

hybrid bomb, 373

hydrochlorofluorocarbons (HCFCs), 288

ideology, 343

illegal drugs, 17

immigration, 114, 121. *see also* migration

immigration rate, 64

imperialism, 346

improvised explosive devices, 353

incineration, 236, 237

income redistribution, 210

Index of Sustainable Economic Welfare, 454

India: cotton industry, 172; and economic disparity, 199; Kerala, 92–95; NGOs, 468; population, 87; population control, 88–90, 92, 92–95; population growth, 85–86; population growth rate, 88; slums, 140; terrorism, 368; and world power structures, 389

Indonesia, 284

Industrial Revolution, 33, 61–63

industry, categories of, 168

infant mortality rate, 65

infanticide, 88

infant-mortality rate, 42, 43, 44, 45, 96

infectious diseases, 411, 413

inflation, 220

influenza, 419–420

informal economy, 138

information sources, 8

infrastructure, 135

integration of immigrants, 121–122

intellectual property rights, 16, 391

intensive farming, 151

Intergovernmental Panel on Climate Change, 321

internal migration, 119, 128–144

internally displaced persons, 124, 125

International Conference on Population and Development, 92, 95–97

international debt: in Africa, 218; burden of, 214–218; comparison table, 216; dealing with, 221–222; debt relief, 222–224; defaults, 221; effects of, 218–219; and GDP, 216; and goods exported, 216; Highly Indebted Poor Countries initiative, 222; lenders, 217; per capita, 215; reasons for, 219–220; restructuring, 221–222; and social development, 218

International Food Policy Research Institute, 149

International Institute for Applied Systems Analysis, 102

International Joint Commission, 263

International Monetary Fund, 221

International Organization for Standardization (ISO), 456–457

International Polar Year, 287

International Union for the Conservation of Nature and Natural Resources, 37

International Year of Planet Earth, 463

Internet users, 42, 43, 44, 45

investment, 201

involuntary migration, 116

Iraq war: dates, 356; and globalization, 360; involuntary migration, 116; and terrorism, 369, 374; and the UN, 398

Ireland, 457

Irgun, 372

Irish Republican Army, 367

iron fertilization, 334

Islam, 24, 354, 360–361, 380, 392–393

isolationist, 380

Israel, 356, 369

issues, 5–7

Japan, 385

Johnson-Sirleaf, Ellen, 429

Jubilee 2000 Campaign, 223–224

Kalimantan, 284

Kenya, 372

Kenyatta, Jomo, 372

Kerala, 92–95

kermode bear, 253

Keynes, John Maynard, 176

Keynesian economics, 176

Kiberia, 128, 130, 139

Kirchner, Cristina Fernandez de, 429

Kitchenuhmaykoosib Inninuwug First Nation, 254

Knights Templar, 182

Kuwait, 292

Kyoto Protocol, 327–329, 403–404

labour shortage, 87, 106–107, 117

Ladakh, 468

land degradation: background, 230; causes of, 233–234; defined, 18, 229; global patterns, 234, 235; impact of, 234; types of, 230–233

land issues, 229

land reform, 94, 157

land tenure, 173

Las Vegas, 259

late transition, 73–74

Laurier, Wilfrid, 189

leaching, 232

leadership, and economic disparity, 202, 204

Lebanon, 369

left wing, 4

legal migration, 118

Lesotho, 120, 266

less globalized periphery, 44, 216–217

Lewis, Stephen, 405

libel, 15

libertarian, 4

life expectancy, 65, 101, 103

life experiences, 3

lifestyle diseases, 411

limits-to-growth thesis, 35

livability, 135

Living Planet Index, 453

local integration, 125

Lomborg, Bjørn, 16

London, 283–284, 410

L'Oréal, 121

Los Angeles, 285–286

loss of genetic diversity, 152

lost decade, 206

Love Canal, 262–263

Lovelock, James, 35, 301

low variant, 102

Lunn, Gary, 301

Maathai, Wangari, 405

Macdonald, Sir John A., 189

MacKinnon, James, 162

MAD, 379, 401

mad cow disease, 420

mainstream media source, 9

malaria, 12–13

Malaysia, 45, 169

malnutrition, 148. *see also* hunger

Malthus, Thomas, 80

Malthusian, 80

Mandela, Nelson, 364, 372

mangrove marsh, 267

Manifest Destiny, 341

Mao Zedong, 4

marriage age, 93

marsh, 267

Marshall Plan, 205, 346

Marx, Karl, 345

Mau-Mau, 372

McDonald's, 29, 42, 43, 44, 45

Médecins Sans Frontières, 405

media, 9, 10

medical geography, 411

medium variant, 102

mega-cities, 133

Memorial Institute for the Prevention of Terrorism, 367

A Memory of Solferino, 404

mercantile system, 172

Merkel, Angela, 429

methane, 237, 320

Mexico, 71, 72, 73, 75, 191

microcredit, 438, 440

Middleton, Nick, 37

migration: brain drain, 119–120; environmental, 116; geopolitical, 116; and global warming, 326; guest workers, 117; illegal, 118, 122–123; and integration, 121–122; internal, 119; involuntary, 116; issues, 119–125; legal, 118; nature of, 115; and population, 101; remittances, 120–121; replacement, 123–124; smuggling, 123; temporary vs. permanent, 117; voluntary, 116; world patterns, 115

Milan, 286
militaristic countries, 359
military authoritarianism, 344
military expenditures, 357–358, 359
Millennium Development Goals, 199, 200
MIPT Terrorism Knowledge Base, 370
mixed economy, 175
mixed farming, 151
monarchy, absolute, 344
money laundering, 16
Mongol Empire, 378
monoculture, 159
Montreal Protocol, 288, 401–402
more globalized core, 43, 46, 103–104
mosquitoes, 12–13
mountain pine beetle, 32
multiculturalism, 121
multilateral aid, 204
multinational companies, 182
Mumbai, 140
Murphy, Cullen, 378
Muslim. see Islam
Mutually Assured Destruction, 379, 401
Myanmar, 345, 356, 371, 405

Nairobi, 128, 130, 139
Nanticoke generating station, 282
narco-terrorism, 142
nation state, 339–340
National Counterterrorism Center, 370
national parks, 33
nationalism, 344
natural gas, 298–299
natural increase rate, 64
natural recovery, 264
Nature Conservancy of Canada, 248
Near-Core Periphery: defined, 46; global involvement, 45; subdivision of, 46; urban changes, 135; urban problems, 138–142
neo-colonialism, 174, 175
neo-liberalism, 176–178
Nepal, 368
net immigration rate, 64
New Core: defined, 46; global involvement, 45; transnational companies, 184, 185; urban changes, 135; urban problems, 138–142
the New Deal, 176
newly industrialized worlds, 51
NGO, 7
9/11, 365, 373
nitrous oxide, 321
Nobel, Alfred, 405
Nobel Peace Prize, 404–406
nomadic hunters and gatherers, 61
non-governmental organizations (NGOs), 204, 405, 468
nonrenewable resource, 36
non-tariff barriers, 176
North, 50
North American Free Trade Agreement (NAFTA), 191, 273
North Atlantic Treaty Organization (NATO), 400–401
Northern Ireland, 356
Northwest Passage, 350–352
nuclear power, 301–302
nuclear terrorism, 373
nuclear weapons, 402
nutrition, 17, 147
nutrition transition, 417–419

obesity, 416–419
objective, 11
oceans, 273–274, 334, 350–352
odious debt, 220
Office Depot, 182
official development assistance, 204
Ogallala Aquifer, 265–266
oil: consumption, 42, 43, 44, 45; crude, 295–297; and debt crisis, 219; and Industrial Revolution, 61;

production and consumption, 296; sands, 306, 382, 383
oil palms, 255
Oklahoma City, 367
Old Core: and debt, 216; defined, 46; and fair trade, 443; and free trade, 193; global involvement, 45; population futures, 102–104; transnational companies, 183–184; urban changes, 134–135; urban problems, 136–138
Old Faithful, 33
old-growth forest, 252
Olympics, 379
Omai gold mine, 207
100-mile diet, 162
one-child policy, 90, 91, 92, 330
one-party nation state, 344
Ontario, 457
opinions, 11, 12
optimistic views of population growth, 79
Oregon Territory, 341
organic farming, 161
Organization for Economic Cooperation and Development, 119, 120, 206
Organization of Petroleum Exporting Countries (OPEC), 219, 295
Ottoman empire, 221
Outbreak, 413
overgrazing, 233
overpopulation, 85
overurbanization, 135
Oxfam, 204
ozone layer, 18, 286–288, 402

Pacala, Stephen, 469
Pacific yew, 36
Palestine, 356
Palestinian Liberation Organization, 372
pandemic, 411, 419–421
parasitic relationship, 37
Paris, 121–122
Paris Declaration, 207
peace dividend, 359
peace, world, 406
peacekeeping, 398–399
peacemaking, 399
peak oil, 305
Pearson, Lester, 206, 207, 405
pension plans, 105
The Pentagon's New Map: War and Peace in the Twenty-First Century, 360
Peres, Shimon, 372
Periphery. see less globalized periphery
persistent organic pollutants (POPs), 278–280
perspective, 3, 4
Peru, 368
pessimistic views of population growth, 80
pesticides, 12–13, 14, 265
petrodollars, 219–220
Pew Global Attitude Survey, 463–464
phantom carrying capacity, 80
Philippines: GDP, 169; global involvement, 45; remittances, 120; soil erosion, 231; terrorism, 368
Phoenix, 266
photochemical smog, 285
physical deterioration, 233
PIR (Planning, Implementation, Review), 446
plantations, 173
plastic bags, 457
Platinex suit, 254
Poland, 45, 169
political consumerism, 255
political globalization, 27
Political Islam, 380, 392–393
political maturity, 41
polls, 8, 11, 12
pollution: acid rain, 280–283; air, 278–286; Beijing, 390; deaths due to, 278, 284; and land degradation, 233; smog, 283–286; water, 260–265; as world issue, 18
population: aging, 105–106, 107; and birth dearth, 104–109; birth rate. see birth rate; control. see population control; Core, 103–104; death rate. see death rate; declining growth rate, 60–61; and economic disparity, 201; economic effects, 107; explosion, 60, 85–86; family size, 70; graphing, 57; growth rate, 60–61; ideas about, 79–80;

migration. see migration; Old Core and eastern Europe, 102–104; projections, 81, 101–102, 107, 108; and sustainability, 104; and technological change, 61–63; theories, 69–83; trends, 58–61; world, 57, 58–59; and world power, 108
population control: China, 90–92; future of, 95–97; government-driven, 86; India, 88–90; success of, 92
population growth rate, 60–61, 64
population implosion: defined, 101; economic effects, 107; labour shortages, 106–107; prevention, 109–110
population migration. see migration
population pyramid: defined, 65–66; early transition, 73; late transition, 74; pre-transition, 71; sequence of, 77
positive feedback loops, 326
post-colonial period, 175
post-transition, 74–75
poverty: and children, 434; distribution, 200; extreme, 199–201; ICPD principles, 96; and urbanization, 137
Poverty Reduction Strategy Paper, 222
Powell, Colin, 397
power structures. see world power structures
precipitation, 322–323
pre-transition, 70–71
primary industries, 168
private development assistance (PDA), 204
progressive thought, 176, 177
pronatalist strategies, 109
protected area, 240–242, 252–253
proxy war, 354
public diplomacy, 352
pull factors, 115, 129
push factors, 115, 129

Quebec, 344, 457

Rabin, Yitzhak, 372
Rainforest Action Network, 248
Ramsar Convention, 267
recentralization, 134, 137
recession, 451
recycle, 239
Red Crescent, 405
Red Cross, 204, 405
reduce, 238
reduced-impact logging, 250–251
refugees, 124–125
relative rate, 64
religion: activists, 28; and conflict, 354; and development assistance, 205; Political Islam, 392–393; and population, 71, 79, 96; and terrorism, 372
religious nation state, 345
remittances, 120–121, 130, 208
renewable resource, 36
replacement migration, 123–124
replacement rate, 66
reserves (energy), 293
resources, 36–37, 354
reuse, 238–239
right wing, 4
Rio Summit, 327, 451, 457
Rockefeller Foundation, 151, 154, 204
Rogers, Everett, 318
Rolls-Royce, 186
Roosevelt, Franklin D., 176
Rostow, Walt, 169
R/P ratio, 293
rule of 70, 66
rule set, 379
rural to urban migration, 129–133
Russia: and Arctic sovereignty, 351–352; economic power, 185; emissions, 328; sovereign default, 221; terrorism, 368; and world power structures, 388
Rwanda, 115, 399; genocide, 173, 356

salinization, 232
sanctions, 202, 353, 397
SARS, 421
Saudi Arabia, 266, 306
Schwarzenegger, Arnold, 331–332
sea level, 323
second world, 50–51

secondary industries, 168
security, 326
Security Council, 397
Seko, Mobutu Sésé, 220
Semmelweis, Ignaz, 72
sewage waste, 261
sex determination, 89, 91
Shake Hands with the Devil, 174
sharecroppers, 157
silence, stigma, discrimination, and denial, 412, 414
Silent Spring, 14, 34
Sillett, Steve, 246
SLAPPs (Strategic Lawsuits Against Public
    Participation), 254
slavery, 435
Slow Cities, 458
slums, 139, 140
slums of despair, 141
slums of hope, 141
smallpox, 72
smart growth, 459
smart meters, 307
Smith, Adam, 176
Smith, Alisa, 162
smog, 283–286
smuggling, of illegal migrants, 123
Snow Brand Milk, 182
Snow, John, 410
social development, 41
socially responsible investing, 439–440
socio-economic status (SES), 3
sociological globalization, 28
Socolow, Robert, 469
soft power, 352–353, 378
solar energy, 308–309
solid waste management, 236, 237–240
source control, 264
source reduction, 238
sources, information, 8, 15
South, 50
South Africa, 12, 356
South Korea, 185
sovereign default, 221
sovereignty, 340, 350–352
Soviet Union, 345–346, 354–355, 378–379
Spaceship Earth concept, 35
Spain, 105, 368
Spanish flu, 419–420
specific indicator, 453
sphere of influence, 346
Spratly Islands, 354
squatter settlements, 135
Sri Lanka, 368
starvation, 147. *see also* hunger
state terrorism, 371
state-sponsored terrorism, 371
Stockholm Convention, 280
structural change model, 94
subjective, 11
subsidies, 16, 158–159
subsistence farming, 151
Suncor, 330
sustainability: agriculture, 161–162; and air pollution,
    141, 285; assessing, 452–453; behaviour change,
    459–560; and biofuels, 255; and biotechnology,
    156; coal, 300; and colonialism, 173; compre-
    hensive indicator, 453–456; defined, 31; and
    development assistance, 207; in Dubai, 31; and
    economic growth, 451; and energy consumption,
    293; Environmental Protection Act, 280; exam-
    ples of, 467–468; extended producer responsibil-
    ity, 457; and family size, 110; forests, 247, 249,
    255; future, 456–460; and global warming, 322;
    and globalization, 451; Green Revolution, 153;
    green taxation, 457–458; historical perspective,
    33–34; ICPD principles, 96, 97; indicators of,
    453–456; Living Planet Index, 453; measuring,
    451–459; microcredit, 442; and migration, 115;
    model, 37; need for, 37; pollution, 281; and pop-
    ulation decline, 104; smart growth, 459; specific

indicator, 453; and urbanization, 137; and waste
    management, 237; water resources, 271; winter,
    325
swamp, 267
Sweden, 70–71, 72, 73, 74–75
symbiotic relationship, 37

Taiwan, 75
Taliban, 345, 435
tar sands, 306, 382, 383
tariffs, 188
taxation, 210
Taylor, P.J., 30
technological globalization, 27
temperate, 50
temperature inversion, 284
Terpstra, John, 248
terrain deformation, 232
terrorism: in Afghanistan, 374; defined, 365–366;
    fighting, 374–375; freedom fighters, 372–373;
    geography of, 366–370; global patterns,
    366–369; and immigration, 122; increasing or
    decreasing?, 369; methods, 373–374; motivations
    for, 371, 372; objectives, 371; organizations,
    368–369; as world issue, 16
tertiary industries, 168
Test Ban Treaty, 402–403
Thailand, 74
theory of demographic regulation, 79
thick-layer capping, 264
Third World, 50–51, 52
third-country resettlement, 125
Three Gorges Dam, 270
3Rs, 237
three-world model, 50–51
tidal marsh, 267
tipping point, 317–318
tokenism, 429
Tokyo, 133
Toronto: affordable housing, 137; deep water lake
    cooling system, 467; immigration, 121; waste
    management, 239, 240
total fertility rate (TFR), 66, 101
total stock, 36
tourism, 23, 42, 43, 44, 45
trade barriers, 16
trade inequities, 203
traditional values, 28
Transboundary Haze Pollution Agreement, 284
transgenic crops, 155–156
transit, 142
transnational companies: annual revenues, 183; back-
    ground, 182; benefits of, 187; criticisms of, 188;
    global distribution, 183–184; ten largest, 183
treaties, 401–404
Treaty of Tordesillas, 171
tropical, 50
Trudeau, Pierre, 242
Tsar Bomba, 379
Turkey, 369
Turner, Chris, 451, 463
Twain, Mark, 454

Uganda, 368
ultraviolet (UV) radiation, 278
underdeveloped worlds, 50
undernutrition, 148
unilateralist, 386
United Arab Emirates, 22
United Nations: General Assembly, 397; history, 397;
    and Iraq war, 398; membership, 41; peacekeep-
    ing, 398–399; peacemaking, 399; and population
    control, 97; population projections, 81; sanc-
    tions, 397; Security Council, 397; success of,
    397–400; veto, 397
United Nations Convention on Long-Range
    Transboundary Air Pollution, 282
United Nations Convention on the Law of the Sea,
    273
United Nations Environment Program, 37

United Nations Food Agency, 156
United Nations Framework Convention on Climate
    Change, 327
United Nations High Commission for Refugees, 124
United Nations Law of the Sea Convention, 351
United Nations Security Council, 108
United States: and Canadian border, 341–342; and cli-
    mate change, 330; and the Cold War, 345–346,
    378–379; Cuban sanctions, 202; debt burden,
    217; and free trade, 193; illegal immigration,
    122–123; sea levels, 323; state terrorism, 371; as
    superpower, 379, 380; terrorism, 368; and world
    power structures, 386
Universal Declaration of Human Rights, 426–427, 428
Unus, Muhammad, 440–441
uranium, 301
urban problems, 138–142, 143
urbanization. *see also* cities; global patterns, 129–133

vaccines, 17
values, 11
variants, 102
vegetation, and land degradation, 233
Venezuela, 221, 306
vertical integration, 160
veto, 397
voluntary migration, 116
voluntary repatriation, 124
voting, 178

Walkerton, 265
Wal-Mart, 182
war, 202, 432–433. *see also* listings of specific wars
War on Terror, 374
Warsaw Pact, 400–401
water power, 61
water resources: Dubai, 31; freshwater, 259–260;
    groundwater, 265–266; irrigation, 270–272;
    managed, 268–272; oceans, 273–274; pollution,
    260–265; preservation, 259; in slums, 139,
    141–142; transfers, 272–273; wetlands,
    266–268; as world issue, 17
wealth distribution, 197, 209
The Wealth of Nations, 175
weapons of mass destruction, 350
wetlands, 266–268
white spirit bear, 252
wind power, 61, 311–312, 311–312, 468
women: in agriculture, 153, 158; changing role, 109;
    and fertility rates, 88; and HIV/AIDS, 415;
    ICPD principles, 96; and microcredit, 438;
    migrating to cities, 130; and political power,
    428–431; status of, 89–90, 92, 93; and war, 433
Woods, Tiger, 21, 22, 31
World Bank, 217
World Commission on Dams, 272
World Conservation Strategy, 37
World Conservation Union, 240
World Council of Churches, 205
World Health Organization, 13
world peace, 406
world power structures: Brazil, 387; Canada, 382–383;
    China, 390–391; Cold War, 379; European
    Union, 384; future of, 379; history, 378–379;
    India, 389; Japan, 385; rule set, 379; Russia, 388;
    United States, 386; US superpower, 379
World Trade Organization, 30
World Trade Organization (WTO), 188–189
World Vision, 204
World War I, 357, 419–420
World War II: and colonialism, 172; impact of, 75;
    and urbanization, 134; and world power struc-
    tures, 378
World Wildlife Fund, 37, 453

Yoruba, 174
Yugoslavia, 356, 401

Zambia, 44, 45, 169
Zimmermann, Erich W., 36

Credits

Documents

Chapter 2: p. 30 Quote from *Political Geography: World, Economy, Nation, State and Locality* (4th ed.), by P.J. Taylor and C. Flint, p.3. © 2000 by Prentice-Hall, Harlow, UK; Fig. 2–8 "Lal Masjid threatens suicide attacks," by Syed Irfan Raza. *Pakistan Herald*, April 7, 2004. http://www.dawn.com/2007/04/07/top1.htm; Fig. 2–17 Adapted from *The Global Casino: An Introduction to Environmental Issues* (2nd ed.), by Nick Middleton, p. 33. © 1999 by Oxford University Press. Reprinted with permission; **Chapter 7:** Figs. 7–1, 7–2, 7–3, and 7–7 From *The Future Population of the World. What Can We Assume Today?* (Revised and Updated Edition), edited by W. Lutz. © 1996 by Earthscan Publications Ltd, London, UK. Reprinted with permission; Fig. 7–8 UN World Population Data Sheet; **Chapter 8:** Fig. 8–9 Balance of Payments Statistic Yearbook 2002. Washington DC: IMF, 2003. International Publication Services; **Chapter 9:** Figs. 9–2, 9–3, 9–4, 9–5, and 9–6 World Urbanization Prospects: The 2007 Revision Population Database; Fig. 9–10 © 2007 The Economist Newspaper Group, Inc. Reprinted with permission. Further reproduction prohibited, www.economist.com; **Chapter 13:** Figs. 13–1 and 13–2 © 2006 The Economist Newspaper Group, Inc. Reprinted with permission. Further reproduction prohibited, www.economist.com; Fig. 13–8 Adapted from Transparency International Global Corruption Report, 2004, Copyright 2004. Transparency International: the Global Coalition Against Corruption. Used with permission, for more information visit, www.transparency.org; **Chapter 14:** WorldWatch Institute, Vital Signs, www.worldwatch.org; **Chapter 15:** Fig. 15–15 Brewers of Ontario, as found at Container Recycling Institute, www.container-recycling.org; **Chapter 16:** p. 248 Poem Reprinted courtesy of John Terpstra; Fig. 16–1 "Last Frontier Forests: Ecosystems and Economies on the Edge" by Dirk Bryant and Daniel Nielsen, and Laura Tangley; World Resources Institute (WRI); **Chapter 17:** Fig. 17–8 www.npwd.org/Ogallala.htm; **Chapter 20:** Fig. 20–4 Compiled by R.S. Bradley and J.A. Eddy based on J.T. Houghton et al. Climate Change: The IPCC Assessment. Cambridge: Cambridge UP, 1990 and published in EarthQuest 5(1), 1991. Courtesy of Thomas Crowley, Remembrance of Things Past: Greenhouse Lessons and the Geologic Record; Fig. 20–5 Pembina Institute for Appropriate Development, Climate Change Basics, Fact Sheet #1; Fig. 20–6 From *Earth Matters: Studies in Physical Geography* by Ron Chasmer. Copyright © Oxford University Press Canada 2001. Reprinted by permission of Oxford University Press Canada; Fig. 20–9 Michael D. Lemonick, "Feeling the Heat: Special Report, Global Warming," *Time* Magazine, April 9, 2001 (vol. 157, no. 14), p. 23. © 2001 Time Inc. Reprinted by Permission. Fig. 20–13 © 2007 The Economist Newspaper Group, Inc. Reprinted with permission. Further reproduction prohibited www.economist.com; **Chapter 22:** Fig. 22–2 © 2007 The Economist Newspaper Group, Inc. Reprinted with permission. Further reproduction prohibited, www.economist.com; **Chapter 23:** p. 365 Quote and Fig. 23–2 © Memorial Institute for the Prevention of Terrorism, http://www.mipt.org/; **Chapter 25:** Fig. 25–3 © 2007 The Economist Newspaper Group, Inc. Reprinted with permission. Further reproduction prohibited, www.economist.com; Fig. 25–6 http://commons.wikimedia.org/wiki/Image:Worldwide_nuclear_testing.png; **Chapter 26:** Figs. 26–1 and 26–6 UNAIDS; Fig. 26–4 © 2000 The Economist Newspaper Group, Inc. Reprinted with permission. Further reproduction prohibited, www.economist.com; Figs. 26–12 and 26–13 © Johns Hopkins Bloomberg School of Public Health; **Chapter 28:** Fig. 28–6 From 2006–2007 Annual Report © Fair Trade Labelling Organization International. Reprinted by permission; **Chapter 29:** Fig. 29–1 From *Assessing Sustainable Development: Principles in Practice*, edited by Peter Hardi and Terrence Zdan. © 1997 by The International Institute for Sustainable Development, www.iisd.org; Figs. 29–3, 29–4, and 29–5 From 2006 Living Planet Report © 2007 World Wildlife Fund. Reprinted by permission; Fig. 29–7 Ontario Ministry of Finance; **Chapter 30:** Figs. 30–3, 30–4, and 30–5 © 2007 World Public Opinion: Global Public Opinion on International Affairs; Fig. 30–6 © Enwave Energy Corporation; p. 469 Quote © 2006 by The Nobel Foundation.

Photographs

AP: Associated Press; CP: Canadian Press; GI: Getty Images; T: Top; B: Bottom; M: Middle; L: Left; R: Right

Chapter 1: p. 1 Phototick - Image and Click/Alamy, AM9DE5; p. 2 B: Sander Meurs/Alamy, A9KYPG; R: RightImage/Alamy, AS076C; p. 3 CP/AP/Alvaro Barrentos, 3555928; p. 4 Time & Life Pictures/Getty, 50615052; p. 9 Dick Hemingway Editorial Photographs; p. 10 © Torstar Syndication Services; p. 13 TL: Art Shay/Time & Life Pictures/Getty, 50662824; TR: Photos.com/Jupiter Images, 5076958; BL: CP/AP/Fredrik Persson, 4019955; BR: James Prout/Alamy, A1A724; p. 14 Alfred Aisentadaedt/Time & Life Pictures/Getty, 50373927; **Chapter 2:** p. 21 R: Andrea Haase/Shutterstock, 3432252; B: Ross Kinnaird/Images Sport/Getty, 3032059; p. 23 Fabrice Bettex/Alamy, AB4X0H; p. 24 © NASA/GSFC/ERSDAC/JAROS and US/Japan ASTER; p. 27 L: Moshe Shai/Israel Images/Alamy, AX92RA; R: © Mike McGregor/mikemcgregor.com; p. 28 © Creatas Images/Jupiter Images, 22820912; p. 29 Scott Peterson/Getty, 1722762; p. 30 Reuters/Bobby Yip, RTR 1B8MD; p. 32 Allen Thornton/Alamy, ACW50R; p. 33 Mike Norton/Shutterstock, 2649619; p. 34 Raghu Rai/Magnum Photos, PAR233003; p. 35 © NASA; **Chapter 3:** p. 44 L: Jo Chambers/Shutterstock, 1406488; R: Tony Cliff/Alamy, A3MF6E; p. 46 T: Paul Springett/Alamy, A77HJ0; M: Thomas Lehne/Alamy, A085CG; **Chapter 4:** p. 55 Walter Bibikow/Jon Arnold Images Ltd/Alamy, AHE8FA; p. 56 R: Greenshoots Communications/Alamy, A3MNP4; B: © Tom Grill/Corbis, 42-15722695; p. 60 Photo Japan/Alamy, ACEM8D; **Chapter 5:** p. 69 R: Will Steeley/Alamy, A8NPPG; B: Bettmann/Corbis, U1391398; p. 79 Mary Lane/Shutterstock, 1599006; **Chapter 6:** p. 84 R: Bettmann/Corbis, BE021687; B: Reuters/Corbis, UT0028940; p. 86 Belinda Lawley/Alamy, AFXH22; p. 89 Sheldan Collins/Corbis, IH033334; p. 94 Robert van de Hilst/Corbis, VH001738; **Chapter 7:** p. 100 R: Tibor Bognar/Alamy, AR157D; B: Jennie Hart/Alamy, AGBBTY; p. 105 Keren Su/Riser/Getty, AF5929-001; p. 106 Comstock Images/Jupiter Images, 4825930; **Chapter 8:** p. 113 R: CP/St. John's Telegram/Keith Gosse, 981680; B: Mark Sykes/Alamy, AFNH40; p. 116 Justin Leighton/Alamy, A1TJEE; p. 119 David R. Frazier Photolibrary Inc/Alamy, A1EX84; p. 121 Laurence Gough/Shutterstock, 3124709; p. 122 Victor Tonelli/Reuters/Corbis, 42-15964053; p. 123 Reuters/China Photo, RTR EZNJ; p. 124 TS Corrigan/Alamy, AR0D0B; **Chapter 9:** p. 128 R: Richard du Toit/Gallo Images/Getty, 71587236; B: Adrian Arbib/Alamy, AG9E02; p. 133 Jo Chambers/Shutterstock, 4361356; p. 134 Maggie Sale Photography; p. 136 TR: Lou Linwei/Alamy, AXPGC6; BR Huw Jones/The Photolibrary Wales/Alamy, A97BRN; p. 137 Kuzma/Shutterstock, 471913; p. 138 Steve Weaver/Shutterstock, 2700788; p. 139 Shadow216/Shutterstock, 3389594; p. 141 CP/Rex Features, 4146746; p. 142 India Images/Dinodia Images/Alamy, A1GW98; **Chapter 10:** p. 145 Alfred Buellesbach/VISUM Foto GmbH/Alamy, A44FBW; p. 146 R: Nic Miller/Organics Image Library/Alamy, ANX69M; B: Peter Donaldson/Alamy, AP917N; p. 147 TR: Jenny Matthews/Alamy ACXGST MR: Dominic Harcourt-Webster/Images of Africa Photobank Alamy, AYG77D; MR: Comstock Images/Jupiter Images, 4825933; BR: Pintailpictures/Alamy, AQN83E; p. 152 Reuters/Ajay Verma, RTR 1CIQ2; p. 153: CP/Rex Features, 3309337; p. 154 Brent Stirton/GI; p. 156 Globe & Mail; p. 158 Allen Brown/ dbimages/Alamy, A2HGRC; p. 160 Miglbauer/WoodyStock/Alamy, AAYFK5; **Chapter 11:** p. 167 R: Tom Tracy Photography/Alamy, A59CAF; B: Redlink/Corbis, 42-17835338; p. 169 L: Horizon International Images Ltd/Alamy, A857Y7; R: Marcia Chambers/dbimages/Alamy, A11GM2; p. 172 LAC/George Hunter PA-166448; p. 174 CP/AP/Ted S. Warren, 881321; p. 175 Rob Atkins/The Image Bank/Getty, 10114800; 176 Source Unknown; p. 178 Don MacKinnon/GI, 5105065; **Chapter 12:** p. 181 R: brianlatino/Alamy, AWH781; B: AfriPics.com/Alamy, A94D2T; p. 185 Mike Fizer/Transtock Inc/Alamy, AT0FE2; p. 188 Lutz Pape/imagebroker/Alamy, A76TNY; p. 192 Reuters/Corbis, UT0011728; p. 193 Reuters/Daniel Aguilar, RTR 2TX7; **Chapter 13:** p. 196 R: Grand Tour/Corbis, 42-19154122; B: AP/Karim Kadim, 3862748; p. 199 TL: Holger Mette/Shutterstock, 3651629; BL © Taolmor/Shutterstock, 1732905; p. 202 CP/AP/Pier Paolo Cito, 1265988; p. 204 Reuters/Zainal Abd Halim, RTR NRFF; **Chapter 14:** p. 213 R: CP/AP/Sayyad Azim, 1346249; B: CP/AP/Michel Euler, 3674137; p. 219 Bruce Clark; p. 220 Bettmann/Corbis, U1819755; p. 214 Doug Garrett/FogStock/Alamy, A4G6Y9; **Chapter 15:** p. 227 JanP/Alamy, AEM5BT; p. 228 R: Reuters/Eric Miller, RTR 1SYC6; B: Javarman/Shutterstock, 2331354; p. 229 TL: CP/Wayne Hanna, 3606243; TR: Brian Atkinson/Alamy, A0B396; BR: Salinity Laboratory, USDA-ARS; BL: Scott Hortop/Alamy, AR7CKF; p. 232 TR: Aaron McCoy/Botanica/First Light, FLR3955551-354; BL: Bruce Clark; p. 233 Naftali Hilger/Israel Images/Alamy, A8H3B7; p. 237 Maciej Dakowicz; p. 241 Danielle Gali/Jon Arnold Images Ltd/Alamy, AHE89B; **Chapter 16:** p. 245 R: Tim Laman/National Geographic/GI, 73477054; B: E. Nugent/FogStock/Alamy, AG5J5K; p. 247 Trevor Smithers ARPS/Alamy, AMPFB1; p. 248 TL: Martina I. Meyer/Shutterstock, 7486861; BR: Sandy Huffaker/GI, 2513108; p. 249 James P. Blair/National Geographic/GI, 78623841; p. 250 © Forest Stewardship Council; p. 251 T: Robin Hanbury-Tenison/Robert Harding Picture Library Ltd/Alamy, A0RCYM; B: Michael Fay/National Geographic/GI, 72328910; p. 252 Ian McAllister/All Canada Photos/Alamy, ANH84R; **Chapter 17:** p. 258 R: Abe Kleinfeld; B: Ethan Meleg/All Canada Photos/GI, 73777952; p. 261 Charlotte Thege/Alamy, AG3HCT; p. 262 Reuters/Mike Segar, RTR X1C; p. 266 Reed Kaestner/Corbis Premium RF/Alamy, AGK7N3; p. 267 TL: Jiri Vondracek/Shutterstock, 2464034; TM Elena Elisseeva/Shutterstock, 1793941; TR: FloridaStock/Shutterstock, 3270949; ML: Nancy Brammer/Shutterstock, 8999800; BL: Johann Helgason/Shutterstock, 3565131; p. 268 TL: City of Phoenix, Water Services Department; B: Walter Dhladhla/AFP/GI, 51419199; p. 271 MR: Reuters/Shamil Zhumatov, RTR 22X6; BL: Worldsat International; BR: Worldsat International; p. 272 James L. Stanfield/National Geographic/GI, 78122757; **Chapter 18:** p. 277 R: CP/Adrian Wyld, 701278; B: H. Reinhard/Arco Images/Alamy, AK29GK; p. 280 CP/Sarnia Observer/Nora Penhale, 980457; p. 282 CP/Dave Chidley, 3600353; p. 283 Ray Pfortner/Peter Arnold Inc/Alamy, ATD0C9; p. 284 Central Press/Hulton Archive/GI, 71531338; p. 285 L: ROM/imagebroker/Alamy, A3TH0H; R: © NASA; p. 287 © NASA; p. 288 © PhotoSky 4t com/Shutterstock, 3398710; **Chapter 19:** p. 291 R: John Li/GI, 1726567; B: blickwinkel/Alamy, AR2N6T; p. 292 Gary Kieffer/Time & Life Pictures/GI, 53368271; p. 293 Robert McGouey/Alamy, A38W65; p. 295 Michael Onisiforou/Shutterstock, 4174132; p. 306 CP/Larry MacDougal, 1679739; p. 308 TL: Jason Smalley/Wildscape/Alamy, AAA5YD; TM: © Solatube International Inc.; TR: Jeff Morgan Cyprus/Alamy, AP065R; BL: Tom Brakefield/Stockbyte/Alamy, AETE3N; BR: Otmar Smit/Shutterstock, 3310536; p. 310 Laurence Gough/Shutterstock, 673891; p. 311 Glenda M. Powers/Shutterstock, 6167149; p. 312 Joe Goodson/Shutterstock, 1454257; **Chapter 20:** p. 316 R: Reuters/Lee Celano, RTR 1MDA0; B: Larry Lee Photography/Corbis, 5044; p. 322 Patrick Chappatte/Globe Cartoon; p. 327 TL Loetscher Chlaus/Alamy, AGM653; TR: Nruboc/Dreamstime.com; BM: © NASA/EROS; p. 332 Steven Greenberg/greenberg-art.com; **Chapter 21:** p. 337 Reuters/Eduardo Munoz, RTR 1L3A9; p. 338 R: China Features/Corbis Sygma, 0000358735-018; B: Ramin Talaie/Corbis, 42-15787063; p. 340 L: CP/Dan Janisse, 3824962; R: CP/Bob Weber, 4059248; p. 344 KCNA VIA Korean News Service/AFP/GI, 55894902; p. 346 Bettmann/Corbis, U830756B; **Chapter 22:** p. 349 R: Shah Marai/AFP/GI, 80329102; B: Reuters/David Gray, RTR 1XL54; p. 351 Reuters/Reuters TV, RTR 1SN29; p. 355 Robert Nickelsberg/GI, 1159563; p. 356 L: Keystone/Hulton Archive/GI, 2659675; R: CP/AP, 3819355; p. 357 Christopher Sprague; p. 358 L: CP/Rex Features, 2212551; TR: Taipan Kid/Shutterstock, 186388; BR: AFP/GI, 77446279; **Chapter 23:** p. 364 R: Ray Stubbline/Reuters/Corbis/DWF15-424223; B: Reuters/Scanfoto, RTR6386; p. 371 CP/AP/Walter Astrada, 1293608; p. 374 CP/Ryan Remiorz, 4144083; **Chapter 24:** p. 377 R: Angus McComiskey/Alamy, ARPYDA; B: Paul Heaton/Alamy, A5K36H; p. 378 Canada Post; p. 379 Valery Bushukhin/ITAR-TASS/Corbis/42-179826; p. 382 Larry MacDougal/First Light, FLM3900851; p. 383 © Torstar Syndication Services; p. 384 CP/Rex Features, 3659139; p. 385 CP/AP/Yuri Kageyama, 3695842; p. 386 Sandra Baker/Alamy, A0HDGX; p. 387 David R. Frazier Photolibrary Inc/Alamy, A5FH4T; p. 388 Iain Masterson/Alamy, ARAPG7; p. 389 1Apix/Alamy, AD46NA; p. 390 Lou Linwei/Alamy, AWG2DR; p. 391 L: Reuters/Rebecca Cook, RTR 1EYUC; R: Shuanghuan Auto Company/epa/Corbis, 42-18836593; p. 393 Mark Lewis/Stone/GI, 880243-001; **Chapter 25:** p. 395 B: Camerique/Classic Stock/Alamy, AAM26Y"; p. 397 CP/Action Press, 1378886; p. 400 CP/Action Press/Henning Schacht, 2143656; p. 402 © NASA/GSFC; p. 404 © Greenpeace; p. 405 CP/AP/Richard Vogel, 3163203; **Chapter 26:** p. 409 Reuters/Radu Sigheti, RTR 11O3"; p. 410 R: Justin Cormack; B: John Snow; p. 414 Brent Stirton/GI, 73165659"; p. 420 CP/AP/Alastair Grant, 13242105"; **Chapter 27:** p. 424 R: Serra Antoine/Corbis Sygma/0000378569-028; B: Hoberman Collection UK/Alamy, A3245T"; p. 425 TL: The Trustees of the British Museum; TR: Alex Wong/GI, 80093375"; BL: © Photothèque des musées de la Ville de Paris/Agence Roget-Viollet; BR: UN Photo/MB, 84570"; p. 432 BL: Reuters/Gleb Garanich, RTR RPI"; BR: Justin Leighton/Alamy, A1TJE4"; p. 433 Terje Lillehaug/Alamy, AAYGTH"; p. 429 Far L: Rainer Unkel/Vario Images GmbH & Co. KG/Alamy, A42ANT"; L: Ian Salas/epa/Corbis/42-19314926; R: Reuters/Jessica Rinaldi, RTR 1HH73"; Far R: Arshad Arbab/epa/Corbis/42-19376021; **Chapter 28:** p. 438 R: Philippe Lissac/Godong/Corbis, 42-17560936; B: Rumi Ahmed Khan/Drishtipat; p. 439 L: Reuters/Bazuki Muhammad, RTR 39XV; R: W. Holger/Shutterstock, 546113; p. 440 David Lyons/Alamy, A60Y0W; p. 441 CP/AP/Pavel Rahman, 4035429; p. 442 Rumi Ahmed Khan/Drishtipat; **Chapter 29:** p. 449 Nigel Cattlin/Holt Studios International Ltd/Alamy, A6P3YD; p. 450 R: Jim Corwin/Alamy, AANGJR; B: Andy Aitchison/Corbis, 42-19638852; p. 458 Danilo Ascine/Shutterstock, 1831605; p. 460 Arko Datta/AFP/GI, 51344116; **Chapter 30:** p. 462 R: © PlayPumps International; B: Bernhard Classen/Alamy, AJJGAX; p. 463 © IYPE; p. 464 Neo Edmund/Shutterstock, 3507671; p. 468 T: Egmont Strigl/Alamy, A2B41Y; M: Pep Roig/Alamy, A6HM15; B: © E+Co; p. Culminating Activity: 472 Grantly Lynch/UK Stock Images Ltd/Alamy; p. 473 Paul Baldesere/Photofusion Picture Library/Alamy; p. 473 Grantly Lynch/UK Stock Images Ltd/Alamy.

TUNDE BIAS
TEMITOPE

TUNDE BIAS
TEMITOPE

ARCTIC OCEAN

80°N

160°W 120°W 80°W 40°W

GREENLAND
(DENMARK)

A

Arctic Circle

ICELAND

BERING STRAIT

U
K

IRELAND

B

CANADA

40°N

UNITED STATES OF AMERICA

PORTUGAL

PACIFIC
OCEAN

NORTH
ATLANTIC
OCEAN

MOROCCO

MEXICO

CUBA

WESTERN SAHARA

Tropic of Cancer

BELIZE
HAITI
HONDURAS

DOMINICAN
REPUBLIC

CAPE VERDE

MAURITANIA

GUATEMALA

JAMAICA

EL SALVADOR NICARAGUA

SENEGAL
GAMBIA
GUINEA-BISSAU
GUINEA
SIERRA LEONE

COSTA RICA

VENEZUELA

GUYANA
SURINAME
FRENCH GUIANA

PANAMA

LIBERIA

COLOMBIA

CÔTE D'IVOIRE

ECUADOR

EQUATORIAL

DEMOCRAT

PERU

BRAZIL

SOUT
ATLANT
OCEA

BOLIVIA

PARAGUAY

CHILE

URUGUAY

ARGENTINA

FALKLAND/MALVINAS
ISLANDS

ANTARCTICA

---

0 1000 2000 3000 4000 5000 6000

kilometres

This world map is a Gall Cylindrical projection.

The Central American Inset map is
a Lambert's Equal Area projection.

The European Inset map is an Azimuthal Equidistant projection.

90°W 80°W 70°W 60°W

Bermuda (UK)

UNITED STATES OF AMERICA

0 500 1000 Kilometres

ATLANTIC OCEAN

30°N

THE BAHAMAS

GULF OF MEXICO

TURKS &
CAICOS
ISLANDS

ANTIGUA
& BARBUDA

Tropic
of
Cancer

CUBA

PUERTO
RICO (US)

VIRGIN Is.

ST. KITTS
& NEVIS

Guadeloupe (Fr.)

MEXICO

HAITI

DOMINICA

Martinique (Fr.)

CAYMAN
ISLANDS

DOMINICAN
REPUBLIC

ST. LUCIA
BARBADOS

20°N

BELIZE

JAMAICA

GRENADA

HONDURAS

CARIBBEAN SEA

TRINIDAD
AND TOBAGO

GUATEMALA

NICARAGUA

EL SALVADOR

VENEZUELA

PANAMA

COSTA
RICA

COLOMBIA

10°N

BRAZIL

80°W 40°W

All three maps are based on Mountain High Maps® © 1997 Digital Wisdom, Inc.